D1094847

THE MODERN LIBRARY

OF THE WORLD'S BEST BOOKS

CLARISSA

OR THE HISTORY OF A YOUNG LADY

CLARISSA

OR THE HISTORY OF A YOUNG LADY

by Samuel Richardson

EDITED, WITH AN INTRODUCTION, BY

JOHN ANGUS BURRELL

THE MODERN LIBRARY · NEW YORK

Distributed in Canada
by Random House of Canada Limited, Toronto.

THE MODERN LIBRARY
is published by RANDOM HOUSE, INC.
BENNETT CERF • DONALD S. KLOPFER

Manufactured in the United States of America by H. Wolff

INTRODUCTION

by John Angus Burrell

Samuel Richardson (1689-1761) is regarded, and rightly, as one of the first and most gifted of English novelists. Whether he should be called *the* first of the novelists is a claim that might be disputed with Defoe. We shall not debate that here. But if we demand of the novelist insight into character with a presentation commanding belief, then Richardson is pre-eminent. We might here make the distinction between a novelist who merely invents, like Defoe, and one who truly creates, like Richardson, and let it go at that.

There can be no disputing the fact, however, that the novel as it has developed from the eighteenth century has owed its greatness to this creative power. And, with all of the characteristics of Richardson's novels that any generation but his own might regard as dated or old-fashioned, Richardson's work still lives through this power of creative imagination.

Richardson was not in our understanding of the term a professional writer. He was past fifty when he produced the works by which he is known. He had all his life been a very busy and successful business man, a printer, who, when there seemed to be some leisure for it, turned to writing as an avocation, as an amateur and a moralist—to amuse and instruct his family and his friends. This is of course too simplified an explanation because it overlooks the deep urge to write that must always have been working in the man. Perhaps we should not try to account for him, but simply accept him as one who was born to write. André Gide tells us that there are two kinds of novelists, the cerebral and the visceral, and, though Richardson might blush at the word, he is clearly the visceral type.

As a boy at school he was nicknamed "Serious and Gravity." He loved to read, to tell stories, and to write letters. In his small circle of family and friends he was treated as something of a prodigy "and encouraged in that native priggishness which the years that developed other and finer qualities never quite eradicated." This man who became master of the epistolary form gives the following account of his early training:

> "As a bashful and not forward boy, I was an early favorite with all the young women of taste and reading in the neighborhood . . . I was not more than thirteen when three of these young women, unknown to each other . . . revealed to me their secret loves in order to induce me to give them copies to write after, or correct, for answers to their lovers' letters . . ."

This is not a very pretty picture, but it does help us to understand the man's expert qualifications when a printing firm asked Richardson to compile a series of letters. This he did, and the result was *The Complete Letter Writer* (1741), consisting of 173 familiar letters. There are letters for every sort of occasion, and the tone throughout is fictional and quite undistinguished. But this gave Richardson the idea for further letters which he loved to write, and eventually we have *Pamela* (1740), *Clarissa* (1748), and *Sir Charles Grandison* (1754).

In addition to the hundreds of letters that constitute the novels, he wrote hundreds more to his family and friends. There have been various editions of his correspondence, and in his letters he revals a good deal about himself. Though many questions and conjectures about the man still remain unanswered or unsolved, many facts about his life are very clear indeed.

Richardson could boast of not even a remote connection with an aristocratic house, nor did he ever pretend to. He tells us that he came from a family of "middling note" in the county of Surrey. His father, a joiner, settled in London, married a lady of a "not ungenteel" family. The father was involved in the rebellion of the Duke of Monmouth, and, probably as a result of these treasonable activities, was obliged to quit London, and to retire to Derbyshire. Samuel Richardson never even revealed the name of the town in Derbyshire where he was born in 1689, and all research has hitherto failed to discover it.

The family returned to London after the accession of William and Mary. It was believed at one time that Samuel was a pupil at Christ Church Hospital, but this rumor has not been substantiated by the school records. It is doubtful if he received so good an education as this school would have provided. Yet there is evidence, especially in *Clarissa,* that Richardson somewhere and somehow acquired a considerable knowledge of the Latin classics.

Richardson's father was evidently in financial straits, and the boy, instead of being educated for the church—which had been intended—was apprenticed to Mr. John Wilde, of Stationers' Hall, a printer. It was a hard and busy life. But his career was from that moment set. All in good time and as a result of stern application, Richardson married his master's daughter, Martha, and eventually set himself up in a printing business which he carried on successfully for many years. Indeed Samuel Richardson, boy and man, might well have served as the prototype of Hogarth's good apprentice.

Of the children of his first wife, all of them died, and the mother followed them in 1731, after five years of marriage. Two years after her death, Richardson married Elizabeth Leake, the daughter of a bookseller at Bath. Two children, a boy and a girl of this marriage, died young, but three daughters survived their father.

In the manner of a nineteenth-century tycoon, Richardson expanded his manner of living, and, while keeping his Westminster house, added an imposing "rural retreat," a very handsome house at North End, Hammersmith. Here eventually he built the famous grotto, or summer-house, where "he would spend the morning hours reading his latest manuscript to a group of admiring friends."

We know that when Richardson began to write, he was distrustful of his own powers, that he needed the stimulus of constant flattery and encouragement. His group of female admirers to whom he read each morning largely supplied this need; but he demanded the same sort of flattery from many friends with whom he corresponded. One such friend was Aaron Hill, and of this friendship the biographer of Hill writes: "Their tastes were similar, they liked to write long letters about their works and their nerves and their medicines, they both had a horror of Milton's prose, and neither had sense of humor enough to disturb the other."

Of Richardson's first book, *Familiar Letters,* published anonymously, we are told, "It seems to have served its end as a complete letter-writer (and moral guide) for the lower classes." Mrs. Barbauld who collected and edited some of the Richardson correspondence in 1804 mentions it as a "favorite book in the servants' kitchen-drawer. But when so found it has not infrequently detained the eye of the mistress, wondering all the while by what secret charm she was induced to turn over a book apparently too low for her perusal, and that charm was—Richardson."

Between the publication of *Pamela* in 1740 and the appearance of *Clarissa* complete in 1748, Richardson was occupied with business affairs. The book was probably begun at the end of 1744 or the beginning of 1745, and published finally three years later. Its success was instantaneous.

There seems to be some conflict among scholars about the appearance of the various volumes of this book. All we need to know here is that the first four volumes were before the reading public by the spring of 1748, and since the volumes appeared serially, the last three were not available until near the end of the year. The fate of Clarissa became something of a national event. During the months of uncertainty readers all over England wrote Richardson letters of excessive praise, many of them begging the author not to let Clarissa die. The book was translated very soon into French and German. There were pirated editions, and even in the eighteenth century there were abridgments. The best of evidence indicates that Goethe read *Clarissa* and wrote *The Sorrows of Werther,* that Rousseau read it and wrote *The New Eloise.* By the mid-nineteenth century there were still ardent readers, and then for a long period, the Victorian novels pushed *Clarissa* to one side, and by 1900 it was regarded something of a literary curiosity, a book placed on the reading list of the history of the novel, and very little read.

The success of the book was indeed very great, but even at the time of its publication there were dissenting voices. Fielding's parody of *Pamela* (*Joseph Andrews*) shows clearly enough his attitude toward Richardson's work, though we may have to include even Fielding as an admirer if we can accept the authenticity of a newly found letter of Fielding to Richardson printed in the *Yale Review* in 1948, a letter filled with praise for *Clarissa.* As for Lord Chesterfield, he found the book tedious and prolix, but patronizingly added that "the middle classes for whom it was written, and whose tone and sentiment it may justly be taken to represent, were seized with wild enthusiasm for it."

Lady Mary Wortley Montagu's emotions were mixed. In 1752 she wrote to her daughter, Lady Bute:

> "I was such an old fool as to weep over Clarissa Harlowe, like any milkmaid of sixteen over the ballad of the Lady's Fall. To say truth, the first volume softened me by a near resemblance of my maiden days; but on the whole 'tis miserable stuff. . . . Even that model of affection, Clarissa, is so faulty in her behaviour as to deserve little compassion. Any girl that runs away with a young fellow, without intending to marry him, should be carried to Bridewell or Bedlam the next day. And, Clarissa follows the maxims of declaring all she thinks to all the people she sees, without reflecting that in this mortal state of imperfection, fig-leaves are as necessary for our minds as our bodies, and 'tis as indecent to show all we think as all we have."

But the praise almost drowned out completely these few though discerning voices of dissent; and of all these paeans let the fulsome words of Richardson's friend Aaron Hill indicate the quality and intensity. Hill wrote: "At this moment, I have three girls around me—each a separate volume in her hand, and all their eyes like a wet flower in April." These were Hill's daughters, and their names, believe it or not, were Astrea, Minerva, and Urania. And it was Urania Hill, in verses patterned on those of her father's, who was sure that the domestic life of generations to come would profit by the book:

"Thence maids shall learn to shun the wiles of art,
And early prudence guard the female heart. . . ."

In the extravagant manner of his time, Aaron Hill suggested the following title for *Clarissa:*

The Lady's Legacy
or
The whole gay & serious Compass of the Human
Heart laid open,
For the service of both sexes.
In the History of the Life and Ruin of
a lately Celebrated Beauty
Miss Clarissa Harlowe.
Including
Great Variety of other Lives & Characters
Occasionally interested in the Moving Story.
Detecting & Exposing
The most secret Arts and Subtlest Practices
of
That endangering Species of Triumphant Rakes
call'd
Women's Men.
Assisted by corrupt & vicious Engines of the Sex
they plot against.
Published in compliance with the Lady's order on her death-bed,
As a Warning to unguarded, vain, or credulous Innocence.

OR, an alternative
The Lady's Remembrancer
or
The Way of a Young Man with a Maid,
Being the whole and so on as above.

There is a wealth of critical material about *Clarissa* in the nineteenth century, but there is space for only a few examples. Macaulay was beguiled by the book. Thackeray records that the station in India "was in a passion of excitement about Miss

Harlowe, and her misfortunes, and her scoundrelly Lovelace." Robert Louis Stevenson, in a letter of December, 1877, to A. Patchett Martin in Australia, writes:

> "Please, if you have not, and I don't suppose you have, institute a search in all Melbourne for one of the rarest and certainly one of the best of books—*Clarissa Harlowe*. For any man who takes an interest in the two sexes, that book is a perfect mine of documents. And it is written, sir, with the pen of an angel. . . . the scene where Clarissa beards her family, with her fan going all the while; and some of the quarrel scenes between her and Lovelace. . . . nothing, nothing could be better! . . . You will bless me when you read it for this recommendation; but, indeed, I can do nothing but recommend *Clarissa*."

One final word from the eighteenth century. Diderot exclaimed that Richardson's works would remain on his shelf with those of Moses, Euripides, and Sophocles.

Of twentieth-century criticism, Joseph Wood Krutch, in his *Five Masters*, has made the most penetrating observations about the work of Richardson. The deepest passions, those that we associate with the French and Russian novels, are not to be found in Richardson, tradesman and conventionalist. For Richardson, novels were justifiable only for their morality. He was afraid that readers would be interested only in the story for entertainment. Actually he was such a great writer that the story of the people is everything—and especially to modern readers:

> "So completely does he enter into their emotions, so lively is his imaginative sympathy with everyone who comes within its narrow range, that his favorite characters cannot fail to engage the interest of the reader, who soon finds himself forgetting his impatience with their limitations in his concern with their experiences."

This is more true of *Clarissa* than of anything else Richardson wrote:

> "Hence *Clarissa* became, above all else, the model for sentimental fiction, by which term we mean here to denominate that vulgar sort of demi-tragedy produced when goodness is substituted for greatness as the necessary qualification of the hero, and when, as a result, the catastrophe reveals him, not going down in rebellious defeat, but tamely acquiescent to the forces which destroy him."

It is a commonplace in Richardson criticism that his women are portrayed much more successfully than his men. No matter what age or social condition, his women characters are flawless. Even Clarissa, laboring as she does under the terms of the plot imposed on her, emerges as a clearly understandable young woman. We have had a hint of the close association that Richardson had all his life with women, and from this may well have come his penetrating knowledge. He said that, in his humble opinion, Shakespeare knew women best of all writers, that he knew them better than they know themselves. Richardson's humility carried him a step further, in a letter to Lady Bradshaigh, where he explains that he does not pretend to know women; he only guessed at them. "And yet I think them not such mysteries as some suppose. A tolerable knowledge of men will lead us to a tolerable knowledge of women." But to be the novelist that Richardson was, more than a tolerable knowledge is necessary.

Now Richardson would not be the important novelist he is if he were wholly unsuccessful in his portrayal of men, as some critics have seemed to feel. A word needs to be said here in his defense. Certainly his older men are very well presented. A single letter of Clarissa's Uncle Antony brings him alive before the reader. The same may be said of Uncle Harlowe, of Lord M., of Mr. Hickman, and of several of the lesser personages. It is in his delineation of younger men that Richardson encounters difficulties. Brother James Harlowe remains an unmotivated caricature; Mr. Belford, for all the part he plays in the novel, is withal a vague and somewhat unbelievable character. But the chief difficulty that has perplexed each generation since *Clarissa* appeared is Lovelace. By many he has been regarded as an incredible, impossible creation. This was true for some contemporary readers, and it has remained true ever since. Whether we believe in him or not, the fact remains that, in some strange way, he captivates the imagination.

An obvious temptation for a present-day reader is to attempt an "analysis" of Lovelace. Vanity rules his life, but we are concerned to discover the basis for that fantastic egotism. We have the comments of members of his family about his indulged and undisciplined childhood; at one point, toward the end of the book, Lovelace himself deplores this indulgence, and feels somehow that it is the cause of his later unhappiness. But he writes one letter to Belford in which he betrays himself clearly as a sadistic person. This letter is usually omitted in abridgments, as are several other details which, taken together, and with even a modicum of Freudian interpretation, make Lovelace a much less enigmatic figure than he has heretofore appeared.

If we accept Lovelace as a cruel, vain, excessively proud young man, one who has little interest in sex, and no real capacity for love, is it then possible, as one critic has suggested, that Lovelace is genuinely and desperately enamored of Clarissa? We are told over and over that Lovelace hates matrimony; that he must be sure that Clarissa loves him above all others; that he must try her virtue to be sure that she will be a faithful wife. He tries her virtue by raping her, and is thus convinced of her virtue. Of course we do not expect Lovelace to behave logically or reasonably; but we do expect Richardson to make the man's pathological behavior credible—at least as a kind of psychic disease, which it is.

That *Clarissa* is too long, everyone who has not read it will admit. Only one who has just removed fifteen hundred of its two thousand pages is in a position to say that most abridgments of the book are too short. It may be, however, that this kind of surgery is necessary if the patient is to live. But, seriously, the length of this book has been under discussion from the beginning. Richardson himself thought it too long, and he asked Aaron Hill to make suggestions for reducing the bulk of manuscript. Hill ventured the statement that "it is the first stages (if at all) that you must look for lopping Places. All your after-growths are sacred, to the smallest Twig." A certain doctor advises Richardson not to cut out any sentiments, but to follow the plan of the Newmarket jockeys who are overweight—sweat away what he takes out. Mr. Colley Cibber was anxious to have whole branches cut off. Hill, once again urged for advice about pruning (having been earlier rebuked for certain suggestions), is this time more cautious, and more flattering than ever. He writes: "You have formed a style . . . where verbosity becomes a virtue; because, in pictures which you draw with such skilful negligence, redundance but conveys resemblance; and to contract the strokes would be to spoil the likeness."

Most readers do not share Hill's conviction. But whether we read Richardson at full length, or Richardson reduced, as in this volume, we find fiction of the very highest order. In his patient analysis of human character Richardson set a pattern that influenced the novel forever after; and it is only fair to say that the greatest of later novelists are very deeply indebted to the work of Samuel Richardson.

Columbia University
1950

CLARISSA

OR THE HISTORY OF A YOUNG LADY

Miss Anna Howe to Miss Clarissa Harlowe

Jan. 10.

I AM EXTREMELY concerned, my dearest friend, for the disturbances that have happened in your family. I long to have the particulars from yourself; and of the usage I am told you receive upon an accident you could not help; and in which, as far as I can learn, the sufferer was the aggressor.

Mr. Diggs the surgeon, told me that there was no danger from the wound, if there were none from the fever.

Mr. Wyerley drank tea with us yesterday; and though he is far from being partial to Mr. Lovelace, yet both he and Mr. Symmes blame your family for the treatment they gave him when he went in person to inquire after your brother's health, and to express his concern for what had happened.

They say that Mr. Lovelace could not avoid drawing his sword: and that either your brother's unskilfulness or passion left him from the very first pass entirely in his power. This, I am told, was what Mr. Lovelace said upon it, retreating as he spoke: "Have a care, Mr. Harlowe, your violence puts you out of your defence. You give me too much advantage. For your sister's sake I will pass by everything—if——"

But this the more provoked his rashness to lay himself open to the advantage of his adversary, who, after a slight wound given him in the arm, took away his sword.

There are people who love not your brother, because of his natural imperiousness and fierce and uncontrollable temper: these say that the young gentleman's passion was abated on seeing his blood gush plentifully down his arm; and that he received the generous offices of his adversary (who helped him off with his coat and waistcoat, and bound up his arm till the surgeon could come) with such patience, as was far from making a visit afterwards from that adversary to inquire after his health appear either insulting or improper.

Be this as it may, everybody pities you.

My mother and all of us talk of nobody but you on this occasion, and of the consequences which may follow from the resentments of a man of Mr. Lovelace's spirit; who, as he gives out, has been treated with high indignity by your uncles. My mother will have it that you cannot now, with any decency, either see him or correspond with him.

Write to me therefore, my dear, the whole of your story from the time that Mr. Lovelace was first introduced into your family; and particularly an account of all that passed between him and your sister; about which there are different reports; some people scrupling not to insinuate that the younger sister has stolen a lover from the elder.

Miss Clarissa Harlowe to Miss Howe

Harlowe Place, Jan. 13.

Our family has indeed been strangely discomposed. —*Discomposed!*—It has been in *tumults* ever since the unhappy transaction; and I have borne all the blame; yet should have had too much concern from myself had I been more justly spared by every one else.

My brother, being happily recovered of his fever and his wound in a hopeful way, although he has not yet ventured abroad, I will be as particular as you desire in the little history you demand of me.

I will begin with Mr. Lovelace's address to my sister. I will recite facts only; and leave you to judge of the truth of the report raised that the younger sister has robbed the elder.

It was in pursuance of a conference between Lord M. and my Uncle Antony, that Mr. Lovelace paid his respects to my sister Arabella. My brother was then in Scotland, busying himself in viewing the condition of the considerable estate which was left him there by his generous godmother, together with one as considerable in Yorkshire. I was also absent at my *Dairy-house*, as it is called,[1] busied in the accounts relating to the estate which my grandfather had the goodness to devise to me; and which once a year are left to my inspection, although I have given the whole into my father's power.

My sister made me a visit there the day after Mr. Lovelace had been introduced, and seemed highly pleased with the gentleman. His birth, his fortune in possession—a clear two thousand pounds a year—as Lord M. had assured my uncle; presumptive heir to that nobleman's large estate; his great expectations from Lady Sarah Sadleir and Lady Betty Lawrance; who with his uncle interested themselves very warmly (he being the last of his line) to see him married.

"So handsome a man!—O her beloved Clary!" "He was but *too* handsome a man for *her!*—Were she but as amiable as *somebody,* there would be a probability of *holding* his affections!—For he was wild, she heard; *very* wild, very gay; loved intrigue. But he was young; *a man of sense:* would see his error, could she but have patience with his faults, if his faults were not cured by marriage."

Thus she ran on; and then wanted me "to see the charming man," as she called him. Again concerned, "that she was not handsome enough for him"; with, "a sad thing, that the man should have the advantage of the woman in that particular!" —But then, stepping to the glass she complimented herself, "That she was very *well*: that there were many women deemed passable who were inferior to herself: that she was always thought comely; and comeliness, let her tell me, having not so much to lose as Beauty had, would hold, when that would evaporate or fly off."

Excuse me, my dear, I never was thus particular before; no, not to you. Nor would I now have written thus freely of a sister, but that she makes a merit to my brother of disowning that she ever liked him.

[1] Her grandfather, in order to invite her to him as often as her other friends would spare her, indulged her in erecting and fitting up a dairy-house in her own taste. When finished, it was so much admired for its elegant simplicity and convenience, that the whole seat (before, of old time, from its situation, called The Grove) was generally known by the name of The Dairy-house. Her grandfather in particular was fond of having it so called.

She liked the gentleman still more at his next visit; and yet he made no particular address to her, although an opportunity was given him for it. This was wondered at, as my uncle had introduced him into our family declaredly as a visitor to my sister. But as we are ever ready to make excuses when in good humour with ourselves, my sister found out a reason much to Mr. Lovelace's advantage for his not improving the opportunity that was given him. It was bashfulness, truly, in him.

"Upon her word, she believed Mr. Lovelace deserved not the bad character he had as to women. He was really, to *her* thinking, a *modest* man. He *would* have spoken out, she believed; but once or twice as he seemed to intend to do so, he was under so *agreeable* a confusion! A perfect *reverence,* she thought: she loved dearly that a man in courtship should show a reverence to his mistress." And she told my Aunt Hervey that she would be a little less upon the reserve next time he came: "She was not one of those *flirts,* not she, who would give pain to a person that deserved to be well treated; and the more pain for the greatness of his value for her."

In his third visit, Bella governed herself by this kind and considerate principle; so that, according to her own account of the matter, the man *might* have spoken out—but he was still *bashful;* he was not able to overcome this *unseasonable reverence.*

But now she began to be dissatisfied with him. "What did the man mean, she wondered? It could not be bashfulness (now she thought of it) since he might have opened his mind to her *uncle,* if he wanted courage to speak directly to *her*. Not that she cared much for the man neither: but it was right, surely, that a woman should be put out of doubt *early* as to a man's intentions in such a case as this from his own mouth. But truly, she had begun to think that he was more solicitous to cultivate her *mamma's* good opinion than *hers!* This distant behaviour, she must take upon her to say, was the more extraordinary as he continued his visits, and declared himself extremely desirous to cultivate a friendship with the whole family. Reserves were painful, she must needs say, to open and free spirits like hers; and yet she must tell my aunt" (to whom all this was directed), "that she should never forget what she owed to her sex, and to herself, were Mr. Lovelace as unexceptionable in his morals as in his figure, and were he to urge his suit ever so warmly."

I was not of her council. And it was agreed upon between my Aunt Hervey and her that she was to be quite solemn and shy in his next visit, if there were not a peculiarity in his address to her.

But my sister had not considered the matter well. This was not the way, to be taken for matters of *mere omission* with a man of Mr. Lovelace's penetration—nor with *any* man; since if love has not taken root deep enough to cause it to shoot out into declaration, there is little room to expect that the blighting winds of anger or resentment will bring it forward. Then my poor sister is not naturally good-humoured. She must therefore, I doubt, have appeared to great disadvantage when she aimed to be worse-tempered than ordinary.

How they managed it in their next conversation I know not. Yet he thought fit to put the question. But, she says, it was not till by some means or other (she knew not how) he had wrought her up to such a pitch of displeasure with him, that it was impossible for her to recover herself at the instant. Nevertheless he re-urged his question, as expecting a definitive answer, without waiting for the return of her temper, or endeavouring to mollify her; so that she was under a necessity of persisting in her denial; yet gave him reason to think she did not dislike his address, only the *manner* of it; his court being rather made to her mother than to herself, as if he were sure of *her* consent at any time.

A good encouraging denial, I must own—as was the rest of her plea, to wit: "A disinclination to change her state. Exceedingly happy as she was; she never could be happier!" And such-like *consenting negatives,* as I may call them, and yet not intend a reflection upon my sister.

Here I am obliged to lay down my pen.

Miss Clarissa Harlowe to Miss Howe

Jan. 13, 14

And thus, as Mr. Lovelace thought fit to *take it,* had he his answer from my sister. It was with very great regret, as he pretended, that he acquiesced in it. "So much determinedness; such a noble firmness in my sister; that there was no hope of prevailing upon her to alter sentiments she had adopted on full consideration." He sighed, as Bella told us, when he took his leave of her: "Profoundly sighed; grasped her hand, and kissed it with *such* an ardour—withdrew with *such* an air of solemn respect—she had him then before her. She could almost find in her heart, although he had vexed her, to pity him." A good intentional preparative to love, this pity; since, at the time, she little thought that he would not renew his offer.

He waited on my mother after he had taken leave of Bella, and reported his ill success in so respectful a manner, as well with regard to my sister as to the whole family, and with so much concern that he was not accepted as a relation to it, that it left upon them all (my brother being then, as I have said, in Scotland) impressions in his favour, and a belief that this matter would certainly be brought on again. But Mr. Lovelace, going directly to town, where he stayed a whole fortnight, and meeting there with my Uncle Antony, to whom he regretted his niece's cruel resolution not to change her state, it was seen that there was a total end of the affair.

My sister made a virtue of necessity, and the man was quite another man with her. "A vain creature! Too well knowing his advantages; yet those not what she had conceived them to be—cool and warm by fits and starts; an ague-like lover. Her sister Clary might think it worth her while perhaps to try to engage such a man; she had patience; she was mistress of persuasion; and indeed, to do the girl justice, had *something* of a person."

But when Mr. Lovelace returned into the country, he thought fit to visit my father and mother; hoping, as he told them, that however unhappy he had been in the rejection of the wished-for alliance, he might be allowed to keep up an acquaintance and friendship with a family which he should always respect. And then, unhappily, as I may say, was I at home and present.

It was immediately observed that his attention was fixed on me.

My Aunt Hervey was there, and was pleased to say we should

make the finest couple in England—if my sister had no objection.—No indeed! with a haughty toss, was my sister's reply.

My mother declared that *her* only dislike of his alliance with either daughter was on account of his reputed faulty morals.

My Uncle Harlowe, that his *daughter* Clary would reform him if any woman in the world could.

My Uncle Antony gave his approbation in high terms; but referred, as my aunt had done, to my sister.

She repeated her contempt of him, and declared, that were there not another man in England, she would not have him.

My father indeed, after a long silence, said that he had a letter from his son, on his hearing of Mr. Lovelace's visits to his daughter Arabella; which he had not shown to anybody but my mother; that treaty being at an end when he received it; that in this letter he expressed great dislike to an alliance with Mr. Lovelace on the score of his immoralities; that he knew indeed, there was an old grudge between them; but that, being desirous to prevent all occasions of disunion and animosity in his family, he would suspend the declaration of his own mind till his son arrived, and till he had heard his further objections; that he was the more inclined to make his son this compliment, as Mr. Lovelace's general character gave but too much ground for his son's dislike of him; adding, that he had heard that he was a very extravagant man; that he had contracted debts in his travels; and, indeed, he had the air of a spendthrift.

But the very next day Lord M. came to Harlowe Place and in his nephew's name made a proposal in form, declaring that it was the ambition of all his family to be related to ours, and he hoped his kinsman would not have such an answer on the part of the younger sister, as he had had on that of the elder.

In short, Mr. Lovelace's visits were admitted as those of a man who had not deserved disrespect from our family; but as to his address to me, with a reservation, as above, on my father's part, that he would determine nothing without his son.

And thus was he admitted to converse with our family almost upon his own terms; for while my friends saw nothing in his behaviour but what was extremely respectful, and observed in him no violent importunity, they seemed to have taken a great liking to his conversation; while I considered him only as a common guest when he came, and thought myself no more concerned in his visits, nor at his entrance or departure, than any other of the family.

But this indifference of my side was the means of procuring him one very great advantage; since upon it was grounded that correspondence by letters which succeeded—and which, had it been to be begun when the family-animosity broke out, would never have been entered into on my part. The occasion was this:

My Uncle Hervey has a young gentleman entrusted to his care, whom he has thoughts of sending abroad a year or two hence, to make the grand tour; and finding Mr. Lovelace could give a good account of everything necessary for a young traveller to observe upon such an occasion, he desired him to write down a description of the courts and countries he had visited.

He consented, on condition that I would *direct* his subjects, as he called it; and as every one had heard his manner of writing commended; and thought his narratives might be agreeable amusements in winter evenings; and that he could have no opportunity particularly to address me in them, since they were to be read in full assembly before they were to be given to the young gentleman, I made the less scruple to write, and to make observations and put questions for our further information.

But I should own, that in the letters he sent me upon the general subject, he more than once enclosed a particular one, declaring his passionate regards for me, and complaining, with fervour enough, of my reserves; but of these I took not the least notice.

I had a little specimen of his temper; for after he had sent me a third particular letter with the general one, he asked me the next time he came to Harlowe Place, If I had not received such a one from him? I told him I should never answer one so sent, and that I had waited for such an occasion as he had now given me to tell him so.

I must break off here. But will continue the subject the very first opportunity. Meantime, I am

Your most affectionate friend and servant,

Cl. Harlowe.

Miss Clarissa Harlowe to Miss Howe

Jan. 15.

Such, my dear, was the situation Mr. Lovelace and I were in when my brother arrived from Scotland.

The moment Mr. Lovelace's visits were mentioned to him, he, without either hesitation or apology, expressed his disapprobation of them. He found great flaws in his character, and took the liberty to say in so many words that he wondered how it came into the heads of his uncles to encourage such a man for *either* of his sisters; at the same time returning his thanks to my father for declining his consent till *he* arrived, in such a manner, I thought, as a superior would do, when he commended an inferior for having well performed his duty in his absence.

He justified his avowed inveteracy by common fame, and by what he had known of him at college; declaring that he had ever hated him; ever should hate him; and would never own *him* for a brother, or *me* for a sister if I married him.

He found my sister, who waited but for the occasion, ready to join him in his resentments against the man he hated. She utterly disclaimed all manner of regard for him: "Never liked him at all; his estate was certainly much encumbered; it was impossible it should be otherwise, so entirely devoted as he was to his pleasures. He kept no house; had no equipage; nobody pretended that he wanted pride; the reason therefore was easy to be guessed at." And then did she boast of, and my brother praise her for refusing him; and both joined on all occasions to depreciate him, and not seldom *made* the occasions.

I told them I did not value him enough to make a difference in the family on his account, and as he was supposed to have given too much cause for their ill opinion of him, I thought he ought to take the consequences of his own faults.

Now and then indeed, when I observed that their vehemence carried them beyond all bounds of probability in their charges against him, I thought it but justice to put in a word for him. But this only subjected me to reproach, as having a prepossession in his favour which I would not own.

Their behaviour to him when they could not help seeing him, was very cold and disobliging; but as yet not directly affrontive. For they were in hopes of prevailing upon my father to forbid his visits. But as there was nothing in his behaviour that might warrant such a treatment of a man of his birth and fortune, they succeeded not; and then they were very earnest with *me* to forbid them. I asked what authority I had to take such a step in my father's house; and when my behaviour to him was so distant, that he seemed to be as much the guest of any other person of the family, themselves excepted, as mine? In revenge, they told me that it was cunning management between us, and that we both understood one another better than we pretended to do. And at last they gave such a loose to their passions, all of a sudden, as I may say, that instead of withdrawing as they used to when he came, they threw themselves in his way purposely to affront him.

Mr. Lovelace, you may believe, very ill-brooked this; but nevertheless contented himself to complain of it to me, in high terms, however, telling me that but for my sake my brother's treatment of him was not to be borne.

My brother had just before, with the approbation of my uncles, employed a person related to a discharged bailiff or steward of Lord M. who had had the management of some part of Mr. Lovelace's affairs (from which he was also dismissed by him) to inquire into his debts, after his companions, into his amours, and the like.

My Aunt Hervey, in confidence, gave me the following particulars of what the man said of him:

"That he was a generous landlord; that he spared nothing for solid and lasting improvements upon his estate; and that he looked into his own affairs, and understood them. That he had been very expensive when abroad, and contracted a large debt (for he made no secret of his affairs); yet chose to limit himself to an annual sum, and to decline equipage in order to avoid being obliged to his uncle and aunts, from whom he might have what money he pleased; but that he was very jealous of their control, had often quarrels with them, and treated them so freely that they were all afraid of him. However, that his estate was never mortgaged, as my brother had heard it was; his credit was always high; and the man believed he was by this time near upon, if not quite, clear of the world.

"He was a sad gentleman, he said, as to women. If his tenants had pretty daughters, they chose to keep them out of his sight. He believed he kept no particular mistress, for he had heard *newelty,* that was the man's word, was everything with him. But for his uncle's and aunt's teasings, the man fancied he would not think of marriage. He was never known to be disguised with liquor; but was a great plotter, and a great writer; that he lived a wild life in town, by what he had heard; had six or seven companions as bad as himself, whom now and then he brought down with him; and the country was always glad when they went up again."

This was his character from an enemy; for, as my aunt observed, everything the man said commendably of him came grudgingly, with a *must needs say*—To do him justice, *etc.*, while the contrary was delivered with a free goodwill. But I doubted not that having so very little encouragement from *any*-body, his pride would soon take fire, and he would of himself discontinue his visits or go to town, where, till he came acquainted with our family, he used chiefly to reside; and in this latter case he had no reason to expect that I would *receive,* much less *answer,* his letters; the occasion which had led me to receive *any* of his being by this time over.

But my brother's antipathy would not permit him to *wait* for such an event; and after several excesses, which Mr. Lovelace still returned with contempt and a haughtiness too much like that of the aggressor, my brother took upon himself to fill up the doorway once when he came as if to oppose his entrance; and upon his asking for me, demanded what his business was with his sister?

The other, with a challenging air, as my brother says, told him he would answer a gentleman *any* question; but he wished that Mr. James Harlowe, who had of late given himself high airs, would remember that he was not *now* at college.

Just then the good Dr. Lewen, who frequently honours me with a *visit of conversation,* as he is pleased to call it, and had parted with me in my own parlour, came to the door; and hearing the words, interposed, both having their hands upon their swords; and telling Mr. Lovelace where I was, he burst by my brother to come to me, leaving him chafing, he said, like a hunted boar at bay.

This alarmed us all. My father was pleased to hint to Mr. Lovelace that he wished he would discontinue his visits for the peace-sake of the family; and I, by his command, spoke a great deal plainer.

But Mr. Lovelace is a man not easily brought to give up his purpose, especially in a point wherein he pretends his heart is so much engaged; and no absolute prohibition having been given, things went on for a little while as before; for I saw plainly that to have denied myself to his visits (which however I declined receiving as often as I could) was to bring forward some desperate issue between the two, since the offence so readily given on one side was brooked by the other only out of consideration to me.

And thus did my brother's rashness lay me under an obligation where I would least have owed it.

The intermediate proposals of Mr. Symmes and Mr. Mullins, both (in turn) encouraged by my brother, induced me to be more patient for a while; as nobody thought me over-forward in Mr. Lovelace's favour; for he hoped that he should engage my father and uncles to approve of the one or the other in opposition to the man he hated. But when he found that I had interest enough to disengage myself from the addresses of those gentlemen, as I had of Mr. Wyerley's, he then kept no measures; and first set himself to upbraid me for a supposed prepossession, which he treated as if it were criminal, and then to insult Mr. Lovelace in person at Mr. Edward Symmes's, the brother of the other Symmes, two miles off; and no good Dr. Lewen being there to interpose, the unhappy rencounter followed. My brother was disarmed, as you have heard; and on being brought home, and giving us ground to suppose he was much worse hurt than he really was, and a fever ensuing, every one flamed out; and all was laid at my door.

Mr. Lovelace for three days together sent twice each day to inquire after my brother's health, and although he received rude and even shocking returns, he thought fit on the fourth day to make in person the same inquiries, and received still greater incivilities from my two uncles who happened to be both there.

My father also was held by force from going to him with his sword in his hand, although he had the gout upon him.

I fainted away with terror, seeing every one so violent, and hearing Mr. Lovelace swear that he would not depart till he had made my uncles ask his pardon for the indignities he had received at their hands, a door being held fast locked between him and them. My mother all the time was praying and struggling to withhold my father in the great parlour. Meanwhile my sister, who had treated Mr. Lovelace with virulence, came in to me and insulted me as fast as I recovered. But when Mr. Lovelace was told how ill I was he departed; nevertheless vowing revenge.

He was ever a favourite with our domestics. His bounty to them, and having always something facetious to say to each, had made them all of his party; and on this occasion they privately blamed everybody else, and reported his calm and gentlemanly behaviour (till the provocations given him ran very high) in such favourable terms, that those reports and my apprehensions of the consequence of this treatment, induced me to *read a letter* he sent me that night, and, it being written in the most respectful terms (offering to submit the whole to my decision and to govern himself entirely by my will), *to answer* it some days after.

To this unhappy necessity was owing our renewed correspondence, as I may call it; yet I did not write till I had informed myself from Mr. Symmes' brother, that he was really insulted into the act of drawing his sword by my brother's repeatedly threatening (upon his excusing himself out of regard to me) to brand him if he did not; and, by all the inquiry I could make, that he was again the sufferer from my uncles in a more violent manner than I have related.

The same circumstances were related to my father and other relations by Mr. Symmes; but they had gone too far in making themselves parties to the quarrel either to retract or forgive, and I was forbidden to correspond with him, or to be seen a moment in his company.

Your kind, your *precautionary* regard for my fame, and the opportunity you have given me to tell my own story previous to any new accident (which Heaven avert!), is so like the warm friend I have ever found in my dear Miss Howe, that, with redoubled obligation, you bind me to be

Your ever grateful and affectionate,

Clarissa Harlowe.

Miss Clarissa Harlowe to Miss Howe

Jan. 20.

I have been hindered from prosecuting my intention. Neither nights nor mornings have been my own. My mother has been very ill, and would have no other nurse but me.

Her disorder was a very violent colic. The contentions of these fierce, these masculine spirits, and the apprehension of mischiefs that may arise from the increasing animosity which all *here* have against Mr. Lovelace, and *his* too well-known resenting and intrepid character, she cannot bear. My brother and sister, who used very often to jar, are now so entirely one and are so much together (*caballing* was the word that dropped from my mother's lips, as if at unawares) that she is very fearful of the consequences that may follow—to my prejudice, perhaps, is her kind concern, since she sees that they behave to me every hour with more and more shyness and reserve; yet would she but exert that authority which the superiority of her fine talents gives her, all these family feuds might perhaps be extinguished in their but yet beginnings.

For if I may say to you, my dear, what I would not to any other person living, it is my opinion that had she been of a temper that would have borne less, she would have had ten times less to bear than she has had.

I know you do not love any of us but my mother and me, and, being above all disguises, make me sensible that you do *not* oftener than I wish. Ought I then to add force to your dislikes of those whom I wish you to like?—of my father especially; for he, alas! has some excuse for his impatience of contradiction. He is not *naturally* an ill-tempered man; and in his person and air, and in his conversation, too, when not under the torture of a gouty paroxysm, everybody distinguishes the gentleman born and educated.

But my father was soured by the cruel distemper I have named, which seized him all at once in the very prime of life, in so violent a manner as to take from the most active of minds, as *his* was, all power of activity, and that in all appearance for life.

But my brother! what excuse can be made for his haughty and morose temper? He is really, my dear, I am sorry to have occasion to say it, an ill-tempered young man, and treats my mother sometimes—indeed he is not dutiful. Once, my dear, it was perhaps in your power to have moulded him as you pleased.—Could you have been my sister!—then had I had a *friend* in a sister. But no wonder that he does not love you now; who could nip in the bud, and that with a disdain, let me say, too much of kin to his haughtiness, a passion that would not have wanted a fervour worthy of the object, and which possibly would have *made* him so.

Your most affectionate and obliged Friend and Servant,

Cl. Harlowe.

Miss Clarissa Harlowe to Miss Howe

Harlowe Place, Jan. 20.

My brother being in a good way, although you may be sure that his resentments are rather heightened than abated by the galling disgrace he has received, my friends (my father and uncles, however, if not my brother and sister) begin to think that I have been treated unkindly.

Nevertheless I believe they all think that I receive letters from Mr. Lovelace. But Lord M. being inclined rather to support than to blame his nephew, they seem to be so much afraid of Mr. Lovelace that they do not put it to me whether I do or not, conniving on the contrary, as it should seem, at the only method left to allay the vehemence of a spirit which they have so much provoked; for he still insists upon satisfaction from my uncles, and this possibly (for he wants not art) as the best way to be introduced again with some advantage into our family. And indeed my Aunt Hervey has put it to my mother, whether it were not best to prevail upon my brother to take a turn to his Yorkshire estate and to stay there till all is blown over.

But this is very far from being his intention; for he has already begun to hint again, that he shall never be easy or satisfied till I am married; and, finding neither Mr. Symmes nor Mr. Mullins will be accepted, has proposed Mr. Wyerley once more, on the score of his great passion for me. This I have again rejected, and but yesterday he mentioned one who has applied to him by letter, making high offers. This is Mr. Solmes; *Rich* Solmes you know they call him. But this application has not met with the attention of one single soul.

If none of his schemes of getting me married take effect, he has thoughts, I am told, of proposing to me to go to Scotland, that, as the compliment is, I may put his house there in such order as our own is in. I have no mind to be his housekeeper, and I am sure, were I to go with him, I should be treated rather as a servant than a sister; perhaps, not the better because I *am* his sister. And if Mr. Lovelace should follow me, things might be worse than they are now.

But I have besought my mother, who is apprehensive of Mr. Lovelace's visits, and for fear of whom my uncles never stir out without arms and armed servants, to procure me permission to be your guest for a fortnight or so. Will your mother, think you, my dear, give me leave?

Just now, my mother has rejoiced me with the news that my requested permission is granted. Everyone thinks it best that I should go to you, except my brother. I am to be sent for into the great parlour, where are my two uncles and my Aunt Hervey, and to be acquainted with this concession in form.

Clary, said my mother, as soon as I entered the great parlour, your request to go to Miss Howe's for a few days has been taken into consideration, and granted——

Much against my liking, I assure you, said my brother.

Son James! said my father, and knit his brows.

He was not daunted. His arm is in a sling. He often has the mean art to look upon *that,* when anything is hinted that may be supposed to lead towards the least favour to or reconciliation with Mr. Lovelace. Let the *girl* then (I am often *the girl* with him) be prohibited seeing that vile libertine.

Do you hear, sister Clary? taking their silence for approba-

tion of what *he* had dictated; you are not to receive visits from Lord M.'s nephew.

Do you so understand the licence you have, miss? interrogated he.

I would be glad, sir, said I, to understand that you are my *brother*—and that *you* would understand that you are *only* my brother.

O the fond, fond heart! with a sneer of insult, lifting up his hands.

Sir, said I to my father, to your justice I appeal. If I have deserved reflection, let me not be spared. But if I am to be answerable for the rashness——

No more! No more of either side, said my father. You are not to receive the visits of that Lovelace, though. Nor are you, son James, to reflect upon your sister.

Sir, I have done, replied he—and yet I have *her* honour at heart, as much as the honour of the rest of the family.

And *hence,* sir, retorted I, your unbrotherly reflections upon me!

Well but you observe, miss, said he, that it is not *I,* but your *father,* that tells you that you are not to receive the visits of that Lovelace.

Cousin Harlowe, said my Aunt Hervey, allow me to say that my cousin Clary's prudence may be confided in.

I am *convinced* it may, joined my mother.

But aunt, but madam (put in my sister), there is no hurt, I presume, in letting my sister know the condition she goes to Miss Howe upon, since, if he gets a knack of visiting her there——

You may be sure, interrupted my Uncle Harlowe, he will endeavour to see her there.

So would such an impudent man *here,* said my Uncle Antony; and 'tis better *there* than *here.*

Better *nowhere,* said my father. I command you (turning to me), on pain of my displeasure, that you see him not at all.

I will not, sir, in any way of encouragement, I do assure you nor at all if I can properly avoid it.

You know with what indifference, said my mother, she h hitherto seen him. Her prudence may be trusted to, as my si Hervey says.

With what *appa*—rent indifference, drolled my brother.

Son James! said my father sternly.

I have done, sir, said he.

Thus ended this conference.

Will you engage, my dear, that the hated man shall not come near your house? But if he does come I charge you never leave us alone together.

Your most affectionate and obliged,

Clarissa Harlowe.

MISS CLARISSA HARLOWE TO MISS HOWE

Harlowe Place, Feb. 20.

MY BROTHER and sister have succeeded in all their views. They have found out another lover for me; an hideous one!—yet he is encouraged by everybody. No wonder that I was ordered home so suddenly. It was for fear, as I have been informed (an unworthy fear!), that I should have entered into any concert with Mr. Lovelace had I known their motive for commanding me home; apprehending, 'tis evident, that I should dislike the man they had to propose to me.

And well might they apprehend so; for who do you think he is?—No other than that *Solmes!*—and they are all determined too, my mother with the rest! Dear, dear excellence! how could she be thus brought over, when I am assured that on his first being proposed she was pleased to say that had Mr. Solmes the *Indies* in possession, and would endow me with them, she should not think him deserving of her Clarissa!

I was struck all of a heap as soon as I entered to see a solemnity which I had been so little used to on the like occasions in the countenance of every dear relation. I ran to my father and kneeled; then to my mother; and met from both a cold salute; from my father a blessing but half pronounced; my mother indeed called me child, but embraced me not with her usual indulgent ardour.

After I had paid my duty to my uncles and my compliments to my sister, which she received with solemn and stiff form, I was bid to sit down. But my heart was full; and I said it became

me to stand, if I *could stand,* upon a reception so awful and unusual.

My unbrotherly accuser hereupon stood forth, and charged me with having received no less than *five or six visits* at Miss Howe's from the man they had all so much reason to hate; notwithstanding the commands I had had to the contrary. And he bid me deny it if I could.

I had never been used, I said, to deny the truth, nor would I now. I owned I had in the three weeks passed seen the person I presumed he meant *oftener* than five or six times. (Pray hear me, brother, said I, for he was going to flame out.) But he always asked for Mrs. or Miss Howe when he came.

My brother seemed ready to give a loose to his passion; my father put on the countenance which always portends a gathering storm; my uncles mutteringly whispered; and my sister aggravatingly held up her hands. While I begged to be heard out, and my mother said, let the *child* be heard.

I hoped, I said, there was no harm done; that it became not me to prescribe to Mrs. or Miss Howe who should be their visitors; that Mrs. Howe was always diverted with the raillery that passed between miss and him; that I had no reason to challenge *her* guest for *my* visitor, as I should seem to have done had I refused to go into their company when he was with them; that I had never seen him out of the presence of one or both of those ladies, and had signified to him once, on his urging for a few moments' private conversation with me, that unless a reconciliation were effected between my family and his, he must not expect that I would countenance his visits, much less give him an opportunity of that sort.

I told them further that Miss Howe so well understood my mind that she never left me a moment while Mr. Lovelace was there; that when he came, if I was not below in the parlour, I would not suffer myself to be called to him, although I thought it would be an affectation which would give him advantage rather than the contrary, if I had left company when he came in, or refused to enter into it when I found he would stay any time.

My brother heard me out with such a kind of impatience as

showed he was resolved to be dissatisfied with me, say what I would. The rest, as the event has proved, behaved as if they *would* have been satisfied had they not further points to carry by intimidating me.

My father, with vehemence both of action and voice (my father has, you know, a terrible voice when he is angry!), told me, that I had met with too much indulgence in being allowed to refuse *this* gentleman, and the *other* gentleman; and it was now *his* turn to be obeyed.

Very true, my *mother* said, and hoped his will would not now be disputed by a child so favoured.

To show they were all of a sentiment, my Uncle *Harlowe* said he hoped his beloved niece only wanted to know her father's will to obey it.

And my Uncle Antony, in his rougher manner, added that surely I would not give them reason to apprehend that I thought my grandfather's favour to me had made me independent of them all. If I did, he would tell me, the will *could* be set aside, and *should*.

I was astonished, you must needs think. Whose addresses now, thought I, is this treatment preparative to?—Mr. Wyerley's again? or whose? But that it could be for Solmes, how should it enter into my head?

I did not know, I said, that I had given occasion for this harshness. I hoped I should always have a just sense of every one's favour to me, superadded to the duty I owed as a daughter and a niece; but that I was so much surprised at a reception so unusual and unexpected, that I hoped my papa and mamma would give me leave to retire in order to recollect myself.

No one gainsaying, I made my silent compliments and withdrew, leaving my brother and sister, as I thought, pleased, and as if they wanted to congratulate each other on having occasioned so severe a beginning to be made with me.

I went up to my chamber.

I had not recovered myself when I was sent for down to tea. I begged by my maid to be excused attending, but on the repeated command, went down with as much cheerfulness as I could assume, and had a new fault to clear myself of; for my brother, so pregnant a thing is determined ill-will, by intimations equally rude and intelligible, charged my desire of being excused coming down to sullens, because a certain person had been spoken against, upon whom, as he supposed, my fancy ran.

I could easily answer you, sir, said I, as such a reflection deserves; but I forbear.

Mr. Solmes came in before we had done tea. My Uncle Antony presented him to me as a gentleman he had a particular friendship for. My Uncle Harlowe in terms equally favourable for him. My father said, Mr. Solmes is my friend, Clarissa Harlowe. My mother looked at him, and looked at me, now and then, as he sat near me, I thought with concern.—I at *her,* with eyes appealing for pity. At *him,* when I could glance at him, with disgust little short of affrightment. While my brother and sister Mr. *Solmes'*d him, and *sirr'd* him up at every word. So caressed, in short, by all—yet such a wretch! But I will at present only add my humble thanks and duty to your honoured mother, and that I am

Your ever obliged
Cl. Harlowe.

Miss Clarissa Harlowe to Miss Howe

Feb. 24.

They drive on here at a furious rate. The man lives here, I think. He courts them, and is more and more a favourite. Such terms, such sentiments!

Oh, my dear, that I had not reason to deplore the family fault, immensely rich as they all are!

Hitherto, I seem to be delivered over to my brother, who pretends as great love to me as ever.

My father and mother industriously avoid giving me opportunity of speaking to them alone. They have not the *interest* in compelling me as my brother and sister have; I say less therefore to them, reserving my whole force for an audience of my father if he will permit me a patient ear.

I have already stood the shock of three of this man's particular visits, besides my share in his more general ones; and find it is impossible I should ever endure him. He has but a very ordinary share of understanding, is very illiterate, knows nothing but the value of estates and how to improve them, and what belongs to land-jobbing and husbandry.

They had endeavoured it seems to influence my good Mrs. Norton before I came home—so intent are they to carry their point! And her opinion not being to their liking, she has been told that she would do well to decline visiting here for the present.

My aunt likewise having said that she did not think her niece could ever be brought to like Mr. Solmes, has been obliged to learn another lesson.

I am to have a visit from her to-morrow. And, since I have refused so much as to hear from my brother and sister what the noble settlements are to be, she is to acquaint me with the particulars and to receive from me my determination; for my father, I am told, will not have patience but to *suppose* that I shall stand in opposition to his will.

Meantime it has been signified to me that it will be acceptable if I do not think of going to church next Sunday.

The same signification was made me for last Sunday, and I obeyed. They are apprehensive that Mr. Lovelace will be there with design to come home with me.

The man, this Solmes, you may suppose, has no reason to boast of his progress with me. His courtship indeed is to *them*, and my brother pretends to court me as his proxy, truly! I utterly to my brother reject his address, but all I say against him is affectedly attributed to coyness; and he, not being sensible of his own imperfections, believes that my avoiding him when I can, and the reserves I express, are owing to nothing else.

February 25.

I have had the expected conference with my aunt.

I have been obliged to hear the man's proposals from her, and have been also told what their motives are for espousing his interest with so much warmth. I hate him more than before. One great estate is already obtained at the expense of the relations to it, though distant relations; my brother's, I mean, by his godmother; and this has given the hope, however chimerical that hope, of procuring others, and that my own at least may revert to the family.

But here, upon my absolute refusal of him upon *any* terms, have I had signification made me that wounds me to the heart. It is, my dear, that I must not for a month to come, or till licence obtained, correspond with *any*body out of the house.

My brother brought me, in authoritative terms, the prohibition.

Not to Miss Howe? I said.

No, not to Miss Howe, *madam,* tauntingly; for have you not acknowledged that Lovelace is a favourite there?

And do you think, brother, this is the way?

Do *you* look to that. But your letters will be stopped, I can tell you. And away he flung.

My sister came to me soon after: Sister Clary, you are going on in a fine way, I understand. But as there are people who are supposed to harden you against your duty, I am to tell you that it will be taken well if you avoid visits or visitings for a week or two till further order.

Can this be from those who have authority——

Ask them, ask them, child, with a twirl of her finger. I have delivered my message. Your father will be obeyed.

I know my duty, said I, and hope I shall not find impossible conditions annexed to it.

A pert young creature, vain and conceited, she called me.

Dear Bella, said I, hand and eyes lifted up, why all this? Dear, dear Bella, why——

None of your dear, dear Bella's to me. I tell you I see through your *witchcrafts* (that was her strange word). And away she flung.

Feb. 25. In the evening.

What my brother and sister have said against me I cannot tell; but I am in heavy disgrace with my father.

I was sent for down to tea.

Such a solemnity in everybody's countenance! My mother's eyes were fixed upon the tea-cups, and when she looked up it was heavily, as if her eyelids had weights upon them, and then not to me. My father sat half-aside in his elbow-chair, that his head might be turned from me; his hands clasped, and waving, as it were, up and down; his fingers, poor dear gentleman! in motion, as if angry to the very ends of them. My sister sat swelling. My brother looked at me with scorn, having measured me, as I may say, with his eyes as I entered, from head to foot. My aunt was there and looked upon me as if with kindness restrained, bending coldly to my compliment to her as she sat; and then cast an eye first on my brother, then on my sister, as if to give the reason (so I am willing to construe it) of her unusual stiffness.

I took my seat. Shall I make tea, madam, to my mother?

No! A very short sentence, in one very short word, was the expressive answer.

My brother bid the footman who attended leave the room. I, said he, will pour out the water.

My heart was up at my mouth. What is to follow? thought I.

Just after the second dish, out stepped my mother.—A word with you, sister Hervey! taking her in her hand. Presently my sister dropped away. Then my brother. So I was left alone with my father.

He looked so very sternly that my heart failed me as twice or thrice I would have addressed myself to him; nothing but solemn silence on all hands having passed before.

At last, I asked, if it were his pleasure that I should pour him out another dish?

He answered me with the same angry monosyllable which I had received from my mother before, and then arose and walked about the room. I arose too, with intent to throw myself at his feet, but was too much overawed by his sternness even to make such an expression of my duty to him as my heart overflowed with.

At last, as he supported himself because of his gout on the back of a chair, I took a little more courage, and approaching him, besought him to acquaint me in what I had offended him?

He turned from me, and in a strong voice, Clarissa Harlowe, said he, know that I will be obeyed.

God forbid, sir, that you should not! I have never yet opposed your will——

Nor I your whimsies, Clarissa Harlowe, interrupted he. Don't let me run the fate of all who show indulgence to your sex, to be the more contradicted for mine to you.

I was going to make protestations of duty—No protestations, girl! No words! I will not be prated to! I will be obeyed!

Sir, you never had reason, I hope——

Tell me not what I never *had*, but what I *have,* and what I *shall* have.

Good sir, be pleased to hear me. My brother and my sister, I fear——

Your brother and sister shall not be spoken against, girl! They have a just concern for the honour of my family.

And I hope, sir——

Hope nothing. Tell me not of *hopes,* but of *facts.* I ask nothing of you but what is in your *power* to comply with, and what it is your *duty* to comply with.

Then, sir, I *will* comply with it; but yet I hope from your goodness——

No expostulations! No *buts,* girl! No qualifyings! I will be obeyed, I tell you; and cheerfully, too!—or you are no child of mine!

I wept.

Let me beseech you, my dear and ever honoured papa (and I dropped down on my knees), that I may have only yours and my mamma's will, and not my brother's, to obey.

I was going on, but he was pleased to withdraw, leaving me on the floor, saying that he would not hear me thus, by subtlety and cunning, aiming to distinguish away my duty, repeating that he *would* be obeyed.

Miss Clarissa Harlowe to Miss Howe

Feb. 26. In the morning.

My aunt, who stayed here last night, made me a visit this morning as soon as it was light. She tells me that I was left alone with my father yesterday on purpose that he might talk with me on my expected obedience, but that he owned he was put beside his purpose by reflecting on something my brother had told him in my disfavour, and by his impatience but to suppose that such a gentle spirit as mine had hitherto seemed to be, should presume to dispute his will in a point where the advantage of the whole family was to be so greatly promoted by my compliance.

I find, by a few words which dropped unawares from my aunt, that they have all an absolute dependence upon what they suppose to be a meekness in my temper. But in this they may be mistaken, for I verily think, upon a strict examination of myself, that I have almost as much in me of my father's as of my mother's family.

My Uncle Harlowe it seems is against driving me upon extremities; but my brother has engaged that the regard I have for my reputation and my principles, will bring me *round to my duty*—that's the expression.

My aunt advises me to submit for the present to the interdicts they have laid me under, and indeed to encourage Mr. Solmes's address. I have absolutely refused the latter, let what will (as I have told her) be the consequence. The visiting prohibition I will conform to. But as to that of not corresponding with you, nothing but the menace that our letters shall be intercepted can engage my observation of it.

But can you, my dear Miss Howe, condescend to carry on a private correspondence with me?

You must remember the Green Lane, as we call it, that runs by the side of the wood-house and poultry-yard where I keep my bantams, pheasants, and peahens, which generally engage my notice twice a day.

The lane is lower than the floor of the wood-house, and in the side of the wood-house the boards are rotted away down to the floor for half an ell together in several places. Hannah can step into the lane and make a mark with chalk where a letter or parcel may be pushed in under some sticks, which may be so managed as to be an unsuspected cover for the written deposits from either.

So your faithful Robert may, without coming near the house, and as only passing through the Green Lane which leads to two or three farm-houses very easily take from thence my letters and deposit yours.

Try, my dear, the success of a letter this way, and give me

your opinion and advice what to do in this *disgraceful* situation.

But beforehand I must tell you that your advice must not run in favour of this Solmes; and yet it is very likely they will endeavour to engage your mother in order to induce you, who have such an influence over me, to favour him.

Yet if you incline to that side of the question, I would have you write your whole mind. Determined as I think I am, and cannot help it, I would at least give a patient hearing to what may be said on the other side. For my regards are not so much engaged to another person as some of my friends suppose; and as you, giving way to your lively vein, upon his last visits affected to suppose.

But why must I be pushed into a state which I have no wish to enter into, although I reverence it?

Your affectionate
Clarissa Harlowe.

MISS HOWE TO MISS CLARISSA HARLOWE

Feb. 27.

MISS CLARISSA HARLOWE to be sacrified in marriage to Mr. Roger Solmes!

I must not, you say, *give my advice in favour of this man!* You now convice me, my dear, that you are nearer of kin than I thought you to the family that could think of so preposterous a match.

You are all too rich to be happy, child. For must not each of you, by the constitutions of your family, marry to be *still* richer? Is true happiness any part of your family view? So far from it that none of your family but yourself could be happy were they *not* rich. So let them fret on, grumble and grudge, and accumulate, and wondering what ails them that they have not happiness when they have riches, think the cause is want of more, and so go on heaping up till Death, as greedy an accumulator as themselves, gathers them into his garner.

That they prohibit your corresponding with *me* is a wisdom I neither wonder at, nor blame them for; since it is an evidence to me that they know their own folly.

I am glad you have found out a way to correspond with me. I approve it much.

We had heard before you wrote that all was not right between your relations and you at your coming home; that Mr. Solmes visited you and that with a prospect of success. But I concluded the mistake lay in the person, and that his address was to Miss Arabella.

I indulged this surmise against rumour, because I could not believe that the absurdest people in England could be so *very* absurd as to think of this man for you.

My mother takes very kindly your compliments in your letter to her. Her words upon reading it were: "Miss Clarissa Harlowe is an admirable young lady. Wherever she goes, she confers a favour; whomever she leaves, she fills with regret." And then a little comparative reflection: "O my Nancy, that you had a little of her sweet obligingness!"

No matter; the praise was yours. You are me, and I enjoyed it. The more enjoyed it because—shall I tell you the truth?—because I think myself as well as I am—were it but for this reason: that had I twenty brother James's, and twenty sister Bell's, not one of them, nor all of them joined together, would dare to treat me as yours presume to treat you.

The result is this: that I am fitter for *this* world than you; you for the *next* than me—that's the difference.

You are pleased to say, and *upon your word too!* that your *regards are not so much engaged, as some of your friends suppose, to another person.* What need you give one to imagine, my dear, that the last month or two has been a period extremely favourable to that *other* person—whom it has made an obliger of the niece for his patience with the uncles.

But, to pass that by—*so much* engaged! *How much,* my dear? Shall I infer? *Some of your friends* suppose *a great deal.* You seem to own *a little.*

Don't be angry. It is all fair; because you have not acknowledged to me that *little.*

O my friend, depend upon it you are in danger. Depend upon it, whether you know it or not, you are a little in for 't. Your native generosity and greatness of mind endanger you; all your friends, by fighting *against* him with impolitic violence, fight *for* him. And Lovelace, my life for yours, notwithstanding all his veneration and assiduities, has seen further than that veneration and those assiduities will let him own he has seen—has seen, in short, that his work is doing for him more effectually than he could do it for himself.

In short, my dear, it is my opinion, and that from the easiness of his heart and behaviour, that he has seen more than *I* have seen, more than you think *could* be seen; more than I believe you *yourself* know, or else you would have let *me* know it.

Already, in order to restrain him from resenting the indignities he has received, and which are daily offered him, he has prevailed upon you to correspond with him privately. By your insisting that he should keep this correspondence private, it appears that there is *one secret* which you do not wish the world should know; and *he* is master of that secret. He is indeed *himself,* as I may say, that secret!

Yet who, as things are situated, can blame you? Your condescension has no doubt hitherto prevented great mischiefs. It must be continued for the same reasons while the cause remains. And I would advise you not to be afraid of entering upon a close examination into the true springs and grounds of this your *generosity* to that happy man.

It is my humble opinion, I tell you frankly, that on inquiry it will come out to be LOVE—don't start, my dear!

I have been tinctured, you know. Nor, on the coolest reflection, could I account how and when the jaundice began; but had been over head and ears, as the saying is, but for some of that advice from you which I now return you. Yet my *man* was not half so—so *what,* my dear. To be sure, Lovelace is a charming fellow. And were he only—but I will not make you *glow,* as you read—upon *my word* I will not. Yet, my dear, don't you find at your heart somewhat unusual make it go throb, throb, throb, as you read just here! If you do, don't be ashamed to own it. It is your *generosity,* my love, that's all.

Your ever affectionate,

Anna Howe.

Miss Clarissa Harlowe to Miss Howe

Wednesday, March 1.

You both nettled and alarmed me, my dearest Miss Howe, by the concluding part of your last. At first reading it I did not think it necessary, said I to myself, to guard against a critic when I was writing to so dear a friend. But then recollecting myself, is there not more in it, said I, than the result of a vein so naturally lively? Surely I must have been guilty of an inadvertence. Let me enter into the close examination of myself which my beloved friend advises.

I did so, and cannot own any of the *glow,* any of the *throbs* you mention. And yet the passages in my letter upon which you are so humorously severe, lay me fairly open to your agreeable raillery.

But, pray now, is it saying so much, when one who has no very particular regard to *any* man, says there are *some* who are preferable to *others?* Mr. Lovelace, for instance, I may be allowed to say, is a man to be preferred to Mr. Solmes, and that I *do* prefer him to that man; but surely, this may be said without its being a necessary consequence that I must be in love with him.

Indeed, my dear, THIS man is not THE man. I have great objections to him. My heart *throbs* not after him. I *glow* not but with indignation against myself for having given room for such an imputation. But if ever I should have the misfortune to think it love, I promise you, *upon my word,* which is the same as *upon my honour,* that I will acquaint you with it.

Be satisfied, my dear, that I am *not* displeased with you; indeed I am not. On the contrary, I give you my hearty thanks for your friendly premonitions.

Your equally affectionate and grateful

Cl. Harlowe.

Miss Howe to Miss Clarissa Harlowe

Thursday morn. March 2.

Indeed you *would not be in love with him for the world!*—Your servant, my dear. Nor would I have you; for I think, with all the advantages of person, fortune, and family, he is not by any means worthy of you.

Well but, if you have not the throbs and glows, you have not; and are not in love; good reason why—because you would not be in love, and there's no more to be said; only, my dear, I shall keep a good look out upon you; and so I hope you will upon yourself; for it is no manner of argument that because you would not be in love, you therefore are not. But before I part entirely with this subject, a word in your ear, my charming friend: 'tis only by way of caution, and in pursuance of the general observation that a stander-by is often a better judge of the game than those that play. May it not be that you have had, and have, such cross creatures and such odd heads to deal with, as have not allowed you to attend to the throbs?

But whether you have a value for Lovelace or not, I know you'll be impatient to hear what Mrs. Fortescue has said of him.

A hundred wild stories she tells of him from childhood to manhood; for, as she observes, having never been subject to contradiction, he was always as mischievous as a monkey.

Mrs. Fortescue owns, what everybody knows, "that he is notoriously, nay, avowedly, a man of pleasure, yet says that in anything he sets his heart upon or undertakes, he is the most industrious and persevering mortal under the sun. He delights in writing. Whether at Lord M.'s, or at Lady Betty's, or Lady Sarah's, he has always a pen in his fingers when he retires. One of his companions (confirming his love of writing) has told her that his thoughts flow rapidly to his pen."

That you and I, my dear, should love to write, is no wonder. We have always, from the time each could hold a pen, delighted in epistolary correspondencies. Our employments are domestic and sedentary, and we can scribble upon twenty innocent subjects, and take delight in them because they *are* innocent, though were they to be seen, they might not much profit or please others. But that such a gay, lively young fellow as this, who rides, hunts, travels, frequents the public entertainments, and has *means* to pursue his pleasures, should be able to set himself down to write for hours together, as you and I have heard him say he frequently does, that is the strange thing.

Mrs. Fortescue says, "that he is a complete master of short-hand writing."

Whatever his other vices are, all the world, as well as Mrs. Fortescue, says "he is a sober man. And among all his bad qualities, *gaming,* that great waster of time as well as fortune, is not his vice." So that he must have his head as cool, and his reason as clear, as the prime of youth and his natural gaiety will permit, and by his early morning hours, a great portion of time upon his hands, to employ in writing, or worse.

A person willing to think favourably of him would hope that a *brave,* a *learned,* and a *diligent* man, cannot be *naturally* a *bad* man. But if he be better than his enemies say he is (and if worse, he is bad indeed), he is guilty of an inexcusable fault in being so careless as he is of his reputation.

Upon the whole, and upon all that I could gather from Mrs. Fortescue, Mr. Lovelace is a very faulty man. You and I have thought him too gay, too inconsiderate, too rash, too little an hypocrite to be *deep.* You see he never would disguise his natural temper (haughty as it certainly is) with respect to your brother's behaviour to him.

But were he deep, and ever so deep, you would soon penetrate him, if they would leave you to yourself. His vanity would be your clue. Never man had more.

Talk *of the devil* is an old saying. The lively wretch has made me a visit and is but just gone away. He is all impatience and resentment at the treatment you meet with, and full of apprehensions, too, that they will carry their point with you.

I told him my opinion that you will never be brought to think of such a man as Solmes; but that it will probably end in a composition never to have either.

No man, he said, whose fortunes and alliances are so considerable, ever had so little favour from a woman for whose sake he had borne so much.

I told him my mind as freely as I used to do. But whoever was in fault, self being judge? He complained of spies set upon his conduct, and to pry into his life and morals, and this by your brother and uncles.

I told him that this was very hard upon him, and the more so as neither his life nor morals perhaps would stand a fair inquiry.

He smiled, and called himself *my servant*. The occasion was too fair, he said, for Miss Howe, who never spared him, to let it pass. But, Lord help the shallow souls of the Harlowes! Would I believe it? they were for turning plotters upon *him*. They had best take care he did not pay them in their own coin. Their *hearts* were better turned for such works than their *heads*.

I asked him if he valued himself upon having a head better turned than theirs for *such works*, as he called them?

He drew off; and then ran into the highest professions of reverence and affection for you.

Though I began this letter with impertinent raillery, knowing that you always loved to indulge my mad vein, yet never was there a heart that more glowed with friendly love than that of

Your own
Anna Howe.

MISS CLARISSA HARLOWE TO MISS HOWE

Wedn., March 1.

I NOW TAKE UP my pen to lay before you the inducements and motives which my friends have to espouse so earnestly the address of this Mr. Solmes.

Now you must know that from the last conversation which passed between my aunt and me, it comes out that this *sudden* vehemence on my brother's and sister's parts, was owing to stronger reasons than to the college-begun antipathy on his side or to slighted love on hers: to wit, to an apprehension that my uncles intended to follow my grandfather's example in my favour, at least in a higher degree than they wish they should.

I have more than once mentioned to you the darling view some of us have long had of *raising a family*, as it is called; a reflection, as I have often thought, upon our own, which is no inconsiderable or upstart one on either side; of my mother's especially. A view too frequently, it seems, entertained by families which having great substance, cannot be satisfied without rank and title.

My uncles had once extended this view to each of us three children, urging, that as they themselves intended not to marry, we each of us might be so portioned, and so advantageously matched, as that our posterity, if not ourselves, might make a first figure in our country. While my brother, as the only son, thought the two girls might be very well provided for by ten or fifteen thousand pounds apiece; and that all the real estates in the family: to wit, my grandfather's, father's, and two uncles', and the remainder of their respective personal estates, together with what he had an expectation of from his godmother, would make such a noble fortune, and give him such an interest, as might entitle him to hope for a peerage. Nothing less would satisfy his ambition.

But when my grandfather's will had lopped off one branch of my brother's expectation, he was extremely dissatisfied with me. Nobody indeed was pleased; for although every one loved me, yet being the youngest child, father, uncles, brother, sister, all thought themselves postponed, as to matter of right and power; and my father himself could not bear that I should be made sole, as I may call it, and independent, for such the will, as to that estate and the powers it gave (unaccountably as they all said), made me.

To obviate therefore every one's jealousy, I gave up to my father's management, as you know, not only the estate, but the money bequeathed me, contenting myself to take as from his bounty what he was pleased to allow me, without desiring the least addition to my annual stipend. And then I hoped I had laid all envy asleep; but still my brother and sister (jealous, as now is evident, of my two uncles' favour for me, and of the pleasure I had given my father and them by this act of duty) were every now and then occasionally doing me covert ill offices.

My brother's acquisition then took place. Then followed Lord M.'s proposal for my sister; and this was an additional felicity for the time.

You know how that went off; you know what came on in its place.

My brother then returned, and we were all wrong again; and Bella, as I observed in my letters above-mentioned, had an opportunity to give herself the credit of having refused Mr. Lovelace on the score of his reputed faulty morals. This united my brother and sister in one cause. They set themselves on all occasions to depreciate Mr. Lovelace, and his *family* too.

My uncle then gave one instance, my aunt told me, as a proof of a generosity in Mr. Lovelace's spirit which convinced him that he was not a bad man in nature, and that he was of a temper, he was pleased to say, like my own; which was, that when he (my uncle) had represented to him, that he might, if he pleased, make three or four hundred pounds a year of his paternal estate more than he did; he answered, "that his tenants paid their rents well; that it was a maxim with his family, from which he would by no means depart, never to rack-rent old tenants, or their descendants, and that it was a pleasure to him to see all his tenants look fat, sleek, and contented."

Although this pleased me when I heard it as giving an instance of generosity and prudence at the same time, not lessening (as my uncle took notice) the yearly value of the farm, yet, my dear, I had no *throbs,* no *glows* upon it!—*upon my word,* I had not.

My uncle went on (as my aunt told me), that, besides his paternal estate, he was the immediate heir to very splendid fortunes; that it was with this view that his relations were all so earnest for his marrying; that as he saw not where Mr. Lovelace could better himself, so truly, he thought there was wealth enough in their own family to build up three considerable ones. That therefore he must needs say he was the more desirous of this alliance, as there was a great probability, not only from Mr. Lovelace's descent, but from his fortunes, that his niece Clarissa might one day be a peeress of Great Britain—and upon that prospect (*here was the mortifying stroke*) he should, for his own part, think it not wrong to make such dispositions as should contribute to the better support of the dignity.

My Uncle Harlowe, it seems, far from disapproving of what his brother had said, declared that there was but one objection to an alliance with Mr. Lovelace: to wit, his faulty morals; especially as so much could be done for Miss Bella and for my brother, too, by my father, and as my brother was actually possessed of a considerable estate by virtue of the Deed of Gift and will of his godmother Lovell.

Had I known this before I should the less have wondered at many things I have been unable to account for in my brother's and sister's behaviour to me, and been more on my guard than I imagined there was a necessity to be.

"See, Sister Bella," said he in an indecent passion before my uncles on the occasion I have mentioned, "See how it is! You and I ought to look about us! This little siren is in a fair way to *out-uncle,* as she has already *out-grandfathered* us both!"

From this time (as I now find it plain upon recollection) did my brother and sister behave to me as to one who stood in their way, and to each other as having but one interest.

But if I will suffer myself to be prevailed upon, how happy (as *they* lay it out) shall we all be! Such presents am I to have, such jewels, and I cannot tell what from every one of the family! Then Mr. Solmes's fortunes are so great, and his proposals so very advantageous (no relation whom he values), that there will be abundant room to raise mine upon them, were the high-intended favours of my own relations to be quite out of the question.

This is the bright side that is turned to my father and uncles to captivate *them;* but I am afraid that my brother's and sister's design is to ruin me with them at any rate. Were it otherwise, would they not on my return from you have rather sought to *court* than *frighten* me into measures their hearts are so much bent to carry?

Meantime, orders are given to all the servants to show the highest respect to Mr. Solmes; the *generous* Mr. Solmes is now his character with some of our family! And *the noble settlements* are echoed from every mouth.

Hatred to Lovelace, family aggrandisement, and this great motive, *paternal authority!* What a force *united* must they be supposed to have, when *singly* each consideration is sufficient to carry all before it!

My BROTHER and my SISTER triumph.

What at present most concerns me is the peace of my mother's mind!

They do indeed value her; but, I am sorry to say, she has purchased that value by her compliances; yet has merit for which she ought to be venerated, prudence which ought of itself to be conformed to in everything.

But you, who know how much I love and reverence my mother, will judge what a difficulty I am under, to be obliged to oppose a scheme which *she* has engaged in. Yet I *must* oppose it (to comply is impossible), and must without delay *declare* my opposition or my difficulties will increase, since as I am just now informed, a lawyer has been this very day consulted (would you have believed it?) in relation to settlements.

Your truly affectionate,

Cl. Harlowe.

Miss Clarissa Harlowe to Miss Howe

Thursday evening, March 2.

I MUST TAKE or seek the occasion to apply to my mother for her mediation; for I am in danger of having a day fixed, and antipathy taken for bashfulness. Should not sisters *be* sisters to each other? Should they not make a common cause of it, as I may say, a cause of sex, on such occasions as the present? Yet mine, in support of my brother's selfishness, and no doubt in concert with him, has been urging in full assembly, it seems, that an absolute day be given me, and if I comply not, to be told, that it shall be to the forfeiture of all my fortunes, and of all their love.

She need not be so officious; my *brother's* interest, without hers, is strong enough, for he has found means to confederate all the family against me. Upon some fresh provocation or new intelligence concerning Mr. Lovelace (I know not what it is), they have bound themselves, or are to bind themselves, by a signed paper, to one another, to carry their point in favour of Mr. Solmes, in support of my *father's authority,* as it is called, and against Mr. Lovelace, as a libertine and an enemy to the family; and if so, I am sure, I may say against *me.* But hang the man, I had almost said, what is he to me? What *would* he be—were not this Mr. Sol—— O my dear, how I hate that man in the light he is proposed to me!

All of them at the same time are afraid of Mr. Lovelace; yet not afraid to provoke him! How am I entangled!—to be obliged to go on corresponding with him for *their* sakes—Heaven forbid that their persisted in violence should so drive me as to make it necessary for *my own!*

But surely *they* will yield—indeed *I* cannot.

An interruption obliges me to conclude myself in some hurry, as well as fright, what I must ever be,

Yours more than my own,
Clarissa Harlowe.

MISS HOWE TO MISS CLARISSA HARLOWE

Friday, March 3.

I HAVE BOTH your letters at once. It is very unhappy, my dear, since your friends will have you marry, that a person of your merit should be addressed by a succession of worthless creatures, who have nothing but their presumption for their excuse.

But where indeed is the man to be found (who has the least share of due diffidence) that dares to look up to Miss Clarissa Harlowe with hope, or with anything but wishes? Hence your Symmes, your Byrons, your Mullins, your Wyerleys (the best of the herd), and your Solmes, in turn invade you—wretches that, looking upon the rest of your family, need not despair of succeeding in an alliance with it—but, to you, what an inexcusable presumption!

Yet I am afraid all opposition will be in vain. You must, you will, I doubt, be sacrificed to this odious man. I know your family. There will be no resisting such baits as he has thrown out. Oh, my dear, my beloved friend! and are such charming qualities, is such exalted merit, to be sunk in such a marriage!

Wonder not, however, at your Bell's unsisterly behaviour in this affair: I have a particular to add to the inducements your insolent brother is governed by, which will account for all her driving. You have already owned that her *outward* eye was from *the first* struck with the figure and address of the man whom she pretends to despise, and who, 'tis certain, thoroughly despises her: but you have not told me that *still* she loves him of all men. She has owned her love, her uneasy days, and sleepless nights, and her revenge grafted upon her love, to her favourite Betty Barnes. To lay herself in the power of a servant's tongue! Poor creature—

And now you will not wonder to find in Miss Bell an implacable rival, rather than an affectionate sister; and for her driving on for a fixed day for sacrificing you to Solmes. I am sure, alas! I am *too* sure, that they will subdue such a fine spirit as yours, unused to opposition; and (*tell it not in Gath*) you *must* be Mrs. Solmes!

And now I am more than ever convinced of the propriety of the advice I formerly gave you, to keep in your own hands the estate bequeathed to you by your grandfather. Had you done so, it would have procured you at least an *outward* respect from your brother and sister, which would have made them conceal the envy and ill-will that now are bursting upon you from hearts so narrow.

I long for your next letter. I can think of no other subject but what relates to you and to your affairs: for I am, and ever will be, most affectionately,

Your own,
Anna Howe.

MISS CLARISSA HARLOWE TO MISS HOWE

[*Her preceding not at the time received*]

Friday, March 3.

O MY DEAR FRIEND, I have had a sad conflict! Trial upon trial; conference upon conference! But what law, what ceremony, can give a man a right to a heart which abhors him more than it does any living creature?

I hope my mother will be able to prevail for me.

I went down this morning when breakfast was ready with a very uneasy heart; wishing for an opportunity to appeal to my mother, in hopes to engage her interest in my behalf, and purposing to try to find one when she retired to her own apartment after breakfast: but, unluckily, there was the odious Solmes sitting asquat between my mother and sister, with *so much* assurance in his looks!

Had the wretch kept his seat, it might have been well enough: but the bent and broad-shouldered creature must needs rise and stalk towards a chair; which was just by that which was set for me.

I removed it to a distance, as if to make way to my own: And down I sat, abruptly I believe.

But this was not enough to daunt him. The man is a very confident, he is a very bold, staring man!

He took the removed chair and drew it so near mine, squatting in it with his ugly weight, that he pressed upon my hoop. I was so offended that I removed to another chair. I own I had too little command of myself. It gave my brother and sister too much advantage. But I did it involuntarily, I think. I could not help it.

I saw that my father was excessively displeased. Clarissa Harlowe! said he with a big voice—and there he stopped. Sir! said I, trembling and curtsying (for I *had* not then sat down again): and put my chair nearer the wretch, and sat down—my face, as I could feel, all in a glow.

Make tea, child, said my kind mamma: sit by me, love, and make tea.

I removed with pleasure to the seat the man had quitted; and being thus indulgently put into employment, soon recovered myself; and in the course of the breakfasting officiously asked two or three questions of Mr. Solmes, which I would not have done, but to make up with my father.

My mother was all kindness and condescension.

Before the usual breakfast-time was over my father withdrew with my mother, telling her he wanted to speak to her. Then my sister and next my aunt dropped away.

My brother gave himself some airs of insult, which I understood well enough; but which Mr. Solmes could make nothing of: and at last he arose from *his* seat. Sister, said he, I have a curiosity to show you. I will fetch it. And away he went; shutting the door close after him.

I saw what all this was for. I arose; the man hemming up

for a speech, rising and beginning to set his splay feet [indeed, my dear, the man in all his ways is hateful to me!] in an approaching posture. I will save my brother the trouble of bringing to me his curiosity, said I. I curtsied—your servant, sir. The man cried, madam, madam, twice, and looked like a fool. But away I went—to find my brother to save my word. But my brother, indifferent as the weather was, was gone to walk in the garden with my sister. A plain case that he had left his *curiosity* with me, and designed to show me no other.

I had but just got into my own apartment, and began to think of sending Hannah to beg an audience of my mother, when Shorey, her woman, brought me her commands to attend her in her closet.

My father, Hannah told me, was just gone out of it with a positive angry countenance.

I went down however; but, apprehending the subject she intended to talk to me upon, approached her trembling and my heart in visible palpitations.

She saw my concern. Holding out her kind arms as she sat, Come kiss me, my dear, said she. Why flutters my jewel so?

O my mamma! was all I could say; and I clasped my arms round her neck, and my face sunk into her bosom.

My child! my child! restrain, said she, your powers of moving! I dare not else trust myself with you.

Lift up your sweet face, my best child, my own Clarissa Harlowe! O my daughter, best-loved of my heart, lift up a face so ever-amiable to me! Why these sobs?—is an apprehended duty so affecting a thing that before I can speak—but I am glad, my love, you can guess at what I have to say to you. I am spared the pains of breaking to you what was a task upon me reluctantly enough undertaken *to* break to you.

Then rising, she drew a chair near her own and made me sit down by her, overwhelmed as I was with tears of apprehension of what she had to say, and of gratitude for her truly maternal goodness to me—sobs still my only language.

And drawing her chair still nearer to mine, she put her arms round my neck, and my glowing cheek, wet with my tears, close to her own: Let me talk to you, my child.

You know, my dear, what I every day forgo, and undergo, for

the sake of peace. Your papa is a very good man and means well; but he will not be controlled, nor yet persuaded. I see your conflict (loosing her arm and rising, not willing I should see how much she herself was affected). I will leave you a moment. I will leave you to recollection: and I charge you, on my blessing, that all this my truly maternal tenderness be not thrown away upon you.

And then she withdrew into the next apartment; wiping her eyes as she went from me; as mine overflowed; my heart taking in the whole compass of her meaning.

She soon returned, having recovered more steadiness.

Still on my knees, I had thrown my face cross the chair she had sat in.

Look up to me, my Clary Harlowe—no sullenness, I hope!

No, indeed, my ever-to-be-revered mamma—and I arose. I bent my knee.

She raised me. No kneeling to me but with knees of duty and compliance. Your heart, not your knees, must bend. It is absolutely determined—prepare yourself, therefore, to receive your *father,* when he visits you by and by, as he would wish to receive *you.* But on this one-quarter of an hour depends the peace of my future life, the satisfaction of all the family, and your own security from a man of violence: and I charge you *besides,* on my blessing, that you think of being Mrs. Solmes.

There went the dagger to my heart, and down I sunk: and when I recovered, found myself in the arms of my Hannah, my sister's Betty holding open my reluctantly-opened palm, my laces cut, my linen scented with hartshorn; and my mother gone.

Shorey came in with a message. Your mamma, miss, is concerned for your disorder: she expects you down again in an hour; and bid me say that she then hopes everything from your duty.

I made no reply; for what could I say? And leaning upon my Hannah's arm, withdrew to my own apartment.

Within that time my mother came up to *me.*

I love, she was pleased to say, to come into *this* apartment!—No emotions, child! No flutters! Am I not your mother! Am I not your fond, your indulgent mother! Do not discompose *me* by discomposing *yourself!* Do not occasion *me* uneasiness, when I would give *you* nothing but pleasure. Come, my dear, we will go into your closet.

She was pleased to tell me that my father and she, in order to spare my natural modesty, had taken the whole affair upon themselves——

Hear me out; and then speak, for I was going to expostulate. You are no stranger to the end of Mr. Solmes's visits——

O madam!——

Hear me out, and then speak. He is not indeed everything I wish him to be: but he is a man of probity, and has no vices——

No vices, madam!——

Hear me out, child.

I shall have done presently—a young creature of your virtuous and *pious* turn, she was pleased to say, cannot surely love a profligate: you love your brother too well to wish to marry one who had like to have killed him, and who threatened your uncles and defies us all. You have had your own way six or seven times: we want to secure you against a man so vile. Tell me (I have a *right* to know) whether you prefer this man to all others? Yet God forbid that I should know you do! for such a declaration would make us all miserable. Yet tell me, are your affections engaged to this man?

I knew what the inference would be if I had said they were not.

You hesitate—you answer me not—you cannot answer me. *Rising*—never more will I look upon you with an eye of favour——

O madam, madam! Kill me not with your displeasure—I would not, I *need* not, hesitate one moment did I not dread the inference, if I answer you as you wish. Yet be that inference what it will, your threatened displeasure will make me speak. And I declare to you that I know not my own heart, if it be not absolutely free.

Well then, Clary, if your heart be free——

O my beloved mamma, let the usual generosity of your dear heart operate in my favour.

I won't be interrupted, Clary. You have seen in my behaviour to you, on this occasion, a truly maternal tenderness; you have observed that I have undertaken this task with some reluctance, because the man is not everything; and because I know you carry your notions of perfection in a man too high——

Dearest madam, forgive me: it was always my pride and my pleasure to obey you. But look upon that man—see but the disagreeableness of his person——

Now, Clary, do I see whose person you have in your eye! Now is Mr. Solmes, I see, but *comparatively* disagreeable; disagreeable only as another man has a much more specious person.

But, madam, are not his manners equally so? Is not his person the true representative of his mind? That other man is not, shall not, be anything to me, release me but from this one man, whom my heart, unbidden, resists.

Condition thus with your father. Will *he* bear, do you think, to be thus dialogued with? And will *you* give up nothing? Have you not refused as many as have been offered to you? If you would not have us guess for whom, comply; for comply you must, or be looked upon as in a state of defiance with your whole family.

And saying this, she arose, and went from me. But at the chamber door stopped and turned back; I will not say below in what a disposition I leave you. Consider of everything. The matter is resolved upon. As you value your father's blessing and mine, and the satisfaction of all the family, resolve to comply. I will leave you for a few moments. I will come up to you again: see that I find you as I wish to find you; and since *your heart is free* let your duty govern it.

In about half an hour my mother returned. She found me in tears. She took my hand: it is my part evermore, said she, to be of the acknowledging side. I believe I have needlessly exposed myself to your opposition by the method I have taken with you.

When I came to you a second time, proceeded she, knowing that your opposition would avail you nothing, I refused to hear your reasons: and in this I was wrong.

You have as much of my pity as of my love. But what is *person,* Clary, with one of your prudence, and *your heart disengaged?*

Should the eye be disgusted when the heart is to be engaged?

O madam, who can think of marrying when the heart is shocked at the first appearance, and where the disgust must be confirmed by every conversation afterwards?

This, Clary, is owing to your prepossession. Let me not have cause to regret that noble firmness of mind in so young a creature which I thought your glory, and which was my boast in your character. In this instance it would be obstinacy, and want of duty. Have you not made objections to several——

That was to their *minds,* to their *principles,* madam—but this man——

Is an honest man, Clary Harlowe. He has a good mind. He is a virtuous man.

He an honest man! *His* a good mind, madam! *He* a virtuous man!

Nobody denies him these qualities.

Can *he* be an honest man who offers terms that will rob all his own relations of their just expectations? Can *his* mind be good——

You, Clary Harlowe, for whose sake he offers so much, are the last person that should make this observation.

Give me leave to say, madam, that a person preferring happiness to fortune, as I do; that want not even what I *have,* and can give up the use of *that,* as an instance of duty——

No more, no more of your merits! You know you will be a gainer by that cheerful instance of your duty; not a loser. You know you have but *cast your bread upon the waters*—so no more of that! For it is not understood as a merit by everybody, I assure you, though I think it a high one; and so did your father and uncles at the time——

At the *time,* madam! How unworthily do my brother and sister, who are afraid that the favour I was so lately in——

I hear nothing against your brother and sister. What family feuds have I in prospect at a time when I hoped most comfort from you all!

Just then, up came my father, with a sternness in his looks that made me tremble. He took two or three turns about my chamber, though pained by his gout. And then said to my mother, who was silent as soon as she saw him:

My dear, you are long absent. Dinner is near ready. What

you had to say lay in a very little compass. Surely, you have nothing to do but to declare *your* will, and *my* will—but perhaps you may be talking of the preparations. Let us have you soon down—your daughter in your hand, if worthy of the name.

And down he went, casting his eye upon me with a look so stern that I was unable to say one word to him, or even for a few minutes to my mother.

My mother, seeing my concern, seemed to pity me. She called me her good child, and kissed me; and told me that my father should not know I had made such opposition. Come, my dear, dinner will be upon table presently; shall we go down? —and took my hand.

This made me start: what, madam, go down to let it be supposed we were talking of *preparations!* O my beloved mamma, command me not down upon such a supposition.

You see, child, that to stay longer together, will be owning that you are debating about an absolute duty: and that will not be borne. I will a third time leave you. I must say something by way of excuse for you: and that you desire not to go down to dinner—that your modesty on the occasion——

O madam! say not my modesty on *such* an occasion: for that will be to give hope——

And design you *not* to give hope? Perverse girl! *Rising, and flinging from me;* take more time for consideration! Since it is necessary, *take* more time—and when I see you next, let me know what blame I have to cast upon myself, or to bear from your father for my indulgence to you.

She made, however, a little stop at the chamber door; and seemed to expect that I would have besought her to make the gentlest construction for me; for, hesitating, she was pleased to say, I suppose you would not have me make a report——

O madam, interrupted I, whose favour can I hope for if I lose my mamma's?

And so my mother went downstairs.

Your sincere and ever affectionate,

Cl. Harlowe.

MISS CLARISSA HARLOWE TO MISS HOWE

MY MOTHER on her return, which was as soon as she had dined, was pleased to inform me, that she told my father, on his questioning her about my *cheerful* compliance, that she was willing, on so material a point, to give a child whom she had so *much reason to love,* liberty to say all that was in her heart to say; letting him know, that when he came up, she was attending to my pleas; for that she found I had rather not marry at all.

She told me that to this my father angrily said, let her take care—let her take care—that she give me not ground to suspect her of a preference somewhere else. But, if it be to ease *her* heart, and not to dispute *my* will, you may hear her out.

So, Clary, said my mother, I am returning in a temper accordingly; and I hope you will not again, by *your* peremptoriness, show *me* how I ought to treat *you.*

But, why, dearest madam, why am I, the *youngest,* to be precipitated into a state, that I am very far from wishing to enter with anybody?

You are going to question me, I suppose, why your sister is not thought of for Mr. Solmes?

I hope, madam, it will not displease you if I were?

I might refer you for an answer to your *father.*—Mr. Solmes has reasons for preferring *you*——

And I have reasons, madam, for disliking *him.* And why am I——

This quickness upon me, interrupted my mother, is not to be borne! I am gone, and your father comes, if *I* can do no good with you.

O madam, I would rather die, than——

She put her hand to my mouth.—No peremptoriness, Clary Harlowe: once you declare yourself inflexible, I have done.

I wept for vexation. This is all, all, my brother's doings—his grasping views——

No reflections upon your brother; he has entirely the honour of the family at heart.

I would no more dishonour my family, madam, than my brother would.

I believe it: but I hope you will allow your father and me and your uncles to judge what will do it honour, what dishonour.

I then offered to live single; never to marry at all; or never but with their full approbation.

If you mean to show your duty and your obedience, Clary, you must show it in *our* way; not in *your own*.

Your patience, my dearest mamma: You were pleased to *say*, you would hear me with patience. PERSON in a man is nothing, because I am supposed to be prudent: so my eye is to be disgusted and my reason not convinced——

Girl, girl!

Thus are my imputed good qualities to be made my punishment; and I am to be wedded to a *monster*——

(Astonishing!—Can this, Clarissa, be from you?)

O my dear mamma, said I, forgive me! But surely you cannot believe I can ever think of having that man!

She was very angry, and seemed to be greatly disappointed. She threatened to turn me over to my father and my uncles: she however bid me (generously bid me) consider, what a handle I gave to my brother and sister, if I thought they had views to serve by making my uncles dissatisfied with me.

I, said she, in a milder accent, have early said all that I thought could be said against the present proposal, on a supposition that you, who have refused several others (whom I own to be preferable as to person), would *not* approve of it; and could I have succeeded, you, Clary, had never heard of it. But if *I* could not, how can *you* expect to prevail? My great ends, in the task I have undertaken, are the preservation of the family peace so likely to be overturned; to reinstate you in the affections of your father and uncles; and to preserve you from a man of violence. Your father, you must needs think, will flame out upon your refusal to comply: your uncles are so thoroughly convinced of the consistency of the measure with their favourite views of aggrandising the family, that they are as much determined as your father—your Aunt Hervey and your Uncle Hervey are of the same party. And it is hard if a father and mother, and uncles and aunt, all conjoined, cannot be allowed to direct your choice—surely, my dear girl, proceeded she (for I was silent all this time), it cannot be that you are the *more* averse because the *family views* will be promoted by the match. This, I assure you, is what everybody must think, if you comply not. Nor, while the man so obnoxious to us all remains unmarried, and *buzzes* about you, will the strongest asseverations you can make of your resolution and wishes to live single, be in the least regarded. And well you know, that were Mr. Lovelace an angel, and your father made it a point that you should not have him, it would be in vain to dispute his will. As to the prohibition laid upon you, (much as I will own against *my* liking,) that is owing to the belief that you corresponded by Miss Howe's means with that man; nor do I doubt that you did so.

I answered to every article in such a manner as I am sure would have satisfied her, could she have been permitted to judge for herself; and I then inveighed with bitterness against the disgraceful prohibitions laid upon me.

They would serve to show me, she was pleased to say, how much in earnest my father was. They might be taken off, whenever I thought fit, and no harm done, nor disgrace received. But if I were to be contumacious, I might thank myself for all that would follow.

I sighed. I wept. I was silent.

Shall I, Clary, said she, shall I tell your father that these prohibitions are as unnecessary as I hoped they would be? That you know your *duty,* and will not offer to controvert his will? What say you, my love?

O madam, what can I say to questions so indulgently put? I do indeed *know* my duty: no creature in the world is more willing to *practise* it: but, pardon me, dearest madam, if I say that I must bear these prohibitions, if I am to pay so dear to have them taken off.

Determined and perverse, my dear mamma called me: and after walking twice or thrice in anger about the room, she turned to me; your heart *free,* Clarissa! How can you tell me your heart is free? Such extraordinary antipathies to a particular person must be owing to extraordinary prepossessions in another's favour! Tell me, Clary, and tell me truly—do you not continue to correspond with Mr. Lovelace?

Dearest madam, replied I, you know my motives: to prevent

mischief, I answered his letters. The reasons for our apprehensions of this sort are not over.

I own to you, Clary (although now I would not have it known), that I once thought a little qualifying among such violent spirits was not amiss. I did not know but all things would come round again by the mediation of Lord M. and his two sisters: but as they all three think proper to resent for their nephew; and as their nephew thinks fit to defy us all; and as terms are offered on the other hand that could not be asked, which will very probably prevent your grandfather's estate going out of the family, and may be a means to bring a still greater into it; I see not, that the continuance of your correspondence with him either can or ought to be permitted. I therefore now forbid it to you, as you value my favour.

Be pleased, madam, only to advise me how to break it off with safety to my brother and uncles; and it is all I wish for. Would to Heaven the man so hated had not the pretence to make of having been too violently treated, when he meant peace and reconciliation! It would always have been in my own power to have broke with him. His reputed immoralities would have given me a just pretence at any time to do so--but, madam, as my uncles and my brother will keep no measures; as he has heard what the view is; and as I have reason to think, that he is only restrained by his regard for me from resenting their violent treatment of him and his family; what can I do? Would you have me, madam, make him desperate?

The law will protect us, child! Offended magistracy will assert itself——

But, madam, may not some dreadful mischief first happen? The law asserts not itself till it *is* offended.

You have made offers, Clary, if you might be obliged in the point in question—are you really earnest, were you to be complied with, to break off all correspondence with Mr. Lovelace? Let me know this.

Indeed, I am; and I will. You, madam, shall see all the letters that have passed between us. You shall see I have given him no encouragement independent of my duty. And when you have seen them, you will be better able to direct me how, on the condition I have offered, to break entirely with him.

I take you at your word, Clarissa—give me *his* letters; and the copies of *yours.*

I am sure, madam, you will keep the knowledge that I write, and what I write——

No conditions with your mother—surely my prudence may be trusted to.

I begged her pardon; and besought her to take the key of the private drawer in my escritoire, where they lay, that she herself might see that I had no reserves to my mother.

She did; and took all his letters and the copies of mine. Unconditioned with, she was pleased to say, they shall be yours again, unseen by anybody else.

I thanked her; and she withdrew to read them, saying she would return them when she had.

You, my dear, have seen all the letters that passed between Mr. Lovelace and me till my last return from you. He earnestly insists (upon what he has so often proposed) that I will give him leave, in company with Lord M., to wait upon my uncles, and even upon my father—and he promises patience, if new provocations, absolutely beneath a man to bear, be not given: which by the way I am far from being able to engage for.

In my answer, I absolutely declare, as I tell him I have often done, "that he is to expect no favour from me against the approbation of my friends: that I am sure their consents for his visiting any of them will never be obtained: that I cannot allow myself to correspond with him any longer in this clandestine manner: it is mean, low, undutiful, I tell him; and has a giddy appearance which cannot be excused: that therefore he is not to expect that I *will* continue it."

To this, in his last, among other things, he replies, "that if I am actually determined to break off all correspondence with him, he must conclude that it is with a view to become the wife of a man whom no woman of honour and fortune can think tolerable. If he shall know that it will have my consent, he must endeavour to resign to his destiny: but if it be brought about by compulsion, he shall not be able to answer for the consequence."

In about an hour my mother returned. Take your letters, Clary: I have nothing, she was pleased to say, to tax your discretion with, as to the wording of yours to him. Your heart, you *say,* is *free:* you own, that you cannot think, as matters are circumstanced, that a match with a man so obnoxious as he now is to us all, is proper to be thought of; what do you propose to do? What, Clary, are your own thoughts of the matter?

Without hesitation thus I answered—what I humbly propose is this: "That I will write to Mr. Lovelace (for I have not answered his last) that he has nothing to do between my father and me: that I neither *ask* his advice nor *need* it: but that since he thinks he has some pretence for interfering, because of my brother's avowal of the interest of Mr. Solmes in displeasure to him, I will assure him (without giving him any reason to impute the assurance to be in the least favourable to himself) that I never will be that man's." And if, proceeded I, I may be permitted to give him this assurance; and Mr. Solmes, in consequence of it, be discouraged from prosecuting his address; let Mr. Lovelace be satisfied or dissatisfied, I will go no further; nor write another line to him; nor ever see him more if I can avoid it: and I shall have a good excuse for it without bringing in any of my family.

Ah! my love! But what shall we do about the *terms* Mr. Solmes offers? He has even given hopes to your brother that he will make exchanges of estates; or at least that he will purchase the northern one; for you know it must be entirely consistent with the family views, that we increase our interest in this country.

And for the sake of these views, for the sake of this plan of my brother's, am I, madam, to be given in marriage to a man I never can endure! O my dear mamma, save me, save me if you can, from this heavy evil! I had rather be buried alive, indeed I had, than have that man!

She chid me for my vehemence; but was so good as to tell me that she would sound my Uncle Harlowe who was then below; and if he encouraged her (or would engage to second her) she would venture to talk to my father herself, and I should hear further in the morning.

She went down to tea, and kindly undertook to excuse my attendance at supper.

MISS CLARISSA HARLOWE TO MISS HOWE

Sat., Mar. 4.

I HAVE NOT BEEN in bed all night; nor am I in the least drowsy. Expectation and hope and doubt (an uneasy state!) kept me sufficiently wakeful. I stepped down at my usual time that it might not be known I had not been in bed.

About eight o'clock Shorey came to me from my mother with orders to attend her in her chamber.

My mother had been weeping, I saw by her eyes: but her aspect seemed to be less tender and less affectionate than the day before; and this, as soon as I entered into her presence, struck me with an awe, which gave a great damp to my spirits.

Sit down, Clary Harlowe; I shall talk to you by and by: and continued looking into a drawer among laces and linen in a way neither busy nor unbusy.

I believe it was a quarter of an hour before she spoke to me (my heart throbbing with the suspense all the time); and then she asked me coldly, what directions I had given for the day?

I showed her the bill of fare for this day and to-morrow, if, I said, it pleased her to approve of it.

She made a small alteration in it; but with an air so cold and so solemn, as added to my emotions.

Mr. Harlowe talks of dining out to-day, I think, at my brother Antony's.

Mr. Harlowe!—not my father! Have I not then a father! thought I?

Sit down when I bid you.

I sat down.

You look very sullen, Clary.

I hope not, madam.

If children would always be children—parents—and there she stopped.

She then went to her toilet, and looked in the glass and gave half a sigh—the other half, as if she would not have sighed could she have helped it, she gently hemmed away.

I don't love to see the girl look so sullen.

Indeed, madam, I am not sullen. And I arose and, turning

from her, drew out my handkerchief, for the tears ran down my cheeks.

I thought, by the glass before me, I saw the *mother* in her softened eye cast towards me: but her words confirmed not the hoped-for tenderness.

One of the most provoking things in the world is to have people cry for what they can help!

I wish to Heaven I could, madam! And I sobbed again.

Tears of penitence and sobs of perverseness are mighty well suited! You may go up to your chamber. I shall talk with you by and by.

I curtsied with reverence.

Mock me not with outward gestures of respect. The heart, Clary, is what I want.

Indeed, madam, you have it. It is not so much mine as my mamma's!

Fine talking! As somebody says, if words were to pass for duty, Clarissa Harlowe would be the dutifullest child breathing.

God bless that somebody! And I curtsied, and, pursuant to her last command, was going.

She seemed struck; but *was* to be angry with me.

So turning from me, she spoke with quickness, whither now, Clary Harlowe?

You commanded me, madam, to go to my chamber.

I see you are very ready to go out of my presence. Is your compliance the effect of sullenness or obedience?

I could hold no longer; but threw myself at her feet: O my dearest mamma! Let me know all I am to suffer: let me know what I am to be! I *will* bear it, if I *can* bear it: but your displeasure I cannot bear!

Leave me, leave me, Clary Harlowe! No kneeling!—limbs so supple; will so stubborn! Rise, I tell you.

I cannot rise! I will disobey my mamma when she bids me leave her without being reconciled to me! No sullens, my mamma: no perverseness: but worse than either: this is direct disobedience! Yet tear not yourself from me! (wrapping my arms about her as I kneeled; she struggling to get from me; my face lifted up to hers with eyes running over, that spoke not my heart if they were not all humility and reverence) you must not, must not, tear yourself from me! (for still the dear lady struggled, and looked this way and that in a sweet disorder, as if she knew not what to do.)—I will neither rise nor leave you, nor let you go till you say you are not angry with me.

O thou ever-moving child of my heart! (folding her dear arms about my neck, as mine embraced her knees) why was this task! But leave me—you have discomposed me beyond expression! Leave me, my dear! I won't be angry with you—if I can help it—if you'll be good.

I arose trembling and hardly knowing what I did, or how I stood or walked, withdrew to my chamber. My Hannah followed me as soon as she heard me quit my mother's presence, and with salts and spring water just kept me from fainting; and that was as much as she could do.

My mother went down to breakfast. I was not fit to appear: but if I had been better, I suppose I should not have been sent for; since the permission for my attending her down, was given by my father (when in my chamber) only on condition that she found me *worthy of the name of daughter*. That, I doubt, I never shall be in *his* opinion, if he be not brought to change his mind as to this Mr. Solmes.

Miss Clarissa Harlowe to Miss Howe

Sat., March 4. 12 o'clock.

As to what you mention of my sister's value for Mr. Lovelace, I am not very much surprised at it. She never tells the story of their parting, and of her refusal of him, but her colour rises, she looks with disdain upon me, and mingles anger with the airs she gives herself: anger as well as airs, demonstrating that she refused a man whom she thought worth accepting: where else is the reason either for anger or boast?

As to what you say of my giving up to my father's control the estate devised me, my motives at the time, as you acknowledge, were not blameable. You were indeed jealous of my brother's views *against me;* or rather of his predominant love of *himself;* but I did not think so hardly of my brother and sister as you always did.

And now for the *most* concerning part of your letter.

You think I must of necessity, as matters are circumstanced, be Solmes's wife. I will not be very rash, my dear, in protesting to the contrary: but I think it never can, and what is still more, never *ought* to be! I repeat, that I *ought* not: for surely, my dear, I should not give up to my brother's ambition the happiness of my future life. The less, surely, ought I to give into these grasping views of my brother, as I myself heartily despise the end aimed at; as I wish not either to change my state, or better my fortunes; and as I am fully persuaded, that happiness and riches are *two* things and very seldom meet together.

I am stopped. Hannah shall deposit this. She was ordered by my mother (who asked where I was) to tell me that she would come up and talk with me in my own closet. She is coming! Adieu, my dear.

MISS CLARISSA HARLOWE TO MISS HOWE

Sat. Afternoon.

THE EXPECTED conference is over: but my difficulties are increased. This, as my mother was pleased to tell me, being the last *persuasory* effort that is to be attempted.

I have made, said she, as she entered my room, a *short* as well as *early* dinner, on purpose to confer with you: and I do assure you that it will be the last conference I shall either be permitted or *inclined* to hold with you on the subject, if you should prove as refractory as it is imagined you will prove by some, who are of opinion that I have not the weight with you which my indulgence deserves. But I hope you will convince as well them as me of the contrary.

Your father both dines and sups at your uncle's, on purpose to give us this opportunity; and according to the report I shall make on his return (which I have promised shall be a very faithful one), he will take his measures with you.

I was offering to speak—hear, Clarissa, what I have to tell you, said she, before you speak, unless what you have to say will signify to me your compliance—say—*will* it? If it *will*, you may speak.

I was silent.

She looked with concern and anger upon me—no compliance,

I find!—such a dutiful young creature hitherto! Will you not, *can* you not, speak as I would have you speak? Then (rejecting me as it were with her hand) continue silent. *I,* no more than your *father,* will bear your *avowed* contradiction.

She paused, with a look of expectation, as if she waited for my consenting answer.

I was still silent, looking down; the tears in my eyes.

O thou determined girl! But say—speak out—are you resolved to stand in opposition to us all, in a point our hearts are set upon?

May I, madam, be permitted to expostulate?

To what purpose expostulate with *me,* Clarissa? Your *father* is determined. Have I not told you there is no receding; that the honour as well as the interest of the family is concerned? Be ingenuous: you *used* to be so, even occasionally against yourself: who at the long run *must* submit—*all* of us to *you;* or *you* to *all* of us? If you intend to yield at *last* if you find you cannot conquer, yield *now,* and with a grace—for yield you must, or be none of our child.

I wept. I knew not what to say; or rather how to express what I had to say.

Take notice, that there are flaws in your grandfather's will: not a shilling of that estate will be yours if you do not yield. Your grandfather left it to you as a reward of your duty to *him* and to *us*. You will *justly* forfeit it, if——

Permit me, good madam, to say that, if it were *unjustly* bequeathed me, I ought not to wish to have it. But I hope Mr. Solmes will be apprised of these flaws.

This is very pertly said, Clarissa: but reflect, that the forfeiture of that estate through your opposition will be attended with the total loss of your father's favour.

I must accommodate myself, madam. It becomes me to be thankful for what I have had.

What perverseness! said my mother. But if you depend upon the favour of either or both your uncles, vain will be that dependence: *they* will give you up, I do assure you, if your father does, and absolutely renounce you.

I am sorry, madam, that I have had so little merit as to have made no deeper impressions of favour for me in their hearts· but I will love and honour them as long as I live.

All this, Clarissa, makes your prepossession in a certain man's favour the more evident. Indeed your brother and sister cannot go any whither but they hear of these prepossessions.

It is a great grief to me, madam, to be made the subject of the public talk: but I hope you will have the goodness to excuse me for observing that the authors of my disgrace within doors, the talkers of my prepossession without, and the reporters of it from abroad, are originally the same persons.

She severely chid me for this.

I received her rebukes in silence.

You are sullen, Clarissa: I see you are *sullen*. And she walked about the room in anger. Then turning to me—you can *bear* the imputation of sullenness, I see! I was afraid of telling you all I was enjoined to tell you, in case you were to be unpersuadable: but I find that I had a greater opinion of your delicacy, of your gentleness than I needed to have—it cannot discompose so steady, so inflexible a young creature, to be told, as I now tell you, that the settlements are actually drawn; and that you will be called down in a very few days to hear them read and to sign them: for it is impossible, if your heart be free, that you can make the least objection to them; except it will be an objection with you, that they are so much in your favour and in the favour of all our family.

I was speechless, absolutely speechless. Although my heart was ready to burst, yet could I neither weep nor speak.

I am sorry, said she, for your averseness to this match [*match* she was pleased to call it!]: but there is no help; and you must comply.

I was still speechless.

She folded the *warm statue,* as she was pleased to call me, in her arms; and entreated me, for Heaven's sake, and for her sake, to comply.

Speech and tears were lent me at the same time. You have given me life, madam, said I, clasping my uplifted hands together, and falling on one knee; a happy one till now has *your* goodness and my *papa's* made it! O do not, do not, make all the remainder of it miserable!

Your father, replied she, is resolved not to see you till he sees you as obedient a child as you used to be. This *is*, this *must* be, my last effort with you. Give me hope, my dear child: my peace is concerned.

To give you hope, my dearest, my most indulgent mamma, is to give you everything. Can I be honest, if I give a hope that I cannot confirm?

She was very angry. She again called me perverse: she upbraided me with regarding only my own prepossessions, and respecting not either her peace of mind or my own duty.

"I have had a very hard time of it, said she, between your father and you; for, seeing your dislike, I have more than once pleaded for you: but all to no purpose."

She went on: "Your father has declared that your unexpected opposition [*unexpected she was pleased to call it*], and Mr. Lovelace's continued menaces and insults, more and more convince him that a short day is necessary in order to put an end to all that man's hopes, and to his own apprehensions resulting from the disobedience of a child so favoured. He has, therefore, actually ordered patterns of the richest silks to be sent for from London——"

I started—I was out of breath—I gasped at this frightful precipitance. I was going to open with warmth against it. But she was pleased to hurry on, that I might not have time to express my disgusts at such a communication—to this effect:

"Your father, added she, at his going out, told me what he expected from me, in case I found that I had not the requisite influence upon you. It was this—that I should directly separate myself from you, and leave you singly to take the consequence of your double disobedience—I therefore entreat you, my dear Clarissa, concluded she, and that in the most earnest and condescending manner, to signify to your father, on his return, your ready obedience; and this as well for my sake as for your own."

Affected by my mother's goodness to me, and by that part of her argument which related to her own peace, I could not but wish it were possible for me to obey. I therefore paused, hesitated, considered, and was silent for some time. But then, recollecting that all was owing to the instigations of a brother and sister, wholly actuated by selfish and envious views; I would, madam said I, folding my hands, with an earnestness in which my whole heart was engaged, bear the cruellest tortures, bear loss of limb, and even of life to give *you* peace. But this man, every moment I would, at your command, think of him with favour, is the more my aversion. You cannot, indeed you cannot, think how my whole soul resists him! And to talk of contracts concluded upon; of patterns; of a short day! Save me, save me, O my dearest mamma, save your child from this heavy, from this insupportable evil!

Never was there a countenance that expressed so significantly, as my mother's did, an anguish, which she struggled to hide under an anger she was compelled to assume—till the latter overcoming the former, she turned from me with an uplifted eye, and stamping—*strange perverseness!* were the only words I heard of a sentence that she angrily pronounced; and was going. I then, half-franticly I believe, laid hold of her gown. Have patience with me, dearest madam! said I. Do not *you* renounce me totally! If you *must* separate yourself from your child, let it not be with *absolute* reprobation on *your own* part! My uncles may be hard-hearted—my father may be immovable. I may suffer from my brother's ambition, and from my sister's envy! But let me not lose my mamma's love; at least, her pity.

She turned to me with benigner rays. You *have* my love! You *have* my *pity!* But, O my dearest girl—I have not *yours*.

Indeed, indeed, madam, you have; and all my reverence, all my gratitude, you have! But in this *one* point: cannot I be this *once* obliged? Will no *expedient* be accepted? Have I not made a very fair proposal as to Mr. Lovelace?

I wish, for both our sakes, my dear unpersuadable girl, that the decision of this point lay with me. But why, when you know it does not, why should you thus perplex and urge me? To renounce Mr. Lovelace is now but *half* what is aimed at. Nor will anybody else believe you in earnest in the offer, if *I* would. While you remain single, Mr. Lovelace will have hopes—and you, in the opinion of others, inclinations.

Permit me, dearest madam, to say, that *your* goodness to me, *your* patience, *your* peace, weigh more with me than all the rest put together: for although I am to be treated by my brother, and, through his instigation, by my father, as a slave in this point, and not as a daughter, yet my mind is not that of a slave. You have not brought me up to be mean.

So, Clary! you are already at defiance with your father! You forget that I must separate myself from you, if you will not comply. You do not remember that your father will take you up, where I leave you. Once more, however, I will put it to you: are you determined to brave your father's displeasure? Do you choose to break with us all, rather than encourage Mr. Solmes? Rather than give me hope?

Dreadful alternative! But is not my sincerity, is not the integrity of my heart, concerned in my answer? May not my everlasting happiness be the sacrifice? Forgive me, madam: bear with your child's boldness in such a cause as *this!* Settlements drawn! Patterns sent for! An early day! Dear, dear madam, how can I give hope, and not intend to be this man's?

Ah, girl, never say your *heart is free!* You deceive yourself if you think it is. You may guess what your father's first question on his return will be. He *must* know that I can do nothing with you. I have done my part. Seek *me,* if your mind change before he comes back: you have yet a little more time as he stays supper. I will no more seek *you* nor *to* you. And away she flung.

What could I do but weep?

Cl. H.

MISS CLARISSA HARLOWE TO MISS HOWE

Sat. Night.

I HAVE been down.

I found my mother and sister together in my sister's parlour.

I entered like a dejected criminal; and besought the favour of a private audience.

You have, said she (looking at me with a sternness that never sits well on her sweet features), rather a *requesting* than a *conceding* countenance, Clarissa Harlowe: if I am mistaken, tell me so; and I will withdraw with you wherever you will. Yet, whether so or not, you may say what you have to say before your sister.

I come down, madam, said I, to beg of you to forgive me for anything you may have taken amiss in what passed above respecting your honoured self; and that you will be pleased to use your endeavours to soften my papa's displeasure against me on his return.

Such aggravating looks; such lifting up of hands and eyes; such a furrowed forehead in my sister!

My mother was angry enough without all that; and asked me to what purpose I came down, if I were still so untractable?

She had hardly spoken the words when Shorey came in to tell her that Mr. Solmes was in the hall, and desired admittance.

Ugly creature! I believe it was contrived, that he should be here at supper, to know the result of the conference between my mother and me, and that my father, on his return, might find us together.

I was hurrying away; but my mother commanded me (since I had come down only, as she said, to mock her) not to stir; and at the same time see if I could behave so to Mr. Solmes, as might encourage her to make the favourable report to my father which I had besought her to make.

My sister triumphed. I was vexed to be so caught, and to have such an angry and cutting rebuke given me.

The man stalked in. His usual walk is by pauses, as if he was telling his steps: and first paid his clumsy respects to my mother; then to my sister; next to me, as if I were already his wife, and therefore to be last in his notice; and sitting down by me, told us in general what weather it was. Then addressing himself to me; and how do *you* find it, miss? and would have taken my hand.

I withdrew it, I believe with disdain enough. My mother frowned. My sister bit her lip.

I could not contain myself: I never was so bold in my life; for I went on with my plea as if Mr. Solmes had not been there.

My mother coloured, and looked at him, at my sister, and at me. My sister's eyes were opener and bigger than ever I saw them before.

The man understood me. He hemmed, and removed from one chair to another.

I went on, supplicating for my mother's favourable report: Nothing but invincible dislike, said I——

What would the girl be at, interrupted my mother? Why, Clary! Is this a subject! Is this!—is this!—is this a time—and again she looked upon Mr. Solmes.

I beg pardon, madam, said I. But my papa will soon return. And since I am not permitted to withdraw, it is not necessary, I humbly presume, that Mr. Solmes's presence should deprive me of this opportunity to implore your favourable report; and at the same time, if he still visit on my account (looking at him) to convince him, that it cannot possibly be to any purpose——

Is the girl mad? said my mother, interrupting me.

My sister, with the affectation of a whisper to my mother: This is—this is *spite,* madam [very *spitefully* she spoke the word] because you commanded her to stay.

I only looked at her, and turning to my mother, Permit me, madam, said I, to repeat my request. I have no brother, no sister! If I lose my mamma's favour I am lost for ever!

Mr. Solmes removed to his first seat, and fell to gnawing the head of his hazel; a carved head, almost as ugly as his own.

My sister rose, with a face all over scarlet, and stepping to the table, where lay a fan, she took it up, and although Mr. Solmes had observed that the weather was cold, fanned herself very violently.

My mother came to me, and angrily taking my hand, led me out of that parlour into my own; which, you know, is next to it. Is not this behaviour very bold, very provoking, think you, Clary?

I beg your pardon, madam, if it has that appearance to you. But indeed, my dear mamma, there seem to be snares laying for me. Too well I know my brother's drift.

My mother was about to leave me in high displeasure.

I besought her to stay: one favour, but one favour, dearest madam, said I, give me leave to beg of you——

What would the girl?

I see how everything is working about. I never, never can think of Mr. Solmes. My papa will be in tumults when he is told I cannot. They will judge of the tenderness of your heart to a poor child who seems devoted by every one else, from the willingness you have already shown to hearken to my prayers. There will be endeavours used to confine me, and keep me out of your presence, and out of the presence of every one who used to love me [*this, my dear Miss* Howe, *is threatened*]. If this be effected; if it be put out of my power to plead my own cause, and to appeal to you, and to my Uncle Harlowe, of whom only I have hope; then will every ear be opened against me, and every tale encouraged—it is, therefore, my humble request, that, added to the disgraceful prohibitions I now suffer under, you will not, if you can help it, give way to my being denied *your* ear.

Your listening Hannah has given you this intelligence, as she does many others.

My Hannah, madam, listens not.

No more in Hannah's behalf—Hannah is known to make mischief—Hannah is known—but no more of that bold intermeddler. 'Tis true your father threatened to confine you to your chamber if you complied not, in order the more assuredly to deprive you of the opportunity of corresponding with those who harden your heart against his will. He bid me tell you so, when he went out, if I found you refractory. But I was loth to deliver so harsh a declaration; being still in hope that you would come down to us in a compliant temper. Hannah has overheard this I suppose; as also that he declared he would break your heart rather than you should break his. And I now assure you, that you will be confined, and prohibited making teasing appeals to any of us: and we shall see who is to submit, you to us, or everybody to you.

And this, said I, is all I have to hope for from my mamma?

It is. But, Clary, this one further opportunity I give you: go in again to Mr. Solmes, and behave discreetly to him; and let your father find you together, upon *civil* terms at least.

My feet moved (of *themselves*, I think) farther from the parlour where he was, and towards the stairs; and there I stopped and paused.

If, proceeded she, you are determined to stand in defiance of us all—then indeed may you go up to your chamber (as you are ready to do)—and God help you!

God help me, indeed! for I cannot give hope of what I cannot intend.

I was moving to go up——

And *will* you go up, Clary?

I turned my face to her: my officious tears would needs plead for me: I could not just then speak; and stood still.

Good girl, distress me not thus! Dear, good girl, do not thus distress me! holding out her hand; but standing still likewise.

What *can* I do, madam? What *can* I do?

Go in again, my child. Go in again, my *dear* child! repeated she; and let your father find you together.

What, madam, to give *him* hope? To give hope to Mr. Solmes?

Obstinate, perverse, undutiful Clarissa! with a rejecting hand and angry aspect; then take your own way and go up!

She flung from me with high indignation: and I went up with a heavy heart; and feet as slow as my heart was heavy.

My father is come home, and my brother with him. Late as it is they are all shut up together.

The angry assembly is broken up. My two uncles and my Aunt Hervey are sent for, it seems, to be here in the morning to breakfast. I shall then, I suppose, know my doom. 'Tis past eleven, and I am ordered not to go to bed.

Twelve o'clock.

This moment the keys of everything are taken from me. It was proposed to send for me down: but my father said he could not bear to look upon me.

Cl. Harlowe.

Miss Clarissa Harlowe to Miss Howe

Sunday Morning, March 5.

Hannah has just brought me, from the private place in the garden wall, a letter from Mr. Lovelace, signed also by Lord M.

He tells me in it, "That Mr. Solmes makes it his boast that he is to be married in a few days to one of the shyest women in England: that my brother explains his meaning; this shy creature, he says, is me; and he assures every one that his younger sister is very soon to be Mr. Solmes's wife. He tells of the patterns bespoken which my mother mentioned to me."

Not one thing escapes him that is done or said in this house.

"He knows not, he says, what my relations' inducements can be to prefer such a man as Solmes to him. If advantageous settlements be the motive, Solmes shall not offer what he will refuse to comply with.

"As to his estate and family; the first cannot be excepted against: and for the second, he will not disgrace himself by a comparison so odious. He appeals to Lord M. for the regularity of his life and manners ever since he has made his addresses to me, or had hope of my favour.

"He desires my leave (in company with my lord, in a pacific manner) to attend my father or uncles, in order to make proposals that *must* be accepted, if they will but see him and hear what they are: and tells me, that he will submit to any measures that I shall prescribe, in order to bring about a reconciliation."

He presumes to be very earnest with me, "to give him a private meeting some night in my father's garden, attended by whom I please."

Really, my dear, were you to see his letter, you would think I had given him great encouragement, and that I am in direct treaty with him; or that he is sure that my friends will drive me into a foreign protection; for he has the boldness to offer, in my lord's name, an asylum to me should I be tyrannically treated in Solmes's behalf.

There are other particulars in this letter which I ought to

mention to you: but I will take an opportunity to send you the letter itself, or a copy of it.

For my own part, I am very uneasy to think how I have been *drawn* on one hand, and *driven* on the other, into a clandestine, in short, into a mere lover-like correspondence which my heart condemns.

It is easy to see, if I do not break it off, that Mr. Lovelace's advantages, by reason of my unhappy situation, will every day increase, and I shall be more and more entangled. Yet if I do put an end to it, without making it a condition of being freed from Mr. Solmes's address.

All my relations are met. Mr. Solmes is expected. I am excessively uneasy. I must lay down my pen.

Sunday Noon.

What a cruel thing is suspense!

I desired to speak with Shorey. Shorey came. I directed her to carry to my mother my request for permission to go to church this afternoon. What think you was the return? Tell her that she must direct herself to her brother for any favour she has to to ask.

I was resolved, however, to ask of *him* this favour. Accordingly, when they sent me up my solitary dinner, I gave the messenger a billet, in which I made it my humble request through him to my father, to be permitted to go to church this afternoon.

This was the contemptuous answer: "Tell her that her request will be taken into consideration *to-morrow*."

Patience will be the fittest return I can make to such an insult.

On recollection, I thought it best to renew my request. The following is a copy of what I wrote, and what follows that of the answer sent me.

SIR,—I know not what to make of the answer brought to my request of being permitted to go to church this afternoon. If you designed to show your pleasantry by it, I hope that will continue; and then my request will be granted.

My present situation is such that I never more wanted the benefit of the public prayers.

I will solemnly engage only to go thither and back again.

Nor will I, but by distant civilities, return the compliments of any of my acquaintance. My disgraces, if they are to have an end, need not to be proclaimed to the whole world.

Your unhappy sister,
Cl. Harlowe.

To Miss Clarissa Harlowe

For a girl to lay so much stress upon going to church, and yet resolve to defy her parents in an article of the greatest consequence to them, and to the whole family, is an absurdity. You are recommended, miss, to the practice of your *private* devotions. The *intention* is, I tell you plainly, to mortify you into a sense of your duty.

Ja. Harlowe.

Miss Clarissa Harlowe to Miss Howe

Monday Morning, March 6

They are resolved to break my heart. My poor Hannah is discharged—disgracefully discharged! Thus it was:

Within half an hour after I had sent the poor girl down for my breakfast, that bold creature Betty Barnes, my sister's confident and servant (if a favourite maid and confident can be deemed a *servant*), came up.

What, miss, will you please to have for breakfast?

I was surprised. What will I have for breakfast, Betty! How! —what!—how comes it! Then I named Hannah. I could not tell what to say.

Don't be surprised, miss: but you'll see Hannah no more in this house.

God forbid! Is any harm come to Hannah? What! What is the matter with Hannah?

Why, miss, the short and the long is this: your papa and mamma think Hannah has stayed long enough in the house to do mischief; and so she is ordered to *troop* (that was the confident creature's word); and I am directed to wait upon you in her stead.

I burst into tears. I have no service for you, Betty Barnes;

none at all. But where is Hannah? Cannot I speak with the poor girl? I owe her half a year's wages. I may never see her again perhaps; for they are resolved to break my heart.

And they think you are resolved to break theirs: so tit for tat, miss.

Impertinent I called her; and asked her if it were upon such confident terms that her service was to begin.

I was so very earnest to see the poor maid that (to *oblige* me, as she said) she went down with my request.

The worthy creature was as earnest to see me; and the favour was granted in presence of Shorey and Betty.

I thanked her when she came up for her past service to me.

Her heart was ready to break.

I gave her a little linen, some laces, and other odd things; and instead of four pounds which were due to her, ten guineas: and said, if ever I were again allowed to be my own mistress, I would think of *her* in the first place.

Hannah told me, before their faces, having no other opportunity, that she had been examined about letters *to* me and *from* me: and that she had given her pockets to Miss Harlowe, who looked into them, and put her fingers in her stays, to satisfy herself that she had not any.

We wept over each other at parting.

Miss Clarissa Harlowe to Miss Howe

Monday near 12 o'clock.

The enclosed letter was just now delivered to me. My brother has carried all his points.

Mond., March 6.

Miss Clary,—By command of your father and mother I write expressly to forbid you to come into their presence or into the garden when *they* are there: nor when they are *not* there, but with Betty Barnes to attend you; except by particular licence or command.

On their blessings, you are forbidden likewise to correspond with the vile Lovelace; as it is well known you did by means of your sly Hannah.

Neither are you to correspond with Miss Howe; who has

given herself high airs of late; and might possibly help on your correspondence with that detested libertine. Nor, in short, with anybody without leave.

You are not to enter into the presence of either of your uncles without their leave first obtained. It is in *mercy* to you, after such a behaviour to your mother, that your father refuses to see you.

You are not to be seen in any apartment of the house you so lately governed as you pleased, unless you are commanded down.

In short, you are strictly to confine yourself to your chamber, except now and then in Betty Barnes's sight (as aforesaid) you take a morning or evening turn in the garden: and then you are to go directly, and without stopping at any apartment in the way, up and down the back stairs, that the sight of so perverse a young creature may not add to the pain you have given everybody.

The hourly threatenings of your fine fellow, as well as your own unheard-of obstinacy, will account to you for all this. What must your perverseness have been, that *such* a mother can give you up!

If anything I have written appear severe or harsh, it is still in your power (but perhaps will not always be so) to remedy it; and that by a single word.

Ja. Harlowe.

To JAMES HARLOWE, JUNIOR, ESQ.

SIR,—I WILL only say that you may congratulate yourself on having *so far* succeeded in all your views, that you may report what you please of me, and I can no more defend myself than if I were dead. Yet one favour, nevertheless, I will beg of you. It is this: that you will not occasion more severities, more disgraces, than are necessary for carrying into execution your further designs, whatever they be, against

Your unhappy sister,

Clarissa Harlowe.

MISS CLARISSA HARLOWE TO MISS HOWE

Tuesday, March 7.

CAN SUCH measures be supposed to soften? But surely they can only mean to try to frighten me into my brother's views! All my hope is to be able to weather this point till my Cousin Morden comes from Florence; and he is soon expected: yet, if they are determined upon a short day, I doubt he will not be here time enough to save me.

I asked Mrs. Betty if she had any orders to watch or attend me; or whether I was to ask *her* leave whenever I should be disposed to walk in the garden or to go to feed my bantams? Lord bless her! what could I mean by such a question!

However, as it behoved me to be assured on this head, I went down directly, and stayed an hour without question or impediment; and yet a good part of the time I walked under and in *sight,* as I may say, of my brother's study window, where both he and my sister happened to be. And I am sure they saw me, by the loud mirth they affected, by way of insult, as I suppose.

Tuesday Night.

Since I wrote the above, I ventured to send a letter by Shorey to my mother.

HONOURED MADAM,—Having acknowledged to you that I had received letters from Mr. Lovelace full of resentment, and that I answered them purely to prevent further mischief; and having showed you copies of my answers, which you did not disapprove of, although you thought fit, after you had read them, to forbid me any further correspondence with him; I think it my duty to acquaint you that another letter from him has since come to my hand, in which he is very earnest with me to permit him to wait on my papa, or you, or my two uncles, in a pacific way, accompanied by Lord M.: on which I beg your commands.

And here I cannot but express my grief that I should have all the punishment and all the blame, who, as I have reason to think, have prevented great mischief, and have not been the occasion of any. For, madam, could *I* be supposed to govern the passions of *either* of the gentlemen? Over the one, indeed, I have had some little influence.

This communication being as voluntarily made as dutifully intended; I humbly presume to hope that I shall not be required to produce the letter itself. I cannot either in honour or prudence do that, because of the vehemence of his style; for having heard of some part of the harsh treatment I have met with; he thinks himself entitled to place it to his own account, by reason of speeches thrown out by some of my relations, *equally* vehement.

If I do *not* answer him, he will be made desperate, and think himself justified in resenting the treatment he complains of: if I *do,* and if, in compliment to me, he forbears to resent what he thinks himself entitled to resent; be pleased, madam, to consider the obligation he will suppose he lays me under.

If I were as strongly prepossessed in his favour as is supposed, I should not have wished this to be considered by you. And permit me, as a still further proof that I am *not* prepossessed, to beg of you to consider, whether, upon the whole, the proposal I made of declaring for the single life (which I will religiously adhere to) is not the best way to get rid of his pretensions with honour. To renounce him, and not be allowed to aver that I will never be the other man's, will make him conclude (driven as I am driven) that I am determined in that other man's favour.

And so leaving the whole to your own wisdom, and whether you choose to consult my papa and uncles upon this humble application, or not; or whether I shall be allowed to write an answer to Mr. Lovelace or not (and if allowed so to do, I beg your direction, by whom to send it); I remain, Honoured Madam,

Your unhappy, but ever dutiful daughter,

Cl. Harlowe.

Wednesday Morning.

I have just received an answer to the enclosed letter.

Clarissa,—Say not all the blame and all the punishment is yours. I am as much blamed, and as much punished as you are; yet am more innocent. When your obstinacy is equal to any other person's passion, blame not your brother.

I don't know what to write about your answering that man of violence. What can you think of it, that such a family as ours, should have such a rod held over it?

I should have been glad to see the letter you tell me of, as I saw the rest: you say, both honour and prudence forbid you to show it to me. O Clarissa! what think you of receiving letters that honour and prudence forbid you to show to a mother! But it is not for me to see it if you would *choose* to show it me. I will not know that you did correspond. And as to an answer, take your own methods. But let him know it will be the last you will write. And if you do write I won't see it: so seal it up (if you do) and give it to Shorey; and she—yet do not think I give you licence to write.

Your father and uncles would have no patience were he to come.

As to the rest, you have by your obstinacy put it out of my power to do anything for you. Your father takes upon himself to be answerable for all consequences. You must not, therefore, apply to me for favour.

I charge you, let not this letter be found. Burn it. There is too much of the *mother* in it to a daughter so unaccountably obstinate.

After this letter, you will believe, that I could have very little hopes, that an application directly to my father would stand me in my stead: but I thought it became me to write, were it but to acquit myself *to* myself, that I have left nothing unattempted that has the least likelihood to restore me to his favour. Accordingly I wrote to the following effect:

"I presume not, I say, to argue with my papa; I only beg his mercy and indulgence in this *one* point, on which depends my present and perhaps my *future* happiness; and beseech him not to reprobate his child for an aversion which it is not in her power to conquer. In everything but this *one* point, I promise implicit duty and resignation to his will. I repeat my offers of a single life; and appeal to him, whether I have ever given him cause to doubt my word. I conclude with hoping that my brother's instigations may not rob an unhappy child of her father."

This is the answer.

Wednesday.

I write, perverse girl; but with all the indignation that your disobedience deserves. Your behaviour to your too indulgent, and too fond mother—but, I have no patience—continue banished from my presence, undutiful as you are, till you know how to conform to my will. Write no more to me till you are convinced of your duty to

A justly-incensed Father.

MISS CLARISSA HARLOWE TO MISS HOWE

Thursday Morn., Mar. 9.

I HAVE another letter from Mr. Lovelace, although I had not answered his former.

He is excessively uneasy upon what he hears; and his expressions both of love to me, and resentment to them, are very fervent. He solicits me "to engage my honour to him, never to have Mr. Solmes."

I think I may fairly promise him that I will not.

You see, my dear, that my mother seems as apprehensive of mischief as myself; and has *indirectly* offered to let Shorey carry my answer to the letter he sent me before.

He is full of the favour of the ladies of his family to me: to whom, nevertheless, I am personally a stranger; except, that once I saw Miss Patty Montague at Mrs. Knollys's.

I have answered his letters.

This is the substance of my letter:

I assure him "that were there not such a man in the world as himself I would not have Mr. Solmes."

I tell him "that to return, as I understand he does, defiances for defiances to my relations, is far from being a proof with me, either of his politeness or of the consideration he pretends to have for me.

"That the moment I hear he visits any of my friends without

their consent, I will a make resolution never to see him more if I can help it."

I apprise him "that I am connived at in sending this letter, provided it shall be the last I will ever write to him: that I had more than once told him that the single life was my choice; and this before Mr. Solmes was introduced as a visitor in our family: that had he even my friends on his side, I should have very great objections to him, were I to get over my choice of a single life; and that I should have declared as much to him, had I regarded him as *more* than a common visiter. On all these accounts, I desire that the one more letter, which I will allow him to deposit in the usual place, may be the very *last;* and that only to acquaint me with his acquiescence that it shall be so; at least till happier times."

In short, my dear, like a restive horse (as I have heard described by sportsmen) he pains one's hands, and half disjoints one's arms to rein him in. And when you see his letters you must form no judgment upon them till you have read my answers. If you do you will indeed think you have cause to attribute *self-deceit,* and *throbs,* and *glows* to your friend—and yet, at other times, the contradictory creature complains that I show him as little favour, and my friends as much inveteracy as if in the rencounter betwixt my brother and him he had been the aggressor; and as if the catastrophe had been as fatal as it might have been.

If he has a design by this conduct (sometimes complaining of my shyness, at others exulting in my imaginary favours) to induce me at one time to acquiesce with his compliments; at another to be more complaisant for his complaints; and if the contradiction be not the effect of his inattention and giddiness; I shall think him as deep and as artful (too probably, as *practised*) a creature as ever lived; and were I to be sure of it, should hate him, if possible, worse than I do Solmes.

Miss Howe to Miss Clarissa Harlowe

Thursday Night, March 9.

I HAVE no patience with any of the people you are with. I know not what to advise you to do. How do you know that you are not punishable for being the cause, though to your own loss, that the will of your grandfather is not complied with? Wills are sacred things, child.

I allow of all your noble reasonings for what you did at the time: but since such a charming, such a generous instance of filial duty is to go thus unrewarded, why should you not resume?

Your Uncle Harlowe is one trustee, your Cousin Morden is the other: insist upon your right to your uncle; and write to your Cousin Morden about it. This, I dare say, will make them alter their behaviour to you.

Your insolent brother—what has *he* to do to control you? Were it me I'd show him the difference. I would be in my own mansion, pursuing my charming schemes and making all around me happy. I would set up my own chariot. I would visit them when they deserved it. But when my brother and sister gave themselves airs, I would let them know that I was their sister, and not their servant: and, if that did not do, I would shut my gates against them; and bid them go and be company for each other.

As to this odious Solmes, I wonder not at your aversion to him. It is needless to say anything to you, who have so sincere an antipathy to him, to strengthen your dislike: yet who can resist her own talents? One of mine, as I have heretofore said, is to give an ugly likeness. Shall I indulge it?—I will.

"I was twice in this wretch's company. At one of the times your Lovelace was there.

"Lovelace entertained the company in his lively gay way, and made everybody laugh at one of his stories. It was before this creature was thought of for you. Solmes laughed, too. It was, however, *his* laugh; for his first three years, at least, I imagine, must have been one continual fit of crying; and his muscles have never yet been able to recover a risible tone."

Yet this is the man they have found out (for considerations as sordid as those he is governed by) for a husband, that is to say, for a lord and master, for Miss Clarissa Harlowe!

But enough, and too much, of such a wretch as this! You must not have him, my dear—that I am clear in, though not so clear how you will be able to avoid it, except you assert the independence to which your estate gives you a title.

Here my mother broke in upon me. She wanted to see what I had written.

She owned that the man was not the most desirable of men; and that he had not the happiest appearance: but what, said she, is *person* in a *man?* And I was chidden for setting you against complying with your father's will.

My mother charged me at last to write that side over again.

"I cannot but think Nancy, said she, after all, that there is a little hardship in Miss Harlowe's case: and yet (as her mother says) it is a grating thing to have a child, who was always noted for her duty in *smaller* points, to stand in opposition to her parents' will, in the *greater;* yea, in the *greatest of all.* And now, to middle the matter between both, it is a pity, that the man *they* favour has not that sort of merit which a person of a mind so delicate as that of Miss Harlowe might reasonably expect in a husband. But then this man is surely preferable to a libertine: to a libertine too, who has had a duel with her own brother: *fathers* and *mothers* must think so, were it *not* for that circumstance—and it is strange if *they* do not know best."

I must needs say that I think duty to parents is a very meritorious excellence: but I bless God I have not your trials.

I will not mention all that is upon my mind in relation to the behaviour of your father and uncles *and the rest of them,* because I would not offend you: but I have now a higher opinion of my own sagacity than ever I had, in that I could never cordially love any one of your family but yourself. I am not *born* to like them. But it is my *duty* to be sincere to my *friend:* and this will excuse her Anna Howe to Miss Clarissa Harlowe.

I ought, indeed, to have excepted your mother; a lady to be reverenced, and now to be pitied. What must have been her treatment to be thus subjugated, as I may call it? Little did the good old viscount think, when he married his darling, his only daughter to so well-appearing a gentleman, and to her own liking, too, that she would have been so much kept down. Another world would call your father a tyrant, if I must not: all the world that know him *do* call him so; and if you love your mother you should not be very angry at the world for taking that liberty.

And now to give up the most deserving of her children against her judgment, a sacrifice to the ambition and selfishness of the least deserving! But I fly from this subject—having I fear, said too much to be forgiven—and yet much less than is in my heart to say upon the over-meek subject.

Mr. Hickman is expected from London this evening. I have desired him to inquire after Lovelace's life and conversation in town. Don't expect a very good account of either. He is certainly an intriguing wretch and full of inventions.

If I have not been clear enough in my advice about what you shall do, let me say that I can give it in one word: it is only by re-urging you to RESUME. If you do all the rest will follow.

RESUME, my dear. And that is all I will give myself time to say further, lest I offend you when I cannot serve you—only this, that I am

Your truly affectionate friend and servant,

Anna Howe.

MISS CLARISSA HARLOWE TO MISS HOWE

Friday, March 10.

YOU WILL permit me, my dear, to touch upon a few passages in your last letter that affect me sensibly.

If you would avoid my highest displeasure, you must spare my mother; and, surely, you will allow me, with her, to pity, as well as to love and honour my father.

I cannot help owning, however, that I am pleased to have you join with me in opinion of the contempt which Mr. Solmes deserves from me. But yet, permit me to say, that he is not *quite* so horrible a creature as you make him: as to his *person,* I mean; for with regard to his *mind,* by all I have heard, you have done him but justice: but you have such a talent at an ugly likeness, and such a vivacity, that they sometimes carry you out of verisimilitude.

As to the advice you give, to resume my estate, I am determined not to litigate with my father, let what will be the consequence to myself.

I knew your mother would be for implicit obedience in a child. I am sorry my case is so circumstanced that I *cannot* comply.

It would be my duty to do so, if I could. You are indeed very happy, that you have nothing but your own agreeable, yet whimsical, humours to contend with, in the choice she invites you to make of Mr. Hickman.

I should be very blameable to endeavour to hide any the least bias upon my mind, from you: and I cannot but say that this man—this Lovelace—is a man that might be liked well enough, if he bore such a character as Mr. Hickman bears; and even if there were hopes of reclaiming him. And further still, I will acknowledge that I believe it possible that one might be driven, by violent measures, step by step, into something that might be called a *conditional kind of liking*. But as to the word LOVE justifiable and charming as it is in some cases it has, methinks, in the narrow, circumscribed, selfish, peculiar sense in which you apply it to me (the man, too, so little to be approved of for his morals, if all that report says of him be true) no pretty sound with it.

MR. LOVELACE TO JOHN BELFORD, ESQ.

Monday, March 13.

IN VAIN dost thou[1] and thy compeers press me to go to town, while I am in such an uncertainty as I am in at present with this proud beauty. All the ground I have hitherto gained with her, is entirely owing to her concern for the safety of people whom I have reason to hate.

The lady's malevolent brother has now introduced another man; the most unpromising in his person and qualities, the most formidable in his offers, that has yet appeared.

But is it not a confounded thing to be in love with one who is the daughter, the sister, the niece of a family I must eternally despise? And, the devil of it, that love increasing, with her—what shall I call it?—'tis not scorn: 'tis not pride: 'tis not the insolence of an adored beauty—but 'tis to *virtue*, it seems, that my difficulties are owing; and I pay for not being a sly sinner,

[1] These gentlemen affected what they called the Roman style (to wit, the *thee* and the *thou* in their letters: and it was an agreed rule with them, to take in good part whatever freedoms they treated each other with, if the passages were written in that style.

an hypocrite; for being regardless of my reputation; for permitting slander to open its mouth against me.

I have boasted that I was once in love before: and indeed I thought I was. It was in my early manhood—with that quality-jilt, whose infidelity I have vowed to revenge upon as many of the sex as shall come into my power. I believe, in different climes, I have already sacrified an hecatomb to my Nemesis, in pursuance of this vow. But upon recollecting what I was *then,* and comparing it with what I find in myself *now,* I cannot say that I was ever in love before.

I could not bear that a woman, who was the first that had bound me in silken fetters (they were not iron ones, like those I now wear) should prefer a coronet to me: and when the bird was flown, I set more value upon it, than when I had it safe in my cage, and could visit it when I pleased.

But now am I *indeed* in love. I can think of nothing, of nobody, but the divine Clarissa Harlowe. *Harlowe!* How that hated word sticks in my throat—but I shall give her for it the name of love.[1]

Is it possible to imagine that I would be braved as I am braved, threatened as I am threatened, by those who are afraid to see me; and by this brutal brother too, to whom I gave a life (a life, indeed, not worth my taking!); had I not a greater pride in knowing, that by means of his very spy upon me, I am playing him off as I please; cooling or inflaming his violent passions as may best suit my purposes; permitting so much to be revealed of my life and actions, and intentions, as may give him such a confidence in his double-faced agent, as shall enable me to dance his employer upon my own wires?

This it is that makes my pride mount above my resentment.

And what my motive, dost thou ask? No less than this, that my beloved shall find no protection out of my family; for, if I know *hers,* fly she must or have the man she hates.

All my fear arises from the little hold I have in the heart of this charming frost-piece: such a constant glow upon her lovely features: eyes so sparkling: limbs so divinely turned: health so florid: youth so blooming: air so animated—to have an heart so

[1] Lovelace.

impenetrable: and *I,* the hitherto successful Lovelace, the addresser—how can it be?

But how much more will my heart rise with indignation against her, if I find she hesitates but one moment (however persecuted) about preferring me to the man she avowedly hates!

That her indifference to me is not owing to the superior liking she has for *any* other man, is what rivets my chains: but take care, fair one; take care, O thou most exalted of female minds, and loveliest of persons, how thou debasest thyself, by encouraging such a competition as thy sordid relations have set on foot in mere malice to me! Thou wilt say I rave. And so I do:

Perdition catch my soul, but I *do* love her.

By the advices I have this moment received, I have reason to think that I shall have occasion for thee here. Hold thyself in readiness to come down upon the first summons.

Let Belton, and Mowbray, and Tourville, likewise prepare themselves. I have a great mind to contrive a method to send James Harlowe to travel for improvement. Never was there booby-'squire that more wanted it. I have *already* contrived it; could I but put it in execution without being suspected to have a hand in it. This I am resolved upon; if I have not his *sister,* I will have *him.*

But be this as it may, there is a present likelihood of room for *glorious* mischief.

Thus, Jack, as thou desirest, have I written; upon nothing; upon REVENGE, which I love; upon LOVE, which I hate, *heartily* hate, because 'tis my master: and upon the devil knows what besides.

[Clarissa had written appealing letters to her brother, sister, and uncles offering to give up her estate and live the single life to be free of Mr. Solmes. Their replies are scornful and rebuking. In desperation she writes to Mr. Solmes. Ed.]

MISS CLARISSA HARLOWE TO MISS HOWE

Thursday, March 16.

HAVING met with such bad success in my application to my relations, I have taken a step that will surprise you. It is no other than writing a letter to Mr. Solmes himself. With these, I shall enclose one from my brother to me, on occasion of mine to Mr. Solmes.

TO ROGER SOLMES, ESQ.

Wednesday, Mar. 15.

SIR,—When you first came acquainted with our family, you found the writer of this one of the happiest creatures in the world; beloved by the best and most indulgent of parents, and rejoicing in the kind favour of two affectionate uncles, and in the esteem of every one.

But how is this happy scene now changed! You was pleased to cast a favourable eye upon me. You addressed yourself to my friends: your proposals were approved of by them—approved of without consulting me; as if my choice and happiness were of the least signification. I had not the felicity to think as they did; almost the first time my sentiments differed from theirs. I besought them to indulge me in a point so important to my future happiness: but, alas, in vain! And then (for I thought it was but honest) I told *you* my mind; and even that my affections were engaged. But, to my mortification and surprise, you persisted and still persist.

Thus distressed and made unhappy, and all for your sake, and through your cruel perseverance, I write, sir, to demand of you the peace of mind you have robbed me of: to demand of you the love of so many dear friends of which you have deprived me; and, if you have the generosity that should distinguish a man, and a gentleman, to adjure you not to continue an address that has been attended with such cruel effects to the creature you profess to esteem.

Your compliance with this request will lay me under the highest obligation to your generosity, and make me ever

Your well-wisher and humble servant,

Clarissa Harlowe.

TO MISS CLARISSA HARLOWE

These most humbly present.

DEAREST MISS,—Your letter has had a very contrary effect upon me, to what you seem to have expected from it. It has doubly convinced me of the excellency of your mind and of the honour of your disposition. Call it *selfish,* or what you please, I must persist in my suit; and happy shall I be, if by patience and perseverance and a steady and unalterable devoir, I may at last overcome the difficulty laid in my way.

As your good parents, your uncles, and other friends, are absolutely determined you shall never have Mr. Lovelace if they can help it; and as I presume no other person is in the way; I will contentedly wait the issue of this matter.

Pardon me, dear miss, but I must persevere, though I am sorry you suffer on my account, as you are pleased to think; for I never before saw the woman I could love: and while there is any hope, and that you remain undisposed of to some happier man, I must and will be

Your faithful and obsequious admirer,

Roger Solmes.

March 16.

MR. LOVELACE TO JOHN BELFORD, ESQ.

Friday, March 17.

I WOULD have thee, Jack, come down as soon as thou canst. I believe I shall not want the others so soon.

Thou wilt find me at a little alehouse; they call it an inn: the White Hart; most terribly wounded (but by the weather only) the sign:—in a sorry village; within five miles from Harlowe Place.

The people here at the Hart are poor but honest; and have gotten it into their heads that I am a man of quality in disguise; and there is no reining-in their officious respect. Here is a pretty little smirking daughter; seventeen six days ago. I call her my Rosebud. Her grandmother (for there is no mother) a good neat old woman, as ever filled a wicker-chair in a chimney corner, has besought me to be merciful to her.

This is the right way with me. Many and many a pretty

rogue had I spared, whom I did *not* spare, had my power been acknowledged, and my mercy in time implored.

This simple chit (for there is a simplicity in her thou wilt be highly pleased with: all humble, all officious, all innocent—I love her for her humility, her officiousness, and even for her *innocence*) will be pretty amusement to thee; while I combat with the weather and dodge and creep about the walls and purlieus of Harlowe Place.

But I charge thee, that thou do not (what I would not permit myself to do for the world—I charge thee, that thou do not) crop my Rosebud.

O Jack! spare thou therefore (for I shall leave thee often alone with her, spare thou) my Rosebud! Unsuspicious of her danger, the lamb's throat will hardly shun thy knife! O be not thou the butcher of my lambkin!

The less be thou so for the reason I am going to give thee—the gentle heart is touched by love: her soft bosom heaves with a passion she has not yet found a name for. I once caught her eye following a young carpenter, a widow neighbour's son, living (to speak in her dialect) *at the little white house over the way.* A gentle youth he also seems to be, about three years older than herself: playmates from infancy, till his eighteenth and her fifteenth year, furnished a reason for a greater distance in show, while their hearts gave a better for their being nearer than ever—for I soon perceived the love reciprocal. A scrape and a bow at first seeing his pretty mistress; turning often to salute her following eye; and when a winding lane was to deprive him of her sight, his whole body turned round, his hat more reverently doffed, than before. This answered (for, unseen, I was behind her) by a low courtesy, and a sigh, that Johnny was too far off to hear! Happy whelp! said I to myself! I withdrew; and in tripped my Rosebud, as if satisfied with the dumb show, and with nothing beyond it.

I have examined the little heart. She has made me her confidante. She owns she could love Johnny Barton very well: and Johnny Barton has told her he could love her better than any maiden he ever saw. But, alas! it must not be thought of. Why not be thought of? She don't know! And then she sighed:

but Johnny has an aunt who will give him a hundred pounds when his time is out: and her father cannot give her but a few things, or so, to set her out with: and though Johnny's mother says she knows not where Johnny would have a prettier or notabler wife, yet—and then she sighed again—what signifies talking? I would not have Johnny be unhappy and poor for me! For what good would that do *me,* you know, sir!

What would I give [by my soul, my angel will indeed reform me, if her friends' implacable folly ruin us not both!—what would I give] to have so innocent and so good a heart as either my Rosebud's or Johnny's!

I have a confounded mischievous one—by *nature* too, I think! A good motion now and then rises from it: but it dies away presently. A love of intrigue. An invention for mischief. A triumph in subduing. Fortune encouraging and supporting. And a constitution—what signifies palliating? But I believe I had been a rogue had I been a plough boy.

Meantime, as I make it my rule, whenever I have committed a very capital enormity, to do some good by way of atonement; and as I believe I am a pretty deal indebted on that score; I intend, before I leave these parts (successfully shall I leave them I hope, or I shall be tempted to double the mischief by way of revenge, though not to my Rosebud any) to join an hundred pounds to Johnny's aunt's hundred pounds, to make one innocent couple happy. I repeat therefore, and for half a dozen *therefores,* spare thou my Rosebud.

Mr. Lovelace to John Belford, Esq.

I HAVE found out by my *watchful spy* almost as many of my charmer's motions, as of those of the rest of her relations.

The interview I am meditating will produce her consent I hope, to other favours of the like kind: for, should she not choose the place in which I am expecting to see her, I can attend her anywhere in the rambling, Dutch-taste garden, whenever she will permit me that honour: for my implement, *hight Joseph Leman,* has procured me the opportunity of getting two keys made to the garden door (one of which I have given him, for reasons good); and Joseph, upon proper notice, will leave it unbolted.

My REVENGE and my LOVE are uppermost by turns. If the latter succeed not, the gratifying of the former will be my only consolation: and by all that's good, they shall feel it; although for it I become an exile from my native country forever.

I will throw myself into my charmer's presence. I have twice already attempted it in vain. I shall then see what I may depend upon from her favour. If I thought I had no prospect of that, I should be tempted to carry her off. That would be a rape worthy of a Jupiter!

But all gentle shall be my movements: all respectful, even to reverence, my address to her—her hand shall be the only witness to the pressure of my lip—my trembling lip: I *know* it will tremble, if I do not *bid* it tremble. By *my* humility will I invite *her* confidence: the loneliness of the place shall give me no advantage: to dissipate her fears and engage her reliance upon my honour for the future, shall be my whole endeavour.

MISS CLARISSA HARLOWE TO MISS HOWE

Sat. Night, Mar. 18.

I HAVE been frighted out of my wits—still am in a manner out of breath. Thus occasioned, I went down under the usual pretence, in hopes to find something from you. Concerned at my disappointment, I was returning from the woodhouse, when I heard a rustling as of somebody behind a stack of wood. I was extremely surprised: but still more to behold a man coming from behind the furthermost stack.

In the same point of time that I saw him, he besought me not to be frighted: and still nearer approaching me, threw open a horseman's coat: and who should it be but Mr. Lovelace! I could not scream out (yet attempted to scream the moment I saw a man; and again, when I saw who it was) for I had no voice: and had I not caught hold of a prop which supported the old roof, I should have sunk.

I had hitherto, as you know, kept him at a distance: and now, as I recovered myself, judge of my first emotions when I recollected his character from every mouth of my family; his enterprising temper; and found myself alone with him in a place so near a by-lane and so remote from the house.

But his respectful behaviour soon dissipated these fears, and gave me others, lest we should be seen together.

As soon, therefore, as I could speak, I expressed with the greatest warmth my displeasure; and told him that he cared not how much he exposed me to the resentment of all my friends, provided he could gratify his own impetuous humour. I then commanded him to leave the place that moment; and was hurrying from him when he threw himself in the way at my feet, beseeching my stay for one moment; declaring that he suffered himself to be guilty of this rashness, as I thought it, to avoid one much greater: for, in short, he could not bear the hourly insults he received from my family, with the thoughts of having so little interest in my favour, that he could not promise himself that his patience and forbearance would be attended with any other issue than to lose me for ever, and be triumphed over and insulted upon it.

This man, you know, has very ready knees.

I must forgive him, he said, if he, who pretended only to a comparative merit (and otherwise thought no man living could deserve me) had presumed to hope for a greater share in my favour than he had hitherto met with, when such men as Mr. Symmes, Mr. Wyerley, and now, lastly, so vile a reptile as this Solmes, however discouraged by myself, were made his competitors.

I was very uneasy to be gone; and the more as the night came on apace.

As he hoped that I would one day make him the happiest man in the world, he assured me that he had so much regard for my fame, that he would be as far from advising any step that was likely to cast a shade upon my reputation (although that step was to be ever so much in his own favour) as I would be to follow such advice. But since I was not to be permitted to live single, he would submit it to my consideration, whether I had any way but *one* to avoid the intended violence to my inclinations.

And then he asked me if I would receive a letter from Lady

Betty Lawrance, on this occasion: for Lady Sarah Sadleir, he said, having lately lost her only child, hardly looked into the world or thought of it farther than to wish him married, and preferably to all the women in the world, with me.

To be sure, my dear, there is a great deal in what the man said—I may be allowed to say this, without an imputed *glow* or *throb*.

He appealed to me, whether ever I knew my father recede from any resolution he had once fixed; especially if he thought either his prerogative or his authority concerned in the question.

He then again pressed me to receive a letter of offered protection from Lady Betty.

I told him that however greatly I thought myself obliged to Lady Betty Lawrance, if this offer came from herself; yet it was easy to see to what it led.

But what would the world conclude would be the end, I demanded, were I in the last resort, as he proposed, to throw myself down into the protection of *his* friends.

And what less did the world think *now*, he asked, than that I was confined that I *might not?* You are to consider, madam, you have not now an option; and to whom it is owing that you have not; and that you are in the power of those (parents why should I call them?) who are determined that you shall *not* have an option. All I propose is, that you will embrace such a protection; but not till you have tried every way to avoid the necessity for it.

And give me leave to say, proceeded he, that if a correspondence on which I have founded all my hopes, is at this critical conjuncture to be broken off; and if you are resolved not to be *provided against* the worst; it must be plain to me, that you will at last yield to that worst—worst to *me* only—it cannot be to *you*—and *then!* (and he put his hand clenched to his forehead) how shall I bear the supposition? *Then* will you be that Solmes's! But by all that's sacred, neither he, nor your brother, nor your uncles, shall enjoy their triumph—perdition seize my soul if they shall!

The man's vehemence frightened me.

I told him that he talked to me in very high language; but he might assure himself that I never would have Mr. Solmes (yet that this I said not in favour to him): and I had declared as much to my relations, were there not such a man as himself in the world.

Would I declare that I would still honour him with my correspondence?

I bid him forbear rashness or resentment to any of my family, and I would, for some time at least, till I saw what issue my present trials were likely to have, proceed with a correspondence, which, nevertheless, my heart *condemned*——

I made many efforts to go; and now it was so dark that I began to have great apprehensions. I cannot say from his behaviour: indeed, he has a good deal raised himself in my opinion by the personal respect, even to reverence, which he paid me during the whole conference: for although he flamed out once, upon a supposition that Solmes might succeed, it was upon a supposition that would excuse passion, if anything could, you know, in a man pretending to love with fervour; although it was so levelled that I could not avoid resenting it.

He recommended himself to my favour at parting, with great earnestness, yet with as great submission; not offering to condition anything with me; although he hinted his wishes for another meeting: which I forbade him ever attempting again in the same place. And I will own to you, from whom I should be really blameable to conceal anything, that his arguments (drawn from the disgraceful treatment I meet with) of what I *am* to expect make me begin to apprehend that I shall be under an obligation to be either the one man's or the other's—and if so, I fancy I shall not incur your blame, were I to say *which* of the two it must be. You have said which it must *not* be. But, O my dear, the single life is by far the most eligible to me: *indeed* it is.

Your affectionate and faithful friend and servant,

Cl. Harlowe.

MISS HOWE TO MISS CLARISSA HARLOWE

Sunday, March 19.

YOU KNOW that I can do nothing but rave at your stupid persecutors: and that you don't like. I have advised you to resume your own estate: that you won't do. You cannot bear the thoughts of having their Solmes: and Lovelace is resolved you shall be his, let who will say to the contrary. I think you must be either the one man's or the other's.

If it must be Lovelace or Solmes, the choice cannot admit of debate. Yet if all be true that is reported, I should prefer almost any of your other lovers to either; unworthy as *they* also are.

I wish you are not *indeed* angry with me for harping so much on one string. I must own, that I should think myself inexcusable so to do (the rather, as I am bold enough to imagine it a point out of all doubt from fifty places in your letters, were I to labour the proof) if you would ingenuously own—

Own what? you'll say. Why, my Anna Howe, I hope you don't think that I am already in love!

No, to be sure! How can your Anna Howe have such a thought? What then shall we call it? You have helped me to a phrase. A *conditional kind of liking!*—that's it.

Let this question divert, and not displease you, my dear. You must recollect the many instances of my impertinence which you have forgiven, and then say, "This is a mad girl: but yet I love her! and she is my own."

Anna Howe.

MISS CLARISSA HARLOWE TO MISS HOWE

Monday, March 20.

I WILL NOW, though midnight (for I have no sleep in my eyes), resume the subject I was forced so abruptly to quit.

In order to acquit myself of so heavy a charge as that of having reserves to so dear a friend, I will acknowledge (and I thought I had over and over) that it is owing to my particular situation, if Mr. Lovelace appears to me in a tolerable light: and I take upon me to say, that had they opposed to him a man of sense, of virtue, of generosity; one who enjoyed his fortune with credit; who had a tenderness in his nature for the calamities of others, which would have given a moral assurance, that he would have been still less wanting in grateful returns to an obliging spirit. Had they opposed such a man as this to Mr. Lovelace, and been as earnest to have me married, as now they are, I do not know myself, if they would have had reason to tax me with that invincible obstinacy which they lay to my charge: and this whatever had been the *figure* of the man; since the *heart* is what we women should judge by in the choice we make, as the best security for the party's good behaviour in every relation of life.

But, situated as I am, thus persecuted, and driven; I own to you, that I have now and then had a little more difficulty than I wished for, in passing by Mr. Lovelace's tolerable qualities, to keep up my dislike to him for his others.

And so you call upon me again, to have no reserves, and so forth.

Why then, my dear, if you will have it, I think, that, with all his preponderating faults, I like him better than I ever thought I should like him; and, those faults considered, better perhaps than I *ought* to like him. And I believe it is possible for the persecution I labour under, to induce me to like him still more—especially while I can recollect to his advantage our last interview, and as every day produces stronger instances of *tyranny,* I will call it, on the other side. In a word, I will frankly own (since you cannot think anything I say too explicit) that were he *now* but a moral man, I would prefer him to all the men I ever saw.

So that this is but *conditional liking* still, you'll say—nor, I hope, is it more. I never was in *love* as it is called; and whether this be *it* or not, I must submit to *you.* But will venture to think it, if it be, no such *mighty* monarch, no such unconquerable power, as I have heard it represented; and it must have met with greater encouragement than I think I have given it, to be so *irresistible*—since I am persuaded that I could yet, without a *throb,* most willingly give up the *one* man to get rid of the *other.*

MISS CLARISSA HARLOWE TO MISS HOWE

Tuesday, March 21.

HOW WILLINGLY would my dear mother show kindness to me, were she permitted! None of this persecution should I labour under, I am sure, if that regard were paid to her prudence and fine understanding, which they so well deserve. Whether owing to her, or to my aunt, or to both, that a new trial was to be made upon me, I cannot tell; but this morning her Shorey delivered into my hand the following condescending letter.

MY DEAR GIRL—for so I must still call you; since *dear* you may be to me, in every sense of the word. We have taken into particular consideration some hints that fell yesterday from your good Norton, as if we had not, at Mr. Solmes's first application, treated you with that condescension, wherewith we have in all other instances treated you. If it even *had been so,* my dear, you were not excusable to be wanting in *your* part, and to set yourself to oppose your father's will in a point into which he had entered too far, to recede with honour. But all yet may be well.

Your father permits me to tell you that if you now at last comply with his expectations, all past disobligations shall be buried in oblivion, as if they had never been: but withal, that this is the last time that that grace will be offered you.

I hinted to you, you must remember, that patterns of the richest silks were sent for. They are come: and as they *are* come, your father, to show how much he is determined, will have me send them up to you. I could have wished they might not have accompanied this letter—but there is no great matter in *that.*

These are the newest, as well as richest, that we could procure; answerable to our station in the world; answerable to the fortune, additional to your grandfather's estate, designed you; and to the noble settlements agreed upon.

Mr. Solmes intends to present you with a set of jewels. You know full well that I, who first and last brought a still larger fortune into the family than you will carry to Mr. Solmes, had not a provision made me of near this that we have made for you.

Wonder not, Clary, that I write to you thus plainly and freely upon this subject. You know I have told you more than once that you must resolve to have Mr. Solmes, or never to be looked upon as our child.

The draft of the settlements you may see whenever you will.

If, upon perusal of them, you think any alteration necessary, it shall be made. Do, my dear girl, send to me within this day or two, or rather *ask* me for the perusal of them.

As a certain person's appearance at church so lately, and what he gives out everywhere, makes us extremely uneasy, and as that uneasiness will continue while you are single, you must not wonder that a short day is intended. This day fortnight we design it to be, if you have no objection to make that I shall approve of. But if you determine as we would have you, and signify it to us, we shall not stand with you for a week or so.

Signify to us, now, therefore, your compliance with our wishes. And then there is an end of your confinement. You may, in this case, directly come down to your father and me in his study; where we will give you our opinions of the patterns, with our hearty forgiveness and blessings.

Come, be a good child, as you used to be, my Clarissa. I have promised never more to interfere between your *father* and *you,* if this my most earnest application succeed not. I expect you down, love. Your father expects you down. You don't know what I have suffered within these few weeks past; nor ever will be able to guess, till you come to be in my situation; which is that of a fond and indulgent mother, praying night and day, and struggling to preserve, against the attempts of more ungovernable spirits, the peace and union of her family.

Your truly affectionate Mother.

Think for me, my dearest friend, how I must be affected by this letter; the contents of it so surprisingly terrifying, yet so sweetly urged! Oh why, cried I to myself, am I obliged to undergo this severe conflict between a command that I cannot obey, and language so condescendingly moving! Could I have been sure of being struck dead at the altar before the ceremony had given the man I hate a title to my vows, I think I could have submitted to have been led to it. But to think of living *with* and living *for* a man one abhors, what a sad thing is that!

Upon the whole, it was not possible for me to go down upon the prescribed condition.

I walked backward and forward. I threw down with disdain the patterns. Now to my closet retired I; then quitting it, threw myself upon the settee; then upon this chair; then upon that; then into one window, then into another—I knew not what to do! And while I was in this suspense, having again taken up the letter to re-peruse it, Betty came in, reminding me, by order, that my papa and mamma waited for me in my father's study.

Tell my mamma, said I, that I beg the favour of seeing her here for one moment; or to permit me to attend her anywhere by herself.

I listened at the stairs-head—You see, my dear, how it is, cried my father, very angrily: all your condescension (as your indulgence heretofore) is thrown away. *You blame your son's violence,* as you call it [*I had some pleasure in hearing this*]; but nothing else will do with her. You shall *not* see her alone. Is *my* presence an exception to the bold creature?

Tell her, said my mother to Betty, she knows upon what terms she may come down to us. Nor will I see her upon any other.

The maid brought me this answer. At last Betty brought me these lines from my father.

UNDUTIFUL AND PERVERSE CLARISSA,—No condescension, I see, will move you. Your mother shall *not* see you: nor will I. Prepare however to obey. You know our pleasure. Your Uncle Antony, your brother, and your sister, and your favourite Mrs. Norton, shall see the ceremony performed privately at your uncle's chapel. And when Mr. Solmes can introduce you to us, in the temper we wish to behold you in, we may perhaps forgive *his* wife, although we never can, in any *other* character, our perverse daughter. As it will be so privately performed, clothes and equipage may be provided afterwards. So prepare to go to your uncle's for an early day in next week. Nor shall you hear from me any more till you have changed your name to my liking. This from

Your Incensed Father.

If this resolution be adhered to, then will my father never see me more! For I will never be the wife of that Solmes—I will die first!

Tuesday Evening.

He, this Solmes, came hither soon after I had received my father's letter. He sent up to beg leave to wait upon me—I wonder at his assurance!

I said to Betty, who brought me his message, let him restore an unhappy creature to her father and mother, and then I may hear what he has to say. But, if my friends will not see *me* on *his* account, I will not see *him* upon his *own.*

I hope, miss, said Betty, you will not send me down with this answer. He is with your papa and mamma.

I am driven to despair, said I. I cannot get used worse. I will not see him.

Oh how I heard my father storm!

The wench says that he would have come up in his wrath, at my refusing to see Mr. Solmes, had not my brother and sister prevailed upon him to the contrary.

I wish he had! And, were it not for his own sake, that he had killed me!

Mr. Solmes condescended [I am mightily obliged to him, truly!] to plead for me.

They are all in tumults! How it will end, I know not; I am quite weary of my life—so happy, till within these few weeks! —so miserable now!

Miss Clarissa Harlowe to Miss Howe

An angry dialogue, a scolding-bout rather, has passed between my sister and me.

She was sent up to me, upon my refusal to see Mr. Solmes—let loose upon me, I think!

She began with representing to me the danger I had been in, had my father come up, as he would have done had he not been hindered—by Mr. *Solmes,* among the rest. She ridiculed me for my supposed esteem for Mr. Lovelace. Was surprised that the *witty,* the *prudent,* nay, the *dutiful* and *pi—ous* (so she sneeringly pronounced the word) Clarissa Harlowe, should be so strangely fond of a profligate man, that her parents were forced to lock her up, in order to hinder her from running into his arms. "Let me ask you, my dear, said she, how you now keep your account of the disposition of your time? *How many hours* in the *twenty-four* do you devote to your needle? How many to your prayers? How many to letter-writing? And how many to love? I doubt, I doubt, my little dear, was her arch expression, the latter article is like Aaron's rod, and swallows up all the rest! Tell me; is it not so?"

To these I answered, that it was a double mortification to me to owe my safety from the effects of my father's indignation to a man I could never thank for anything. With warmth I resented her reflections upon me on Mr. Lovelace's account. As to the disposition of my time in the twenty-four hours, I told her it would better have become her to pity a sister in distress, than to exult over her, especially when I could too justly attribute to the disposition of some of her wakeful hours no small part of that distress.

She raved extremely at this last hint: but reminded me of the gentle treatment of all my friends, my mother's in particular, before it came to this: she said that I had discovered a spirit they never had expected: that, if they had *thought* me such a championess, they would hardly have ventured to engage with me: but that now, the short and the long was, that the matter had gone too far to be given up: that it was become a contention between *duty* and *wilfulness;* whether a parent's authority were to yield to a daughter's obstinacy, or the contrary: that I must therefore bend or break, that was all, child.

I told her that I wished the subject were of such a nature that I could return her pleasantry with equal lightness of heart: but that, if Mr. Solmes had such merit in everybody's eyes, in *hers* particularly, why might he not be a *brother* to me, rather than a *husband?*

O child, says she, methinks you are as pleasant to the full as I am: I begin to have some hopes of you now. But do you think I will rob my sister of her humble servant? Had he first addressed himself to me, proceeded she, something might have been said: but to take my younger sister's refusal! No, no, child; it is not come to that neither! Besides, that would be to leave the door open in your heart for you know who, child; and we would fain bar him out, if possible. In short (and then she changed both her tone, and her looks) had I been as forward as somebody, to throw myself into the arms of one of the greatest profligates in England, who had endeavoured to support his claim to me through the blood of my brother, then might all my family join together to save me from such a wretch, and to marry me as fast as they could, to some worthy man, who might *opportunely* offer himself. And now, Clary, all's out, and make the most of it.

Alas! for my poor sister! said I! The man was not *always* so great a profligate. How true is the observation, *that unrequited love turns to deepest hate!*

I thought she would have beat me. But I proceeded: And, as to *opportune* offers, would to heaven someone had offered *opportunely* to somebody! It is not my fault, Bella, the *opportune* gentlemen don't come!

I expected to feel the weight of her hand. She did come up to me with it held up: then, speechless with passion, ran down half-way of the stairs and came up again.

When she could speak: God give me patience with you!

And so, that wicked wretch is to be allowed such a control over you that you are not to be civil to your father's friends, at his own house, for fear of incensing *him!* When this comes to be represented, be so good as to tell me what is it you expect from it?

Everything, I said, or *nothing,* as she was pleased to represent it. Be so good as to give it your interest, Bella: and say further, "that I will by any means I can in the law, or otherwise, make over to my father, to my uncles, or even to my brother, all I am entitled to by my grandfather's will, as a security for the performance of my promises. And as I shall have no reason to expect any favour from my father, if I break them, I shall not be worth anybody's having. And further still, unkindly as my brother has used me, I will go down to Scotland privately as his housekeeper [I now see I may be spared here] if he will promise to treat me no worse than he would do an hired one. Or I will go to Florence to my Cousin Morden, if his stay in Italy will admit of it. In *either case,* it may be given out that I am gone to the *other;* or to the world's end. I care not whither it is said I am gone, or do go."

So down she went. But, it seems, my Aunt Hervey and my

Uncle Harlowe were gone away: and as they have all engaged to act in concert, messengers were dispatched to my uncle and aunt to desire them to be there to breakfast in the morning.

Tuesday Noon, March 21.

I have as yet heard no more of my sister: and have not courage enough to insist upon throwing myself at the feet of my father and mother, as I thought in my heat of temper I should be able to do. And I am now grown as calm as ever; and were Bella to come up again, as fit to be played upon as before.

But what shall I do with this Lovelace? I have just now by the unsuspected hole in the wall (*that I told you of in my letter by Hannah*) got a letter from him. So uneasy is he for fear I should be prevailed upon in Solmes's favour; so full of menaces, if I am; so resenting the usage I receive (for, how I cannot tell; but he has undoubtedly intelligence of all that is done in the family); such protestations of inviolable faith and honour; such vows of reformation; such pressing arguments to escape from this disgraceful confinement—O my Nancy, what shall I do with this Lovelace?

MISS HOWE TO MISS CLARISSA HARLOWE

Wednesday Night, March 22.

YOU AND I have often *retrospected* the faces and minds of grown people; that is to say, have formed images from their present appearances, outside and in what sort of figures they made when boys and girls. And I'll tell you the lights in which Hickman, Solmes, and Lovelace, our three heroes, have appeared to me, supposing them boys at school.

Solmes I have imagined to be a little sordid pilfering rogue, who would purloin from everybody, and beg every boy's bread and butter from him; while, as I have heard a reptile brag, he would in a winter morning spit upon his thumbs, and spread his own with it, that he might keep it all to himself.

Hickman, a great overgrown, lank-haired, chubby boy, who would be hunched and punched by everybody; and go home with his finger in his eye, and tell his mother.

While Lovelace I have supposed a curl-pated villain, full of fire, fancy, and mischief; an orchard-robber, a wall-climber, a horse-rider without saddle or bridle, neck or nothing: a sturdy rogue, in short, who would kick and cuff, and do no right, and take no wrong of anybody; would get his head broken, then a plaster for it or let it heal of itself; while he went on to do more mischief, and if not to get, to deserve, broken bones. And the same dispositions have grown up with them, and distinguish them as *men,* with no very material alteration.

Only, that all men are monkeys more or less, or else that you and I should have such baboons as these to choose out of, is a mortifying thing, my dear.

Miss Howe to Miss Clarissa Harlowe

Tuesday Morn., 7 o'clock.

I MUST BEGIN with blaming you, my dear, for your resolution not to litigate for your right, if occasion were to be given you. Justice is due to ourselves, as well as to everybody else. Still more must I blame you for declaring to your aunt and sister, that you will *not:* since (as they will tell it to your father and brother) the declaration must needs give advantage to spirits who have so little of that generosity for which you are so much distinguished.

You have chidden me, and again will, I doubt not, for the liberties I take with some of your relations. But, my dear, need I tell *you,* that pride in *ourselves* must, and for ever will, provoke contempt, and bring down upon us abasement from *others?* I am very loth to offend you; yet I cannot help speaking of your relations, as well as of others, as I think they deserve. I despise them all, but your mother: indeed I do: and as for her —but I will spare the good lady for your sake. God forgive me; but with such usage I should have been with Lovelace before now! Yet remember, my dear, that the step which would not be wondered at from such a hasty-tempered creature as me, would be inexcusable in such a considerate person as you.

Must I, my dear, call such a creature your *brother?* I believe I must; because he is your *father's son.* There is no harm, I hope, in saying that.

I repeat, you know that I will speak my mind, and *write* it too. He is not *my* brother. Can you say he is *yours?* So, for your life, if you are just, you can't be angry with me: for would you side with a *false brother* against a *true friend?* A brother may *not* be a friend: but a friend will be *always* a brother—*mind that,* as your Uncle *Tony* says!

I cannot descend so low as to take very particular notice of the epistles of those poor souls, whom you call *uncles*. Yet I love to divert myself with such grotesque characters too. But I know *them,* and love *you;* and so cannot make the jest of them which their absurdities call for.

Did I think you would have any manner of doubt, from the style or contents of this letter, whose saucy pen it is that has run on at this rate, I would write my name at length; since it comes too much from my heart to disavow it: but at present the initials shall serve; and I will go on again directly.

A. H.

MISS HOWE TO MISS CLARISSA HARLOWE

Thursday Morn, 10 o'clock (Mar. 23.)

I WILL POSTPONE, or perhaps pass by, several observations which I had to make on other parts of your letters; to acquaint you that Mr. Hickman, when in London, found an opportunity to inquire after Mr. Lovelace's town life and conversation.

At the Cocoa Tree in Pall Mall he fell in with two of his intimates, the one named Belton, the other Mowbray; both very free of speech, and probably as free in their lives: but the waiters paid them great respect, and on Mr. Hickman's inquiry after their characters, called them men of fortune and honour.

They began to talk of Mr. Lovelace of their own accord; and upon some gentlemen in the room asking when they expected him in town, answered, that very day. Mr. Hickman (as they both went on praising Lovelace) said, he had indeed heard that Mr. Lovelace was a very fine gentleman—and was proceeding, when one of them interrupting him, said—only, sir, the finest gentleman in the world; that's all.

And so he led them on to expatiate more particularly on his qualities; which they were very fond of doing: but said not one single word in behalf of his morals—*mind that* also, in your uncle's style.

Mr. Hickman said that Mr. Lovelace was very happy, as he understood, in the esteem of the ladies; and, smiling, to make them believe he did not think amiss of it, that he pushed his good fortune as far as it would go.

Well put, Mr. Hickman! thought I; equally grave and sage—thou seemest not to be a stranger to their dialect, as I suppose this is. But I said nothing; for I have often tried to find out this *mighty* sober man of my mother's: but hitherto have only to say that he is either very moral or very cunning.

No doubt of it, replied one of them; and out came an oath, with a who would not? That he did as every young fellow would do.

Very true! said my mother's Puritan. But I hear he is in treaty with a fine lady——

So he was, Mr. Belton said—the devil fetch her! [Vile brute!] for she engrossed all his time. But the lady's family ought to be —something—[Mr. Hickman desired to be excused repeating what—though he had repeated what was worse] and might dearly repent their usage of a man of his family and merit.

Perhaps they may think him too wild, cried Hickman: and theirs is, I hear, a very sober family——

SOBER! said one of them: a good honest word, Dick! Where the devil has it lain all this time? D— me if I have heard of it in this sense, ever since I was at college! And then, said he, we bandied it about among twenty of us, as an obsolete.

These, my dear, are Mr. Lovelace's companions: you'll be pleased to take *notice of that!*

Yet it must be said too that if there be a woman in the world that can reclaim him, it is you. And by your account of his behaviour in the interview between you, I own I have some hope of him. At least, this I will say, that all the arguments he then used with you seem to be just and right: and if you *are* to be his—but no more of that: he cannot, after all, deserve you.

Miss Howe to Miss Clarissa Harlowe

Thursday Afternoon, March 23.

An unexpected visitor has turned the course of my thoughts, and changed the subject I had intended to pursue. The only one for whom I would have dispensed with my resolution not to see anybodv all the dedicated day: a visitor, whom, according to Mr. Hickman's report from the expectations of his libertine friends, I supposed to be in town. Now, my dear, have I saved myself the trouble of telling you that it was your too agreeable rake. Our sex is said to love to trade in surprises: yet have I, by my promptitude, surprised myself out of mine. I had intended, you must know, to run twice the length, before I had suffered you so much as to guess who, and whether man or woman, my visitor was: but since you have the discovery at so cheap a rate, you are welcome to it.

The end of his coming was to engage my interest with my *charming friend;* and as he was sure that I knew all your mind, to acquaint him what he had to trust to.

He mentioned what had passed in the interview between you; but could not be satisfied with the result of it, and with the little satisfaction he had obtained from you; the malice of your family to him increasing, and their cruelty to you not abating. His heart, he told me, was in tumults, for fear you should be prevailed upon in favour of a man despised by everybody.

He gave me fresh instances of indignities cast upon himself by your uncles and brother; and declared that if you suffered yourself to be forced into the arms of the man for whose sake he was loaded with undeserved abuses, you should be one of the youngest, as you would be one of the lovliest widows in England: and that he would moreover call your brother to account for the liberties he takes with his character to every one he meets with.

He proposed several schemes for you to choose some one of them, in order to enable you to avoid the persecutions you labour under: one I will mention: that you will resume your estate; and if you find difficulties that can be no otherwise surmounted, that you will, either avowedly or privately, as he had proposed to you, accept of Lady Betty Lawrance's or Lord M.'s assistance to instate you in it. He declared that if you did he would leave it absolutely to your own pleasure afterwards, and to the advice which your Cousin Morden on his arrival should give you, whether to encourage his address or not, as you should be convinced of the sincerity of the reformation which his enemies make him so much want.

I had now a good opportunity to sound him, as you wished Mr. Hickman would Lord M. as to the continued or diminished favour of the ladies, and of his lordship, towards you, upon their being acquainted with the animosity of your relations to them, as well as to their kinsman. I laid hold of the opportunity; and he satisfied me by reading some passages of a letter he had about him from Lord M. That an alliance with you, and that on the foot of your own single merit, would be the most desirable event to them that could happen: and so far to the purpose of your wished inquiry does his lordship go in this letter, that he assures him, that whatever you suffer in fortune from the violence of your relations on *his* account, he and Lady Sarah and Lady Betty will join to make it up to him. And yet that the reputation of a family so splendid, would, no doubt, in a case of such importance to the honour of both, make them prefer a general consent.

I told him, as you yourself I knew had done, that you were extremely averse to Mr. Solmes; and that, might you be left to your own choice, it would be the single life. As to himself, I plainly said that you had great and just objections to him on the score of his careless morals: that it was surprising that men who gave themselves the liberties he was said to take, should presume to think that whenever they took it into their heads to marry, the most virtuous and worthy of the sex were to fall to heir lot: that as to the resumption, it had been very strongly urged by myself, and would be still further urged; though you had been hitherto averse to that measure: that your chief reliance and hopes were upon your Cousin Morden: and that to suspend or gain time till he arrived was, as I believed, your principal aim.

I told him that with regard to the mischief he threatened, neither the act nor the menace could serve any end but theirs who persecuted you; as it would give them a pretence for carrying into effect their compulsatory projects; and that with the approbation of all the world; since he must not think the public would give its voice in favour of a violent young man, of no extraordinary character as to morals, who should seek to rob a family of eminence of a child so valuable; and who threatened, if he could not obtain her in preference to a man chosen by themselves, that he would avenge himself upon them all by acts of violence.

I added that he was very much mistaken if he thought to intimidate *you* by such menaces: for that, though your disposition was all sweetness, yet I knew not a steadier temper in the world than yours; nor one more inflexible (as your friends had found, and would still further find, if they continued to give occasion for its exertion) whenever you thought yourself in the right; and that you were ungenerously dealt with in matters of too much moment to be indifferent about. Miss Clarissa Harlowe, Mr. Lovelace, let me tell you, said I, timid as her foresight and prudence may make her in some cases, where she apprehends dangers to those she loves, is above fear, in points where her honour, and the true dignity of her sex, are concerned. In short, sir, you must not think to frighten Miss Clarissa Harlowe into such a mean or unworthy conduct as only a weak or unsteady mind can be guilty of.

He was so very far from intending to intimidate you, he said, that he besought me not to mention one word to you of what had passed between us: that what he hinted at, which carried the air of a menace, was owing to the fervour of his spirits, raised by his apprehensions of losing all hope of you for ever; and on a supposition that you were to be actually forced into the arms of a man you hated: that were this to be the case, he must own, that he should pay very little regard to the world or its censures: especially as the menaces of some of your family now, and their triumph over him afterwards, would both provoke and warrant all the vengeance he could take.

He added, that all the countries in the world were alike to him, but on your account: so that whatever he should think fit to do, were you lost to *him,* he should have nothing to apprehend from the laws of this.

I did not like the determined air he spoke this with: he is certainly capable of great rashness.

And now, my dear, upon the whole, I think it behoves you to make yourself independent: all then will fall right. This man is a violent man. I should wish, methinks, that you should not have either him or Solmes. You will find, if you get out of your brother's and sister's way, what you *can* or *cannot* do, with regard to either. If your relations persist in their foolish scheme, I think I will take his hint, and, at a proper opportunity, sound my mother. I am, my dearest friend, and will be ever,

Your most affectionate and faithful

Anna Howe.

MISS CLARISSA HARLOWE TO MISS HOWE

Wedn. Night, March 22.

ON THE REPORT made by my aunt and sister of my *obstinacy,* my assembled relations have taken an *unanimous* resolution (as Betty tells me it is) against me. This resolution you will find signified to me in the enclosed letter from my brother, just now brought me.

MISS CLARY,—I am commanded to let you know that my father and uncles having heard your Aunt Hervey's account of all that has passed between her and you: having heard from your sister what sort of treatment she has had from you: having recollected all that has passed between your mother and you: having weighed all your pleas and proposals: having taken into consideration their engagements with Mr. Solmes; that gentleman's patience and great affection for you; and the little opportunity you have given yourself to be acquainted either with his merit, or his proposals: having considered two points more; to wit, the wounded authority of a father; and Mr. Solmes's continual entreaties (little as you have deserved regard from him) that you may be freed from a confinement to which he is desirous to attribute your perverseness to him [*averseness* I should have said, but let it go] he being unable to account otherwise for so strong a one, supposing you told truth to your mother, when you asserted that your heart *was free;* and which Mr. Solmes is willing to believe, though nobody else does—for all these reasons it is resolved that you shall go to your Uncle Antony's: and you must accordingly prepare yourself so to do. You will have but short notice of the day, for obvious reasons.

I will honestly tell you the motive for your going: it is a double one; first, that they may be sure that you shall not correspond with anybody they do not like (for they find from Mrs. Howe that, by some means or other, you *do* correspond with her daughter; and, through her, perhaps with somebody else): and next, that you may receive the visits of Mr. Solmes; which you have thought fit to refuse to do here; by which means you have deprived yourself of the opportunity of knowing *whom* and *what* you have hitherto refused.

If after one fortnight's conversation with Mr. Solmes, and after you have heard what your friends shall further urge in his behalf, unhardened by clandestine correspondencies, you shall convince them that Virgil's *Amor omnibus idem* (for the application of which I refer you to the Georgic, as translated by Dryden) is verified in you, as well as in the rest of the animal creation; and that you cannot, or will *not,* forego your prepossession in favour of the *moral,* the *virtuous,* the *pious* Lovelace it will then be considered, whether to humour you, or to renounce you for ever.

It is hoped, that as you *must* go, you will go cheerfully. Your Uncle Antony will make everything at his house agreeable to you. But indeed he won't promise, that he will not, *at proper times,* draw up the bridge.

Your visitors, besides Mr. Solmes, will be myself, if you permit me that honour, Miss Clary; your sister; and, as you behave to Mr. Solmes, your Aunt Hervey, and your Uncle Harlowe; and yet the two latter will hardly come neither, if they think it will be to hear your *whining vocatives.* Betty Barnes will be your attendant: and, I must needs tell you, miss, that we none of us think the worse of the faithful maid, for your dislike of her: although Betty, who would be glad to oblige you, laments it as a misfortune.

Your answer is required whether you *cheerfully* consent to go? And your indulgent mother bids me remind you from her, that a fortnight's visits from Mr. Solmes are all that is meant at present.

I am, as you shall be pleased to deserve,

Yours, etc.,
James Harlowe, Jun.

So here is the master-stroke of my brother's policy! Called upon to consent to go to my Uncle Antony's, *avowedly* to receive Mr. Solmes's visits! A chapel! A moated house! Deprived of the opportunity of corresponding with you!—or of any possibility of escape, should violence be used to compel me to be that odious man's! [1]

Late as it was when I received this insolent letter, I wrote an answer to it directly, that it might be ready for the writer's time of rising. You will see by it how much his vile hint from the Georgic, and his rude one of my *whining vocatives,* have set me up.

YOU MIGHT have told me, brother, in three lines, what the determination of my friends was; only, that then you would not have had room to display your pedantry by so detestable an allusion or reference to the Georgic.

The time is indeed come that I can no longer bear those contempts and reflections which a brother, least of all men, is entitled to give. And let me beg of you one favour, officious sir: it is *this,* that you will not give yourself any concern about a husband for *me,* till I shall have the forwardness to propose a wife to *you.* Pardon me, sir; but I cannot help thinking that could I have the art to *get my father* on my side, I should have as much right to prescribe for you, as you have for me.

As to the communication you make me, I must take upon me to say, that although I will receive, as becomes me, any of my father's commands; yet, as this signification is made by a brother, who has shown of late so much of an unbrotherly animosity to me (for no reason in the world that I know of, but

[1] These violent measures, and the obstinate perseverance of the whole family in them, will be the less wondered at, when it is considered, that all the time they were but as so many puppets danced upon Mr. Lovelace's wires, as he boasts

that he believes he has, in me, *one* sister too many for his interest) I think myself entitled to conclude, that such a letter as you have sent me is all your own—and of course to declare that, while I *so* think it, I will not, willingly, nor even without violence, go to any place, avowedly to receive Mr. Solmes's visits.

One more word, provoked as I am, I will add: that had I been thought as really obstinate and perverse as of late I am said to be, I should not have been so disgracefully treated as I have been. Lay your hand upon your heart, brother, and say, by whose instigations—and examine what I have done to deserve to be made thus unhappy, and to be obliged to style myself

Your injured sister,
Cl. Harlowe.

Miss Clarissa Harlowe to Miss Howe

Thursday Morning, Mar. 23.

My letter has set them *all* in tumults: for, it seems, none of them went home last night; and they all were desired to be present to give their advice, if I should refuse compliance with a command thought so reasonable as it seems this is.

The result was that my brother (having really, as my mother and aunt insisted, taken wrong measures with me) should write again in a more *moderate* manner: for nobody else was permitted or cared to write to such a *ready scribbler*. And, I having declared that I would not receive any more of his letters without command from a superior authority, my mother was to give it *hers:* and accordingly has done so in the following lines, written on the superscription of his letter to me: which letter also follows; together with my reply.

Clary Harlowe,—Receive and read this with the temper that becomes your sex, your character, your education, and your duty: and return an answer to it, directed to your brother.

Charlotte Harlowe.

To Miss Clarissa Harlowe

Thursday Morning.

Once more I write, although imperiously prohibited by a younger sister. Your mother will have me do so that you may be destitute of all defence, if you persist in your *pervicacy.* Shall I be a *pedant,* miss, for this word? She is willing to indulge in you the *least* appearance of that delicacy for which she once, as well as everybody else, admired you—before you knew Lovelace; I cannot, however, help saying *that:* and she, and your Aunt Hervey, will have it—[they would fain favour you if they could] that I may have provoked from you the answer they nevertheless own to be so exceedingly *unbecoming.* I am now learning, you see, to take up the softer language, where you have laid it down. This then is the case:

They *entreat,* they *pray,* they *beg,* they *supplicate*—[will either of these do, Miss Clary?] that you will make no scruple to go to your Uncle Antony's: and fairly I am to tell you, for the very purpose mentioned in my last—or, 'tis presumable, they need not *entreat, pray, beg, supplicate.* Thus much is promised to Mr. Solmes's, who is your advocate, and very uneasy, that you should be under constraint, supposing that your dislike to him arise from that. And, if he finds that you are not to be moved in his favour, when you are absolutely freed from what you call a *control,* he will forbear thinking of you, whatever it costs him. He loves you too well: and in *this,* I really think his understanding, which you have reflected upon, is to be questioned.

Only for one fortnight, therefore, permit his visits. Your *education* [you tell me of *mine,* you know] ought to make you incapable of rudeness to anybody. He will not, I hope, be the first man, myself excepted, whom you ever treated rudely, purely because he is esteemed by us all. I am, what you have a mind to make me, friend, brother, or servant—I wish I could be still *more* polite, to so polite, so delicate, a sister.

Ja. Harlowe.

To James Harlowe, Junior, Esq.

Thursday, March 23.

Permit me, my ever-dear and honoured papa and mamma, in this manner to surprise you into an *audience* (presuming this will be read to you) since I am denied the honour of writing to you directly. Let me beg of you to believe that nothing but the most unconquerable dislike could make me stand against your pleasure. What are riches, what are settlements, to happiness? Let me not thus cruelly be given up to a man my very soul is averse to. Permit me to repeat that I cannot *honestly* be his. Had I a slighter notion of the matrimonial duty than I have, perhaps I might. But when I am to bear all the misery, and that for *life;* when my *heart* is less concerned in this matter than my *soul;* my *temporary,* perhaps, than my *future* good; why should I be denied the liberty of *refusing?* That liberty is all I ask.

It were easy for me to give way to hear Mr. Solmes talk for the mentioned fortnight, although it is impossible for me, say what he would, to get over my dislike to him. But the moated house, the chapel there, and the little mercy my brother and sister, who are to be there, have hitherto shown me, are what I am extremely apprehensive of. And why does my brother say my restraint is to be taken off (and that too at Mr. Solmes's desire) when I am to be a still closer prisoner than before; the bridge threatened to be drawn up; and no dear papa and mamma near me, to appeal to, in the last resort?

Transfer not, I beseech you, to a brother and sister your own authority over your child; to a brother and sister who treat me with unkindness and reproach; and, as I have too much reason to apprehend, misrepresent my words and behaviour; or, greatly favoured as I used to be, it is impossible I should be sunk so low in your opinions, as I unhappily am!

Let but this my hard, my disgraceful confinement, be put an end to. Let me not, however, be put out of your own house. Let Mr. Solmes come and go, as my papa pleases: let me but stay or retire when he comes, as I can; and leave the rest to Providence.

Forgive me, brother, that thus, with an appearance of art,

I address myself to my father and mother, to whom I am forbidden to approach, or to write. Hard it is to be reduced to such a contrivance! Forgive likewise the plain dealing I have used in the above, with the nobleness of a gentleman, and the gentleness due from a brother to a sister.

Your unhappy sister,
Cl. Harlowe.

[Her brother replies to this letter, denying for the family all her requests. Ed.]

Friday, Ten o'clock.

Going down to my poultry-yard just now, I heard my brother and sister and that Solmes laughing and triumphing together. The high yew hedge between us, which divides the yard from the garden, hindered them from seeing me.

My brother, as I found, had been reading part, or the whole perhaps, of the copy of his last letter.

Indeed you was up with her there, brother, said my sister. You need not have bid her not write to you. I'll engage, with all her wit, she'll never pretend to answer it.

Why, indeed, said my brother, with an air of college-sufficiency, with which he abounds (for he thinks nobody writes like himself,) I believe I have given her a *choke-pear*. What say you, Mr. Solmes?

Why, sir, said he, I think it is unanswerable. But will it not exasperate her more against me?

Never fear, Mr. Solmes, said my brother, but we'll carry our point, if she do not tire *you* out first. We have gone too far in this method to recede. Her Cousin Morden will soon be here: so all must be over before that time, or she'll be made independent of us all.

Mr. Solmes declared that he was determined to persevere while my brother gave him any hopes, and while my father stood firm.

Some lively, and I suppose, witty answer, my brother returned; for he and Mr. Solmes laughed outrageously upon it, and Bella, laughing too, called him a naughty man: but I heard no more of what they said; they walking on into the garden.

Miss Clarissa Harlowe to Miss Howe

Friday, Midnight.

You again insist (strengthened by Mr. Lovelace's opinion) upon my *assuming* my own estate [I cannot call it *resuming,* having never been in possession of it]: and I have given you room to expect that I will consider this subject more closely than I have done before.

You would not, I am sure, have me accept of Mr. Lovelace's offered assistance in such a claim. If I would embrace any *other* person's, who else would care to appear for a child against parents, ever, till of late, so affectionate? But were such a protector to be found, what a length of time would it take up in a course of litigation? The will and the deeds have flaws in them, they say. My brother sometimes talks of going to reside at *The Grove:* I suppose, with a design to make ejectments necessary, were I to offer at assuming; or were I to marry Mr. Lovelace, in order to give him all the opposition and difficulty the law would help him to give.

These cases I have put to myself for argument sake: but they are all out of the question, although anybody *were* to be found who would espouse my cause: for I do assure you, I would sooner beg my bread than litigate for my right with my father: since I am convinced that whether the parent do his duty by the child or not, the child cannot be excused from doing hers to him. And to go to law with my *father,* what a sound has that?

Upon the whole, then, what have I to hope for, but a change in my father's resolution? And is there any probability of *that;* such an ascendency as my brother and sister have obtained over everybody; and such an interest to pursue the enmity they have now openly avowed against me?

As to Mr. Lovelace's approbation of your assumption-scheme, I wonder not at it. He very probably penetrates the difficulties I should have to bring it to effect, without *his* assistance. Were I to find myself as free as I would wish myself to be, perhaps Mr. Lovelace would stand a worse chance with me than his vanity may permit him to imagine; notwithstanding the pleasure you take in raillying me on his account.

Then am I utterly displeased with him. To threaten as he

threatens; yet to pretend, that it is not to intimidate me; and to beg of you *not to tell me,* when he must know you *would,* and no doubt *intended* that you *should,* is so meanly artful! The man must think he has a frighted fool to deal with.

Meantime, give me leave to tell you, that it goes against me, in my cooler moments, unnatural as my brother is to me, to have you, my dear, who are my other self, write such very severe reflections upon him, in relation to the advantage Lovelace had over him. He is not indeed *your* brother: but remember, that you write to *his* sister. Upon my word, my dear Miss Howe, you dip your pen in gall whenever you are offended. And yet I am so angry both at my brother and sister, that I should not have taken this liberty with my dear friend, notwithstanding I know you *never* loved them, had you not made so light of so shocking a transaction, where a brother's life was at stake: when his credit in the eye of the mischievous sex has received a still deeper wound than he *personally* sustained; and when a revival of the same wicked resentments (which may end more fatally) is threatened.

I shall deposit this the first thing. When you have it, lose no time, I pray you, to advise (lest it be too late).

Your ever obliged

Cl. Harlowe.

Miss Howe to Miss Clarissa Harlowe

Sat., March 25.

What *can* I advise you to do, my noble creature? Your merit is your crime. You can no more change *your* nature than your persecutors can *theirs*. Your distress is owing to the vast disparity between you and them. What would you have of them? Do they not act in character? And to whom? To an alien You are not one of them. They have two dependencies in their hope to move you to compliance: upon their *impenetrableness* one (I'd give it a more proper name, if I dared); the other, on the regard you have always had for your *character* (have they not heretofore owned as much?) and upon your apprehensions from *that* of Lovelace, which would discredit you, should you take any step by his means to extricate yourself. Then they know that resentment and unpersuadableness are not natural to you; and that the anger they have wrought you up to, will subside, as all *extraordinaries* soon do; and that once married, you will make the best of it.

As to that wretch's perseverance, those only who know not the man, will wonder at it. He has not the least delicacy. His principal view in marriage is not to the mind. How shall those beauties be valued, which cannot be comprehended? Were you to be his, and show a visible want of tenderness to him, it is my opinion, he would not be much concerned at it.

Were it not YOU, I should know how (barbarously used as you are used) to advise you in a moment. But such a noble character to suffer from a (supposed) rashness and indiscretion of such a nature, would, as I have heretofore observed, be a wound to the sex.

While I was in hope that the asserting of your own independence would have helped you, I was pleased that you had *one* resource, as I thought: but now that you have so well proved that such a step would not avail you, I am entirely at a loss what to say.

One thing you must consider, that if you leave your parents, your duty and love will not suffer you to justify yourself by an appeal against them; and so you'll have the world against you. And should Lovelace continue his wild life, and behave ungratefully to you, will not his baseness seem to justify their conduct to *you,* as well as their resentments against *him?*

May Heaven direct you for the best! I can only say that, for my own part, I would do anything, go any whither, rather than be compelled to marry the man I hate; and (were he such a man as Solmes) must always hate; nor could I have borne what you have borne, if from father and uncles, not from brother and sister.

My mother will have it that after they have tried their utmost efforts to bring you into their measures, and find them ineffectual, they will recede. But I cannot say I am of her mind. She does not own she has any other authority for this but her own conjecture.

You must, if possible, avoid being carried to that uncle's. The man, the parson, your brother and sister present—they'll certainly there marry you to the wretch.

Yet, after all, I must leave the point undetermined, and only to *be* determined, as you find they recede from their avowed purpose, or resolve to remove you to your Uncle Antony's. But I must repeat my wishes, that something may fall out, that *neither* of these men may call you *his!* And may you live single, my dearest friend, till some man shall offer, that may be as worthy of you as man *can* be!

I will add nothing (though I could an hundred things on occasion of your latest communications) but that I am

Your ever-affectionate and faithful

Anna Howe.

MISS CLARISSA HARLOWE TO MISS HOWE

Sunday Morning, March 26.

HOW SOOTHING a thing is praise from those we love!

Most heartily I thank you for the kind dispatch of your last favour.

But let me answer the kind contents of it, as well as I may.

As to getting over my disgusts to Mr. Solmes, it is impossible to be done; while he wants generosity, frankness of heart, benevolence, manners, and every qualification that distinguishes a worthy man. O my dear! what a degree of patience, what a greatness of soul is required in the wife, not to despise a husband who is more ignorant, more illiterate, more low-minded, than herself? How much easier to bear the *temporary* persecutions I labour under, *because* temporary, than to resolve to be *such* a man's for *life?* Were I to comply, must I not leave my relations, and go to him?

I have received two letters from Mr. Lovelace, since his visit to you; which make three that I have not answered. I doubt not his being very uneasy; but in his last he complains in high terms of my silence; not in the still small voice, or, rather, style of an humble lover, but in a style like that which would probably be used by a slighted protector. And his pride is again touched, that like a *thief* or *eavesdropper,* he is forced to dodge about in hopes of a letter, and return five miles without any.

I will give you the substance of what I wrote to him yesterday.

I take him severely to task, for his freedom in threatening me, through you, with a visit to Mr. Solmes, or to my brother.

"As to the solemn vows and protestations he is so ready, upon all occasions, to make, they have the less weight with me, I tell him, as they give a kind of demonstration, that he himself, from his own character, thinks there is *reason* to make them. *Deeds* are to me the only evidences of *intentions*. And I am more and more convinced of the necessity of breaking-off a correspondence with a person, whose address I see it is impossible either to expect my friends to encourage, or him to deserve that they should.

"What therefore I repeatedly desire is, that since his birth, alliances, and expectations, are such as will at any time, if his immoral character be not an objection, procure him at least equal advantages in a woman whose taste and inclinations moreover might be better adapted to his own; I insist upon it, as well as advise it, that he give up all thoughts of me: and the rather, as he has all along (by his threatening and unpolite behaviour to my friends, and whenever he speaks of them) given me reason to conclude, that there is more malice to *them*, than regard to *me*, in his perseverance."

Your mother is of opinion, you say, that *at last* my friends will relent. Heaven grant that they may! But my brother and sister have such an influence over everybody, and are so determined; so pique themselves upon subduing me, and carrying their point; that I despair that they will: and yet, if they do not, I frankly own, I would not scruple to throw myself upon any not disreputable protection, by which I might avoid my present persecutions, on one hand, and not give Mr. Lovelace advantage over me, on the other. That is to say, were there manifestly *no other* way left me: for, if there *were*, I should think the leaving my father's house, without his consent, one of the most inexcusable actions I could be guilty of, were the protection to be ever so unexceptionable; and this notwithstanding the independent fortune willed me by my grandfather.

But, upon the whole, this I do repeat—that nothing but the *last* extremity shall make me abandon my father's house, if they will permit me to stay; and if I can, by any means, by any honest pretences, but keep off my evil destiny in it till my

Cousin Morden arrives. As one of my trustees, *his* is a protection into which I may without discredit throw myself, if my other friends should remain determined. And this (although they seem too well aware of it) is all my hope: for, as to Lovelace, were I to be sure of his tenderness, and even of his reformation, must not the thoughts of embracing the offered protection of his family, be the same thing in the world's eye, as accepting of his own? Could I avoid receiving his visits at his own relations? Must I not be his whatever (on seeing him in a *nearer* light) I should find him out to be? For you know, it has always been my observation, that very few people in courtship see each other as they are.

. . . . . .

Mr. Solmes is almost continually here: so is my Aunt Hervey: so are my two uncles. Something is working against me, I doubt. What an uneasy state is suspense! When a naked sword, too, seems hanging over one's head!

I will deposit thus far. Adieu, my dear.

Clarissa Harlowe.

MISS HOWE TO MISS CLARISSA HARLOWE

Sat., March 25.

I FOLLOW my last of this date by command. I mentioned in my former, my mother's opinion of the merit you would have, if you could oblige your friends against your own inclination.

My mother argues upon this case in a most discouraging manner for all such of our sex as look forward for happiness in marriage with the *man of their choice.*

What is there in it, says she, that all this bustle is about? Is it such a mighty matter for a young woman to give up her inclinations to oblige her friends?

Very well, my mamma, thought I! Now, may you ask this. At FORTY, you may—but what would you have said at EIGHTEEN is the question?

Either, said she, the lady must be thought to have very violent inclinations (and what nice young creature would have that supposed?) which she *could* not give up; or a very stubborn will, which she *would* not; or, thirdly, have parents she was indifferent about obliging.

I told my mother that if *you* were to take any rash step, it would be owing to the indiscreet violence of your friends. I was afraid, I said, that this must be allowed me, that if children weighed not these matters so thoroughly as they ought, neither did parents make those allowances for youth, inclination, and inexperience, which had been found necessary to be made for themselves at their children's time of life.

She then touched upon the moral character of Mr. Lovelace; and how reasonable the aversion of your relations is, to a man who gives himself the liberties he is said to take; and who indeed himself denies not the accusation; having been heard to declare, that he will do all the mischief he can to the sex in revenge for the ill usage and broken vows of his first love, at a time when he was *too young* (his own expression, it seems) to be insincere.

I insisted upon the extraordinary circumstances in your case; particularizing them. I took notice, that Mr. Lovelace's morals were at one time no objection with your relations for Arabella: that then much was built upon his family, and more upon his parts and learning, which made it out of doubt, that he might be reclaimed by a woman of virtue and prudence: and (pray forgive me for mentioning it) I ventured to add, that although your family might be good sort of folks, as the world went, yet nobody imputed to any of them but you, a *very* punctilious concern for religion or piety. Therefore were they the less entitled to object to defects of that kind in others. Then, what an odious man, said I, have they picked out, to supplant in a lady's affections one of the finest figures of a man, and one noted for his brilliant parts and other accomplishments, whatever his morals may be!

To avoid entering further into such an *incomparable* comparison, I said I did not believe, had they left you to your own way, and treated you generously, that you would have had the thought of encouraging any man whom they disliked.

Then, Nancy, catching me up, the excuse is less; for, if so, must there not be more of *contradiction* than *love*, in the case?

Not so, neither, madam: for I know Miss Clarissa Harlowe would prefer Mr. Lovelace to all men, if morals——

If, Nancy! That *if* is everything. Do you really think she loves Mr. Lovelace?

What would you have had me to say, my dear? I won't tell you what I *did* say: but had I *not* said what I *did*, who would have believed me?

Besides, I *know* you love him! Excuse me, my dear: yet, if you deny it, what do you but reflect upon yourself, as if you thought you *ought not* to allow yourself in what you cannot help doing?

Indeed, madam, said I, the man is worthy of any woman's love (*If*, again, I *could* say)—but her parents——

Her parents, Nancy—(you know, my dear, how my mother, who accuses her daughter of quickness, is evermore interrupting one!)

May take wrong measures, said I——

Cannot do wrong. They have reason, I'll warrant, said she——

By which they may provoke a young woman, said I, to do rash things, which otherwise she would not do.

And thus, my dear, have I set my mother's arguments before you. And the rather, as I cannot myself tell what to advise you to do.

Heaven guide and direct you for the best, is the incessant prayer of

Your ever affectionate,
Anna Howe.

Miss Clarissa Harlowe to Miss Howe

Sunday Afternoon.

I am in great apprehensions. Yet cannot help repeating my humble thanks to your mother and you, for your last favour.

Before I come to what most nearly affects me, I must chide you, once more, for the severe, the *very* severe things you mention of our family, to the disparagement of their *morals*. Indeed, my dear, I wonder at you! A slighter occasion might have passed me, after I have written to you so often to so little purpose, on this topic. But, affecting as my own circumstances are, I cannot pass by without animadversion the reflection I need not repeat in words.

I had reason to fear, as I mentioned in mine of this morning, that a storm was brewing. Mr. Solmes came home from church this afternoon with my brother. Soon after, Betty brought me up a letter, without saying from whom. It was in a cover, and directed by a hand I never saw before; as if it were supposed that I would not receive and open it, had I known from whom it came.

These are the contents:

TO MISS CLARISSA HARLOWE

Sunday, March 26.

DEAREST MADAM,—I think myself a most unhappy man, in that I have never yet been able to pay my respects to you with your consent, for one half-hour. I have something to communicate to you that concerns you much, if you be pleased to admit me to your speech. Your honour is concerned in it, and the honour of all your family. It relates to the designs of one whom you are said to value more than he deserves; and to some of his reprobate actions; which I am ready to give you convincing proofs of the truth of. I may appear to be interested in it: but nevertheless, I am ready to make oath that every tittle is true: and you will see what a man you are said to favour. But I hope not so, for your own honour.

Pray, madam, vouchsafe me a hearing, as you value your honour and family: which will oblige, dearest miss,

Your most humble and most faithful servant,

Roger Solmes.

I wait below *for* the hope of admittance.

I was obliged either to see him, or to write to him. I wrote therefore an answer. And now my heart aches for what may follow from it; for I hear a great hurry below.

To Roger Solmes, Esq.

Sir,—Whatever you have to communicate to me, which concerns my honour, may as well be done by writing as by word of mouth. If Mr. Lovelace is any of *my* concern, I know not that *therefore* he ought to be *yours:* for the usage I receive on *your* account (I *must* think it so!) is so harsh, that were there not such a man in the world as Mr. *Lovelace,* I would not wish to see Mr. *Solmes,* no, not for one half-hour, in the way he is pleased to be desirous to see me. I never can be in any danger from Mr. Lovelace (and of consequence, cannot be affected by any of your discoveries) if the proposal I made be accepted. You have been acquainted with it, no doubt. If not, be pleased to let my friends know, that if they will rid *me* of my apprehensions of one gentleman, I will rid them of *theirs* of another: and then, of what consequence to *them,* or to *me,* will it be, whether Mr. Lovelace be a good man, or a bad? And if not to *them* nor to *me,* I see not how it can be of any to *you.* But if *you* do, I have nothing to say to that; and it will be a Christian part, if you will expostulate with him upon the errors you have discovered, and endeavour to make him as good a man, as, no doubt, you are *yourself,* or you would not be so ready to detect and expose *him.*

Cl. Harlowe.

Sunday Night.

My father was for coming up to me in great wrath it seems; but was persuaded to the contrary. My Aunt Hervey was permitted to send me this that follows.

To Miss Clarissa Harlowe

Niece,—Everybody is now convinced that nothing is to be done with you by way of gentleness or persuasion. Your mother will not permit you to stay in the house; for your father is so incensed by your strange letter to his friend, that she knows not what will be the consequence if you do. So you are commanded to get ready to go to your Uncle Antony's out of hand.

You must not answer me. There will be no end of that.

You know not the affliction you give to everybody; but to none more than to

Your affectionate aunt,
Dorothy Hervey.

Forbid to write to my aunt, I took a bolder liberty. I wrote a few lines to my mother; beseeching her to procure me leave to throw myself at my father's feet, and hers, if I *must* go (nobody else present) to beg pardon for the trouble I have given them both and their blessings; and to receive their commands as to my removal, and the time for it, from their own lips.

"What new boldness this! Take it back; and bid her learn to obey," was my mother's angry answer, with my letter returned, unopened.

But that I might omit nothing that had an appearance of duty, I wrote a few lines to my father to the same purpose begging that he would not turn me out of his house without his blessing. But this, torn in two pieces, and unopened, was brought me up again by Betty, with an air, one hand held up, the other extended, the torn letter in her open palm, and a See here! What a *sad* thing is this! Nothing will do but duty, miss! Your papa said, let her tell me of *deeds!* I'll receive no *words* from her: and so he tore the letter, and flung the pieces at my head.

So desperate my case, I was resolved not to stop even at this repulse. I took my pen and addressed myself to my Uncle Harlowe, enclosing that which my mother had returned unopened, and the torn unopened one sent to my father; having first hurried off a transcript for you.

To John Harlowe, Esq.

My dear and ever-honoured Uncle,—I have nobody now but you to whom I can apply, with hope, so much as to have my humble addresses opened and read. My Aunt Hervey has given me commands which I want to have explained; but she has forbid me writing to *her*. Hereupon I took the liberty to write to my father and mother: you will see, sir, by the torn one, and by the other (both unopened) what has been the result. This sir, perhaps you already know: but, as you know not the *con-*

tents of the disgraced letters, I beseech you to read them both, that you may be a witness for me, that they are not filled either with complaints or expostulations, nor contain anything undutiful. I beseech you, dear, good sir, to let me know what is meant by sending me to my Uncle Antony's house, rather than to yours, or to my Aunt Hervey's, or elsewhere? If it be for what I apprehend it to be, life will not be supportable under the terms. I beg also to know, WHEN I am to be turned out of doors! My heart strongly gives me, *that if once I am compelled to leave this house, I never shall see it more.*

It becomes me, however, to declare, that I write not this through perverseness or in resentment. God knows my heart, I do not! But the treatment I apprehend I shall meet with, if carried to my other uncle's, will, in all probability, give the finishing stroke to the distresses, the *undeserved* distresses I will be bold to call them, of

Your once highly favoured,
But now most unhappy,
Cl. Harlowe.

MISS CLARISSA HARLOWE TO MISS HOWE

Monday Morning, March 27.

THIS MORNING early my Uncle Harlowe came hither. He sent up the enclosed very tender letter. It has made me wish I *could* oblige him.

Sunday Night, or rather Monday Morning.

I must answer you, though against my own resolution. Everybody loves you, and you know they do. The very ground you walk upon is dear to most of us. But how can we resolve to see you? There is no standing against your looks and language. It is our love makes us decline to see you. How *can* we, when you are resolved *not* to do what we are resolved you *shall* do? I never, for my part, loved any creature, as I loved you from your infancy till now.

We are all afraid to see you, because we know we shall be made as so many fools. Nay, your mother is so afraid of you that once or twice, when she thought you were coming to force yourself into her presence, she shut the door, and locked herself in, because she knew she must not see you upon *your* terms, and you are resolved you will not see her upon *hers*.

Resolve but to oblige us all, my dearest Miss Clary, and you shall see how we will clasp you every one by turns to our rejoicing hearts.

Dear, sweet creature, oblige us: and oblige us with a grace. It *must* be done, whether with a grace or not. I do assure you it *must*. You must not conquer father, mother, uncles, everybody: depend upon that.

I have sat up half the night to write this. You do not know how I am touched at reading yours and writing this. Yet will I be at Harlowe Place early in the morning. So, upon reading this, if you will oblige us all, send me word to come up to your apartment: and I will lead you down, and present you to the embraces of every one: and you will then see, you have more of a brother and sister in them both, than of late your prejudices will let you think you have. This from one who used to love to style himself,

Your paternal uncle,
John Harlowe.

DEAR AND HONOURED SIR,—How you rejoice me by your condescending goodness! So kind, so paternal a letter! so soothing to a wounded heart; and of late what I have been so little used to! Tell me not, dear sir, of my way of writing: your letter has more moved *me* than I have been able to move *anybody!* It has made me wish with all my heart that I could entitle myself to be visited upon your own terms; and to be led down to my father and mother by so good and so kind an uncle.

I will tell you, dearest sir, what I will do to make my peace. I have a doubt that Mr. Solmes, upon consideration, would greatly prefer my sister to such a strange averse creature as me. His chief, or one of his chief motives in his address to me, is, as I have reason to believe, the contiguity of my grandfather's estate to his own. I will resign it; for ever I will resign it: and the resignation must be good, because I will never marry at all. I will make it over to my sister, and her heirs for ever.

I beg of you, dearest sir, to propose it, and second it with your interest. This will answer every end. My sister has a high opinion of Mr. Solmes. I never can have *any* in the light he is proposed to me. But as my sister's husband, he will be always entitled to my respect; and shall have it.

I wait, sir, for your answer to this proposal, made with the whole heart of

Your dutiful and most obliged niece,
Cl. Harlowe.

Monday Noon.

I hope this will be accepted. And what a charming pretence will this afford me of breaking with Mr. Lovelace!

Monday Evening.

Betty, by anticipation, tells me that I am to be refused. I am "a vile, artful creature. My Uncle Harlowe has been *taken in,* that's the phrase. A pretty thing truly in the eyes of the world would it be, were they to take me at my word! It was equally against law and equity: and a fine security Miss Bella would have, or Mr. Solmes, when I could resume it when I would! My *brother* and *she* my heirs! Oh, the artful creature! *I* to resolve to live single, when Lovelace is so *sure* of me—and everywhere declares as much!—and can whenever he pleases, if my husband, claim under the will!"

Monday Night.

This moment the following letter is brought me by Betty.

Monday, 5 o'clock.

Miss Cunning-ones,—Your fine new proposal is thought unworthy of a particular answer. Your Uncle Harlowe is ashamed to be so taken in. To-morrow you go to my Uncle Antony's. That's all, child.

James Harlowe.

I opened Mr. Lovelace's letter.

He says, "he has more reason than ever, from the contents of my last, to apprehend, that I shall be prevailed upon by force, if not by fair means, to fall in with my brother's measures; and sees but too plainly that I am preparing him to expect it.

"He begs, in the most earnest and humble manner, for one half-hour's interview; undertaking by a key, which he owns he has to the garden door, leading into the *coppice,* as we call it (if I will but unbolt the door) to come into the garden at night, and wait till I have an opportunity to come to him, that he may reassure me of the truth of all he writes, and of the affection, and, if needful, protection, of all his family.

"He presumes not, he says, to write by way of menace to me; but, if I refuse him this favour, he knows not (so desperate have some strokes in my letter made him) what his despair may make him do."

He beseeches me, "to unbolt the door, *as that very night;* or, if I receive not this time enough, *this night;* and he will in a disguise that shall not give a suspicion who he is, if he should be seen, come to the garden door, in hopes to open it with his key; nor will he have any other lodging than in the coppice both nights: watching every wakeful hour for the propitious unbolting, unless he has a letter with my orders to the contrary, or to make some other appointment."

MISS CLARISSA HARLOWE TO MISS HOWE

Tuesday Morning, 7 o'clock.

MY UNCLE has vouchsafed to answer me.

Monday Night.

MISS CLARY,—Since you are grown such a bold challenger, and teach us all our duty, though you will not practise your own, I *must* answer you. Nobody wants your estate from you. Are *you,* who refuse everybody's advice, to prescribe a husband to your *sister?* Your letter to Mr. Solmes is inexcusable. Your parents *will* be obeyed. Your mother has nevertheless prevailed to have your going to your Uncle Antony's put off till Thursday: yet owns you deserve not that, or any other favour from her. I will receive no more of your letters.

Your displeased uncle,

John Harlowe.

To be carried away on Thursday—to the moated house—to the chapel—to Solmes! How can I think of this! They will make me desperate.

Tuesday Morning, Eight o'clock.

I have another letter from Mr. Lovelace. I opened it with the expectation of its being filled with bold and free complaints, on my not writing to prevent his two nights watching, in weather not extremely agreeable. But, instead of complaints, he is full of tender concern lest I may have been prevented by indisposition, or by the closer confinement which he has frequently cautioned me that I may expect.

"He had no shelter, he says, but under the great overgrown ivy, which spreads wildly round the heads of two or three oaklings; and that was soon wet through."

He owns, "that he has an intelligencer in our family; who has failed him for a day or two past: and not knowing how I do, or how I may be treated, his anxiety is increased."

This circumstance gives me to guess who this intelligencer is: Joseph Leman: the very creature employed and confided in, more than any other, by my brother.

So, possibly, this man may be bribed by both, and yet betray both.

"He presses with the utmost earnestness for an interview. He would not presume, he says, to disobey my last personal commands, that he should not endeavour to attend me again in the wood-house. But says he can give me such reasons for my permitting him to wait upon my father or uncles, as he hopes will be approved by me: for he cannot help observing that it is no more suitable to my own spirit than to his, that he, a man of fortune and family, should be obliged to pursue such a clandestine address as would only become a vile fortune-hunter. But, if I will give my consent for his visiting me like a man and a gentleman, no ill-treatment shall provoke him to forfeit his temper.

"Lord M. will accompany him, if I please: or Lady Betty Lawrance will first make the visit to my mother, or to my Aunt Hervey, or even to my uncles, if I choose it. And such terms shall be offered as *shall* have weight upon them.

"He begs, that I will not deny him making a visit to Mr. Solmes. By all that's good, he vows that it shall not be with the least intention either to hurt or affront him; but only to set before him, calmly and rationally, the consequences that may possibly flow from so fruitless a perseverance, as well as the ungenerous folly of it, to a mind so noble as mine. He repeats his own resolution to attend my pleasure, and Mr. Morden's arrival and advice, for the reward of his own patience.

"He renews his professions of reformation: he is convinced, he says, that he has already run a long and dangerous course; and that it is high time to think of returning: it *must be* from proper convictions, he says, that a person who has lived too gay a life, resolves to reclaim before age or sufferings come upon him.

"All generous spirits, he observes, hate compulsion. Upon this observation he dwells; but regrets, that he is likely to owe all his hopes to this compulsion; this *injudicious* compulsion, he justly calls it; and none to my esteem for him. Although he presumes upon some merit—in his implicit regard to my will—in the bearing the daily indignities offered not only to him, but to his relations, by my brother. In the nightly watchings, and risks which he runs in all weathers; and which his present indisposition makes him mention, or he had not debased the nobleness of his passion for me by such a selfish instance."

I cannot but say, I am sorry the man is not well.

But what I *have* done, I *have* done. In a word, I wrote, "that I would, if possible, give him a meeting tomorrow night, between the hours of nine and twelve, by the ivy summer house, or in it, or near the great cascade, at the bottom of the garden; and would unbolt the door, that he might come in by his own key. But that, if I found the meeting impracticable, or should change my mind, I would signify as much by another line; which he must wait for until it were dark."

Tuesday, Eleven o'clock.

I am just returned from depositing my billet. How diligent is this man! It is plain he was in waiting: for I had walked but a few paces, after I had deposited it, when, my heart misgiving me, I returned, to have taken it back, in order to reconsider it as I walked, and whether I should, or should not, let it go. But I found it gone.

In all probability there was but a brick wall, of a few inches thick, between Mr. Lovelace and me, at the very time I put the letter under the brick!

I am come back dissatisfied with myself. But I think, my dear, there can be no harm in meeting him. If I do *not,* he may take some violent measures. What he requires is not unreasonable, and cannot affect my future choice and determination: it is only to assure him from my own lips, that I will never be the wife of a man I hate.

MISS CLARISSA HARLOWE TO HER UNCLE HARLOWE

Tuesday Afternoon

HONOURED SIR,—Let me this once be heard with patience, and have my petition granted. It is only that I may not be hurried away so soon as next Thursday.

Procure for me, sir, one fortnight's respite. One fortnight's respite is but a *small favour* for them to grant, except I am to be refused everything I ask; but it is of the *highest import* to my peace of mind.

Your dutiful, though greatly afflicted niece,

Cl. Harlowe.

I sent this down: my uncle was not gone: and he now stays to know the result of the question put to me in the enclosed answer which he has given to mine.

Your going to your uncle's was absolutely concluded upon for next Thursday. Nevertheless, your mother, seconded by Mr. Solmes, pleaded so strongly to have you indulged, that your request for a delay will be complied with, upon one condition; and whether for a fortnight, or a shorter time, that will depend upon yourself.

This condition is, that you admit of a visit from Mr. Solmes, for one hour, in company of your brother, your sister, or your Uncle Antony, choose which you will.

If you comply not, you go next Thursday to a house which is

become strangely odious to you of late, whether you get ready to go or not. Answer therefore directly to the point. No evasion. Name your day and hour. Mr. Solmes will neither eat you, nor drink you. Let us see whether *we* are to be complied with *in anything* or not.

John Harlowe.

After a very little deliberation, I resolved to comply with this condition. All I fear is that Mr. Lovelace's intelligencer may inform him of it; and that his apprehensions upon it may make him take some desperate resolution: especially as now (having more time given me here) I think to write to him to suspend the interview he is possibly so sure of. I sent down the following to my uncle:

Honoured Sir,—Although I see not what end the proposed condition can answer, I comply with it. I wish I could with everything expected of me. If I must name one, in whose company I am to see the gentleman, and that one *not* my mamma, whose presence I could wish to be honoured by on the occasion, let my uncle, if he pleases, be the *person.* If I must name the *day* (a long day, I doubt, will not be permitted me) let it be next Tuesday. The *hour,* four in the afternoon. The *place* either the ivy summer-house, or in the little parlour I used to be permitted to call mine.

Be pleased, sir, nevertheless, to prevail upon my mamma to vouchsafe me her presence on the occasion. I am, sir,

Your ever dutiful

Cl. Harlowe.

A reply is just sent me. I thought it became my averseness to this meeting, to name a distant day: but I did not expect they would have complied with it. So here is one week gained!

This is the reply:

You have done well to comply. Yet have you seemed to consider the day as an evil day, and so put it far off. This nevertheless is granted you if you are as generous *after* the day as we are condescending *before* it. Let me advise you not to harden your mind; nor take up your resolution beforehand. Mr. Solmes has more awe, and even terror, at the thoughts of seeing you than you can have at the thoughts of seeing him. *His* motive is *love;* let not yours be *hatred.* My brother, Antony, will be present, in hopes you will deserve well of *him,* by behaving well to the friend of the family.

Your loving uncle,
John Harlowe.

Repenting of my appointment with Mr. Lovelace *before* I had this favour granted me, you may believe I hesitated not a moment to revoke it *now* that I had gained such a respite. Accordingly, I wrote, "that I found it inconvenient to meet him, as I had intended: that the risk I should run of a discovery, and the mischiefs that might flow from it, could not be justified by any end that such a meeting could answer: that things drawing towards a crisis between my friends and me, an interview could avail nothing; especially as the method by which this correspondence was carred on was not suspected, and he could write all that was in his mind to write: that I expected to be at liberty to judge of what was proper and fit upon this occasion: especially as he might be assured that I would sooner choose death than Mr. Solmes."

Tuesday Night.

I have deposited my letter to Mr. Lovelace. Threatening as things look against me, I am much better pleased with myself for declining the interview than I was before.

Pray, my dear, be so kind as to make inquiry by some safe hand, after the disguises Mr. Lovelace assumes at the inn he puts up at in the poor village of *Neale,* he calls it.

As he must, to be so constantly near us, be much there. I would be glad to have some account of his behaviour; and what the people think of him. In such a length of time, he must by his conduct either give scandal, or hope of reformation. Pray, my dear, humour me in this inquiry. I have reasons for it which you shall be acquainted with another time, if the result of the inquiry discover them not.

MISS CLARISSA HARLOWE TO MISS HOWE

Wednesday Morning, Nine o'clock.

I AM JUST returned from my morning walk, and already have received a letter from Mr. Lovelace in answer to mine deposited last night. He must have had pen, ink, and paper with him; for it was written in the coppice; with this circumstance; on one knee, kneeling with the other. *Not* from reverence to the written to, however, as you'll find!

This man has vexed me heartily. I see his gentleness was *art:* fierceness and a temper like what I have been too much used to at home are *nature* in him. Nothing, I think, shall ever make me forgive him; for surely, there can be no good reason for his impatience on an expectation given with reserve, and revocable. *I* so much to suffer *through* him; yet, to be treated as if I were obliged to bear insults *from* him!

TO MISS CLARISSA HARLOWE

GOOD GOD!

What is *now* to become of me! How shall I support this disappointment! No new cause! On one knee, kneeling with the other, I write! My feet benumbed with midnight wanderings through the heaviest dews that ever fell: my wig and my linen dripping with the hoar frost dissolving on them! Day but just breaking—sun not risen to exhale. May it never rise again! Unless it bring healing and comfort to a benighted soul! In proportion to the joy you had inspired (ever lovely promiser!) in such proportion is my anguish!

And *are things drawing towards a crisis between your friends and you?* Is not this a reason for me to expect, the *rather* to expect, the promised interview?

CAN *I write all that is in my mind,* say you? Impossible! Not the hundredth part of what is in my mind, and in my apprehension, can I write!

Oh, the wavering, the changeable sex! But can Miss Clarissa Harlowe——

Forgive me, madam! I know not what I write!

You would sooner choose death than Solmes (How my soul spurns the competition!) O my beloved creature, what are these but *words! Whose* words? Sweet and ever adorable—what? Promise-breaker, must I call you? How shall I believe the asseveration (your *supposed duty* in the question! Persecution so flaming! Hatred to me so strongly avowed!) after this instance of your so lightly dispensing with your promise?

If, my dearest life! you would prevent my distraction, or, at least, distracted consequences, renew the promised hope! My *fate* is indeed upon its crisis.

Forgive me, dearest creature, forgive me! I know I have written in too much anguish of mind! Writing this in the same moment that the just-dawning light has imparted to me the heavy disappointment.

I dare not re-peruse what I have written. I *must* deposit it—it may serve to show you my distracted apprehension that this disappointment is but a prelude to the greatest of all. But if, exerting your usual generosity, you will excuse and *reappoint,* may that God, whom you profess to serve, and who is the God of *truth* and of *promises,* protect and bless you, for both; and for restoring to Himself, and to hope,

Ivy-Cavern in the Coppice— Your ever-adoring,
Day but just breaking. yet almost desponding
Lovelace.

This is the answer I shall return.

Wednesday Morning.

I AM AMAZED, sir, at the freedom of your reproaches. Pressed and teased, against convenience and inclination, to give you a private meeting, am *I* to be thus challenged and upbraided, and my sex reflected upon, because I thought it prudent to change my mind? A liberty I had reserved to myself, when I made the *appointment,* as you call it. I wanted not instances of your impatient spirit to other people: yet may it be happy for me, that I have this new one; which shows, that you can as little spare *me,* when I pursue the dictates of my own reason, as you do *others,* for acting up to theirs. I am too much alarmed, not to wish and desire, that your letter of this day may conclude all the trouble you have had from, or for,

Your humble servant,

Cl. Harlowe.

Wednesday Noon, March 29.

We cannot always answer for what we *can* do: but to convince you that I can keep my above resolution, with regard to Mr. Lovelace, angry as my letter is, and three hours as it is since it was written, I assure you, that I repent it not, nor will soften it, although I find it is not taken away. And yet I hardly ever before did anything in anger, that I did not repent in half an hour; and question myself in *less* than that time, whether I were right or wrong.

In this respite till Tuesday, I have a little time to look about me, as I may say, and to consider of what I *have* to do, and *can* do. And Mr. Lovelace's insolence will make me go very home with myself.

But, with all my courage, I am exceedingly apprehensive about the Tuesday next, and about what may result from my stedfastness; for stedfast I am sure I shall be.

Adieu, my beloved friend.

Cl. Harlowe.

MISS HOWE TO MISS CLARISSA HARLOWE

Thursday morning.

YOUR RESOLUTION not to leave your father's house is right—if you can stay in it and avoid being Solmes's wife.

I think you answered Solmes's letter as *I* should have answered it. Will you not compliment me and yourself at once by saying that *that* was right?

You have, in your letters to your uncle and the rest, done all that you ought to do. You are wholly guiltless of the consequence, be it what it will. To offer to give up your estate! That would not I have done! You see this offer staggered them: they took time to consider of it. I was afraid they would have taken you at your word: and so, but for shame, and for fear of Lovelace, I dare say, they would. You are too noble for them. Let me beg of you, my dear, never to repeat the temptation to them.

I freely own to you, that their usage of you upon it, and Lovelace's different treatment of you in his letter received at the same time, would have made *me* his, past redemption. The deuce take the man, I was going to say, for not having had so much regard to his character and morals, as would have entirely justified such a step in a CLARISSA, persecuted as she is!

I wonder not at your appointment with him.

I shall be all impatience to know how this matter ends between you and him. But a *few inches of brick wall* between you so lately; and now such *mountains!* And you think to hold it?

You see, you say, that the temper he showed in his preceding letter was not *natural* to him. And did you before think it *was?* Wretched creepers and insinuators! Yet when opportunity serves as insolent encroachers!

All good-natured men are passionate, says Mr. Lovelace. A pretty plea to a beloved object in the plenitude of her power! As much as to say, "Greatly as I value you, madam, I will not take pains to curb my passions to oblige you."

Indeed, we are too apt to make allowances for such tempers as *early* indulgence has made uncontrollable; and therefore habitually evil. But if a boisterous temper, when under *obligation,* is to be thus allowed for, what, when the tables are turned, will it expect?

How artfully has Lovelace, in the abstract you give me of one of his letters, calculated to your meridian; *generous spirits hate compulsion!* He is certainly a deeper creature by much than once we thought him. He knows, as you intimate, that his own wild pranks cannot be concealed; and so owns just enough to palliate (because it teaches you not to be surprised at) any new one, that may come to your ears; and then, truly, he is, however faulty, a mighty *ingenuous* man; and by no means a *hypocrite:* a character, when found out, the most odious of all others, to *our sex,* in the *other;* were it only because it teaches us to doubt the justice of the praises such a man gives us, when we are willing to believe them to be our due.

But now the unheard-of cruelty and perverseness of some of

your friends [*relations,* I should say—I am always blundering thus!]; the *as* strange determinedness of others; your present quarrel with Lovelace; and your approaching interview with Solmes, from which you are right to apprehend a great deal; are such considerable circumstances in your story, that it is fit they should engross all my attention.

You ask me to advise you how to behave upon Solmes's visit. I *cannot* for my life. I know they expect a great deal from it: you had not else had your long day complied with. All I will say is that if Solmes cannot be prevailed for now that Lovelace has so much offended you, he never will.

Only let me advise you to pull up a spirit, even to your uncle, if there be occasion. Resent the vile and foolish treatment you meet with, in which he has taken so large a share, and make him ashamed of it, if you can.

I know not, upon recollection, but this interview may be a good thing for you, however designed. For when Solmes sees (if that be to *be* so) that it is impossible he should succeed with you; and your relations see it too; the one must, I think, recede, and the other come to terms with you, upon offers, that it is my opinion, will go hard enough with you to comply with; when the *still* harder are dispensed with.

But, upon the whole, I have no patience to see you thus made the sport of your brother's and sister's cruelty: for what, after *so much steadiness* on your part, in *so many trials,* can be their hope? *Except indeed it be to drive you to extremity, and to ruin you in the opinion of your uncles, as well as father.*

I urge you by all means to send out of their reach all the letters and papers you would not have them see. Methinks, I would wish you to deposit likewise a parcel of clothes, linen, and the like, before your interview with Solmes; lest you should not have an opportunity for it afterwards. Robin shall fetch it away on the first orders, by day or by night.

I am in hopes to procure from my mother, if things come to extremity, leave for you to be privately with us.

I will condition to be good-humoured, and even *kind,* to HER favourite [Hickman. Ed.], if she will show me an indulgence that shall make me serviceable to MINE.

I depend upon your forgiveness of all the perhaps unseasonable flippancies of your naturally too lively, yet most sincerely sympathizing,

Anna Howe

Miss Clarissa Harlowe to Miss Howe

Friday, March 31.

You have taught me what to say to, and what to think of, Mr. Lovelace. Only one thing must be allowed for me; that whatever course I shall be *permitted* or be *forced* to steer, I must be considered as a person out of her own direction. Tossed to and fro by the high winds of passionate control (and, as I think, unreasonable severity) I behold the desired port, the *single state,* which I would fain steer into; but am kept off by the foaming billows of a brother's and sister's envy, and by the raging winds of a supposed invaded authority; while I see in Lovelace the rocks on one hand, and in Solmes, the sands on the other; and tremble lest I should split upon the former or strike upon the latter.

I am afraid I must not venture to take the hint you give me, to deposit some of my clothes; although I will some of my linen as well as papers.

I will tell you why: Betty had for some time been very curious about my wardrobe, whenever I took out any of my things before her.

Observing this, I once, on taking one of my garden-airings, left my keys in the locks; and on my return surprised the creature with her hand upon the keys as if shutting the door.

She was confounded at my sudden coming back. I took no notice: but, on her retiring, I found my clothes were not in the usual order.

What I was principally leading to was to tell you how ingenious I am in my contrivances and pretences to blind my gaoleress, and to take off the jealousy of her principals on my going down so often into the garden and poultry-yard. People suspiciously treated are never, I believe, at a loss for invention. Sometimes I want *air,* and am better the moment I am out of my chamber—sometimes *spirits;* and then my bantams and pheasants or the cascade divert me; the former, by their inspiriting liveliness; the latter, more solemnly, by its echoing dashings and hollow murmurs. Sometimes solitude is of all things my wish; and the awful silence of the night, the spangled element, and the rising and setting sun, how promotive of contemplation! Sometimes, when I intend nothing, and expect not letters, I am officious to take Betty with me; and at others, bespeak her attendance, when I know she is otherwise employed, and cannot give it me.

Friday Morning, Eleven o'Clock.

I have already made up my parcel of linen. My heart ached all the time I was employed about it; and still aches, at the thoughts of its being a necessary precaution.

When the parcel comes to your hands, as I hope it safely will, you will be pleased to open it. You will find in it two parcels sealed up; one of which contains the letters you have not yet seen; being those written since I left you: in the other are all the letters and copies of letters that have passed between you and me since I was last with you; with some other papers on subjects so much above me, that I cannot wish them to be seen by anybody whose indulgence I am not so sure of as I am of yours. If my judgment ripen with my years, perhaps I may review them.

In a third division, folded up separately, are all Mr. Lovelace's letters written to me since he was forbidden this house, and copies of my answers to them.

By the way, not a line from that man!—not *one* line!—Wednesday I deposited mine. It remained there on Wednesday night. What time it was taken away yesterday I cannot tell: for I did not concern myself about it till towards night; and then it was not there. No return at ten this day. I suppose he is as much out of humour, as I. With all my heart!

He may be mean enough perhaps, if ever I should put it into his *power*, to avenge himself for the trouble he has had with me. But that now, I dare say, I never shall.

I see what sort of a man the encroacher is. And I hope we are equally sick of one another. My heart is *vexedly* easy, if I may so describe it. *Vexedly,* because of the apprehended interview with Solmes, and the consequences it may be attended with: or else I should be *quite* easy; for why? I have not *deserved* the usage I receive: and could I be rid of Solmes, as I presume I am of Lovelace, *their* influence over my father, mother, and uncles against me, could not hold.

The five guineas tied up in one corner of a handkerchief under the linen, I beg you will let pass as an acknowledgment for the trouble I give your trusty servant. You must not chide me for this. You know I cannot be easy unless I have my way in these little matters.

Friday, One o'Clock, in the Wood-house.

No letter yet from this man! I have luckily deposited my parcel, and have your letter of last night. If Robert take this without the parcel, pray let him return immediately for it. But he cannot miss it, I think; and must conclude that it is put there for him to take away. You may believe, from the contents of yours that I shall immediately write again.

Clarissa Harlowe.

Miss Howe to Miss Clarissa Harlowe

Thursday Night, March 30.

The fruits of my inquiry after your abominable wretch's behaviour and baseness at the paltry alehouse, which he calls an inn, prepare to hear.

Wrens and sparrows are not too ignoble a quarry for this villainous goshawk! His assiduities; his watchings; his nightly risks; the inclement weather he journeys in; must not be all placed to *your* account. He has opportunities of making everything light to him of that sort. A sweet pretty girl, I am told—innocent till he went hither—now! (Ah! poor girl!) who knows what?

But just turned of seventeen! His friend and brother rake (a man of humour and intrigue) as I am told, to share the social bottle with. And sometimes another disguised rake or two. No sorrow comes near their hearts. Be not disturbed, my dear, at his *hoarsenesses!* His pretty Betsy, his Rosebud, as the vile wretch calls her, can *hear* all he says.

He is very fond of her. They say she is innocent even yet—her father, her grandmother, believe her to be so. He is to fortune her out to a young lover. Ah! the poor young lover! Ah! the poor simple girl!

A vile wretch! Cannot such purity in pursuit, in view, restrain him? But I leave him to you! There can be no hope of him. Yet I wish I may be able to snatch the poor young creature out of his villainous paws. I have laid a scheme to do so; if *indeed* she be hitherto innocent and heart-free.

. . . . . .

I have sent for this girl and her father; and am just now informed that I shall see them. I will sift them thoroughly. I shall soon find out such a simple thing as this, if he has not corrupted her already—and if he has, I shall soon find that out too. If more art than nature appear either in her or her father, I shall give them both up; but depend upon it, the girl's undone.

He is said to be fond of her. He places her at the upper end of his table. He sets her a-prattling. He keeps his friend at a distance from her. She prates away. He admires for nature all she says. Once was heard to call her charming little creature! An hundred has he called so no doubt. He puts her upon singing. He praises her wild note. O my dear, the girl's undone!—must be undone! The man, you know, is LOVELACE.

Let 'em bring Wyerley to you, if they will have you married—anybody but Solmes and Lovelace be yours! So advises

Your

Anna Howe.

MISS CLARISSA HARLOWE TO MISS HOWE

Friday, Three o'Clock.

YOU incense, alarm, and terrify me, at the same time. Hasten, my dearest friend, hasten to me, what further intelligence you can gather about this vilest of men.

But never talk of innocence, of simplicity, and this unhappy girl, together! Must she not know that such a man as that, dignified in his very aspect; and no disguise able to conceal his being of condition; must mean too much, when he places her at the upper end of his table, and calls her by such tender names: would a girl, modest as simple, above seventeen, be set a singing at the pleasure of such a man as that? A stranger, and professedly in disguise! Would her father and grandmother, if honest people, and careful of their simple girl, permit such freedoms?

Keep his friend at distance from her!—To be sure his *designs* are villainous, if they have not been already effected.

Warn, my dear, if not too late, the unthinking father, of his child's danger. There cannot be a father in the world who would sell his child's virtue. No mother!—the poor thing!

I long to hear the result of your intelligence. You shall *see* the simple creature, you tell me. Let me know what sort of a girl she is. A *sweet pretty girl!* you say. A *sweet* pretty *girl,* my dear!—they are sweet pretty words from your pen. But are they *yours* or *his* of her? If she be so simple, if she have ease and nature in her manner, in her speech, and warbles prettily her *wild notes,* why, such a girl as that must engage such a profligate wretch (as now indeed I doubt this man is) accustomed, perhaps, to town-women, and their confident ways—must *deeply* and for a *long season* engage him: since perhaps when her innocence is departed, she will endeavour by art to supply the loss of the natural charms which now engage him.

Fine hopes of such a wretch's reformation! I would not, my dear, for the world have anything to say—but I need not make resolutions. I have not opened, nor will I open, his letter. A sycophant creature! With his hoarsenesses—got perhaps by a midnight revel, singing to his wild-note singer, and only increased in the coppice!

To be already on a foot!—in *his* esteem, I mean: for myself, I despise him. I hate myself almost for writing so much about *him,* and of such a simpleton as *this sweet pretty girl* as you call her: but nothing can be either *sweet* or *pretty,* that is not modest, that is not virtuous.

And now, my dear, I will tell you, how I came to put you upon this inquiry.

This vile *Joseph Leman* had given a hint to *Betty,* and she to *me,* as if Lovelace would be found out to be a very bad man, at a place where he had been lately seen in disguise. But he would see further, he said, before he told her more; and she promised *secrecy,* in hope to get at *further intelligence.* I thought it could be no harm, to get you to inform yourself, and me, of what could be gathered. And now I see, his enemies are but too well warranted in their reports of him: and, if the ruin of this poor young creature be his aim, and if he had not known her but for his visits to Harlowe Place, I shall have reason to be doubly concerned for her; and doubly incensed against so vile a man.

I think I hate him worse than I do Solmes himself.

But I will not add one other word about him; after I have told you, that I wish to know, as soon as possible, what further occurs from your inquiry. I have a letter from him; but shall not open it till I do: and then, if it come out as I dare say it will, I will directly put the letter unopened into the place I took it from, and never trouble myself more about him, Adieu, my dearest friend.

Cl. Harlowe.

MISS HOWE TO MISS CLARISSA HARLOWE

Friday Noon, March 31.

JUSTICE obliges me to forward this after my last on the wings of the wind, as I may say. I really believe the man is innocent. Of this *one* accusation, I think, he must be acquitted.

I have seen the girl. She is really a very pretty, a very neat, and, what is still a greater beauty, a very innocent young creature. He who could have ruined such an undesigning home-bred, must have been indeed infernally wicked. Her father is an honest simple man: entirely satisfied with his child, and with her new acquaintance.

I am almost afraid for your heart, when I tell you, that I find, now I have got to the bottom of this inquiry, something noble come out in this Lovelace's favour.

The girl is to be married next week; and this promoted and brought about by him. He is resolved, her father says, to make one couple happy, and wishes he could make more so (*There's for you, my dear!*): and having taken a liking also to the young fellow whom she professes to love, he has given her an hundred pounds: the grandmother actually has it in her hands, to answer to the like sum given to the youth by one of his own relations: while Mr. Lovelace's companion, attracted by the example, has given twenty-five guineas to the father, who is poor, towards clothes to equip the pretty rustic.

Mr. Lovelace and his friend, the poor man says, when they first came to his house, affected to appear as *persons of low degree;* but now he knows the one (but mentioned it in confidence) to be Colonel Barrow, the other Capt. Sloane. The colonel he owns was at first very *sweet upon his girl:* but upon her grandmother's begging of him to spare her innocence, he vowed, that he never would offer anything but good counsel to her. He kept his word; and the pretty fool acknowledged that she never could have been better instructed by the minister himself from the *Bible-book!* The girl pleased me so well, that I made her visit to me worth her while.

But what, my dear, will become of us now? Lovelace not only reformed, but turned preacher! What will become of us now? Why, my sweet friend, your *generosity* is now engaged in his favour!—What before was only a *conditional liking,* I am now afraid will turn to *liking unconditional.*

Upon the whole, Mr. Lovelace comes out with so much advantage from this inquiry, that were there the least room for it, I should suspect the whole to be a *plot set on foot to wash a blackmoor white.* Adieu, my dear.

Anna Howe.

MISS CLARISSA HARLOWE TO MISS HOWE

Saturday, April 1.

MR. LOVELACE has faults enow to deserve very severe censure, although he be not guilty of this. If I were upon such terms with him as he would wish me to be, I should give him a hint, that this treacherous Joseph Leman cannot be *so much* attached to him, as perhaps he thinks him to be. I must needs own, that as I should for ever have despised this man, had he been capable of such a vile intrigue in his way to Harlowe Place, and as I believed he *was* capable of it, it has indeed proportionably engaged my *generosity* in his favour: perhaps *more than I may have reason to wish it had.*

Then the *real* generosity of the act. I protest, my beloved friend, if he would be good for the rest of his life from this time,

I would forgive him a great many of his past errors, were it only for the demonstration he has given in this, that he is *capable* of so good and bountiful a manner of thinking.

You may believe I made no scruple to open his letter, after the receipt of your second on this subject: nor shall I of answering it, as I have no reason to find fault with it.

It is lucky enough that this matter was cleared up to me by your friendly diligence so soon: for had I written before it was, it would have been to reinforce my dismission of him; and perhaps I should have mentioned the very motive; for it affected me more than I think it ought: and then, what an advantage would that have given him, when he could have cleared up the matter so happily for himself!

He complains heavily of my "readiness to take mortal offence at him, and to dismiss him for ever: it is a *high* conduct, he says he must be frank enough to tell me; a conduct that must be very far from contributing to allay his apprehensions of the possibility that I may be persecuted into my relations' measures in behalf of Mr. Solmes."

You will also see, "that he has already heard of the interview I am to have with Mr. Solmes"; and with what vehemence and anguish he expresses himself on the occasion.

You will see how passionately he presses me to oblige "him with a few lines, before the interview between Mr. Solmes and me take place" (if, as he says, it *must* take place) "to confirm his hope, that I have no view, in my present displeasure against *him*, to give encouragement to *Solmes*. An apprehension, he says, that he must be excused for repeating: especially as the interview is a favour granted to that man, which I have refused to him; since, as he infers, were it not with such an expectation, why should my *friends* press it?

"I tell him, that I have submitted to this interview with Mr. Solmes, purely as an act of duty, to show my friends, that I will comply with their commands as far as I can; and that I hope, when Mr. Solmes himself shall see how determined I am, he will cease to prosecute a suit, in which it is impossible he should succeed with my consent.

"I assure him, that my aversion to Mr. Solmes is too sincere to permit me to doubt myself on this occasion. But, nevertheless, he must not imagine that my rejecting of Mr. Solmes is in favour to him. That I value my freedom and independency too much, if my friends will but leave me to my own judgment, to give them up to a man so uncontrollable, and who shows me beforehand what I have to expect from him, were I in his power.

"I inform him, that I have been lately made acquainted" (And so I have by Betty, and she by my brother) "with the weak and wanton airs he gives himself of declaiming against matrimony. I severely reprehend him on this occasion: and ask him, with what view he can take so witless, so despicable a liberty, in which only the most abandoned of men allow themselves, and yet presume to address *me?*"

But while you give me the charming hope, that, in order to avoid one man, I shall not be under the necessity of throwing myself upon the friends of the other; I think my case not absolutely desperate.

. . . . . .

I see not any of my family, nor hear from them in any way of kindness. This looks as if they themselves expected no great matters from that Tuesday's conference which makes my heart flutter every time I think of it.

My Uncle Antony's presence on the occasion I do not much like: but I had rather meet him than my brother or sister: yet my uncle is very impetuous. I can't think Mr. Lovelace can be much more so; at least he cannot *look* anger, as my uncle, with his harder features, can. These sea-prospered gentlemen, as my uncle has often made me think, not used to any but elemental control, and even ready to buffet that, bluster often as violently as the winds they are accustomed to be angry at.

Your
Clarissa Harlowe

Miss Clarissa Harlowe to Miss Howe

Sunday Night, April 2.

I HAVE many new particulars to acquaint you with that show a great change in the behaviour of my friends to me.

I did not think we had so much art among us, as I find we have.

All the family was at church in the morning. They brought good Dr. Lewen with them, in pursuance of a previous invitation. And the doctor sent up to desire my permission to attend me in my own apartment.

You may believe it was easily granted.

We had a conversation of near an hour before dinner: but, to my surprise, he waived everything that would have led to the subject I supposed he wanted to talk about.

I was prodigiously disappointed: but supposing that he was thought too just a man to be made a judge of in this cause; I led no more to it: nor, when he was called down to dinner, did he take the least notice of leaving me behind him there.

He left me so dissatisfied, yet so perplexed with this new way of treatment, that I never found myself so much disconcerted, and out of my train.

But I was to be more so.

In the afternoon, all but my brother and sister went to church with the good doctor; who left his compliments for me. I took a walk in the garden: my brother and sister walked in it too, and kept me in their eye a good while, on purpose, as I thought, that I might see how gay and good-humoured they were together. At last they came down the walk that I was coming up, hand in hand, lover-like.

Your servant, miss—your servant, sir—passed between my brother and me.

Is it not coldish, Sister Clary? in a kinder voice than usual, said my sister, and stopped. I stopped, and curtsied low to her half-curtsey. I think not, sister, said I.

She went on. I curtsied without return; and proceeded; turning to my poultry-yard.

By a shorter turn, arm-in-arm, they were there before me.

I think, Clary, said my brother, you must present me with some of this breed, for Scotland.

If you please, brother.

I'll choose for you, said my sister.

And while I fed them, they pointed to half a dozen: yet intending nothing by it, I believe, but to show a deal of love and good-humour to each other before me.

My uncles next (at their return from church) were to do me the honour of *their* notice. They bid Betty tell me, they would drink tea with me in my own apartment.

But they contradicted the order for tea, and only my Uncle Harlowe came up to me.

Half-distant, half-affectionate, at his entering my chamber, as the air he put on to his *daughter-niece,* as he used to call me; and I threw myself at his feet, and besought his favour.

None of these discomposures, child. None of these apprehensions. You will now have everybody's favour. All is coming about, my dear. I was impatient to see you. I could no longer deny myself this satisfaction.

He then raised me, and kissed me, and called me charming creature!

But he waived entering into any interesting subject. All will be well now. All will be right. No more complainings! Everybody loves you! And let every past disagreeable thing be forgotten; as if nothing had happened.

O my cunning brother! This is *his* contrivance. And then my anger made me recollect the triumph in his and my sister's fondness for each other, as practised before me; and the mingled indignation flashing from their eyes, as arm in arm they spoke to me, and the forced condescension playing upon their lips, when they called me Clary, and sister.

Do you think I could, with these reflections, look upon my Uncle Harlowe's visit as the favour he seemed desirous I should think it to be?

Will you give me your hand? Will you see your father? Can you stand his displeasure, on first seeing the dear creature who has given him and all of us so much disturbance? Can you promise future——

He saw me rising in my temper. Nay, my dear, interrupting himself, if you cannot be all resignation, I would not have you think of it.

My heart, struggling between duty and warmth of temper, was full. You know, my dear, I never could bear to be dealt meanly with! How—how *can* you, sir! You, my papa-uncle. How *can* you, sir! The poor girl! For I could not speak with connection.

Nay, my dear, if you cannot be all duty, all resignation—better stay where you are. But after the instance you have given——

Instance I have given! What instance, sir?

Well, well, child, better stay where you are, if your past confinement hangs so heavy upon you. But now there will be a sudden end to it. Adieu, my dear! Three words only. Let your compliance be sincere! And love me, as you used to love me. Your grandfather did not do so much for you, as I will do for you.

Without suffering me to reply he hurried away, as I thought, like one who had been employed to act a part against his will, and was glad it was over.

It is plain from what I have *related,* that they think they have got me at some advantage by obtaining my consent to this interview: but if it were *not,* Betty's impertinence just now would make it evident. She has been complimenting me upon it; and upon the visit of my Uncle Harlowe. She says, the difficulty now is more than half over with me. She is sure I would not see Mr. Solmes, but to have him.

I found in the afternoon a reply to my answer to Mr. Lovelace's letter. It is full of promises, full of vows of gratitude, of *eternal* gratitude, is his word, among others still more hyperbolic.

"He excuses himself for the liberties he owns he has heretofore taken in ridiculing the marriage-state. It is a subject, he says, that he has not of late treated so lightly. He owns it to be so trite, so beaten a topic with all libertines and witlings; so frothy, so empty, so nothing-meaning, so worn-out a theme, that he is heartily ashamed of himself ever to have made it *his.* He condemns it as a stupid reflection upon the laws and good order of society, and upon a man's own ancestors: and in himself who has some reason to value himself upon his descent and alliances, more censurable, than in those who have not the same advantage to boast of. He promises to be more circumspect than ever, both in his words and actions, that he may be more and more worthy of my approbation; and that he may give an assurance beforehand that a foundation is laid in his mind for my example to work upon with equal reputation and effect to us both; if he may be so happy as to call me his."

Your kind, your generous endeavours to interest your mother in my behalf, will, I hope, prevent those harsher extremities to which I might be otherwise driven. And to you I will fly, if permitted, and keep all my promises, of not corresponding with anybody, not seeing anybody, but by your mother's direction and yours.

It is not necessary to say, how much I am

Your ever affectionate and obliged

Cl. Harlowe.

Miss Clarissa Harlowe to Miss Howe

I am glad my papers are safe in your hands.

I have another letter from Mr. Lovelace. He is extremely apprehensive of the meeting I am to have with Mr. Solmes to-morrow. "He assures me that Solmes has actually talked with tradesmen of new equipages, and names the people in town with whom he has treated: that he has even allotted this and that apartment in his house, for a nursery, and other offices."

How shall I bear to hear such a creature talk of love to me?

Upon this confidence of Solmes, you will less wonder at that of Lovelace, "in pressing me in the name of all his family to escape from so determined a violence as is intended to be offered to me at my uncle's: that the forward contriver should propose Lord M.'s chariot and six to be at the stile that leads up to the lonely coppice adjoining to our paddock. You will see how audaciously he mentions settlements ready drawn; horsemen ready to mount; and one of his cousins Montague to be in the chariot, or at the George in the neighbouring village, waiting to accompany me to Lord M.'s, or to Lady Betty's, or Lady Sarah's, or to town, as I please; and upon such orders, or conditions and under such restrictions as to himself, as I shall prescribe."

You will see how he threatens "to watch and waylay them, and to *rescue* me as he calls it, by an armed force of friends and servants, if they attempt to carry me against my will to my uncle's; and this, whether I give my consent to the enterprise, or not: since he shall have no hopes if I am once there."

To-morrow is Tuesday! How soon comes upon us the day we dread! Oh, that a deep sleep of twenty-four hours would seize my faculties! But then the next day would be Tuesday, as to all the effects and purposes for which I so much dread it.

Your
Clarissa Harlowe.

MISS CLARISSA HARLOWE TO MISS HOWE

Tuesday Evening, and continued thro' the Night.

WELL, my dear, I am alive, and here! But how long I shall be either here, or alive, I cannot say. Nevertheless, I must tell you how the saucy Betty again discomposed me, when she came up with this Solmes's message.

Miss! Miss! Miss! cried she, as fast as she could speak, with her arms spread abroad, and all her fingers distended and held up, will you be pleased to walk down into your own parlour? There is everybody, I will assure you, in full *congregation!* And there is Mr. Solmes, as fine as a lord, with a charming white peruke, fine laced shirt and ruffles, coat trimmed with silver, and a waistcoat standing on end with lace! Quite handsome, believe me! You never saw such an alteration! Ah! miss, shaking her head, 'tis pity you have said so much against him! But you know how to come off, for all that! I hope it will not be too late!

Impertinence! said I—wert thou bid to come up in this fluttering way? And I took up my fan, and fanned myself.

Bless me! said she, how soon these fine young ladies will be put into *flusterations!* I meant not either to offend or frighten you, I am sure.

Everybody there, do you say? Who do you call everybody?

Why, miss, holding out her left palm opened, and with a flourish, and a saucy leer, patting it with the forefinger of the other, at every mentioned person, there is your papa! There is your mamma! There is your Uncle Harlowe! There is your

Uncle Antony! Your Aunt Hervey! *My* young lady! And my young master! And Mr. Solmes, with the air of a great courtier, standing up, because he named you: Mrs. Betty, said he (then the ape of a wench bowed and scraped as awkwardly as I suppose the person did whom she endeavoured to imitate) pray give my humble service to miss, and tell her I wait her commands.

Come, dear madam, taking up my fan, which I had laid down, and approaching me with it, fanning, shall I——

None of thy impertinence! But say you, *all* my friends are below with him? And am I to *appear* before them *all?*

I can't tell if they'll stay when you come. I think they seemed to be moving when Mr. Solmes gave me his orders. But what answer shall I carry to the squire?

Say, I can't go! But yet when 'tis over, 'tis over! Say, I'll wait upon—I'll attend—I'll come presently—say anything; I care not what—but give me my fan, and fetch me a glass of water.

She went, and I fanned myself all the time, for I was in a flame; and hemmed and struggled with myself all I could; and, when she returned, drank my water; and finding no hope presently of a quieter heart, I sent her down, and followed her with precipitation; trembling so that, had I not hurried, I question if I could have gone down at all.

There are two doors to *my* parlour, as I used to call it. As I entered at one, my friends hurried out at the other. I saw just the gown of my sister, the last who slid away. My Uncle Antony went out with them; but he stayed not long, as you shall hear: and they all remained in the next parlour, a wainscot partition only parting the two. I remember them both in one: but they were separated in favour of us girls, for each to receive her visitors in at her pleasure.

Mr. Solmes approached me as soon as I entered, cringing to the ground, a visible confusion in every feature of his face. After half a dozen choked-up madams—he was very sorry—he was very much concerned—it was his misfortune—and there he stopped, being unable presently to complete a sentence.

This gave me a little more presence of mind.

I turned from him, and seated myself in one of the fireside chairs, fanning myself.

He hemmed five or six times, as I had done above; and these produced a sentence—that I could not but see his confusion.

He had hemmed himself into more courage.

You could not, madam, imagine any creature so blind to your merits, and so little attracted by them, as easily to forego the interest and approbation he was honoured with by your worthy family, while he had any hope given him, that one day he might, by his perseverance and zeal, expect your favour.

I am but too much aware, sir, that it is upon the interest and approbation you mention, that you build such hope.

He had seen many instances, he told me, and had heard of more, where ladies had seemed as averse, and yet had been induced, some by motives of compassion, others by persuasion of friends, to change their minds; and had been very happy afterwards: and he hoped this might be the case here. I am sure you should not tell me of any fault, that I would be unwilling to correct in myself.

Then, sir, correct *this* fault—do not wish to have a young creature compelled in the most material article of her life, for the sake of motives she despises; and in behalf of a person she cannot value: one that has, in her own right, sufficient to set her above all your offers, and a spirit that craves no more than what is *has,* to make itself easy and happy.

I don't see, madam, how you would be happy, if I were to discontinue my address: for——

That is nothing to you, sir, interrupted I; do you but withdraw your pretensions; and if it be thought fit to start up another man for my punishment, the blame will not lie at your door. You will be entitled to my thanks; and most heartily will I thank you.

He paused and seemed a little at a loss; and I was going to give him still stronger and more personal instances of my plain-dealing; when in came my Uncle Antony.

So, niece, so! Sitting in state like a queen, giving audience! *haughty* audience! Mr. Solmes, why stand you thus humbly?

I arose, as soon as he entered—and approached him with a bent knee: let me, sir, reverence my uncle, whom I have not for so long a time seen! Let me, sir, bespeak your favour and compassion!

You'll have the favour of everybody, niece, when you know how to deserve it.

If ever I deserved it, I deserve it now.

I will engage never to marry any man, without my father's consent, and yours, sir, and everybody's. And here I will take the solemnest oath that can be offered me——

That is the matrimonial one, interrupted he, with a big voice —and to this gentleman. It shall, it shall, Cousin Clary! And the more you oppose it the worse it shall be for you.

This, and before the man, who seemed to assume courage upon it, highly provoked me.

Then, sir, you shall sooner follow me to the grave *indeed.* I will undergo the cruellest death—I will even consent to enter into the awful vault of my ancestors, and to have that bricked up upon me, rather than consent to be miserable for life. And, Mr. Solmes, turning to him, take notice of what I say: *This* or *any* death, I will sooner undergo (that will soon be over) than be yours, and for *ever* unhappy!

My uncle was in a terrible rage upon this. He took Mr. Solmes by the hand, shocked as the man seemed to be, and drew him to the window. Don't be surprised, Mr. Solmes, don't be concerned at *this.* We know, and rapped out a sad oath, what women will say in their wrath: the wind is not more boisterous, or more changeable; and again he swore to that. If you think it worth your while to wait for such an ungrateful girl as this, I'll engage she'll *veer about;* I'll engage she *shall.* And a third time violently swore to it.

Then coming up to me (who had thrown myself, very much disordered by my vehemence, into the most distant window) as if he would have beat me; his face violently working, his hands clenched, and his teeth set. Yes, yes, yes, hissed the poor gentleman, you shall, you shall, you shall, Cousin Clary, be Mr. Solmes's wife; we will see that you shall; and this in one week at farthest.

I am sorry, sir, said I, to see you in such a passion. It is best for me to withdraw. I shall but provoke you further, I fear: for although I would gladly obey you if I could, yet this is a point determined with me; and I cannot so much *as wish* to get it over.

I was going out at the door I came in at; and who should I meet at the door but my brother, who had heard all that had passed!

He bolted upon me so unexpectedly, that I was surprised. He took my hand, and grasped it with violence. Return, pretty miss, said he; return, if you please. You shall not yet be *bricked up*. O thou fallen angel, said he, peering up to my down-cast face—such a sweetness *here!*—and such an obstinacy *there!* tapping my neck. O thou true woman—though so young! But you shall not have your rake: remember that; in a loud whisper, as if he would be decently indecent before the man. You shall be redeemed, and this worthy gentleman, raising his voice, will be so good as to redeem you from ruin—and here after you will bless him, or have reason to bless him, for his *condescension;* that was the brutal brother's word!

He had led me up to meet Mr. Solmes, whose hand he took, as he held mine. Here, sir, said he, take the rebel daughter's hand: I give it you now: she shall confirm the gift in a week's time; or will have neither father, mother, nor uncles, to boast of.

I snatched my hand away.

How now, miss!

And how now, sir! What right have *you* to dispose of my hand? If you govern everybody else, you shall not govern me; especially in a point so immediately relative to myself, and in which you neither have, nor ever shall have, anything to do.

I would have broken from him; but he held my hand too fast.

Let me go, sir! Why am I thus treated? You *design,* I doubt not, with your unmanly grippings, to hurt me, as you do: but again I ask, wherefore is it that I am going to be thus treated by *you?*

He tossed my hand from him with a whirl, that pained my very shoulder. I wept, and held my other hand to the part.

Mr. Solmes blamed him. So did my uncle.

Mr. Solmes said he would sooner give up all his hopes of me, than that I should be used unkindly: and he offered to plead in my behalf to them both; and applied himself with a bow, as if for my approbation of his interposition.

Interpose not, Mr. Solmes, said I, to save me from my brother's violence. I cannot wish to owe an obligation to a man whose ungenerous perseverance is the occasion of *that* violence, and of all my disgraceful sufferings.

How generous in you, Mr. Solmes, said my brother, to interpose so kindly in behalf of such an immovable spirit! I beg of you to persist in your address! Let us save her, if possible, from ruining herself. Look at her person! (and he gazed at me, from head to foot, pointing at me, as he referred to Mr. Solmes) think of her fine qualities! She is worth saving; and, after two or three more struggles, she will be yours, and, take my word for it, will reward your patience. Talk not, therefore, of giving up your hopes, for a little whining folly.

Mr. Solmes, with a self-satisfied air, presumptuously said he would suffer everything to *oblige* my family and to *save* me: and doubted not to be amply rewarded, could he be so happy as to succeed at last.

Mr. Solmes, said I, if you have any regard for your own happiness (*mine* is out of the question with you: you have not generosity enough to make *that* any part of your scheme) prosecute no further your *address,* as my brother calls it.

Excuse me, sir, turning to my uncle—to you, as to my father's brother, I owe duty. I beg *your* pardon, that I cannot obey you: but as for my *brother;* he is *but* my brother; he shall not constrain me: and (turning to the unnatural wretch—I will call him wretch) knit your brows, sir, and frown as you will, I will ask you, would *you,* in my case, make the sacrifices I am willing to make, to obtain every one's favour? If *not,* what right have you to treat me thus? and to procure me to be treated as I have been for so long a time past?

I had put myself by this time into great disorder: they were silent, and seemed by their looks to want to talk to one another, walking about (in violent disorders too) between whiles. I sat down fanning myself (as it happened, against the glass) and I could perceive my colour go and come; and being sick to the very heart, and apprehensive of fainting, I rung.

Betty came in. I called for a glass of water, and drank it: but nobody minded me. I heard my brother pronounce the words, Art! Female art! to Solmes; which, together with the apprehension that he would not be welcome, I suppose kept *him* back. Else I could see the man was affected. And (still fearing I should faint) I arose, and taking hold of Betty's arm, Let me hold by you, Betty, said I; let me withdraw. And moved with trembling feet towards the door, and then turned about, and made a courtesy to my uncle—Permit me, sir, said I, to withdraw.

Whither go you, niece? said my uncle: we have not done with you yet. I charge you depart not. Mr. Solmes has something to open to you, that will astonish you—and you *shall* hear it.

Only, sir, by your leave, for a few minutes into the air. I will return, if you command it. I will hear all that I am to hear; that it may be over *now* and *for ever*. You will go with me, Betty?

And so, without any further prohibition, I retired into the garden; and there, casting myself upon the first seat, and throwing Betty's apron over my face, leaning against her side, my hands between hers, I gave way to a violent burst of grief, or passion, or both; which, as it seemed, saved my heart from breaking; for I was sensible of an immediate relief.

It was near an hour before I was sent for in again. The messenger was my Cousin Dolly Hervey, who, with an eye of compassion and respect told me, my company was desired.

Betty left us.

Who commands my attendance, miss? said I. Have you not been in tears, my dear?

Who can forbear tears, said she.

Why, what is the matter, Cousin Dolly? Surely nobody is entitled to weep in this family but *me!*

Yes, I am, madam, said she, because I love you.

I kissed her.

You must take no notice of what I tell you, said the dear girl: but my mamma has been weeping for you, too, with me; but durst not let anybody see it: O my Dolly, said my mamma, there never was so set a malice in man as in your Cousin James Harlowe. They will ruin the flower and ornament of their family.

As how, Miss Dolly? Did she not explain herself?

Yes; she said, Mr. Solmes would have given up his claim to you; for he said, you hated him, and there were no hopes; and your mamma was willing he should; and to have you taken at your word, to renounce Mr. Lovelace, and to live single: my mamma was for it too; for they heard all that passed between you and Uncle Antony, and Cousin James; saying it was impossible to think of prevailing upon you to have Mr. Solmes. But your papa was immovable, and was angry at your mamma and mine upon it: and hereupon your brother, your sister, and my Uncle Antony joined in, and changed the scene entirely.

I asked what *she* would do, were she in my case?

Without hesitation she replied, Have Mr. Lovelace out-of-hand, and take up her own estate, if she were me; and there would be an end of it—and Mr. Lovelace, she said, was a fine gentleman; Mr. Solmes was not worthy to *buckle his shoes*.

By this time we entered the house. Miss Hervey accompanied me into the parlour, and left me, as a person devoted, I then thought.

Nobody was there.

They were all in my sister's parlour adjoining: for I heard a confused mixture of voices, some louder than others, which drowned the more compassionating accents.

I believe I was above a quarter of an hour enjoying my own comfortless contemplations, before anybody came in to me; for they seemed to be in full debate. My aunt looked in first; O my dear, said she, are you there? and withdrew hastily to apprise them of it.

And then (as agreed upon, I suppose) in came my Uncle Antony, crediting Mr. Solmes with the words, *Let me lead you in, my dear friend,* having hold of his hand; while the new-made beau awkwardly followed, but more edgingly, as I may say, setting his feet mincingly, to avoid treading upon his leader's heels.

I stood up. My uncle looked very surly. Sit down! sit down,

girl, said he—and drawing a chair near me, he placed his *dear* friend in it, whether he would or not, I having taken my seat. And my uncle sat on the other side of me.

Well, niece, taking my hand, we shall have very little more to say to you than we have already said, as to the subject that is so distasteful to you—unless, indeed, you have better considered the matter—and first, let me know if you have?

The matter wants no consideration, sir.

Very well, very well, *madam!* said my uncle, withdrawing his hands from mine: could I ever have thought of this from you?

For God's sake, dearest madam, said Mr. Solmes, folding his hands—and there he stopped.

For God's sake, *what,* sir? How came God's sake and your sake, I pray you, to be the same?

This silenced *him.* My uncle could *only* be angry; and that he was before.

Well, well, well, Mr. Solmes, said my uncle, no more of supplication.

He then was pleased to hint what great things he had designed to do for me.

I told him that I most sincerely thanked him for all his kind intentions to me: but that I was willing to resign all claim to any *other* of his favours than kind looks and kind words.

He looked about him this way and that.

Mr. Solmes looked pitifully down.

But both being silent, I was sorry, I added, that I had too much reason to say a very harsh thing, as it might be thought; which was, that if he would but be pleased to convince my brother and sister, that he was absolutely determined to alter his generous purposes towards me, it might possibly procure me better treatment from both than I was otherwise likely to have.

My uncle was very much displeased. But he had not the opportunity to express his displeasure, as he seemed preparing to do; for in came my brother in exceeding great wrath; and called me several vile names.

Was this my spiteful construction? he asked—was this the interpretation I put upon his brotherly care of me, and concern for me, in order to prevent my ruining myself?

It *is,* indeed it *is,* said I: I know no other way to account for your late behaviour to me: and before your face I repeat my request to my uncle, and I will make it to my other uncle whenever I am permitted to see him, that they will confer all their favours upon you, and upon my sisters; and only make me happy (it is all I wish for!) in their kind looks and kind words.

How they all gazed upon one another!—but could I be less peremptory before the man?

And as to *your* care and concern for me, sir, turning to my brother; once more I desire it not. You are but my brother. My father and mother, I bless God, are both living; and, were they *not,* you have given me abundant reason to say that you are the very last person I would wish to have any concern for me.

How, niece! And is a brother, an *only* brother, of so little consideration with you as this comes to? And ought he to have no concern for his sister's honour and the family's honour?

My honour, sir! I desire none of his concern for that! It never was endangered till it had his undesired concern! Forgive me, sir—but when my brother knows how to act like a brother or behave like a gentleman, he may deserve more consideration from me than it is possible for me now to think he does.

I thought my brother would have beat me upon this: but my uncle stood between us.

Violent girl, however, he called me.

Then was Mr. Solmes told that I was unworthy of his pursuit.

But Mr. Solmes warmly took my part: he could not bear, he said, that I should be treated so roughly.

And so very much did he exert himself on this occasion, and so patiently was his warmth received by my brother, that I began to suspect that it was a contrivance to make me think myself obliged to him; and that this might perhaps be one end of the pressed-for interview.

The very suspicion of this low artifice, violent as I was thought to be before, put me still more out of patience; and my uncle and my brother again praising his wonderful generosity and his noble return of good for evil. You are a happy man, Mr. Solmes, said I, that you can so *easily* confer obligations upon a whole family, except upon one ungrateful person of it, whom you seem to intend *most* to oblige; but who being made unhappy by your favour, desires not to owe to *you* any protection from the violence of a brother.

Then was I a rude, an ungrateful, an unworthy creature.

I own it all—all, all you can call me, or think me, brother, do I own. I own my unworthiness with regard to this gentleman. I take your word for his abundant merit, which I have neither leisure nor inclination to examine into—it may perhaps be as great as your own—but yet I cannot thank him for his mediation: for who sees not, looking at my uncle, that this is giving himself a merit with everybody at my expense?

Then turning to my brother, who seemed surprised into silence by my warmth, I must also acknowledge, sir, the favour of *your* superabundant care for me. But I discharge you of it; at least, while I have the happiness of nearer and dearer relations. I am independent of *you,* sir; though I never desire to be so of my father: and although I wish for the good opinion of my uncles, it is *all* I wish for from them: and this, sir, I repeat, *to make you and my sister easy.*

Instantly almost came in Betty, in a great hurry, looking at me as spitefully as if she were my *sister:* Sir, said she to my brother, my master desires to speak with you this moment at the door.

He went to that which led into my sister's parlour; and this sentence I heard thundered from the mouth of one who had a right to all my reverence: Son James, let the rebel be this moment carried away to my brother's—this very moment—she shall not stay one hour more under my roof!

I trembled; I was ready to sink. Yet, not knowing what I did or said, I flew to the door, and would have opened it: but my brother pulled it to, and held it close by the key. O my papa!—my dear papa, said I, falling upon my knees at the door—admit your child to your presence! Let me but plead my cause at your feet!

My uncle put his handkerchief to his eyes: Mr. Solmes made a still more grievous face than he had before. But my brother's marble heart was untouched.

I will not stir from my knees, continued I, without admission. At this door I beg it! O let it be the door of mercy! and open it to me, honoured sir, I beseech you! But this once, this once! although you were afterwards to shut it against me for ever!

The door was endeavoured to be opened on the inside, which made my brother let go the key on a sudden; and I pressing against it (all the time remaining on my knees) fell flat on my face into the other parlour; however without hurting myself. But everybody was gone, except Betty, who I suppose was the person that endeavoured to open the door. She helped to raise me up; and when I was on my feet I looked round that apartment, and seeing nobody there, re-entered the other, leaning upon her; and then threw myself into the chair which I had sat in before; and my eyes overflowed, to my great relief: while my Uncle Antony, my brother, and Mr. Solmes left me, and went to my other relations.

What passed among them I know not: but my brother came in by the time I had tolerably recovered myself, with a settled and haughty gloom upon his brow. Your father and mother command you instantly to prepare for your Uncle Antony's. You need not be solicitous about what you shall take with you. You may give Betty your keys—take them, Betty, if the perverse one has them about her, and carry them to her mother. She will take care to send everything after you that you shall want—but another night you will not be permitted to stay in this house.

I don't choose to give my keys to anybody, except to my mother, and into her own hands. You see how much I am disordered. It may cost me my life, to be hurried away so suddenly. I beg to be indulged till next Monday at least.

That will not be granted you. So prepare for this very night. And give up your keys. Give them to *me,* miss. I'll carry them to your mother.

Excuse me, brother. Indeed, I won't.

Indeed you must. Have you anything you are afraid should be seen by your mother?

Not if I be permitted to attend her.

I'll make a report accordingly.

He went out.

In came Miss Dolly Hervey: I am sorry, madam, to be the

messenger—but your mamma insists upon your sending up all the keys of your cabinet, library, and drawers.

Tell my mother that I yield them up to her commands: tell her I make no conditions with my mother: but if she find nothing she shall disapprove of, I beg that she will permit me to tarry here a few days longer. Try, my Dolly (the dear girl sobbing with grief); try if your gentleness cannot prevail for me.

She took the keys, and wrapped her arms about me; and begged me to excuse her for her message.

But being a little heavy (for it is now past two in the morning) I will lie down in my clothes, to indulge the kind summons, if it will be indulged.

Three o'clock, Wednesday Morning.

I could not sleep—only dozed away one half-hour.

My Aunt Hervey accosted me thus: O my dear child, what troubles do you give your parents, and to everybody!

I am sorry for it, madam.

Sorry for it, child! *Why* then so very obstinate! Come, sit down, my dear. I will sit next you; taking my hand.

My uncle placed Mr. Solmes on the other side of me: himself over against me, almost close to me.

Your brother, child, said my aunt, is too passionate—his zeal for *your* welfare pushes him on a little too vehemently.

Very true, said my uncle: but no more of this. We would now be glad to see if milder means will do with you.

I asked my aunt if it were necessary that that gentleman should be present?

There is a reason that he should, said my aunt, as you will hear by and by. But I must tell you, first, that, thinking you were a little too angrily treated by your brother, your mother desired me to try what gentler means would do upon a spirit so generous as we used to think yours.

Nothing can be done, madam, I must presume to say, if this gentleman's address be the end.

She looked upon my uncle, who bit his lip, and looked upon Mr. Solmes, who rubbed his cheek; and shaking her head, Good, dear creature, said she, be calm. Let me ask you if something would have been done had you been more gently used than you seem to think you have been?

No, madam, I cannot say it would, in this gentleman's favour. You know, madam, you know, sir, to my uncle, I ever valued myself upon my sincerity: and once indeed had the happiness to be valued for it.

My uncle took Mr. Solmes aside. I heard him say whisperingly: She must, she shall, still be yours. We'll see who'll conquer, parents or child, uncles or niece. I doubt not to be witness to all this being got over, and many a good-humoured jest made of this high frenzy!

I was heartily vexed.

Though we cannot find out, continued he, yet we *guess,* who puts her upon this obstinate behaviour. It is not natural to her, man. Nor would I concern myself so much about her, but that I know what I say to be true, and intend to do great things for her.

I will hourly pray for that happy time, whispered, as audibly, Mr. Solmes. I never will revive the remembrance of what is now so painful to me.

Well, but, niece, I am to tell you, said my aunt, that the sending up your keys, without making any conditions, has wrought for you what nothing else could have done. That, and the not finding anything that could give them umbrage, together with Mr. Solmes's interposition——

O madam, let me not owe an obligation to Mr. Solmes. I cannot repay it, except by my *thanks;* and *those* only on condition that he will decline his suit.

O madam, cried he, believe, believe, believe me, it is impossible. While you are single, I *will* hope. While that hope is encouraged by so many worthy friends, I *must* perservere. I must not slight *them,* madam, because you slight *me.*

I answered him only with a look; but it was of high disdain; and turning from him—But what favour, dear madam (to my aunt) has the instance of duty you mention procured me?

Your mother and Mr. Solmes, replied my aunt, have prevailed, that your request to stay here till Monday next shall be granted, if you will promise to go cheerfully then.

Let me but choose my own visitors, and I will go to my uncle's house with pleasure.

Well, niece, said my aunt, we must waive this subject, I find. We will now proceed to another, which will require your utmost attention. It will give you the reason why Mr. Solmes's presence is requisite——

Ay, said my uncle, and show you what sort of a man somebody is. Mr. Solmes, pray favour us, in the first place, with the letter you received from your anonymous friend.

I will, sir. And out he pulled a letter-case, and, taking out a letter: It is written in answer to one sent to the person. It is superscribed, *To Roger Solmes, Esq.* It begins thus: *Honoured Sir*——

I beg your pardon, sir, said I: but what, pray, is the intent of reading this letter to me?

To let you know what a vile man you are thought to have set your heart upon, said my uncle in an audible whisper.

If, sir, it be suspected, that I have set my heart upon any other, why is Mr. Solmes to give himself any further trouble about me?

Only hear, niece, said my aunt; only hear what Mr. Solmes has to read and to say to you on this head.

If, madam, Mr. Solmes will be pleased to declare, that he has no view to serve, no end to promote, for himself, I will hear anything he shall read. But if the contrary, you must allow me to say, that it will abate with me a great deal of the weight of whatever he shall produce.

Hear it but read, niece, said my aunt.

Hear it read, said my uncle. You are so ready to take part with——

With anybody, sir, that is accused anonymously, and from interested motives.

He began to read; and there seemed to be a heavy load of charges in this letter against the poor criminal: but I stopped the reading of it, and said: It will not be my *fault*, if this vilified man be not as indifferent to me as one whom I never saw.

Still—Proceed, Mr. Solmes—hear it out, niece, was my uncle's cry.

But to what purpose, sir? said I. Has not Mr. Solmes a *view* in this? And, besides, can anything worse be said of Mr. Lovelace, than I have heard said for several months past?

But this, said my uncle, and what Mr. Solmes can tell you besides, amounts to the *fullest proof*——

Was the unhappy man, then, so freely treated in his character before, *without* full proof? I beseech you, sir, give me not *too good* an opinion of Mr. Lovelace; as I *may* have, if such pains be taken to make him guilty, by one who means not his reformation by it; nor to do good, if I may presume to say so in this case, to anybody but himself.

I see very plainly, girl, said my uncle, your prepossession, your fond prepossession, for the person of a man without morals.

Indeed my dear, said my aunt, you too much justify all our apprehensions. Surprising! that a young creature of virtue and honour should thus esteem a man of a quite opposite character!

Dear madam, do not conclude against me too hastily. I believe Mr. Lovelace is far from being so good as he ought to be: but if every man's private life were searched into by *prejudiced people,* set on for that purpose, I know not whose reputation would be safe.

Permit me to observe further, that Mr. Solmes himself may not be absolutely faultless. I never heard of his virtues. Some vices I have heard of. Excuse me, Mr. Solmes, I speak to your face.

He looked down; but was silent.

Mr. Lovelace may have vices *you* have not. You may have others, which *he* has not. I speak not this to defend him, or to accuse you. No man is bad, no one is good, in *everything*. Mr. Lovelace, for example, is said to be implacable, and to hate my friends: that does not make me value him the more: but give me leave to say, that *they* hate him as much. Mr. Solmes has his antipathies likewise; very *strong* ones, and those to his *own relations;* which I don't find to be the other's fault; for he lives well with *his*—yet he may have as bad: worse, pardon me, he cannot have, in my poor opinion: for what must be the man who *hates his own flesh?*

You know not, madam;
You know not, niece; } all in one breath.
You know not, Clary;

I may not, nor do I desire to know Mr. Solmes's reasons. It *concerns* not me to know them: but the world, even the impartial part of it, accuses him. If the world is unjust, or rash, in *one* man's case, why may it not be so in *another's?* That's all I mean by it. Nor can there be a greater sign of want of merit than where a man seeks to pull down another's character, in order to build up his own.

The poor man's face was all this time overspread with confusion, twisted, as it were, and all awry, neither mouth nor nose standing in the middle of it. My uncle said, There was no talking to me. And I should have absolutely silenced both gentlemen, had not my brother come in again to their assistance.

This was the strange speech he made at his entrance, his eyes flaming with anger: This prating girl has struck you all dumb, I perceive. Persevere, however, Mr. Solmes. I have heard every word she has said: and I know no other method of being even with her, than, after she is yours, to make her as sensible of your power as she now makes you of her insolence.

Fie, Cousin Harlowe! said my aunt. Could I have thought a *brother* would have said this to a gentleman, of a *sister?*

I must tell you, madam, said he, that *you* give the rebel courage.

But you see, sir, to Mr. Solmes, what a conduct is thought necessary to enable you to arrive at your ungenerous end. You see how my brother *courts* for you!

I disclaim Mr. Harlowe's violence, madam, with all my soul. I will never remind you——

Silence, worthy sir! said I; I will take care you never shall have the opportunity.

Less violence, Clary, said my uncle. Cousin James, you are as much to blame as your sister.

In then came my sister. Brother, said she, you kept not your promise. You are *thought* to be to blame within, as well as here. Were not Mr. Solmes's generosity and affection to the girl *well* known, what you have said would be inexcusable. My father desires to speak with you; and with you, aunt; and with you, uncle; and with you, Mr. Solmes, if you please.

They all four withdrew into the next apartment.

Mr. Solmes, after a little while, came in again by himself, to take leave of me: full of scrapes and compliments; but too well tutored and encouraged, to give me hope of his declining his suit.

What! said I, will you still persist, when I declare, as I now do, that my affections are engaged? And let my brother make the most of it.

Dearest madam, what can I say? On my knees I beg——

And down the ungraceful wretch dropped on his knees.

Let me not kneel in vain, madam: let me not be thus despised. And he looked most odiously sorrowful.

I have kneeled too, Mr. Solmes: often have I kneeled: and I will kneel again—even to *you,* sir, will I kneel, if there be so much merit in kneeling; provided you will not be the implement of my cruel brother's undeserved persecution.

What I ask you for is mercy to myself: that, since you seem to have some power over my relations, you will use it in my behalf. Tell them that you see I cannot conquer my aversion to you: tell them, if you are a wise man, that you value too much your own happiness to risk it against such a determined antipathy: tell them that I am unworthy of your offers: and that, in mercy to yourself, as well as to me, you will not prosecute a suit so impossible to be granted.

I will risk all consequences, said the fell wretch, rising, with a countenance whitened over, as if with malice, his hollow eyes flashing fire, and biting his underlip, to show he could be *manly.* Your hatred, madam, shall be no objection with me: and I doubt not in a few days to have it in my power to show you——

You have it in your power, sir——

He came well off. *To show you* more generosity than, noble as you are said to be to others, you show to me.

The man's face became his anger: it seems formed to express the passion.

At that instant, again came in my brother. Sister, sister, sister, said he, with his teeth set, act on the termagant part you have so newly assumed—most wonderfully well does it become you. It is but a short one, however. Tyranness in your turn, accuse others of your own guilt—but leave her, leave her, Mr. Solmes; her time is short. You'll find her humble and mortified enough very quickly.

More he said, as he flew out, with a glowing face, upon Shorey's coming in to recall him on his violence.

I removed from chair to chair, excessively frighted and disturbed at this brutal treatment.

The man attempted to excuse himself, as being sorry for my brother's passion.

Leave me, leave me, sir, fanning—or I shall faint. And indeed I thought I should.

He recommended himself to my favour with an air of assurance; augmented, as I thought, by a distress so visible in me; for he even snatched my trembling, my struggling hand; and ravished it to his odious mouth.

I flung from him with high disdain: and he withdrew, bowing and cringing; self-gratified, and enjoying, as I thought, the confusion he saw me in.

Upon his withdrawing, Betty brought me word, that I was permitted to go up to my own chamber: and was bid to consider of everything: for my time was short. Nevertheless, she believed I might be permitted to stay till Saturday.

How lucky it was that I had got away my papers! They made a strict search for them; that I can see, by the disorderly manner they have left all things in. The same in my books; which they have strangely disordered and mismatched; to look *behind* them, and *in* some of them, I suppose. To your hint, I thank you, are they indebted for their disappointment.

Your for ever obliged and affectionate

Cl. Harlowe.

MISS CLARISSA HARLOWE TO MISS HOWE

Wednesday, Eleven o'clock, April 5.

I MUST write as I have opportunity; making use of my concealed stores: for my pens and ink (all of each that they could find) are taken from me.

About an hour ago, I deposited a billet to Mr. Lovelace, lest his impatience should put him upon some rashness; signifying, in four lines, "That the interview was over; and that I hoped my steady refusal of Mr. Solmes would discourage any further applications to me in his favour."

[Clarissa is forced into an interview with her aunt; then she is tricked down to the parlor to her brother and Mr. Solmes. Ed.]

Down I went: and to whom should I be sent for, but to my brother and Mr. Solmes? The latter standing sneaking behind the door, so that I saw him not, till I was mockingly led by the hand into the room by my brother. And then I started as if I had beheld a ghost.

You are to sit down, Clary.

And what then, brother?

Why then, you are to put off that scornful look, and hear what Mr. Solmes has to say to you.

Madam, said Mr. Solmes, as if in haste to speak, lest he should not have opportunity given him, Mr. Lovelace is a declared *marriage-hater,* and has a design upon your honour, if ever——

Base accuser! said I, in a passion, snatching my hand from my brother, who was insolently motioning to give it to Mr. Solmes; he has not! he dares not! But *you* have, if endeavouring to force a free mind be to dishonour it!

O thou violent creature! said my brother. But not gone yet—for I was rushing away.

What mean you, sir (struggling vehemently to get away), to detain me thus against my will?

You shall not go, Violence; clasping his unbrotherly arms about me.

Then let not Mr. Solmes stay. Why hold you me thus? He shall not, for *your own* sake, if I can help it, see how barbarously a brother can treat a sister who deserves not evil treatment.

And I struggled so vehemently to get from him, that he was forced to quit my hand; which he did with these words: Begone then, Fury! How strong is will! There is no holding her.

And up I flew to my chamber, and locked myself in, trembling, and out of breath.

In less than a quarter of an hour, up came Betty.

The Lord have mercy upon us! said she. What a *confusion of a house* is this! (hurrying up and down, fanning herself with her handkerchief). Such angry masters and mistresses!—such an obstinate young lady!—such a humble lover!—such enraged uncles!—Such—O dear!—dear! What a topsy-turvy house is this!—and all for what, trow? Only because a young lady *may* be happy, and will *not?* Only because a young lady *will* have a husband, and will *not* have a husband? What hurly-burlies are here, where all used to be peace and quietness!

Thus she ran on to herself; while I sat as patiently as I could (being assured that her errand was not designed to be a welcome one to me) to observe when her soliloquy would end.

At last, turning to me: I must do as I am bid. I can't help it. Don't be angry with me, miss. But I must carry down your pen and ink: and that, this moment.

By whose order?

By your papa's and mamma's.

How shall I know that?

She offered to go to my closet: I stepped in before her: Touch it, if you dare.

Up came my Cousin Dolly. Madam!—madam! said the poor weeping good-natured creature, in broken sentences—you must—indeed you must—deliver to Betty—or to me—your pen and ink.

Must I, my sweet cousin? Then I will to you; but not to this bold body. And so I gave my standish to her.

I am sorry, very sorry, said miss, to be the messenger: but your papa will not have you in the same house with him: he is resolved you shall be carried away to-morrow, or Saturday at furthest. And therefore your pen and ink is taken away, that you may give nobody notice of it.

And away went the dear girl, very sorrowful, carrying down with her my standish, and all its furniture, and a little parcel of pens beside, which having been seen when the great search was made, she was bid to ask for. As it happened, I had not diminished it, having hid half a dozen crow-quills in as many different places. It was lucky; for I doubt not they had numbered how many were in the parcel.

All my dependence, all my hopes, are in your mother's favour. But for that, I know not *what* I might do: for who can tell what will come next?

Miss Clarissa Harlowe to Miss Howe

Wednesday Night.

All is in a hurry below-stairs. Betty is in and out like a spy. Something is working, I know not what. I am really a good deal disordered in body as well as mind. Indeed I am quite heartsick.

I will go down, though 'tis almost dark, on pretence of getting a little air and composure. Robert has my two former, I hope, before now: and I will deposit this, with Lovelace's enclosed, if I can, for fear of another search.

I know not what I shall do! All is so strangely busy!—doors clapped to—going out of one apartment, hurryingly, as I may say, into another. Betty in her alarming way, staring, as if of frighted importance; twice with me in half an hour; called down in haste by Shorey the last time; leaving me with still *more* meaning in her looks and gestures—yet possibly nothing in all this worthy of my apprehensions.

Here again comes the creature, with her deep-drawn affected sighs, and her *O dears! O dears!*

. . . . . .

More dark hints thrown out by this saucy creature. But she will not explain herself. "Suppose this pretty business ends in murder, she says? Parents will not be *baffled* out of their children by impudent gentlemen; nor is it fit they should. It may come home to me, when I least expect it."

These are the gloomy and perplexing hints this impertinent throws out. Probably they arise from the information Mr. Lovelace says he has secretly permitted them to have (from his vile double-faced agent, I suppose!) of his resolution to prevent my being carried to my uncle's.

How *justly,* if so, may this exasperate them! How am I driven to and fro, like a feather in the wind, at the pleasure of the rash, the selfish, and the headstrong! and when I am as averse to the proceedings of the one, as I am to those of the other! For although I was induced to carry on this unhappy correspondence, as I think I ought to call it, in hopes to prevent mischief; yet indiscreet measures are fallen upon by the rash man, before I, who am so much concerned in the event of the present contentions, can be consulted: and between his violence on one hand, and that of my relations on the other, I find myself in danger from both.

If I am prevented depositing this and the enclosed (as I intend to try to do, late as it is) I will add to it as occasion shall offer. Meantime, believe me to be

Your ever-affectionate and grateful

Cl. Harlowe.

Miss Howe to Miss Clarissa Harlowe

Thursday Morning (*April 6.*)

I have your letters. Never was there a creature more impatient on the most interesting uncertainty than I was, to know the event of the interview between you and Solmes.

Just as I was risen, in came Kitty with your letters. I was not a quarter dressed; and only slipped on my morning sacque; proceeding no further till I had read them all through, long as they are: and yet I often stopped to rave aloud (though by myself) at the devilish people you have to deal with.

As to going to your uncle's, that you must not do if you can help it. Nor must you have Solmes, that's certain: not only because of his unworthiness in every respect, but because of the aversion you have so openly avowed to him; which everybody knows and talks of; as they do of your approbation of the other. For your reputation's sake therefore, as well as to prevent mischief, you must either live single or have Lovelace.

If you think of going to London, let me know; and I hope you will have *time* to allow me a further concert as to the manner of your getting away, and thither, and how to procure proper lodgings for you.

You will observe from what I have written, that I have not succeeded with my mother.

I am extremely mortified and disappointed. We have had very strong debates upon it. But, besides the narrow argument of *embroiling ourselves with other people's affairs,* she will have it that it is your duty to comply.

Think, my dear, if in any way I can serve you. If you allow of it, I protest I will go off privately with you, and we will live and die together.

Adieu! and Heaven direct for the best my beloved creature, prays

Her
Anna Howe.

MISS CLARISSA HARLOWE TO MISS HOWE

Thursday, April 6.

ALL MY consolation is, as I have frequently said, that I have not, by my own inadvertence or folly, brought myself into this sad situation. If I *had,* I should not have dared to look up to anybody with the expectation of protection or assistance, nor to you for excuse of the trouble I give you. But nevertheless we should not be angry at a person's not doing that for ourselves, or for our friend, which she thinks she ought *not* to do; and which she has it in her option either to *do,* or to *let it alone.* Much less have you a right to be displeased with so prudent a mother, for not engaging herself so warmly in my favour, as you wished she would. If my own aunt can give me up, and that against her judgment, as I may presume to say; and if my father and mother, and uncles, who once loved me so well, can join so strenuously against me; can *I* expect, or ought *you,* the protection of your mother, in *opposition* to them?

Your partial love will be ready to acquit me of *capital* and *intentional* faults: but oh, my dear! my calamities have humbled me enough, to make me turn my gaudy eye inward; to make me look into myself! And what have I discovered there? Why, my dear friend, more *secret* pride and vanity than I could have thought had lain in my unexamined heart.

But I will not oppress you, my dearest friend, with further reflections of this sort. I will take them all into myself. Surely I have a mind that has room for them. My afflictions are too sharp to last long. The crisis is at hand. Happier times you bid me hope for. I *will* hope.

. . . . . .

If, my dear, you can procure a vehicle for us *both,* you can perhaps procure one for me *singly:* but can it be done without embroiling *yourself* with your mother, or *her* with our family? Be it coach, chariot, chaise, wagon, or horse, I matter not, provided you appear not to have a hand in my withdrawing. Only, in case it be one of the two latter, I believe I must desire you to get me an ordinary gown and coat, or habit, of some servant; having no concert with any of our own: the more ordinary the better.

But were I even to get safely to London, I know nobody there but by name; and those the tradesmen to our family; who no doubt would be the first wrote to and engaged to find me out. And should Mr. Lovelace discover where I was, and he and my brother meet, what mischiefs might ensue between them, whether I were willing or not to return to Harlowe Place!

But supposing I could remain there concealed, to what might not my youth, my sex, and unacquaintedness with the ways of that great, wicked town, expose me!--I should hardly dare to go to church for fear of being discovered. People would wonder how I lived. Who knows but I might pass for a kept mistress; and that, although nobody came to me, yet, that every time I went out, it might be imagined to be in pursuance of some assignation?

Were Lovelace to find out my place of abode, that would be the same thing in the eye of the world as if I had actually gone off with him: for would he, do you think, be prevailed upon to forbear visiting me? And then his unhappy character (a foolish man!) would be no credit to any young creature desirous of concealment. Indeed the world, let me escape whither, and to whomsoever I could, would conclude *him* to be the contriver of it.

I had thoughts indeed several times of writing to my cousin: but by the time an answer could have come, I imagined all would have been over, as if it had never been: so from day to day, from week to week I hoped on: and, after all, I might as reasonably fear (as I have heretofore said) that my cousin would be brought to side against me, as that some of those I have named would.

MISS CLARISSA HARLOWE TO MISS HOWE

Thursday Night.

THE ALARMING hurry I mentioned under my date of last night, and Betty's saucy dark hints, come out to be owing to what I guessed they were; that is to say, to the private intimation Mr. Lovelace contrived our family should have of his insolent resolution (*insolent* I must call it) to prevent my being carried to my uncle's.

About six o'clock this evening, my aunt came up, and tapped at my door; for I was writing, and had locked myself in. I opened it; and she entering, thus delivered herself:

You will not be hurried away to your uncle's, child; let that comfort you. They see your aversion to go.

How you revive me, madam! This is a cordial to my heart!

And then I ran over with blessings for this good news.

Hold, niece, said she at last. You must not give yourself too much joy upon the occasion neither. But you must be Mrs. Solmes, for all that.

I was dumb.

She then told me that they had had undoubted information, that a certain desperate *ruffian* (I must excuse her that word, she said) had prepared armed men to waylay my brother and uncles, and seize me, and carry me off. Surely, she said, I was not consenting to a violence that might be followed by murder on one side or the other; perhaps on both.

I was still silent.

That therefore my father had changed his resolution as to my going to my uncle's; and was determined next Tuesday to set out thither *himself* with my mother; and that on Wednesday I must give my hand—as they would have me.

She proceeded, that orders were already given for a licence: that the ceremony was to be performed in my own chamber, in presence of all my friends, except my father and mother; who would not return, nor see me, till all was over, and till they had a good account of my behaviour.

But let me ask you, and do not be displeased, will you choose to see what generous stipulations for you there are in the settlements? You have knowledge beyond your years—give the writings a perusal: do, my dear: they are engrossed, and ready for signing, and have been for some time. Your father would oblige me to bring them up, and to leave them with you. He commands you to read them. *But* to read them, niece—since they are engrossed, and *were* before you made them absolutely hopeless.

And then, to my great terror, out she drew some parchments from her handkerchief, which she had kept (unobserved by me) under her apron: and rising, put them in the opposite window. Had she produced a serpent I could not have been more frighted.

Oh! my dearest aunt, turning away my face, and holding out my hands: hide from my eyes those horrid parchments! Let me conjure you to tell me—by all the tenderness of near relationship, and upon your honour, and by your love for me, say, are they absolutely resolved that, come what will, I must be that man's?

My dear, you must have Mr. Solmes: indeed you must.

Indeed I never will! This, as I have said over and over, is not originally my father's will. Indeed I never will—and that is all I will say!

She withdrew; leaving me full of grief and indignation.

I wrote to Mr. Lovelace, to let him know: "That all that was threatened at my Uncle Antony's, was intended to be executed *here*. That I had come to a resolution to throw myself upon the protection *of either of his two aunts,* who would afford it me—in short, that by endeavouring to obtain leave on Monday to dine in the ivy summer-house, I would, if possible, meet him without the garden door, at two, three, four, or five o'clock on Monday afternoon, as I should be able. That in the meantime he should acquaint me, *whether I should hope for either of those ladies' protection:* and if I might, I absolutely insisted that *he should leave me with either, and go to London himself,* or *remain at Lord M.'s; nor offer to visit me, till I was satisfied that nothing could be done with my friends in an amicable way; and that I could not obtain possession of my own estate,* and leave to live upon it: and particularly, *that he should not hint marriage to me, till I consented to hear him upon that subject.*

I added, that if he could prevail upon one of the Misses Montague to *favour me with her company on the road*, it would make me abundantly more easy in the thoughts of carrying into effect a resolution which I had not come to, although so driven, but with the utmost reluctance and concern; and which would throw such a slur upon my reputation in the eye of the world, as perhaps I should never be able to wipe off."

And now, that I am come to this part, my uneasy reflections begin again to pour in upon me. Yet what can I do? I believe I shall take it back again the first thing I do in the morning—yet what *can* I do?

But these strange forebodings! Yet I can, if you advise, cause the chariot he shall bring with him to carry me directly for town, whither in my London scheme, if you were to approve it, I had proposed to go: and this will save you the trouble of procuring for me a vehicle; as well as prevent any suspicion from your mother of your contributing to my escape.

Adieu, my dearest friend, adieu!

MISS CLARISSA HARLOWE TO MISS HOWE

Friday Morning, Seven o'clock (April 7).

MY AUNT HERVEY, who is a very early riser, was walking in the garden (Betty attending her, as I saw from my window this morning) when I arose; for after such a train of fatigue and restless nights, I had unhappily overslept myself: so all I durst venture upon was to step down to my poultry-yard, and deposit mine of yesterday and last night. And I am just come up; for she is still in the garden. This prevents me from going to resume my letter, as I think still to do; and hope it will not be too late.

I said I had unhappily overslept myself. I went to bed at about half an hour after two. I told the quarters till five; after which I dropped alseep, and awaked not till past six, and then in great terror, from a dream, which has made such an impression upon me that, slightly as I think of dreams, I cannot help taking this opportunity to relate it to you.

"Methought my brother, my Uncle Antony, and Mr. Solmes, had formed a plot to destroy Mr. Lovelace; who discovering it, and believing I had a hand in it, turned all his rage against me. I thought he made them all fly into foreign parts upon it; and afterwards seizing upon me, carried me into a churchyard; and there, notwithstanding all my prayers and tears, and protestations of innocence, stabbed me to the heart, and then tumbled me into a deep grave ready dug, among two or three half-dissolved carcasses; throwing in the dirt and earth upon me with his hands, and trampling it down with his feet."

I awoke in a cold sweat, trembling, and in agonies; and still the frightful images raised by it remain upon my memory.

Eight o'clock.

The man, my dear, has got the letter! What a strange diligence! I wish he mean me well, that he takes so much pains! Yet, to be ingenuous, I must own that I should be displeased if he took less. I wish, however, he had been a hundred miles off! What an advantage have I given him over me!

My dearest friend, tell me, have I done wrong? Yet do not *say* I have, if you *think* it; for should all the world besides condemn me, I shall have some comfort, if *you* do not. The first time I ever besought you to flatter me. That, of itself, is an indication that I have done wrong, and am afraid of hearing the truth. O tell me (but yet do not tell me) if I have done wrong!

Friday, Eleven o'clock.

My aunt has made me another visit. She began what she had to say with letting me know that my friends are all persuaded that I still correspond with Mr. Lovelace; as is plain, she said, by hints and menaces he throws out, which show that he is apprised of several things that have passed between my relations and me, sometimes within a very little while after they have happened.

Although I approve not of the method he stoops to take to come at his intelligence, yet it is not prudent in me to clear myself by the ruin of the corrupted servant (although his vileness has neither my connivance nor approbation), since my doing so might occasion the detection of my own correspondence; and so frustrate all the hopes I have to avoid this Solmes. Yet it is not at all unlikely that this very agent of Mr. Lovelace acts a double part between my brother and him: how else can *our* family know (so *soon* too) his menaces upon the passages they hint at?

I perceive you are going to speak with warmth, proceeded she (*and so I was*). For my own part I am sure, you would not write anything, if you *do* write, to inflame so violent a spirit.

Cl. Harlowe.

MISS CLARISSA HARLOWE TO MISS HOWE

Friday, One o'clock.

I HAVE a letter from Mr. Lovelace, full of transports, vows, and promises.

You would imagine, by what he writes, that I have given him reason to think that my aversion to Mr. Solmes is all owing to my favour for him.

The dreadful thing is that, comparing what he writes from his intelligencer of what is designed against me (though he seems not to know the threatened day) with what my aunt and Betty assure me of, there can be no hope for me, but that I must be Solmes's wife if I stay here.

However, I have replied to the following effect: "That although I had given him room to expect, that I would put myself into the *protection of one of the ladies of his family,* yet as I have three days to come, between this and Monday, and as I still hope that my friends will relent, or that Mr. Solmes will give up a point they will find it impossible to carry; I shall not look upon myself as *absolutely bound by the appointment:* and expect therefore, if I recede, that I shall not again be called to account for it by him. That I think it necessary to acquaint him, that if by throwing myself upon Lady Betty Lawrance's protection, as he proposed, he understands, *that I mean directly to put myself into his power, he is very much mistaken:* for that there are *many points in which I must be satisfied; several matters to be adjusted,* even after I have left this house (if I *do* leave it) *before I can think of giving him any particular encouragement:* that in the *first place* he must expect that I will do my utmost to *procure my father's reconciliation and approbation of my future steps;* and that *I will govern myself entirely by his commands,* in every reasonable point, *as much as if I had not left his house:* that if he imagines I shall not reserve to myself this liberty, but that my withdrawing is to give him any advantages which he would *not otherwise have had;* I am determined to stay where I am, and abide the event, in hopes that my friends will still accept of my reiterated promise, *never to marry him, or anybody else, without their consent.*"

This I will deposit as soon as I can. And as he thinks things are near their crisis, I dare say it will not be long before I have an answer to it.

Friday, Four o'clock.

I am really ill. I was used to make the best of any little accidents that befell me, for fear of making my *then* affectionate friends uneasy: but now I shall make the worst of my indisposition, in hopes to obtain a suspension of the threatened evil of Wednesday next. And if I do obtain it, I will postpone my appointment with Mr. Lovelace.

Betty has told them that I am very much indisposed. But I have no pity from anybody.

I believe I am become the object of every one's aversion; and that they would all be glad I were dead. Indeed I believe it. "What ails the perverse creature," cries one? "Is she lovesick," another?

I was in the ivy summer-house, and came out shivering with cold, as if aguishly affected.

Friday, Six o'clock.

My aunt, who again stays all night, has just left me. She came to tell me the result of my friends' deliberations about me.

Next Wednesday morning they are all to be assembled: to wit, my father, mother, my uncles, herself, and my Uncle Hervey; my brother and sister of course: my good Mrs. Norton is likewise to be admitted: and Dr. Lewen is to be at hand, to exhort me, it seems, if there be occasion: but my aunt is not certain whether he is to be among them, or to tarry till called in.

When this awful court is assembled, the poor prisoner is to be brought in, supported by Mrs. Norton.

What is hoped from me, she says, is that I will cheerfully, on Tuesday night, if not before, sign the articles; and so turn the succeeding day's solemn convention into a day of festivity. I am to have the licence sent up, however, and once more the settlements, that I may see how much in earnest they are.

They are sure, she says, something is working on Mr. Lovelace's part, and perhaps on mine: and my father would sooner follow me to the grave than see me *his* wife.

I said I was not well: that the very apprehensions of these trials were already insupportable to me; and would increase upon me, as the time approached; and I was afraid I should be extremely ill.

I'll only tell you one thing, my dear: and that is; ill or well, the ceremony will probably be performed before Wednesday night.

Friday, Nine o'clock.

I have been down, and already have another letter from Mr. Lovelace [*the man lives upon the spot, I think*]: and I must write to him, either that I will or will not stand to my first resolution of escaping hence on Monday next.

"He is full of alternatives and proposals. He offers *to attend me directly to Lady Betty's;* or, if I had rather, *to my own estate;* and that my Lord M. shall protect me there. In either case, as soon as he sees me safe, he will go up to London, or whither I please; and not come near me, but by my own permission; and till I am satisfied in everything I am doubtful of, as well with regard to his reformation, as to settlements, etc.

"*To conduct me to you,* my dear, is another of his proposals; not doubting, he says, but your mother will receive me; or, if that be not agreeable to you, or to your mother, or to me, he will put me *into Mr. Hickman's protection;* whom, no doubt, he says, you can influence; and that it may be given out, that I am gone to Bath, or Bristol, or abroad; wherever I please.

"Again, if it be more agreeable, he proposes *to attend me privately to London,* where he will procure handsome lodgings for me, and *both his Cousins Montague to receive me in them, and to accompany me till all should be adjusted to my mind;* and *till a reconciliation shall be effected;* which he assures me nothing shall be wanting in him to facilitate; greatly as he has been insulted by all my family.

"He conjures me, in the solemnest manner, if I would not throw him into utter despair, to keep to my appointment.

"In short, he solemnly vows that his *whole* view at present is to free me from my imprisonment; and to restore me to my own free will, in a point so absolutely necessary to my future happiness."

Mr. Lovelace concludes "with repeatedly begging an interview with me; and that, *this* night, if possible: an honour, he says, he is the more encouraged to solicit for, as I had twice before made him hope for it.

He renews all his vows and promises on this head in so earnest and so solemn a manner that (his own *interest,* and his family's *honour,* and their *favour* for me, co-operating) I can have no room to doubt of his sincerity.

Miss Clarissa Harlowe to Miss Howe

Sat. Morn. 8 o'clock (*April 8*).

Whether you will blame me or not, I cannot tell, but I have deposited a letter confirming my resolution to leave this house on Monday next, within the hours mentioned in my former, if possible.

I tell him "That I have no way to avoid the determined resolution of my friends in behalf of Mr. Solmes, but by abandoning this house by his assistance."

I have not pretended to make a merit with him on this score; for I plainly tell him: "That could I, *without an unpardonable sin,* die when I *would,* I would sooner make death my choice than take a step which all the world, if not my own heart, will condemn me for taking."

I tell him: "That I shall not try to bring any other clothes with me than those I shall have on; and those but my common wearing apparel; lest I should be suspected. That I must expect to be denied the possession of my estate: but that I am determined never to consent to a litigation with my father, were I to be reduced to ever so low a state: so that the protection I am to be obliged for to any one must be alone for the distress sake. That, therefore, he will have nothing to hope for from this step, *that he had not before:* and that, in every light, I reserve to myself to *accept or refuse his address, as his behaviour and circumspection shall appear to me to deserve.*"

I tell him: "That I think it best to go into a private lodging, in the neighbourhood of Lady Betty Lawrance; and not to her ladyship's house; that it may not appear to the world, *that I have refuged myself in his family;* and that a reconciliation with my friends may not, on that account, be made impracticable: that I will send for thither my faithful Hannah; and apprise only Miss Howe where I am: that *he shall instantly leave me,* and go to London, or to one of Lord M.'s seats; and (as he had promised) not come near me, but by my leave; consenting himself with a correspondence by letter only.

"That if I find myself in danger of being discovered, and carried back by violence, I will then throw myself directly into the protection either of Lady Betty or Lady Sarah: but *this is only in case of absolute necessity;* for that it will be more to my reputation, for me, by the best means I can (taking advantage of my privacy) to enter by a second or third hand *into a treaty of reconciliation with my friends.*

"That I must, however, plainly tell him that if, in this treaty, my friends *insist upon my resolving against marrying him, I will engage to comply with them;* provided they will allow me to promise him *that I will never be the wife of any other man while he remains single, or is living:* that this is a compliment I am willing to pay him in return for the trouble and pains he has taken, and the usage he has met with on my account: Although I intimate that he may, in a great measure, thank himself (by reason of the little regard he has paid to his reputation) for the slights he has met with.

"As to the meeting he is desirous of, I think it by no means proper; especially as it is so likely that I may soon see him. But that if anything occurs to induce me to change my mind, as to withdrawing, I will *then take the first opportunity to see him, and give him my reasons for that change.*"

Saturday, Ten o'clock.

Mr. Solmes is here. He is to dine with his new relations, as Betty tells me he already calls them.

He would have thrown himself in my way once more: but

I hurried up to my prison, in my return from my garden-walk, to avoid him.

I had, when in the garden, the curiosity to see if my letter were gone: I cannot say with an intention to take it back again if it were not, because I see not how I could do otherwise than I have done; yet, what a caprice! when I found it gone, I began (as yesterday morning) to wish it had not: for no other reason, I believe, than because it was out of my power.

Your most affectionate and faithful

Cl. Harlowe.

Miss Howe to Miss Clarissa Harlowe

Sat. Afternoon.

By your last date of ten o'clock in your letter of this day, you could not long have deposited it before Robin took it. He rode hard, and brought it to me just as I had risen from table.

I had been inquiring privately how to procure you a conveyance from Harlowe Place, and yet not appear in it; knowing that to oblige in the *fact,* and to disoblige in the *manner,* is but obliging by halves: my mother being moreover very suspicious, and very uneasy; made more so by daily visits from your Uncle Antony; who tells her that everything is now upon the point of being determined; and hopes that her daughter will not so interfere as to discourage your compliance with their wills.

I found more difficulty than I expected (as the time was confined, and secrecy required, and as you so earnestly forbid me to accompany you in your enterprise) in procuring you a vehicle. Had you not obliged me to keep measures with my mother, I could have managed it with ease. I could even have taken our own chariot, on one pretence or other, and put two horses extraordinary to it, if I had thought fit; and I could, when we had got to London, have sent it back, and nobody the wiser as to the lodgings we might have taken.

I say, and I insist upon it, such a step would *ennoble* your friend: and if still you will permit it, I will take the office out of Lovelace's hands; and, to-morrow evening, or on Monday before his time of appointment takes place, will come in a chariot or chaise: and then, my dear, if we get off as I wish, will we make terms (and what terms we please) with them all. My mother will be glad to receive her daughter again I warrant: and Hickman will cry for *joy* on my return: or he shall for *sorrow*.

But you are so very earnestly angry with me for proposing such a step, and have always so much to say for your side of *any* question that I am afraid to urge it further. Only be so good (let me add) as to encourage me to resume it, if, upon further consideration, and upon weighing matters well (and in *this* light, whether best to go off with *me* or with *Lovelace*), you can get over your punctilious regard for my reputation. A woman going away with a *woman* is not so discreditable a thing, surely! and with no view but to *avoid the fellows!*

A time, I hope, will come, that I shall be able to read your affecting narratives without that impatient bitterness, which now boils over in my heart, and would flow to my pen, were I to enter into the particulars of what you write.

But one thing, in your present situation and prospects, let me advise: it is this: That if you *do* go off with Mr. Lovelace, you take the first opportunity to marry.

Give this matter your most serious consideration. Punctilio is out of doors the moment you are out of your father's house. I know how justly severe you have been upon those inexcusable creatures whose giddiness, and even want of decency, have made them, in the *same hour* as I may say, leap from a parent's window to a husband's bed. But, considering Lovelace's character, I repeat my opinion that your *reputation* in the eye of the world requires that no delay be made in *this* point when once you are in his power.

From this critical and distressful situation it shall be my hourly prayers that you may be delivered without blemish to that fair fame, which has hitherto, like your heart, been unspotted.

Your ever affectionate
Anna Howe.

MISS CLARISSA HARLOWE TO MISS HOWE

Saturday afternoon.

ALREADY have I an ecstatic answer, as I may call it, to my letter.

"He promises compliance with my will in every article.

"He will this afternoon, he says, write to Lord M. and to Lady Betty and Lady Sarah, that he is now within view of being the happiest man in the world, if it be not his own fault; since the only woman upon earth that can make him so will be soon out of danger of being another man's; and cannot possibly prescribe any terms to him that he shall not think it his duty to comply with.

"He assures me that I shall govern him as I please, with regard to anything in *his* power towards effecting a reconciliation with my friends": a point he knows my heart is set upon.

"He is afraid that the time will hardly allow of his procuring Miss Charlotte Montague's attendance upon me at St. Albans, as he had proposed she should; because, he understands, she keeps her chamber with a violent cold and sore throat. But both she and her sister, the first moment she is able to go abroad, shall visit me at my private lodgings; and introduce me to Lady Sarah and Lady Betty, or those ladies to me, as I shall choose; and accompany me to town, if I please; and stay as long in it with me as I shall think fit to stay there.

. . . . . .

After all, far as I have gone, I know not but I may still recede: and if I do, a mortal quarrel I suppose will ensue. And what if it does? Could there be any way to escape this Solmes, a breach with Lovelace might make way for the single life to take place.

What to do I know not. The more I think, the more I am embarrassed—and the stronger will be my doubts as the appointed time draws near.

But I will go down and take a little turn in the garden; and deposit this.

Meantime, my dear friend—but what can I desire you to pray for? Adieu then—let me only say—adieu!

MISS CLARISSA HARLOWE TO MISS HOWE

Sunday Morning, April 9.

THE TWO POINTS in your letter which most sensibly concern me: thus you put them:

"Whether I choose not rather to go off [shocking words!] with one of my *own* sex; with my ANNA HOWE—than with one of the *other;* with Mr. LOVELACE?"

And if *not,*

"Whether I should not marry him as soon as possible?"

You know, my dear, my reasons for rejecting your proposal, and even for being earnest that you should not be *known* to be assisting me in an enterprise in which a cruel necessity induced *me* to think of engaging; and for which *you* have not the same plea.

I do assure you, that were I to take this step myself, I would run all risks rather than you should accompany me in it.

But, my dearest, kindest friend, let me tell you that we will *neither* of us take such a step. The manner of putting your questions abundantly convinces me that I ought not, in *your* opinion, to *attempt* it. You no doubt *intend* that I shall *so* take it; and I thank you for the equally polite and forcible conviction.

It is some satisfaction to me (taking the matter in this light) that I had begun to waver before I received your last. And now I tell you that it has absolutely determined me *not* to go off; at least, not to-morrow.

I resolve then, upon the whole, to stand this one trial of Wednesday next—or, perhaps I should rather say, of Tuesday evening, if my father hold his purpose of endeavouring, in person, to make me *read,* or *hear* read, and then *sign,* the settlements. *That, that* must be the greatest trial of all.

My heart, in short, misgives me less when I resolve *this* way than when I think of the *other:* and in so strong and involuntary a bias, the *heart* is, as I may say, *conscience.*

I will close here: and instantly set about a letter of revocation to Mr. Lovelace; take it as he will. It will only be another trial of temper to *him.* To *me* of infinite importance.

MISS CLARISSA HARLOWE TO MISS HOWE

Sunday Morning, April 9.

THIS IS the substance of my letter to Mr. Lovelace:

"That I have reasons of the greatest consequence to *myself* (and which, when known, must satisfy *him*) to suspend, for the present, my intention of leaving my father's house: that I have hopes that matters may be brought to a happy conclusion without taking a step which nothing but the last necessity could justify: and that he may depend upon my promise that I will die rather then consent to marry Mr. Solmes."

And so I am preparing myself to stand the shock of his exclamatory reply. But be that what it will, it cannot affect me so much as the apprehensions of what may happen to me next Tuesday or Wednesday; for now those apprehensions engage my whole attention, and make me sick at the very heart.

Sunday, Four in the Afternoon.

My letter is not yet taken away. If he should not send for it, or take it, and come hither on my not meeting him to-morrow, in doubt of what may have befallen me, what shall I do? Why had I any concerns with this sex—I that was so happy till I knew this man!

I dined in the ivy summer-house. My request to do so was complied with at the first word. To show I meant nothing, I went again into the house with Betty as soon as I had dined. I thought it was not amiss to ask this liberty; the weather seeming to be set in fine. Who knows what Tuesday or Wednesday may produce?

Sunday Evening, Seven o'clock.

There remains my letter still! He is busied, I suppose, in his preparations for to-morrow. But then he has servants. Does the man think he is so *secure* of me, that having appointed he need not give himself any further concern about me till the very moment? He knows how I am beset. He knows not what may happen. I *might* be ill, or still more closely watched or confined than before. The correspondence *might* be discovered. It *might* be necessary to vary the scheme. I *might* be forced into measures which might entirely frustrate my purpose. I *might* have new doubts. I *might* suggest something more convenient for anything he knew. What can the man mean, I wonder! Yet it shall lie; for if he has it any time before the appointed hour it will save me declaring to him personally my changed purpose, and the trouble of contending with him on that score. If he send for it at all he will see by the date that he might have had it in time; and if he be put to any inconvenience from shortness of notice let him take it for his pains.

Monday Morn., April 10, Seven o'clock.

O my dear! There yet lies the letter, just as I left it! I begin now to see this rashness in the light every one else would have seen it in, had I been guilty of it. But what can I do if he come to-day at the appointed time! If he receive not the letter I must see him, or he will think something has befallen me; and certainly will come to the house. As certainly he will be insulted. And what, in that case, may be the consequence! Then I as good as promised that I would take the first opportunity to see him, if I changed my mind, and to give him my reasons for it.

After I have disappointed him more than once before, on a requested *interview* only, it is impossible he should not have *curiosity* at least to know if something has not happened; and whether my mind hold or not in this more *important case*. And yet, as I rashly confirmed my resolution by a second letter, I begin now to doubt it.

Miss Clarissa Harlowe to Miss Howe

Ivy Summer-house, Eleven o'clock.

He has not yet got my letter: and while I was contriving here how to send my officious gaoleress from me, that I might have time for the intended interview, and had hit upon an expedient which I believe would have done, came my aunt, and furnished me with a much better. She saw my little table covered, preparatory to my solitary dinner; and hoped, she told me, that this would be the last day that my friends would be deprived of my company at table.

You may believe, my dear, that the thoughts of meeting Mr. Lovelace, for fear of being discovered, gave me great and visible emotions. She took notice of them. Why these sighs, why these heavings here? said she, patting my neck. O my dear niece, who would have thought so much natural sweetness could be so very unpersuadable?

I could not answer her, and she proceeded: I am come, I doubt, upon a very unwelcome errand. Some things that have been told us yesterday, which came from the mouth of one of the most desperate and insolent men in the world, convince your father, and all of us, that you still find means to write out of the house. Your mother has also some apprehensions concerning yourself, which yet she hopes are groundless; but, however, cannot be easy, nor will be permitted to be easy, if she would, unless (while you remain here in the garden or in this summer-house) you give her the opportunity once more of looking into your closet, your cabinet, and drawers. It will be the better taken if you give me cheerfully your keys.

I artfully made some scruples and not a few complaints of this treatment: after which I not only gave her the keys of all, but even officiously emptied my pockets before her, and invited her to put her fingers in my stays, that she might be sure I had no papers there.

And I assured her that, take what time they pleased, I would not go in to disturb them, but would be either in or near the garden, in this summer-house, or in the cedar one, or about my poultry-yard, or near the great cascade, till I was ordered to return to my prison. With like cunning I said that I supposed the unkind search would not be made till the servants had dined; because I doubted not that the pert Betty Barnes, who knew all the corners of my apartment and closet, would be employed in it.

I may tell you more perhaps, said she (but in confidence, in absolute confidence), if the inquiry within come out in your favour. Do you know of anything above that can be found to your disadvantage?

Some papers they will find, I doubt: but I must take consequences. My brother and sister will be at hand with their good-natured constructions. I am made desperate, and care not what is found.

I hope, I *earnestly* hope, said she, that nothing can be found that will impeach your discretion; and then—but I may say too much——

And away she went, having added to my perplexity.

But I now can think of nothing but this interview. Would to Heaven it were over! To meet to quarrel—but, let him take what measures he will, I will not stay a *moment* with him if he be not quite calm and resigned.

But, after all, should I, *ought* I, to meet him? How have I taken it for granted that I should!

I should have mentioned that in the course of this conversation I besought my aunt to stand my friend, and to put in a word for me on my approaching trial; and to endeavour to procure me *time for consideration,* if I could obtain nothing else.

She told me that, after the ceremony was performed I should have what time I pleased to reconcile myself to my lot before cohabitation.

This put me out of all patience.

She requested of me in *her* turn, she said, that I would resolve to meet them all with cheerful duty, and with a spirit of absolute acquiescence.

Here comes Betty Barnes with my dinner.

. . . . . .

The wench is gone. The time of meeting is at hand. Oh, that he may not come! But should I, or should I not, meet him?

Betty, according to my leading hint to my aunt, boasted to me that she was to be *employed,* as she called it, after she had eaten her own dinner.

She should be sorry, she told me, to have me found out. Yet 'twould be all for my good.

But why do I trouble you (and myself, at such a crisis) with these impertinences? Yet I would forget, if I could, the nearest evil, the interview; because, my apprehensions increasing as the hour is at hand, I should, were my attention to be engrossed by them, be unfit to see him if he does come: and then he will have too much advantage over me, as he will have seeming reason to reproach me with change of resolution.

I dare say we shall be all to pieces. But I don't care for that. It would be hard if I, who have held it out so sturdily to my father and uncles, should not—but he is at the garden door——

. . . . . .

I was mistaken! How may noises *unlike* be made *like* what one fears!

. . . . . .

I will hasten to deposit this. Then I will, for the last time, go to the usual place, in hopes to find that he has got my letter. If he *has,* I will not meet him. If he has *not* I will take it back, and show him what I have written. That will break the ice, as I may say, and save me much circumlocution and reasoning: and a steadfast adherence to that my written mind is all that will be necessary. The interview must be as short as possible; for should it be discovered it would furnish a new and strong pretence for the intended evil of Wednesday next.

Perhaps I shall not be able to write again one while. Perhaps not, till I am the miserable property of that Solmes! But that shall never, never be while I have my senses.

If your servant find nothing from me by Wednesday morning, you may conclude that I can then neither write to you nor receive your favours.

Your
Cl. Harlowe.

MISS CLARISSA HARLOWE TO MISS HOWE

St. Albans, Tuesday Morn., past One.

O MY DEAREST FRIEND!—After what I had resolved upon, as by my former, what shall I write? You will soon hear (if already you have not heard from the mouth of common fame) that your Clarissa Harlowe is gone off with a man!

Rest is departed from me. I have no call for that: and that has no balm for the wounds of my mind.

But will you receive, shall you be *permitted* to receive, my letters after what I have done?

O, my dearest friend! But I must make the best of it. Yet am I convinced that I did a rash and inexcusable thing in meeting him; and all his tenderness, all his vows, cannot pacify my inward reproaches on that account.

The bearer comes to you, my dear, for the little parcel of linen which I sent you with far better and more agreeable hopes.

Send the linen only: except you will favour me with one line, to tell me you love me still; and that you will suspend your censures till you have the whole before you.

Adieu, my dearest friend! I beseech you to love me still. But, alas! what will your mother say? What will mine? What my other relations?—and what my dear Mrs. Norton? And how will my brother and sister triumph?

I cannot at present tell you how or where you can direct to me. For very early shall I leave this place; harassed and fatigued to death. Once more adieu. Pity and pray for

Your
Cl. Harlowe.

Miss Howe to Miss Clarissa Harlowe

Tuesday, Nine o'clock.

I WRITE because you enjoin me to do so. Love you still!—how can I help it if I would? You may believe how I stand aghast, your letter communicating the first news. Good God of heaven and earth!—but what shall I say? I am all impatience for particulars.

My mother will *indeed* be astonished! How can I tell it her? It was but last night that I assured her, and this upon the strength of your *own* assurances, that neither man nor devil would be able to induce you to take a step that was in the least derogatory to the most punctilious honour.

Let nothing escape you in your letters. Direct them for me, however, to Mrs. Knollys's, till further notice.

. . . . . .

Observe, my dear, that I don't blame *you* by all this—your relations only are in fault! Yet how you came to change your mind is the surprising thing.

How to break it to my mother I know not. Yet, if she hear it first from any other, and find I knew it before, she will believe it to be by my connivance! Yet, as I hope to live, I know not how to break it to her.

Let me now repeat my former advice. If you are *not* married by this time, be sure delay not the ceremony. Since things are as they are, I wish it were thought that you were privately married before you went away.

. . . . . .

Miss Lloyd and Miss Biddulph this moment send up their names. They are out of breath, Kitty says, to speak to me—easy to guess their errand! I must see my mother before I see them. I have no way but to show her your letter to clear myself.

I send what you write for. If there be anything else you want that is in my power, command without reserve

Your ever affectionate

ANNA HOWE.

MISS CLARISSA HARLOWE TO MISS HOWE

Tuesday Night.

I THINK myself obliged to thank you, my dear Miss Howe, for your condescension in taking notice of a creature who has occasioned you so much scandal.

Tell me—but yet I am afraid to know—what your mother said.

I long, and yet I dread to be told, what the young ladies my companions, now never more perhaps to be so, say of me.

They cannot, however, say worse of me than I will of myself.

. . . . . .

After I had deposited my letter to you, written down to the last hour, I returned to the ivy summer-house; first taking back my letter from the loose bricks: and I began to hope that I needed not to be so very apprehensive as I have been of next Wednesday. And thus I argued with myself:

"Wednesday cannot possibly be the day they intend, although to intimidate me they may wish me to think it is: for the settlements are unsigned: nor have they been offered me to sign.

"Nor have I reason to doubt but that I shall be able to bring over some of my relations to my party; and, being brought face to face with my brother, that I shall expose his malevolence, and of consequence weaken his power.

"Then, supposing the very worst, challenging the minister as I shall challenge him, he will not presume to proceed: nor surely will Mr. Solmes dare to accept my refusing and struggling hand."

Revolving curiously these things, I congratulated myself that I had resolved against going away with Mr. Lovelace.

As the above kind of reasoning had lessened my apprehensions as to the Wednesday, it added to those I had of meeting Mr. Lovelace—now, as it seemed, not only the nearest but the heaviest evil; principally indeed because *nearest;* for little did I dream (foolish creature that I was, and every way beset!) of the event proving what it has proved. I expected a contention with him, 'tis true, as he had not my letter: but I thought it would be very strange, if I, who had so steadily held out against characters so venerable, against authorities so sacred when I thought them unreasonably exerted, should not find myself more equal to such a trial as this; especially as I had so much reason to be displeased with him for not having taken away my letter.

When the bell rang to call the servants to dinner, Betty came to me and asked if I had any commands before she went to hers; repeating her hint that she should be *employed;* adding that she believed it was expected that I should not come up till she came down, or till I saw my aunt or Miss Hervey.

I asked her some questions about the cascade, which had been out of order, and lately mended; and expressed a curiosity to see how it played, in order to induce her (how cunning to cheat myself, as it proved!) to go thither if she found me not where she left me; it being at a part of the garden most distant from the ivy summer-house.

She could hardly have got into the house when I heard the first signal—Oh, how my heart fluttered! But no time was to be lost. I stepped to the garden door; and seeing a clear coast, unbolted the already unlocked door. And there was he, all impatience, waiting for me.

A panic next to fainting seized me when I saw him. My heart seemed convulsed; and I trembled so, that I should hardly have kept my feet had he not supported me.

Fear nothing, dearest creature, said he. Let us hasten away—the chariot is at hand and, by this sweet condescension, you have obliged me beyond expression or return.

Recovering my spirits a little, as he kept drawing me after him, O Mr. Lovelace, said I, I cannot go with you—*indeed* I cannot—I wrote you word so—let go my hand and you shall see my letter. It has lain there from yesterday morning till within this half-hour. I bid you watch to the last for a letter from me, lest I should be obliged to revoke the appointment; and had you followed the direction you would have found it.

I have been watched, my dearest life, said he, half out of breath—I have been watched in every step I took: and my trusty servant has been watched too, ever since Saturday; and dared not to come near your wall. And here we shall be discovered in a moment. Speed away, my charmer—this is the moment of your deliverance—if you neglect this opportunity you *never* can have such another.

What is it you mean, sir? Let go my hand: for I tell you (struggling vehemently) that I will sooner die than go with you.

Good God! said he, with a look of wildness and surprise, what is it I hear! But (still drawing me after him as he retreated farther from the door) it is no time to argue—by all that's good you must go. Surely you cannot doubt my honour, nor give me cause to question your own.

As you value me, Mr. Lovelace, urge me no further. I come fixed and resolved. Let me give you the letter I had written. My further reasons shall follow; and they will convince you that I ought not to go.

Nothing, madam, can convince me. By all that's sacred I will not leave you. To leave you now would be to lose you for ever——

Am I to be thus compelled? interrupted I, with equal indignation and vehemence. Let go my hands. I am resolved not to go with you—and I will convince you that I *ought* not.

All my friends expect you, madam—all your own are determined against you. Wednesday next is the day, the important, perhaps the fatal day! Would you stay to be Solmes's wife? Can this be your determination at last?

No, never, never, will I be that man's—but I will not go with you! (Draw me not thus—how dare you, sir? I would not have seen you but to tell you so.) I had not met you but for fear you would have been guilty of some rashness. And, once more, I will *not* go. What mean you!—striving with all my force to get from him.

What can have possessed my angel, said he (quitting my hands, and with a gentler voice) that after so much ill-usage from your relations; vows so solemn on my part; an affection so ardent; you stab me with a refusal to stand by your own appointment?

We have no time to talk, Mr. Lovelace. I will give you my reasons at a better opportunity. I cannot go with you now. And, once more, urge me no further—surely I am not to be compelled by everybody!

I see how it is, said he, with a dejected but passionate air. What a severe fate is mine! At length your spirit is subdued! Your brother and sister have prevailed; and I must give up all my hopes to a wretch so *truly* despicable——

Once more I tell you, interrupted I, I never will be his. All may end on Wednesday differently from what you expect——

And it may *not!* And then, good Heaven!——

It is to be their last effort, as I have reason to believe——

And I have reason to believe so too—since, if you stay, you will inevitably be Solmes's wife.

Not so, interrupted I. I have obliged them in one point. They will be in good humour with me. I shall gain time at least. I have several ways to gain time.

And what, madam, will gaining time do? O my dearest, dearest life! let me beseech you not to run a risk of this consequence. I can convince you that it will be *more* than a risk if you go back, that you will on Wednesday next be Solmes's wife.

While I have any room for hope it concerns *your* honour, Mr. Lovelace, as well as mine (if you have the value for me you pretend, and wish me to believe you), that my conduct in this great point should justify my prudence.

Your prudence, madam! When has that been questionable? Yet what stead has either your prudence or your duty stood you in with people so strangely determined?

And then he pathetically enumerated the different instances of the harsh treatment I had met with; imputing all to the malice and caprice of a brother who set everybody against him: and insisting that I had no other way to bring about a reconciliation with my father and uncles than by putting myself out of the power of my brother's inveterate malice.

Your brother's whole reliance, proceeded he, has been upon your easiness to bear his insults. Your whole family will seek to *you,* when you have freed yourself from this disgraceful oppression. When they know you are with those who *can* and *will* right you, they will give up to you your own estate. Why then, putting his arm round me, and again drawing me with a gentle force after him, do you hesitate a moment? Now is the time. Fly with me then, I beseech you, my dearest creature! Trust your persecuted adorer. Have we not suffered in the same cause? If any imputations are cast upon you, give me the honour (*as I shall be found to deserve it*) to call you mine; and, when you are so, shall I not be able to protect both your person and character?

Urge me no more, Mr. Lovelace. I am convinced that Wednesday next (if I had time I would give you my reasons) is not intended to be the day we had both so much dreaded: and if after that day shall be over I find my friends determined in Mr. Solmes's favour, I will then contrive some way to meet you with Miss Howe, who is not your enemy: and when the solemnity has passed I shall think that step a duty which *till* then will be criminal to take: since now my father's authority is unimpeached by any greater.

Dearest madam——

Nay, Mr. Lovelace, if you now dispute—if, after this more favourable declaration than I had the thought of making, you are not satisfied, I shall know what to think both of your gratitude and generosity.

The case, madam, admits not of this alternative. I am all gratitude upon it. I cannot express how much I should be delighted with the charming hope you have given me, were you not next Wednesday, if you stay, to be another man's.

Depend, depend upon it, I will die sooner than be Mr. Solmes's. If you would have me rely upon *your* honour, why should you doubt of *mine?*

I doubt not your *honour,* madam; your *power* is all I doubt. You never, never can have such another opportunity. Dearest creature, permit me. And he was again drawing me after him.

Whither, sir, do you draw me? Leave me this moment. Do you seek to keep me till my return shall grow dangerous or impracticable? This moment let me go if you would have me think tolerably of you.

My happiness, madam, both here and hereafter, and the safety of all your implacable family, depend upon this moment.

To Providence, Mr. Lovelace, and to the law, will I leave the safety of my friends. Shall *I,* to promote your happiness, as you call it, destroy all my future peace of mind?

You trifle with me, my dear life, just as our better prospects begin to open. The way is clear; just now it is clear; but you may be prevented in a moment. What is it you doubt? May I perish eternally if your will shall not be a law to me in everything! All my relations expect you. Your own appointment calls upon you. Next Wednesday—dearest creature! think of next Wednesday! And to what is it I urge you, but to take a step that sooner than any other will reconcile you to all whom you have most reason to value in your family?

Let me judge for myself, sir. Do not you, who blame my friends for endeavouring to compel me, *yourself* seek to compel me. I won't bear it. Your earnestness gives me greater apprehensions and greater reluctance. Let me go back, then—let me, before it is too late, go back, that it may not be worse for both. What mean you by this forcible treatment? Is it thus that I am to judge of the entire submission to my will which you have so often vowed? Unhand me this moment, or I will cry out for help.

I will obey you, my dearest creature!—and quitted my hand with a look full of tender despondency, that, knowing the violence of his temper, half-concerned me for him. Yet I was hastening from him when, with a solemn air, looking upon his sword, but catching, as it were, his hand from it, he folded both his arms, as if a sudden thought had recovered him from an intended rashness.

Stay one moment—but one moment stay, O best beloved of my soul! Your retreat is secure, if you *will* go: the key lies down at the door. But, O madam, next *Wednesday,* and you are Mr. Solmes's! Fly me not so eagerly—hear me but a few words.

When near the garden door I stopped; and was the more satisfied, as I saw the key there, by which I could let myself in again at pleasure. But, being uneasy lest I should be missed, I told him I could stay no longer. I had already stayed too long. I would write to him all my reasons. And depend upon it, Mr. Lovelace, said I (just upon the point of stooping for the key, in order to return) I will die rather than have that man. You know what I have promised if I find myself in danger.

One word, madam, however; one word more (approaching me, his arms still folded, as if, I thought, he would not be tempted to mischief). Remember only that I come at your appointment, to redeem you, at the hazard of my life, from your gaolers and persecutors, with a resolution, God is my witness, or may He for ever blast me! (that was his shocking imprecation) to be a father, uncle, brother, and, as I humbly hoped, in your own good time, a *husband* to you, all in one. But since I find you are so ready to cry out for help against me, which must bring down upon me the vengeance of all your family, I am contented to run all risks. I will not ask you to retreat with *me;* I will attend you into the garden, and into the *house,* if I am not intercepted. Nay, be not surprised, madam. The help you would have called for, I will attend you to; for I will face them all: but not as a revenger, if they provoke me not too much. You shall see what I can further bear for your sake. And let us both see if expostulation, and the behaviour of a gentleman *to* them, will not procure me the treatment due to a gentleman *from* them.

Had he offered to draw his sword upon himself I was prepared to have despised him for supposing me such a poor novice as to be intimidated by an artifice so common. But this resolution, uttered with so serious an air, of accompanying me in to my friends, made me gasp with terror.

What mean you, Mr. Lovelace? said I: I beseech you leave me—leave me, sir, I beseech you.

Excuse me, madam! I beg you to excuse me. I have long enough skulked like a thief about these lonely walls. Long, too long, have I borne the insults of your brother, and other of your relations. I am desperate. I have but this one chance for it; for is not the day after to-morrow *Wednesday?* You shall see, madam, what I will bear for your sake. My sword shall be put sheathed into your hands (and he offered it to me in the scabbard). My heart, if you please, clapping one hand upon his breast, shall afford a sheath to your brother's sword. Life is nothing if I lose you. Be pleased, madam, to show me the way into the garden; (moving towards the door). I will attend you, though to my fate! But too happy, be it what it will, if I receive it in your presence. Lead on, dear creature! (putting his sword into his belt)—you shall see what I can bear for you. And he stooped and took up the key; and offered it to the lock; but dropped it again, without opening the door, upon my earnest expostulations.

What can you mean, Mr. Lovelace? said I. Would you thus expose *yourself?* Would you thus expose *me?* Is this your generosity? Is everybody to take advantage thus of the weakness of my temper?

And I wept. I could not help it.

He threw himself upon his knees at my feet. Who can bear, said he (with an ardour that could not be feigned, his own eyes glistening), who can bear to behold such sweet emotion? O charmer of my heart (and, respectfully still kneeling, he took my hand with both his, pressing it to his lips), command me *with* you, command me *from* you; in every way I am all implicit obedience. But I appeal to all you know of your relations' cruelty to *you,* their determined malice against *me,* and as determined favour to the *man* you tell me you hate I appeal to everything you know, to all you have suffered, whether you have not reason to be apprehensive of *that* Wednesday which is my terror! Whether you can possibly have such another opportunity—the chariot ready: my friends with impatience expecting the result of *your own* appointment: a man whose will shall be entirely your will, imploring you thus, on his knees, imploring you to be *your own mistress;* that is all: *nor will I ask for your favour but as upon full proof I shall appear to deserve it.* Fortune, alliance, unobjectible! O my beloved creature! pressing my hand once more to his lips, let not such an opportunity slip. You never, never, will have such another.

I bid him rise. He arose; and I told him that were I not thus unaccountably hurried by his impatience, I doubted not to convince him that both he and I had looked upon next Wednesday with greater apprehension than was necessary. I was proceeding to give him my reasons; but he broke in upon me——

Had I, madam, but the shadow of a probability to hope what *you* hope, I would be all obedience and resignation. But the licence is actually got: the parson is provided: that pedant Brand is the man. O my dearest creature, do these preparations mean only a trial?

You know not, sir, were the worst to be intended, and weak as you think me, what a spirit I have: you know not what I can do, and how I can resist when I think myself meanly or unreasonably dealt with: nor do you know what I have already suffered, what I have already borne, knowing to whose unbrotherly instigations all is to be ascribed——

I may expect all things, madam, interrupted he, from the nobleness of your mind. But your spirits may fail you. What may not be apprehended from the invincible temper of a father so positive to a daughter so dutiful? Fainting will not save you: they will not, perhaps, be sorry for such an effect of their barbarity. What will signify expostulations against a ceremony performed? Must not *all,* the *dreadful all* follow, that is torture to my heart but to think of? Nobody to appeal to, of what avail will your resistance be against the consequences of a rite witnessed to by the imposers of it; and those your nearest relations?

I was sure, I said, of procuring a delay at least. Many ways I had to procure delay. Nothing could be so fatal to us both as for me now to be found with him. My apprehensions on this score, I told him, grew too strong for my heart. I should think very hardly of him if he sought to detain me longer. But his acquiescence should engage my gratitude.

And then stooping to take up the key to let myself into the garden, he started, and looked as if he had heard somebody near the door, on the inside; clapping his hand on his sword.

This frightened me so that I thought I should have sunk down at his feet. But he instantly reassured me: he thought, he said, he had heard a rustling against the door: but *had* it been so the noise would have been stronger. It was only the effect of his apprehension for me.

And then taking up the key, he presented it to me. If you *will* go, madam—yet I cannot, cannot leave you! I must enter the garden with you—forgive me, but I *must* enter the garden with you.

And will you, will you thus ungenerously, Mr. Lovelace, take advantage of my fears?—of my wishes to prevent mischief?

Dearest creature! interrupted he, holding my hand as I tremblingly offered to put the key to the lock. Let *me,* if you *will* go, open the door. But once more consider, could you possibly obtain that delay which seems to be your only dependence, whether you may not be closer confined? I know they have already had *that* in consideration. Will you not, in this case, be prevented from corresponding either with Miss Howe or with me? Who then shall assist you in your escape, if escape you would? If you go back it must be from the impulses of a yielding (which you'll call a dutiful) heart, tired and teased out of your own will.

I have no patience, sir, to be thus constrained. Must I never be at liberty to follow my own judgment? Be the consequence what it may, I will not be thus constrained.

And then, freeing my hand, I again offered the key to the door.

Down the ready kneeler dropped between me and that: And can you, can you, madam, once more on my knees let me ask you, look with an indifferent eye upon the evils that may follow? Provoked as I have been, and triumphed over as I shall be if your brother succeeds, my *own* heart shudders, at times, at the thoughts of what *must* happen; and can *yours* be unconcerned? Let me beseech you, dearest creature, to consider all these things; and lose not this only opportunity. My intelligence——

Never, Mr. Lovelace, interrupted I, give so much credit to the words of a traitor.

I was once more offering the key to the lock when, starting from his knees, with a voice of affrightment, loudly whispering, and as if out of breath, *They are at the door, my beloved creature!* And taking the key from me, he fluttered with it, as if he would double-lock it. And instantly a voice from within cried out, bursting against the door, as if to break it open, the person repeating his violent pushes: *Are you there? Come up this moment!—this moment! Here they are—here they are both together! Your pistol this moment!—your gun!* Then another push, and another. He at the same moment drew his sword, and clapping it naked under his arm, took both my trembling hands in his; and, drawing me swiftly after him: Fly, fly, my charmer; this moment is all you have for it, said he. Your brother!—your uncles!—or this Solmes! They will instantly burst the door. Fly, my dearest life, if you would not be more cruelly used than ever—if you would not see two or three murders committed at your feet, fly, fly, I beseech you.

Now behind me, now before me, now on this side, now on that, turned I my affrighted face in the same moment; expecting a furious brother here, armed servants there, an enraged sister screaming, and a father armed with terror in his countenance more dreadful than even the drawn sword which I saw, or those I apprehended. I ran as fast as he; yet knew not that I ran; my fears adding wings to my feet, at the same time that they took all power of thinking from me. My fears, which probably would not have suffered me to know what course to take, had I not had him to urge and draw me after him: especially as I beheld a man, who must have come out of the door, keeping us in his eye, running now towards us; then back to the garden; beckoning and calling to others, whom I supposed *he* saw, although the turning of the wall hindered *me* from seeing them; and whom I imagined to be my brother, my father, and their servants.

Thus terrified, I was got out of sight of the door in a very few minutes: and then, although quite breathless between running and apprehension, he put my arm under his, his drawn sword in the other hand, and hurried me on still faster: my voice, however, contradicting my action; crying, No, no, no, all the while, straining my neck to look back, as long as the walls of the garden and park were within sight, and till he brought me to the chariot: where, attending, were two armed servants of his own, and two of Lord M.'s, on horseback.

Here I must suspend my relation for a while: for now I am come to this said period of it my indiscretion stares me in the face; and my shame and my grief give me a compunction that is more poignant methinks than if I had a dagger in my heart. To have it to reflect, that I should so inconsiderately give in to an interview which, had I known either myself or him, or in the least considered the circumstances of the case, I might have supposed would put me into the power of his resolution, and out of that of my own reason.

For, might I not have believed that *he,* who thought he had cause to apprehend that he was on the point of losing a person who had cost him so much pains and trouble, would not hinder her, if possible, from returning?

But if it shall come out that the person within the garden was his corrupted implement, employed to frighten me away with him, do you think, my dear, that I shall not have reason to hate him and myself still more? I hope his heart cannot be so deep and so vile a one: I hope it cannot! But how came it to pass that one man could get out at the garden door, and no more? How that that man kept aloof, as it were, and pursued us not; nor ran back to alarm the house? My fright and my distance would not let me be certain; but really this man, as I now recollect, had the air of that vile Joseph Leman.

Would to Heaven that I had stood it, however! Then, if I had afterwards done what now I have been prevailed upon, or perhaps foolishly frightened to do, I should not have been stung so much by inward reproach as now I am: and this would have been a great evil avoided.

You know, my dear, that your Clarissa's mind was ever above

justifying her own failings by those of others. God forgive those of my friends who have acted cruelly by me! But their faults *are* their own, and not excuses for mine. And mine began early: for I ought not to have corresponded with him.

O the vile encroacher! how my indignation, at times, rises at him! Thus to lead a young creature (too much indeed relying upon her own strength) from evil to evil! This last evil, although the *remote* yet *sure* consequence of my first—my prohibited correspondence! by a father *early* prohibited.

But I thought I could *proceed* or *stop* as I pleased. I supposed it concerned *me, more than any other, to be the arbitress of the quarrels of unruly spirits*—and now I find my presumption punished—punished, as other sins frequently are, by *itself!*

And what vexes me more is, that it is plain to me now, by all his behaviour, that he had as great a confidence in my weakness as I had in my own strength. And so, in a point entirely relative to my honour, he has triumphed; for he has not been mistaken in me, while I have in myself!

You charge me *to marry the first opportunity*. Ah! my dear! *another* of the blessed effects of my folly. That's as much in my power now as—as I am myself! And can I besides give a sanction immediately to his deluding arts? You don't know, nor can you imagine, my dear, how I am mortified!—how much I am sunk in my own opinion—I that was proposed for an example, truly, to others!

. . . . . .

This is the Wednesday morning I dreaded so much, that I once thought of it as the day of my doom: but of the Monday, it is plain, I ought to have been most apprehensive. Had I stayed, and had the worst I dreaded happened, my friends would then have been answerable for the consequences, if any bad ones had followed: but now I have this *only* consolation left me, that I have cleared *them* of blame and taken it all upon *myself!*

[Omitted here is a long letter, Lovelace to Joseph Leman, giving specific directions for tricking Clarissa in the garden scene, which Clarissa's letter records. Ed.]

MR. LOVELACE TO JOHN BELFORD, ESQ.

St. Albans, Monday night.

I SNATCH a few moments while my beloved is retired (as I hope, to rest) to perform my promise. No pursuit—nor have I apprehensions of any; though I must make my charmer dread that there will be one.

And now, let me tell thee, that never was joy so complete as mine! But let me inquire—is not the angel flown away?

. . . . . .

Oh, no! she is in the next apartment! Securely mine!—mine for ever!

O ecstasy!—My heart will burst my breast,
To leap into her bosom!

I knew that the whole stupid family were in a combination to do my business for me. I told thee that they were all working for me like so many underground moles; and still more blind than the moles are said to be, unknowing that they did so. I myself, the director of their principal motions; which falling in with the malice of their little hearts they took to be all their own.

But did I say my joy was perfect? Oh, no! It receives some abatement from my disgusted pride. For how can I endure to think that I owe more to her relations' persecutions than to her favour for me?

Tuesday, Day-dawn.

Yet it must be allowed that such a sudden transition must affect her; must ice her over. When a little more used to her new situation; when her hurries are at an end; when she sees how religiously I shall observe all her INJUNCTIONS, she will undoubtedly have the gratitude to distinguish between the confinement she has escaped from and the liberty she has reason to rejoice in.

Miss Clarissa Harlowe to Miss Howe

Wednesday, April 12.

I will pursue my melancholy story.

Being thus hurried to the chariot, it would have been to no purpose to have refused entering into it, had he not in my fright lifted me in as he did: and it instantly drove away at full gallop, and stopped not till it brought us to St. Albans; which was just as the day shut in.

I thought I should have fainted several times by the way. With uplifted hands and eyes, God protect me, said I often to myself! Can it be I that am here! My eyes running over, and my heart ready to burst with sighs as involuntary as my flight.

How different, how inexpressibly different, the gay wretch; visibly triumphing (as I could not but construe his almost rapturous joy) in the success of his arts! But overflowing with complimental flourishes, yet respectfully distant his address, all the way we *flew;* for that, rather than *galloping,* was the motion of the horses; which took, as I believe, a roundabout way to prevent being traced.

Think, my dear, what were my thoughts on alighting from the chariot; having no attendant of my own sex; no clothes but what I had on, and those little suited for such a journey as I had *already* taken, and was *still* to take: neither hood nor hat, nor anything but a handkerchief about my neck and shoulders: fatigued to death: my mind still more fatigued than my body: and in such a foam the horses that every one in the inn we put up at guessed (they could not do otherwise) that I was a young giddy creature who had run away from her friends.

The mistress of the house, whom he sent in to me, showed me another apartment; and, seeing me ready to faint, brought me hartshorn and water; and then, upon my desiring to be left alone for half an hour, retired: for I found my heart ready to burst, on revolving everything in my thoughts: and the moment she was gone, fastening the door, I threw myself into an old great chair, and gave way to a violent flood of tears; which a little relieved me.

Mr. Lovelace, sooner than I wished, sent up the gentlewoman, who pressed me, in his name, to admit my brother or to come down to him: for he had told her I was his sister; and that he had brought me, against my will and without warning, from a friend's house, where I had been all the winter, in order to prevent my marrying against the consent of my friends; to whom he was now conducting me; and that, having given me no time for a travelling dress, I was greatly offended at him.

So, my dear, your frank, your open-hearted friend, was forced to countenance this tale; which indeed suited me the better, because I was unable for some time to talk, speak, or look up; and so my dejection, and grief, and silence, might very well pass before the gentlewoman and her niece who attended me, as a fit of sullenness.

The room I was in being a bedchamber, I chose to go down, at his repeated message, attended by the mistress of the house, to that in which he was. He approached me with great respect, yet not exceeding a brotherly politeness, where a brother *is* polite; and, calling me his dearest sister, asked after the state of my mind; and hoped I would forgive him; for never brother half so well loved a sister as he me.

When we were alone, he besought me (I cannot say but with all the tokens of a passionate and respectful tenderness) to be better reconciled to myself, and to him: he repeated all the vows of honour and inviolable affection that he ever made me: he promised to be wholly governed by me in every future step: he asked me to give him leave to propose, whether I chose to set out next day to either of his aunts?

I was silent.

Whether I chose to have private lodgings procured for me in either of those ladies' neighbourhood, as were once my thoughts?

I was still silent.

Whether I chose to go to either of Lord M.'s seats; that of Berks, or that in the county we were in?

In lodgings, I said, anywhere, where he was not to be.

He had *promised this,* he owned; and he would religiously keep to his word as soon as he found all danger of pursuit over; and that I was settled to my mind. But, if the place were indifferent to me, London was the safest, and the most private:

and his relations should all visit me there the moment I thought fit to admit them. His Cousin Charlotte, particularly, should attend me as my companion if I would accept of her, as soon as she was able to go abroad.

I told him, I wished not to go (immediately, however, and in the frame I was in, and likely not to be out of) to any of his relations: that my reputation was concerned to have *him* absent from me: that, if I were in some private lodging (the meaner the less to be suspected, as it would be known that I went away by his means; and he would be supposed to have provided me handsome accommodation) it would be most suitable both to my mind and to my situation: that this might be best, I should think, in the country for *me;* in town for *him.*

Even messages and letters, where none used to be brought, would occasion inquiry. He had not provided a lodging anywhere, supposing I would choose to go either to London, where accommodation of that sort might be fixed upon in an hour's time, or to Lady Betty's; or to Lord M.'s Hertfordshire seat, where was housekeeper an excellent woman, Mrs. Greme, such another as my Norton.

He had lodgings in town; but he did not offer to propose them. He knew I would have more objection to go to them than I could have to go to Lord M.'s or to Lady Betty's.

No doubt of it, I replied, with such an indignation in my manner as made him run over with professions, that he was far from proposing them or wishing for my acceptance of them.

I thought myself, I said, extremely unhappy. I knew not what to determine upon; my reputation now, no doubt, utterly ruined: destitute of clothes; unfit to be seen by anybody: my very indigence, as I might call it, proclaiming my folly to every one who saw me; who would suppose that I had been taken at advantage, or had given an undue one; and had no power over either my will or my actions: that I could not but think I had been dealt artfully with: that he had seemed to have taken what he might suppose the just measure of my weakness, founded on my youth and inexperience: that I could not forgive myself for meeting him: that my heart bled for the distress of my father and mother on this occasion: that I would give the world, and all my hopes in it, to have been still in my father's house, whatever had been my usage: that, let him protest and vow what he would, I saw something low and selfish in his love, that he could study to put a young creature upon making such a sacrifice of her duty and conscience: when a person actuated by a generous love must seek to oblige the object of it in everything essential to her honour and to her peace of mind.

"He was inexpressibly grieved and surprised, he said, to hear me say he had acted *artfully* by me. He came provided, according to my *confirmed* appointment" (*a wretch, to upbraid me thus!*) "to redeem me from my persecutors; and little expected a change of sentiment, and that he should have so much difficulty to prevail upon me as he had met with: that perhaps I might think his offer to go *into the garden with me,* and to face my assembled relations, was a piece of *art* only: but that if I did I wronged him: since, to this hour, seeing my excessive uneasiness, he wished with all his soul he had been permitted to accompany me in. It was always his maxim to brave a threatened danger."

So, my dear, what I have to do is to hold myself inexcusable for meeting such a determined and audacious spirit; that's all!

He concluded this part of his talk with saying: "That he doubted not but that had he attended me in he should have come off in every one's opinion so well, that he should have had general leave to renew his visits."

He went on: "He must be so bold as to tell me that he should have paid a visit of this kind (but indeed accompanied by several of his trusty friends) had I *not* met him; and that very afternoon, too; for he could not tamely let the dreadful Wednesday come without making some effort to change their determinations."

What, my dear, was to be done with such a man!

"As to what further remained for him to say, in answer to what I had said, he hoped I would pardon him; but, upon his soul, he was concerned, infinitely concerned, he repeated (his colour and his voice rising) that it was *necessary* for him to observe how much I chose rather to have run the risk of being Solmes's wife than to have it in my power to reward a man who, I must forgive him, had been as much insulted on *my* account as *I* had been on *his*—who had watched my commands and (pardon me, madam) every *changeable* motion of your pen, all hours, in all weathers, and with a cheerfulness and ardour that nothing but the most faithful and obsequious passion could inspire."

I now, my dear, began to revive into a little more warmth of attention.

"And all, madam, for what?" How I stared! for he stopped then a moment or two. *"Only,* went he on, to prevail upon you to free yourself from ungenerous and base oppression——"

Sir, sir! indignantly said I——

"Hear me but out, dearest madam! My heart is full—I *must* speak what I have to say—to be told (for your words are yet in my ears and at my heart!) that you would give the world, *and all your hopes in it,* to have been still in your cruel and gloomy father's house——"

Not a word, sir, against my father! I will not bear that——

"Whatever had been your usage: and you have a credulity, madam, against all probability, if you believe you should have avoided being Solmes's wife: that I have put you upon *sacrificing your duty and conscience.* Yet, dearest creature! see you not the contradiction that your warmth of temper has surprised you into, when the reluctance you showed to the last to leave your persecutors has cleared your conscience from the least reproach of this sort——?"

O sir! sir! are you so critical then? Are you so light in your anger as to dwell upon words——?

"Forgive me, madam—I have just done. Have I not, in your own opinion, hazarded my life to redeem you from oppression? Yet is not my reward, after all, precarious? For, madam, *have you not conditioned with me* (and, hard as the condition is, *most sacredly will I observe it*) *that all my hope must be remote?* That you are determined to have it in your power *to favour or reject me totally,* as you please?"

See, my dear! In every respect my condition changed for the worse!

"And have you not furthermore declared, proceeded he, *that you will engage to renounce me for ever, if your friends insist upon that cruel renunciation as the terms of being reconciled to you?*

"But nevertheless, madam, all the merit of having saved you from an odious compulsion shall be mine. I glory in it, though I were to lose you for ever—*as I see I am but too likely to do,* from your present displeasure; and especially *if your friends insist upon the terms you are ready to comply with.*

"That you are *your own mistress,* through *my* means, is, I repeat, my boast. *As such,* I humbly implore your favour—and *that only upon the conditions I have yielded to hope for it.* As I do now *thus humbly* (the proud wretch falling on one knee) your forgiveness for so long detaining your ear, and for all the plain-dealing that my undesigning heart would not be denied to utter by my lips."

O sir, pray rise! Let the *obliged* kneel if one of us must kneel! But nevertheless, proceed not in this strain I *beseech* you. You have had a great *deal* of trouble about me: but had you let me know *in time,* that you expected to be rewarded for it at the price of my duty, I should have spared you much of it.

Far be it from me, sir, to depreciate merit so *extraordinary.* But let me say that had it not been for the forbidden correspondence I was teased by you into; and which I had not continued but because I thought you a sufferer from my friends; I had not been either confined or ill-treated: nor would my brother's low-meant violence have had a foundation to work upon.

I am far from thinking my case would have been so very desperate as you imagine, had I stayed. My father loved me in his heart: he would not see me before; and I wanted *only* to *see* him, and to be *heard;* and a *delay of his sentence* was the least thing I expected from the trial I was to stand.

You are boasting of your merits, sir: let merit be your boast: nothing else can attract me. If *personal* considerations had principal weight with me, either in Solmes's disfavour, or in your favour, I should despise *myself:* if you value yourself upon them in preference to the *person* of the poor Solmes I shall despise *you!*

You may glory in your fancied merits in getting me away: but the cause of *your* glory, I tell you plainly, is *my* shame.

All that I desire of you now is to leave it to myself to seek for some private abode: to take the chariot with you to London or elsewhere: and, if I have any further occasion for your assistance and protection I will signify it to you, and be still *further* obliged to you.

You are warm, my dearest life! But indeed there is no occasion for it. Had I any views unworthy of my faithful love for you I should not have been so honest in my declarations.

Then he began again to vow the sincerity of his intentions.

But I took him up short: I am willing to *believe* you, sir. It would be insupportable but to suppose there were a *necessity* for such solemn declarations (at this he seemed to collect himself, as I may say, into a little more circumspection). If I thought there *were,* I would not sit with you here, in a public inn, I assure you, although *cheated* hither, as far as I know, by methods (you must excuse me, sir!) which but to *suspect* will hardly let me have patience either with you or with myself. But no more of this just now: let me, I beseech you, *good sir,* bowing (I was very angry!) let me only know whether you intend to leave me; or whether I have only escaped from one confinement to another?

Cheated hither, as far as you know, madam! Let you *know* (and with that air too, charming, though grievous to my heart!) *if you have only escaped from one confinement to another.* Amazing! perfectly amazing! And can there be a necessity for me to answer this? You are absolutely your own mistress. *The moment you are in a place of safety* I will leave you. To one condition only, give me leave to beg your consent: "That, make up how you please with your relations, you will never marry any other man while I am living and single, unless I should be so wicked as to give new cause for high displeasure."

I hesitate not to confirm this promise, sir, upon your *own* condition. In what manner do you expect me to confirm it?

Only, madam, by your word.

Then I never will.

He had the assurance (*I was now in his power*) to salute me as a sealing of my promise, as he called it. His motion was so sudden that I was not aware of it. It would have looked *affected* to be very angry; yet I could not be pleased, considering this as a *leading freedom* from a spirit so audacious and encroaching: and he might see that I was not.

I broke from him to write to you my preceding letter; but refused to send it by his servant, as I told you. The mistress of the house helped me to a messenger, who was to carry what you should give him to Lord M.'s seat in Hertfordshire, directed for Mrs. Greme, the housekeeper there. And early in the morning, for fear of pursuit, we were to set out that way: and there he proposed to exchange the chariot-and-six for a chaise-and-pair of his own, which he had at that seat, as it would be a less-noticed conveyance.

I looked over my little stock of money; and found it to be no more than seven guineas and some silver: the rest of my stock was but fifty guineas, and that five more than I thought it was, when my sister challenged me as to the sum I had by me: and those I left in my escritoire, little intending to go away with him.

Indeed my case abounds with a shocking number of indelicate circumstances. Among the rest, I was forced to account to *him*, who knew I could have no clothes but what I had on, how I came to have linen with you (for he could not but know I sent for it); lest he should imagine I had an early design to go away with him, and made that a *part of the preparation*.

. . . . . .

Before five o'clock (Tuesday morning) the maidservant came up to tell me my *brother* was ready, and that breakfast also waited for me in the parlour. I went down with a heart as heavy as my eyes, and received great acknowledgments and compliments from him on being so soon dressed, and ready (as he interpreted it) to continue our journey.

He had the thought, which I had not (for what had I to do with thinking, who had it not when I stood most in need of it?) to purchase for me a velvet hood, and a short cloak, trimmed with silver, without saying anything to me. He must reward himself, the artful encroacher said before the landlady and her maids and niece, for his forethought; and would salute his pretty sullen sister! He took his reward; and, as he said, a tear with it. While he assured me, still before them (a vile wretch!), that I had nothing to fear from meeting with parents who so dearly loved me.

How could I be complaisant, my dear, to such a man as this?

When we had got into the chariot, and it began to move, he asked me whether I had any objection to go to Lord M.'s Hertfordshire seat? His lordship, he said, was at his Berkshire one.

I told him I chose not to go, *as yet,* to any of his relations; for that would indicate a plain defiance to my own. My choice was to go to a private lodging, and for him to be at a distance from me: at least till I heard how things were taken by my friends.

He proposed, and I consented, to put up at an inn in the neighbourhood of *The Lawn* (as he called Lord M.'s seat in this county), since I chose not to go thither. And here I got two hours to myself: which I told him I should pass in writing another letter to you and in one to my sister, to apprise the family (whether they were solicitous about it or not) that I was well; and to beg that my clothes, some particular books, and the fifty guineas I had left in my escritoire, might be sent me.

He asked if I had considered whither to have them directed?

Indeed not I, I told him: I was a stranger to——

So was he, he interrupted me; but it struck him by chance——

But, added he, I will tell you, madam, how it shall be managed. If you don't choose to go to London, it is, nevertheless, best that your relations should *think* you there; for then they will absolutely despair of finding you. If you write, be pleased to direct: To be left for you at Mr. Osgood's, near Soho Square.

I had no objection to this: and I have written accordingly. But what answer I shall have, or whether any, that is what gives me no small anxiety.

This, however, is one consolation: that if I have an answer, and although my brother should be the writer, it cannot be more severe than the treatment I have of late received from him and my sister.

Mr. Lovelace stayed out about an hour and a half; and then came in; impatiently sending up to me no less than four times, to desire admittance. But I sent him word as often, that I was busy; and at last, that I should be so till dinner were ready.

Mrs. Greme came to pay her *duty* to me, as Mr. Lovelace called it; and was very urgent with me to go to her lord's house; letting me know what handsome things she had heard her lord, and his two nieces, and all the family, say of me; and what wishes for several months past they had put up for the honour she now hoped would soon be done them all.

This gave me some satisfaction, as it confirmed from the mouth of a very good sort of woman all that Mr. Lovelace had told me.

Upon inquiry about a private lodging, she recommended me to a sister-in-law of hers, eight miles from thence—where I now am. And what pleased me the better was that Mr. Lovelace (of whom I could see she was infinitely observant) obliged her, of his own motion, to accompany me in the chaise; himself riding on horseback, with his two servants and one of Lord M.'s. And here we arrived about four o'clock.

But, as I told you in my former, the lodgings are inconvenient. Mr. Lovelace indeed found great fault with them: and told Mrs. Greme (who had said that they were not worthy of us) that they came not up even to her account of them. As the house was a mile from town, it was not proper for him, he said, to be so far distant from me, lest anything should happen: and yet the apartments were not separate and distinct enough for me to like them, he was sure.

This must be agreeable enough from him, you will believe.

Mrs. Greme and I had a good deal of talk in the chaise about him: she was very easy and free in her answers to all I asked; and has, I find, a very serious turn.

I led her on to say to the following effect; some part of it not unlike what Lord M.'s dismissed bailiff had said before; by which I find that all the servants have a like opinion of him.

"That Mr. Lovelace was a generous man: that it was hard to say whether the servants of her lord's family loved or feared him most: that her lord had a very great affection for him: that his two noble aunts were no less fond of him: that his cousins Montague were as good-natured young ladies *as ever lived:* that Lord M. and Lady Sarah and Lady Betty had proposed several ladies to him before he made his addresses to me; and even since; despairing to move me and my friends in his favour. But that he had no thoughts of marrying at all, she had heard him say, if it were not to me: that as well her lord as the two ladies his sisters were a good deal concerned at the ill-usage he received from my family: but admired my character, and wished to have him married to me (although I were not to have a shilling) in preference to any other person, from the opinion that they had of the influence I should have over him. That, to be sure, Mr. Lovelace was a wild gentleman: but wildness was a distemper which would cure itself. She mingled a thousand pities often, that he acted not up to the talents lent him—yet would have it that he had fine qualities to found a reformation upon; and, when the happy day came, would make amends for all: and of this all his friends were so assured that they wished for nothing so earnestly as for his marriage."

This, indifferent as it is, is better than my brother says of him.

The people of the house here are very honest-looking industrious folks: Mrs. Sorlings is the gentlewoman's name. She is a widow; has two sons, men grown, who vie with each other which shall take most pains in promoting the common good; and they are both of them, I already see, more respectful to two modest young women their sisters than my brother was to his sister.

I believe I must stay here longer than at first I thought I should.

We have been alarmed with notions of a pursuit, founded upon a letter from his intelligencer.

I condemned in Mr. Lovelace the corrupting of a servant of my father's; and now I am glad to give a kind of *indirect* approbation of that fault, by inquiring of him what he hears, by that or any other way, of the manner in which my relations took my flight.

Most heavily, he says, they take it; but show not so much grief as rage. And he can hardly have patience to hear of the virulence and menaces of my brother against himself.

What a satisfaction am I robbed of, my dearest friend, when I reflect upon my inconsiderateness! O that I had it still in my power to say I *suffered* wrong rather than did wrong!

Fie upon me! for *meeting the seducer!* Let all end as happily as it now may, I have laid up for myself *remorse for my whole life.*

What still more concerns me is, that every time I see this man I am still at a greater loss than before what to make of him.

I watch every turn of his countenance: and I think I see very deep lines in it. He looks with more meaning, I verily think, than he used to look; yet not more serious; not less gay—I don't know how he looks—but with more confidence a great deal than formerly; and yet he never wanted that.

But here is the thing: I behold him with *fear* now, as conscious of the power my indiscretion has given him over me.

If you hear anything of my father and mother, and of their health, and how my friends were affected by my unhappy step, pray be so good as to write me a few lines.

Your unhappy
Clarissa Harlowe.

MR. LOVELACE TO JOHN BELFORD, ESQ.

Tuesday, Wedn., April 11, 12.

I TOLD THEE my reasons for not going in search of a letter of countermand. I was right; for, if I had, I should have found such a one; and had I received it she would not have met me. Did she think that, after I had been more than once disappointed, I would not keep her to her promise; that I would not hold her to it, when I had got her in so deeply?

The moment I heard the door unbolt I was sure of her. That motion made my heart bound to my throat. But when that was followed with the presence of my charmer, flashing upon me all at once in a flood of brightness, sweetly dressed, though all unprepared for a journey, I trod air, and hardly thought myself a mortal.

Thou shalt judge of her dress as, at the moment I first beheld her, she appeared to me, and as, upon a nearer observation, she really was. I am a critic, thou knowest, in women's dresses. Many a one have I taught to dress, and helped to undress.

Expect therefore a faint sketch of her admirable person with her dress.

Her wax-like flesh (for, after all, flesh and blood I think she is), by its delicacy and firmness, answers for the soundness of her health. Thou hast often heard me launch out in praise of her complexion. I never in my life beheld a skin so *illustriously* fair. The lily and the driven snow it is nonsense to talk of: her lawn and her laces one might indeed compare to those: but what a whited wall would a woman appear to be who had a complexion which would justify such unnatural comparisons? But this lady is all glowing, all charming flesh and blood; yet so clear that every meandering vein is to be seen in all the lovely parts of her which custom permits to be visible.

Thou hast heard me also describe the wavy ringlets of her shining hair, needing neither art nor powder; of itself an ornament defying all other ornaments; wantoning in and about a neck that is beautiful beyond description.

Her head-dress was a Brussels lace mob, peculiarly adapted to the charming air and turn of her features. A sky-blue ribbon illustrated that. But although the weather was somewhat sharp, she had not on either hat or hood; for, besides that she loves to use herself hardily (by which means, and by a temperance truly exemplary, she is allowed to have given high health and vigour to an originally tender constitution), she seems to have intended to show me that she was determined not to stand to her appointment. O Jack! that such a sweet girl should be a rogue!

Her morning gown was a pale primrose-coloured paduasoy: the cuffs and robings curiously embroidered by the fingers of this ever-charming Arachne, in a running pattern of violets and their leaves; the light in the flowers silver; gold in the leaves. A pair of diamond snaps in her ears. A white handkerchief, wrought by the same inimitable fingers, concealed—O Belford! what still more inimitable beauties did it not conceal! And I saw, all the way we rode, the bounding heart (by its throbbing motions I saw it!) dancing beneath the charming umbrage.

Her ruffles were the same as her mob. Her apron a flowered lawn. Her coat white satin, quilted: blue satin her shoes, braided with the same colour, without lace; for what need has the prettiest foot in the word of ornament? Neat buckles in them: and on her charming arms a pair of black velvet glove-like muffs of her own invention; for she makes and gives fashions as she pleases. Her hands, velvet of themselves, thus uncovered the freer to be grasped by those of her adorer.

I have told thee what were *my* transports, when the undrawn bolt presented to me my long-expected goddess. *Her* emotions were more sweetly feminine after the first moments; for then the fire of her starry eyes began to sink into a less dazzling languor. She trembled: nor knew she how to support the agitations of a heart she had never found so ungovernable. She was even fainting, when I clasped her in my supporting arms. What a precious moment that! How near, how sweetly near, the throbbing partners!

But seest thou not now the wind-outstripping fair one flying *from* her love *to* her love? Is there not such a game? Nay, flying from friends she was resolved not to abandon to the man she was determined not to go off with? *The sex! the sex all over!*—charming contradiction! Ha, ha, ha, ha! I must here—I must here lay down my pen to hold my sides; for I must have my laugh out now the fit is upon me.

. . . . . .

"Thou wilt not dare, methinks I hear thee say, to attempt to reduce such a goddess as this to a standard unworthy of her excellences. It is impossible, Lovelace, that thou shouldst intend to break through oaths and protestations so solemn."

That I did *not* intend it is certain. That I *do* intend it I cannot (my heart, my reverence for her, will not let me) say. But knowest thou not my aversion to the state of shackles? And is she not IN MY POWER?

"And wilt thou, Lovelace, abuse that power, which——"

Which what, Belford?—which I obtained not by her own consent, but *against* it.

"But which thou never hadst obtained had she not esteemed thee above all men."

And which I had never taken so much pains to obtain had I not loved her above all women. Thou knowest the whole progress of our warfare: for a warfare it has truly been; and far, very far, from an amorous warfare too. Doubts, mistrusts, upbraidings on her part: humiliations the most abject on mine.

Does she not deserve to pay for all this?

Then, I fancy, by her circumspection and her continual grief, that she *expects* some mischief from me. I don't care to disappoint anybody I have a value for.

But O the noble, the exalted creature!

But I resolve not *any way*. I will see how *her* will works; and how *my* will leads me on. And yet, every time I attend her, I find that she is less in *my* power; I more in *hers.*

Yet a foolish little rogue! to forbid me to think of marriage till I am a reformed man! Till the implacables of her family change their natures and become placable!

How it swells my pride to have been able to outwit such a vigilant charmer! Last night I was still more extravagant. I took off my hat as I walked, to see if the lace were not scorched, supposing it had brushed down a star; and, before I put it on again, in mere wantonness, and heart's ease, I was for buffeting the moon.

In short, my whole soul is joy. When I go to bed I laugh myself asleep: and I awake either laughing or singing. Yet nothing *nearly* in view, neither. For why? *I am not yet reformed enough!* Marriage will always be in my power. When I reform, I'll marry.

Miss Howe to Miss Clarissa Harlowe

Wednesday Night, April 12.

I have your narrative, my dear. You are the same noble creature you ever were.

The only family in the world, yours, surely, that could have driven such a daughter upon such extremities.

You lay the blame so properly and so unsparingly *upon your meeting him,* that nothing can be added to that subject by your worst enemies.

I am not surprised, now I have read your narrative, that so bold and so contriving a man—I am forced to break off——

. . . . . .

You stood it out much better and longer—— Here again comes my bustling, jealous mother!

. . . . . .

Don't be so angry at yourself. Did you not do for the best at the time? As to your first fault, *the answering his letters;* it was almost incumbent upon you to assume the guardianship of such a family, when the bravo of it had run riot, as he did, and brought himself into danger.

Except your mother, who has no will of her own, have any of them common sense?

Forgive me, my dear—here is that stupid Uncle Antony of yours. He came yesterday, in a fearful pucker, and puffed, and blowed, and stumped about our hall and parlour.

The *issue* showed what the errand was. Its first appearance, after the old fusty fellow was marched off (*you must excuse me, my dear*), was in a kind of gloomy, Harlowe-like reservedness in my mother; which, upon a few resenting flirts of mine, was followed by a rigorous prohibition of correspondence.

This put us, you may suppose, upon terms not the most agreeable. I desired to know if I were prohibited *dreaming* of you?

I should think myself the unworthiest of creatures could I be brought to slight a dear friend, and such a meritorious one, in her distress. I would die first—and so I told my mother.

Mr. Hickman, who greatly honours you, has, unknown to me, interposed so warmly in your favour with my mother that it makes for him no small merit with me.

If this ever-active, ever-mischievous monkey of a man, this Lovelace, contrived as you suspect—— But here comes my mother again—Ay, stay a little longer, my mamma, if you please.

Bless me!—how impatient she is!—how she thunders at the door! This moment, madam!

. . . . . .

You may believe, my dear, that I took care of my papers before I opened the door. We have had a charming dialogue. She flung from me in a passion——

So—what's now to be done? Sent for down in a very peremptory manner, I assure you. What an incoherent letter will you have, when I can get it to you! But now I know where to send it, Mr. Hickman shall find me a messenger.

Thursday, April 13.

I have this moment your continuation letter.

Dear creature! I can account for all your difficulties. A young lady of your delicacy!—and with such a man! I must be brief——

The man's a fool, my dear, with all his pride, and with all his complaisance, and *affected regards to your injunctions.* Yet his ready inventions——

Sometimes I think you should go to Lady Betty's. I *should,* if you were not so intent upon reconciling yourself to your relations. Yet they are implacable. You can have no hopes from them. Your uncle's errand to my mother may convince you of that; and if you have an answer to your letter to your sister, that will confirm you, I dare say.

You need not to have been afraid of asking me whether, upon reading your narrative, I thought any extenuation could lie for what you have done. I have, as above, before I had your question, told you my mind as to that. And I repeat, that I think, your *provocations* and *inducements* considered, you are free from blame: at least the freest that ever young creature was who took such a step.

But *you took it not.* You were *driven on one side,* and, possibly, *tricked on the other.*

All your acquaintance, you may suppose, talk of nobody but you. Some indeed bring your admirable character for a plea against you: but nobody does, or *can,* acquit your father and uncles.

Everybody seems apprised of your brother's and sister's motives. Your flight is, no doubt, the very thing they aimed to drive you to, by the various attacks they made upon you; unhoping (as they must do all the time) the success of their schemes in Solmes's behalf.

Your father is all rage and violence. He ought, I am sure, to turn his rage inward. All your family accuse you of acting with *deep art;* and are put upon supposing that you are actually *every hour exulting over them,* with your man, in the success of it.

They all pretend now, that your trial of Wednesday was to be the last.

They own, however, that a minister was to be present. Mr. Solmes was to be at hand. And your father was previously to try his authority over you, in order to make you sign the settlements. All of it a romantic contrivance of your wild-headed foolish brother, I make no doubt.

How they took your flight, when they found it out, may be better supposed than described.

Your Aunt Hervey, it seems, was the first that went down to the ivy summer-house in order to acquaint you that their search was over. Betty followed her; and they not finding you there, went on towards the cascade, according to a hint of yours.

Returning by the garden door, they met a servant (*they don't say it was that Joseph Leman; but it is very likely that it was he*) running, as he said, from pursuing Mr. Lovelace (a great hedge-stake in his hand, and out of breath) to alarm the family.

If it were this fellow, and if he were employed in the double agency of cheating them and cheating you, what shall we think of the wretch you are with? Run away from him, my dear, if so—no matter to whom—or marry him, if you cannot.

Your aunt and all your family were accordingly alarmed by this fellow—*evidently when too late for pursuit*. They got together and, when a *posse,* ran to the place of interview; and some of them as far as to the tracks of the chariot-wheels, without stopping. And having heard the man's tale upon the spot, a general lamentation, a mutual upbraiding, and rage, and grief, were echoed from the different persons, according to their different tempers and conceptions. And they returned like fools as they went.

Your brother, at first, ordered horses and armed men to be got ready for a pursuit. Solmes and your Uncle *Tony* were to be of the party. But your mother and your Aunt Hervey dissuaded them from it, for fear of adding evil to evil; not doubting but Lovelace had taken measures to support himself in what he had done; and especially when the servant declared that he saw you run with him as fast as you could set foot to ground; and that there were several armed men on horseback at a small distance off.

. . . . . .

My mother's absence was owing to her suspicion that the Knollys's were to assist in our correspondence. She made them a visit upon it. *She does everything at once.* And they have promised that no more letters shall be left there without her knowledge.

But Mr. Hickman has engaged one Filmer, a husbandman, in the lane we call Finch Lane, near us, to receive them. Thither you will be pleased to direct yours, under cover, to Mr. John Soberton; and Mr. Hickman himself will call for them there; and there shall leave mine.

Plotting wretch as I doubt your man is, I wish to heaven that you were married, that you might brave them all; and not be forced to hide yourself and be hurried from one inconvenient place to another.

You have a nice, a very nice part to act with this wretch—who yet has, I think, but one plain path before him.

If you think not of marrying soon, I approve of your resolution to fix somewhere out of his reach: and if he know not where to find you, so much the better. Yet I verily believe they would force you back, could they but come at you, if they were not afraid of *him*.

I think, by all means, you should demand of both your trustees to be put in possession of your own estate. Meantime I have sixty guineas at your service. I don't think you'll have a shilling or a shilling's worth of your own from your relations, unless you extort it from them.

As they believe you went away by your own consent, they are, it seems, equally surprised and glad that you have left your jewels and money behind you, and have contrived for clothes so ill.

Indeed every one who knows not what I *now* know, must be at a loss to account for your *flight,* as they call it. And how, my dear, can one report it with any tolerable advantage to you? To say you *did not intend it* when you met him, who will believe it? To say that a person of your known steadiness and punctilio was *over-persuaded* when you gave him the meeting, how will that sound? To say you were *tricked out of yourself,* and people were to give credit to it, how disreputable! And while *un-*

married, and *yet with him,* the man a man of such a character, what would it not lead a censuring world to think?

Your relations, according to what old Antony says to *my mother,* and *she* to *me* (by way of threatening that you will not gain your supposed ends upon them by your flight), seem to expect that you will throw yourself into Lady Betty's protection; and that she will offer to mediate for you: and they vow that they will never hearken to any terms of accommodation that shall come from that quarter. They might speak out, and say from *any* quarter; for I dare aver that your brother and sister will not let them cool—at least till their uncles have made such dispositions, and perhaps your father too, as they would have them make.

As this letter will apprise you of an alteration in the place to which you must direct your next, I send it by a friend of Mr. Hickman, who may be depended upon. He will return to Mr. Hickman this night; and bring back any letter you shall have ready to send, or can get ready.

I hear at this instant my mother calling about her, and putting everybody into motion.

Adieu, my dear. May Heaven preserve you, and restore you with honour as unsullied as your mind to

Your ever affectionate

Anna Howe.

Miss Clarissa Harlowe to Miss Howe

Thursday Afternoon, April 13.

I AM infinitely concerned, my ever dear and ever kind friend, that I am the sad occasion of the displeasure between your mother and you. How many persons have I made unhappy!

I think that you should obey your mother; and decline a correspondence with me; at least for the present.

I thank you, my dear, most cordially I thank you, for your kind offers.

I am willing to hope (notwithstanding what you write) that my friends will send me my little money, together with my clothes. Perhaps they will not be in haste to oblige me. But if not, I cannot yet want.

Small hopes indeed of a reconciliation from your account of my uncle's visit to your mother, in order to set her against an almost friendless creature whom once he loved! *But is it not my duty to try for it?* Ought I to widen my error by obstinacy and resentment because of *their* resentment; which must appear reasonable to them, as they suppose my flight premeditated; and as they are made to believe that I am capable of triumphing *in it,* and *over them,* with the *man they hate?*

These considerations make me waver about following your advice in relation to marriage; and the rather, as he is so full of complaisance with regard to my former conditions, which he calls my *injunctions.* Nor can I, now that my friends, as you inform me, have so strenuously declared *against accepting of the mediation of the ladies of Mr. Lovelace's family,* put myself into their protection, unless I am resolved to give up all hopes of a reconciliation with my own.

Yet if any happy introduction *could* be thought of to effect this desirable purpose, how shall terms be proposed to my father while this man is with me, or near me? Meanwhile, to what censures, as you remind me, do I expose myself while he and I are together and unmarried! Yet (can I with patience ask the question?) *is it in my power?* O my dear Miss Howe! And am I so reduced, as that, to save the poor remains of my reputation in the world's eye, I must *watch the gracious motion* from this man's lips?

Were my Cousin Morden in England, all might still perhaps be determined happily.

Hitherto I have not discovered anything in his behaviour that is *very* exceptionable.

But he has doubtless an arrogant and encroaching spirit. Nor is he so polite as his education, and other advantages, might have made one expect him to be. He seems, in short, to be one who has always had too much of his own will to study to accommodate himself to that of others.

Indeed, indeed, my dear, I could tear my hair, on reconsidering what you write (as to the probability that the dreaded Wednesday was more dreaded than it needed to be), to think that I should be thus tricked by this man; and that, in all likelihood, through his vile agent Joseph Leman. So premeditated and elaborate a wickedness as it must be!

I am obliged to Mr. Hickman for the assistance he is so kindly ready to give to our correspondence.

I am now in a state of obligation: so must rest satisfied with whatever I cannot help. Whom have I the power, once so precious to me, of obliging?

You must permit me (severe as your mother is against an undesigning offender) to say that I think your liveliness to her inexcusable—to pass over, for this time, what nevertheless concerns me not a little, the free treatment you almost *indiscriminately* give to my relations.

If you will not, for your *duty's sake,* forbear your tauntings and impatience, let me beseech you that you will for *mine:* since otherwise your mother may apprehend that my example, like a leaven, is working itself into the mind of her beloved daughter.

I enclose the copy of my letter to my sister. You will observe that, although I have not demanded my estate in form, and of my trustees, yet that I have hinted at leave to retire to it.

Your ever obliged and affectionate

Cl. Harlowe.

To Miss Arabella Harlowe

[*Enclosed to Miss Howe in the preceding*]

St. Albans, Apr. 11.

My dear Sister,—I have, I confess, been guilty of an action which carried with it a rash and undutiful appearance. But what is done, is done—perhaps I could wish it had not; and that I had trusted to the relenting of my dear and honoured parents. To whom I am ready to return (if I may not be permitted to retire to *The Grove*) on conditions which I before offered to comply with.

Nor shall I be in any sort of dependence upon the person by whose means I have taken this *truly reluctant step,* inconsistent with any reasonable engagement I shall enter into if I am not further precipitated. Let me not have it to say now, at this important crisis! that I have a sister, but not a friend in that sister. My reputation, dearer to me than life, is suffering. A little lenity will, even yet, in a great measure, restore it, and make that pass for a temporary misunderstanding only which otherwise will be a stain as durable as life, upon a creature who has already been treated with great *unkindness,* to use no harsher a word.

For your own sake therefore, for my brother's sake, by whom (I *must* say) I have been thus precipitated, and for all the family's sake, aggravate not my fault, if, on recollecting everything, you think it one; nor by widening the unhappy difference, expose a sister for ever—prays

Your affectionate
Cl. Harlowe.

I shall take it for a very great favour to have my clothes directly sent me, together with fifty guineas, which you will find in my escritoire; as also the divinity and miscellany classes of my little library; and, if it be thought fit, my jewels.

MR. LOVELACE TO JOHN BELFORD, ESQ.

MR. LOVELACE *gives an account to his friend of all that passed between them at the inns, in the journey, and till their fixing at Mrs. Sorlings's. To avoid repetition, those passages in his narrative are only extracted which will serve to embellish hers; to open his views; or to display the humorous talent he was noted for.*

At their alighting at the inn at St. Albans on Monday night, thus he writes:

To the mistress of the house I instantly changed her into a sister, brought off by surprise from a near relation's to prevent her marrying a confounded rake whom her father and mother, her elder sister, and all her loving uncles, aunts, and cousins abhorred. This accounted for my charmer's expected sullens; for her displeasure when she was to join me again, were it to hold; for her unsuitable dress upon the road.

To that part where she tells him of the difficulty she made to correspond with him at first, thus he writes:

Very true, my precious! But one day thou mayest wish that thou hadst spared this boast; as well as those other pretty haughtinesses: "That thou didst not reject Solmes for *my* sake: that *my* glory, if I valued myself upon carrying thee off, was *thy* shame: that I have more merit with *myself* than with thee or anybody else (*what a coxcomb she makes me, Jack!*): that thou wishest thyself in thy father's house again, *whatever were to be the consequence*." If I forgive thee, charmer, for these hints, for these reflections, for these wishes, for these contempts, I am not the Lovelace I have been reputed to be; and that thy treatment of me shows that thou thinkest I am.

Thou has heard me often expatiate upon the pitiful figure a man must make, whose wife *has,* or *believes* she has, more sense than himself. A thousand reasons could I give why I ought not to think of marrying Miss Clarissa Harlowe: at least till I can be sure that she loves me with the preference I must expect from a wife.

Thinkest thou, Jack, that I should have spared my Rosebud, had I been set at defiance thus? Her grandmother besought me, at first, *to spare her Rosebud;* and when a girl is put, or puts herself, into a man's power, what can he wish for *further?* while I always considered opposition and resistance as a challenge to do my worst.

This is Wednesday; the day that I was to have lost my charmer for ever to the hideous Solmes! With what high satisfaction and heart's ease can I now sit down and triumph over my men in straw at Harlowe Place! Yet 'tis perhaps best for them that she got off as she did.

But had I even gone in with her unaccompanied, I think I had but little reason for apprehension: for well thou knowest that *the tame spirits* which value themselves upon reputation, and are held within the skirts of the law by political considerations only, may be compared to an infectious spider; which will run into his hole the moment one of his threads is touched by a finger that can crush him, leaving all his toils defenceless, and to be brushed down at the will of the potent invader.

Nevertheless, to recur; I cannot but observe that these *tame spirits* stand a poor chance in a fairly offensive war with such of us mad fellows as are above all law, and scorn to skulk behind the hypocritical screen of reputation.

So that upon the whole, the law-breakers have the advantage of the law-keepers all the world over; at least for a time, and till they have run to the end of their race. Add to this, in the question between me and the Harlowes, that the whole family of them must know that they have injured me—must therefore be afraid of me. Did they not, at their own church, cluster together like bees when they saw me enter it?

I have rambled enough.

Adieu, for the present.

Miss Clarissa Harlowe to Miss Howe

Thursday Night, April 13.

I HAVE HAD another very warm debate with Mr. Lovelace. It brought on the subject which you advised me not to decline when it handsomely offered.

The impatient wretch sent up to me several times, to desire my company: yet his business nothing particular; only to hear *him* talk. The man seems pleased with his own volubility; and, whenever he has collected together abundance of smooth things, he wants me to find an ear for them!

Nothing, as I said, to any new purpose had he to offer; but complainings; and those in a manner, and with an air, as I thought, that bordered upon insolence. He could not live, he told me, unless he had more of my company, and of my *indulgence* too, than I had yet given him.

We began instantly our angry conference. He provoked me; and I repeated several of the plainest things I had said in our former conversations; and particularly told him that I was every hour more and more dissatisfied with myself and with him; that he was not a man who, in my opinion, improved upon acquaintance: and that I should not be easy *till he had left me to myself.*

I told him *that I desired his absence,* of all things. I saw not, I said, that my friends thought it worth their while to give me disturbance: therefore, if he would set out for London, or Berkshire, or whither he pleased, it would be most agreeable to me, and most reputable too.

He would do so, he said, he *intended to do so,* the moment I was in a place to my liking—in a place convenient for me. But fix upon any place in England where I could be out of danger, and he would go to the furthermost part of the king's dominions, if by doing so he could make me easy.

I told him plainly that I should never be in humour with myself for *meeting him;* nor with him, for *seducing me away:* that my regrets increased, instead of diminished: that my reputation was wounded: that nothing I could do would now retrieve it: and that he must not wonder, if I every hour grew more and more uneasy both with myself and him: that upon the whole I was willing to take care of myself; and when *he* had left me, I should best know what to resolve upon and whither to go.

He wished, he said, he were at liberty, without giving me offence, or being thought to intend to *infringe the articles I had stipulated and insisted upon,* to make one humble proposal to me. But the *sacred regard* he was determined *to pay to all my injunctions* (reluctantly as I had on Monday last put it into his power to serve me) would not permit him to make it, unless I would promise to excuse him if I did not approve of it.

I asked, in some confusion, what he would say?

He prefaced and paraded on; and then out came, with great diffidence, and many apologies, and a bashfulness which sat very awkwardly upon him, a proposal of speedy solemnization: which, he said, would put all right; and make my first three or four months (which otherwise must be passed in obscurity and apprehension) a round of visits and visitings to and from all his relations; to Miss Howe; to whom I pleased: and would pave the way to the reconciliation I had so much at heart.

Your advice had great weight with me just then, as well as *his reasons,* and the consideration of my *unhappy situation:* but what could I say?

The man saw I was not angry at his motion. I only blushed; and that I am sure I did up to the ears; and looked silly, and like a fool.

Would he have had me catch at his first, at his *very* first word? Having also declared to him in my letters, before I had your advice, that I would not think of marriage till he had passed through a state of probation, as I may call it. How was it possible I could encourage, with *very* ready signs of approbation, such as an early proposal? especially so soon after the free treatment he had provoked from me. If I were to die, I could not.

He looked at me with great confidence; as if (notwithstanding his contradictory bashfulness) he would look me through; while my eye but now and then could glance at him. He begged my pardon with great humility: he was *afraid* I would think he deserved no other answer but that of a *contemptuous silence.* True love was fearful of offending. Indeed so *sacred a regard* (foolish man!) would he have *to all my declarations made before I honoured him*——

I would hear him no further; but withdrew in a confusion *too visible,* and left him to make his nonsensical flourishes to himself.

I will only add that, if he really wishes for a speedy solemnization, he never could have had a luckier time to press for my consent to it. But he let it go off; and indignation has taken place of it: and now it shall be a point with me to get him at a distance from me.

Your ever faithful and obliged

Cl. H.

MR. LOVELACE TO JOHN BELFORD, ESQ.

Thursday, Apr. 13.

WHY, Jack, thou needst not make such a *wonderment,* as the girls say, if I should have taken large strides already towards reformation; for dost thou not see, that while I have been so assiduously, night and day, pursuing this single charmer, I have infinitely less to answer for than otherwise I should have had?

By a moderate computation, a dozen kites might have fallen while I have been only trying to ensnare this single lark; nor yet do I see when I shall be able to bring her to my lure; so more innocent days yet!

Thou knowest nothing, Jack, of the delicacies of intrigue; nothing of the glory of outwitting the witty and the watchful;

of the joys that fill the mind of the inventive or contriving genius, ruminating which to use of the different webs that offer to him for the entanglement of a haughty charmer, who in her day has given him unnumbered torments. Thou, Jack, who, like a dog at his ease, contentest thyself to growl over a bone thrown out to thee, dost not know the joys of the chase, and in pursuing a winding game; these I will endeavour to rouse thee to, and thou wilt have reason doubly and trebly to thank me, as well because of thy present delight, as with regard to thy prospects beyond the moon.

. . . . . .

What can be done with a woman who is above flattery, and despises all praise but that which flows from the approbation of her own heart?

'Tis certain I can have no pretence for holding her, if she will go. No such thing as force to be used, or so much as hinted at; Lord send us safe at London!

Is it prudent, thinkest thou, in *her* circumstances, to tell me, *repeatedly* to tell me, "That she is every hour more and more dissatisfied with herself and me? That I am not one who improve upon her in my conversation and address? That she shall not be easy while she is with me? That she was thrown upon me by a perverse fate? That she shall never forgive herself for *meeting me*, nor me for *seducing* her away? That her regrets increase instead of diminish? That she will take care of herself; and since her friends think it not worth while to pursue her, she will be left to her own care? That I shall make Mrs. Sorlings's house more agreeable by my absence?—And go to Berks, to town, or wherever I will (to the devil, I suppose), with all her heart?"

And do I not see that I shall need nothing but patience in order to have all power with me? What shall we say if all were to mean nothing but MATRIMONY? And what if my forbearing to enter upon that subject come out to be the true cause of her petulance and uneasiness?

And shall I marry a woman who has given me reason to doubt the preference she has for me?

Then what a triumph would it be to the *Harlowe pride* were

I now to marry this lady! A family beneath my own! No one in it worthy of an alliance with, but her! My own estate not contemptible! My expectations still so much *more* considerable! My person, my talents—not to be despised, surely—yet rejected by them with scorn. To be forced to *steal* her away, not only from *them,* but from *herself!* And must I be brought to implore forgiveness and reconciliation from the Harlowes? Beg to be acknowledged as the *son* of a gloomy tyrant whose only boast is his riches? As a *brother* to a wretch who has conceived immortal hatred to me; and to a sister who was beneath my attempts, or I would have had her *in my own way;* and finally, as a *nephew* to uncles who, valuing themselves upon their *acquired* fortunes, would insult me as creeping to them on that account? Forbid it the blood of the Lovelaces, that your last, and let me say, not the *meanest* of your stock, should thus creep, thus fawn, thus lick the dust, for a WIFE!—

MR. LOVELACE TO JOHN BELFORD, ESQ.

BUT IS IT NOT the divine CLARISSA (*Harlowe* let me not say; my soul spurns them all but her) whom I am thus by implication threatening?

And what! (methinks thou askest with surprise): Dost thou question this most admirable of women?—The virtue of a CLARISSA dost thou question?

I do not, I dare not question it. My reverence for her will not let me *directly* question it. But let me, in my turn, ask thee: Is not, may not, her virtue be founded rather in *pride* than in *principle?* The pride of setting an example to her sex has run away with her hitherto, and may have made her till *now* invincible. But is not that pride abated? What may not both *men* and *women* be brought to do in a *mortified state?* Pride is perhaps the principal bulwark of female virtue. Humble a woman, and may she not be *effectually* humbled?

And what results? "Is then the divine Clarissa capable of *loving* a man whom she ought *not* to love? And is she capable of *affectation?* And is her virtue founded in *pride?* And, if the answer to these questions be affirmative, must she not then be a *woman?*"

I own that I hardly think there ever was such an angel of a woman. But has she not already taken steps which she herself condemns? Steps which the world and her own family did not think her *capable* of taking? And for which her own family will not forgive her?

"May not then the success of him who could carry her *thus far,* be allowed to be an encouragement for him to try to carry her *farther?"* 'Tis but to try. Who will be afraid of a trial for this divine creature? Is not the whole sex concerned that this trial should be made? And who is it that knows this lady, that would not stake upon her head the honour of the whole?

I must assure thee that I have a prodigious high opinion of virtue; as I have of all those graces and excellences, which I have not been able to attain myself.

To my point: "What must that virtue be which will not stand a trial?"

Well then, a trial seems necessary for the *further* establishment of the honour of so excellent a creature.

And who shall put her to this trial? Who but the man who has, as she thinks, already induced her in lesser points to swerve?—And this for her *own* sake in a double sense; not only as he has been able to make *some* impression, but as she *regrets* the impression made; and so may be presumed to be guarded against his further attempts.

Shun not, therefore, my dear soul, further trials, nor hate me for making them. "For what woman can be said to be virtuous till she has been tried?

"Nor is *one* effort, *one* trial, to be sufficient. Why? Because a woman's heart may be at one time *adamant,* at another *wax"* —as I have often experienced.

And be this one of the morals of my tedious discussion:

But what, methinks thou askest, is to become of the lady if she fail?

What?—Why will she not, *"if once subdued,* be *always subdued?"* And what an immense pleasure to a marriage-hater, what rapture to thought, to be able to prevail upon such a woman as Miss Clarissa Harlowe to live with him without *real* change of name!

But if she resist—if nobly she stand her trial?

Why then I will marry her, and bless my stars for such an angel of a wife.

But will she not hate thee? Will she not refuse?

No, no, Jack! Circumstanced and situated as we are, I am not afraid of that. And hate me! Why should she hate the man who loves her upon proof?

And then for a little hint at *reprisal.* Am I not justified in my resolutions of trying *her* virtue, who is resolved, as I may say, to try *mine?* Who has declared that she will not marry me till she has hopes of my reformation?

And now, to put an end to this sober argumentation, wilt thou not thyself allow me to try if I cannot awaken the *woman* in her? To try if she, with all that glowing symmetry of parts, and that full bloom of vernal graces, by which she attracts every eye, be really inflexible as to the grand article?

If she be a *woman* and *love* me, I shall surely catch her once tripping; for love was ever a traitor to its harbourer. And love *within,* and I *without,* she will be *more* than woman, as the poet says, or I *less* than man, if I succeed not.

Now, Belford, all is out. The lady is mine—shall be *more* mine. Marriage, I see, is in my power, now *she* is so. Else perhaps it had not. If I can have her *without* marriage, who can blame me for trying? If *not,* great will be her glory and my future confidence.

Now wilt thou see all my circulation; as in a glass wilt thou see it. CABALA, however, is the word; nor let the secret escape thee even in thy dreams.

Nobody doubts that she is to be my wife. Let her pass for such when I give the word. "Meantime reformation shall be my stalking-horse; some one of the women in London, if I can get her thither, my bird."

MISS HOWE TO MISS CLARISSA HARLOWE

DO NOT BE so much concerned, my dearest friend, at the bickerings between my mother and me. We love one another dearly notwithstanding. If my mother had not me to find fault with, she must find fault with somebody else.

Don't advise me, my dear, to subscribe to my mother's prohibition of correspondence with you. She has no reason for it. Nor would she of her own judgment have prohibited it. That odd old ambling soul your uncle (whose visits are frequenter than ever), instigated by your malicious and selfish brother and sister, is the occasion. Don't let dejection and disappointment, and the course of oppression which you have run through, weaken your mind, my dearest creature, and make you see inconveniences where there possibly cannot be any. If *your* talent is *scribbling,* as you call it, so is *mine*—and I will scribble on at all opportunities, and to you, let 'em say what they will. Nor let your letters be filled with the self-accusations you mention; there is no cause for them.

I will say nothing upon your letter to your sister till I see the effect it will have. You hope, you tell me, that you shall have your money and clothes sent you, notwithstanding my opinion to the contrary. I am sorry to have it to acquaint you that I have just now heard that they have sat in council upon your letter; and that your mother was the only person who was for sending you your things, and was overruled. I charge you, therefore, to accept of my offer as by my last, and give me particular directions for what you want, that I can supply you with besides.

Don't set your thought so much upon a reconciliation as to prevent your laying hold of any handsome opportunity to give yourself a protector; such a one as the man will be who, I imagine, husband-like, will let nobody insult you but himself.

What could he mean by letting slip such a one as that you mention? I don't know how to blame you; for how could you go beyond silence and blushes, when the foolish fellow came with his observances of the restrictions which you laid him under when in another situation? But, you really strike people into awe.

I repeat what I said in my last, that you have a very nice part to act; and I will add that you have a mind that is much too delicate for your part. He is naturally proud and saucy. I doubt you must engage his *pride,* which he calls his *honour;* and that you must throw off a little more of the veil. And I would have you restrain your wishes before him, that you had not met him, and the like. What signifies wishing, my dear? He will not bear it.

Methinks I see the man hesitating, and looking like the fool you paint him, under your corrective superiority! But he is not a fool. Don't put him upon mingling resentment with his love.

I have only to add that I am, and will ever be,

Your affectionate friend and servant,

Anna Howe.

MISS CLARISSA HARLOWE TO MISS HOWE

YOU TELL ME, my dear, that my clothes and the little sum of money I left behind me will not be sent me—but I will still hope. When their passions subside, they will better consider of the matter; and especially as I have my ever dear and excellent mother for my friend in this request.

You advise me not to depend upon a reconciliation. I do not, I cannot depend upon it. But nevertheless it is the wish next my heart. And as to this man, what can I do? You see *that marriage is not absolutely in my own power,* if I were *inclined* to prefer it to the trial which I think I ought to have principally in view to make for a reconciliation.

You say he is proud and insolent—indeed he is. But can it be your opinion that he intends to humble me down to the level of his mean pride?

And what mean you, my dear friend, when you say that I must throw off a *little more of the veil?* Let me assure you, that if I see anything in Mr. Lovelace that looks like a design to humble me, his insolence shall never make me discover a weakness unworthy of a person distinguished by your friendship, that is to say, unworthy either of my sex or of my *former self.*

But I hope, as I am out of all other protection, that he is not capable of mean or *low* resentments. Did I ever profess a love for him? Did I ever wish for the continuance of his address? Had not my brother's violence precipitated matters, would not my indifference to him in all likelihood have tired out his proud spirit, and made him set out for London, where he used chiefly to reside? And if he *had,* would there not have been an end of all his pretensions and hopes? For no encouragement had I given him; nor did I then correspond with him.

You give me very good advice in relation to this man, and I thank you for it. When you bid me be more upon the *reserve* with him in expressing my displeasure, perhaps I may try for it; but to *palliate,* that, my dear Miss Howe, cannot be done by

Your own
Clarissa Harlowe.

Miss Clarissa Harlowe to Miss Howe

You may believe, my dear Miss Howe, that the circumstance of the noise and outcry within the garden door on Monday last gave me no small uneasiness, to think that I was in the hands of a man who could, by such vile premeditation, lay a snare to trick me out of myself, as I have so frequently called it.

I was resolved to task him upon this subject, the first time I could have patience to enter upon it with him.

I have had the opportunity I waited for.

He was making his court to my good opinion in very polite terms, and with great seriousness lamenting that he had lost it; declaring that he knew not how he had deserved to do so; attributing to me an indifference to him that seemed, to his infinite concern, hourly to increase. And he besought me to let him know my whole mind, that he might have an opportunity either to confess his faults and amend them, or clear his conduct to my satisfaction, and thereby entitle himself to a greater share of my confidence.

I answered him with quickness: Then, Mr. Lovelace, I will tell you one thing with a frankness that is, perhaps, more suitable to *my* character than to *yours* (*He hoped not, he said,*) which gives me a very bad opinion of you as a designing, artful man.

I never can think tolerably of you, while the noise and voice I heard at the garden door, which put me into the terror you took so much advantage of, remains unaccounted for. Tell me fairly, tell me candidly, the whole of that circumstance, and of your dealings with that wicked Joseph Leman; and according to your explicitness in this particular, I shall form a judgment of your future professions.

I will, without reserve, my dearest life.

"I knew nothing, *said he,* of this man—this Leman, and should have scorned a resort to so low a method as bribing the servant of any family to let me into the secrets of that family, if I had not detected him in attempting to corrupt a servant of mine, to inform him of all my motions, of all my supposed intrigues, and, in short, of every action of my private life.

"My servant told me of his offers, and I ordered him, unknown to the fellow, to let me hear a conversation that was to pass between them.

"In the midst of it, and just as he had made an offer of money for a particular piece of intelligence, promising more when procured, I broke in upon them, and by bluster, calling for a knife to cut off his ears (one of which I took hold of) in order to make a present of it, as I said, to his employers, I obliged him to tell me who they were.

"Your brother, madam, and your Uncle Antony he named.

"It was not difficult, when I had given him my pardon on naming them (after I had set before him the enormity of the task he had undertaken, and the honourableness of my intentions to your dear self), to prevail upon him, by a larger reward, to serve me; since at the same time he might preserve the favour of your uncle and brother, as I desired to know nothing but what related to myself and to you, in order to guard us both against the effects of an ill-will, which all his fellow-servants, as well as himself, as he acknowledged, thought undeserved.

"I was the more pleased with his services, as they procured to you, unknown to yourself, a safe and uninterrupted egress to the garden and wood-house; for he undertook, to them, to watch all your motions; and the more cheerfully (for the fellow loves you) as it kept off the curiosity of others."

So my dear, it comes out that I *myself* was obliged to this deep contriver.

But pray, sir, interrupting him, how came you to apprehend that I should revoke my intention? I had indeed deposited a letter to that purpose; but you had it not; and how, as I had reserved to myself the privilege of a revocation, did you know but I might have prevailed upon my friends, and so have revoked upon good grounds?

"I will be very ingenuous, madam. You had made me hope that if you changed your mind, you would give me a meeting to apprise me of the reasons for it. I went to the loose bricks and I saw the letter there; and as I knew your friends were immovably fixed in their schemes, I doubted not but the letter was to revoke or suspend your resolution, and probably to serve instead of a meeting too. I therefore let it lie, that if you *did* revoke, you might be under the necessity of meeting me for the sake of the expectation you had given me; and as I came prepared, I was resolved, pardon me, madam, whatever were your intentions, that you should not go back."

Wicked wretch! said I. It is my grief that I gave you opportunity to take so exact a measure of my weakness! But *would* you have presumed to visit the family had I not met you?

Indeed I would. I had some friends in readiness, who were to have accompanied me to them. And had your father refused to give me audience, I would have taken my friends with me to Solmes.

And what did you intend to do to Mr. Solmes?

Not the least hurt, had the man been passive.

But had he *not* been passive, as you call it, what would you have done to Mr. Solmes?

He was loath, he said, to tell me—yet not the least hurt to his *person.*

I repeated my question.

If he *must* tell me, he only proposed to carry off the *poor fellow,* and to hide him for a month or two. And this he would have done, let what would have been the consequence.

Was ever such a wretch heard of! I sighed from the bottom of my heart; but bid him proceed from the part I had interrupted him at.

"I ordered the fellow, as I told you, madam, said he, to keep within view of the garden door; and if he found any parley between us, and anybody coming (before you could retreat undiscovered) whose coming might be attended with violent effects, he would cry out; and this not only in order to save himself from their suspicions of him, but to give me warning to make off, and, if possible, to induce you (I own it, madam) to go off with me, according to your own appointment. And I hope, all circumstances considered, and the danger I was in of losing you for ever, that the acknowledgment of *this* contrivance, or if you had *not* met me, *that* upon Solmes, will not procure me your hatred; for had they come as *I* expected as well as *you,* what a despicable wretch had I been, could I have left you to the insults of a brother and others of your family, whose mercy was cruelty when they had *not* the pretence with which this detected interview would have furnished them!"

What a wretch, said I! But if, sir, taking your *own* account of this strange matter to be fact, anybody were coming, how happened it that I saw only that man Leman (I *thought* it was he) out of the door, and at a distance, look after us?

Very lucky! said he, putting his hand first in one pocket, then in another—I hope I have not thrown it away—it is, perhaps, in the coat I had on yesterday—little did I think it would be necessary to be produced—but I love to come to a demonstration whenever I can—I *may* be giddy—I *may* be heedless. I *am* indeed—but no man, as to *you,* madam, ever had a sincerer heart.

He then, stepping to the parlour door, called his servant to bring him the coat he had on yesterday.

And in the pocket, rumpled up as a paper he regarded not, he pulled out a letter written by that Joseph, dated Monday night; in which "he begs pardon for crying out so soon—says that his fears of being discovered to act on both sides, had made him take the rushing of a little dog (that always follows him) through the phyllirea-hedge, for Betty's being at hand, or some of his masters; and that when he found his mistake, he opened the door by his own key (which the contriving wretch confessed he had furnished him with) and inconsiderately ran out in a hurry, to have apprised him that his crying-out was owing to his fright only": and he added: "that they were upon the hunt for me by the time he returned."

I shook my head. Deep! deep! deep! said I, at the best! O Mr. Lovelace! God forgive and reform you! But you are, I see plainly, a very artful, a very designing man.

Love, my dearest life, is ingenious. Night and day have I

racked my stupid brain to contrive methods to prevent the sacrifice designed to be made of you, and the mischief that must have ensued upon it; so little hold in your affections; such undeserved antipathy from your friends; so much danger of losing you for ever from *both* causes.

But his resolution to run away with and to hide the poor Solmes for a month or so—O my dear! what a wretch have I let run away with *me,* instead of *Solmes!*

I had no patience with him. I told him so. I see, sir, said I, I see what a man I am with. Your *rattle* warns me of the *snake.* And away I flung, leaving him seemingly vexed and in confusion.

Miss Clarissa Harlowe to Miss Howe

Friday, April 14.

I WILL NOW give you the particulars of a conversation that has just passed between Mr. Lovelace and me, which I must call agreeable.

It began with his telling me that he had just received intelligence that my friends were on a sudden come to a resolution to lay aside all thoughts of pursuing me, or of getting me back; and that therefore he attended me to know my pleasure, and what *I* would do or have *him* do?

I told him that I would have him leave me directly; and that when it was known to everybody that I was absolutely independent of him, it would pass that I had left my father's house because of my brother's ill-usage of me; which was a plea that I might make with justice, and to the excuse of my father as well as of myself.

He mildly replied that if he could be certain that my relations would *adhere* to this their new resolution, he could have no objection, since such was my pleasure; but as he was well assured that they had taken it only from apprehensions that a more *active* one might involve my brother (who had breathed nothing but revenge) in some fatal misfortune, there was too much reason to believe that they would resume their former purpose the moment they should think they *safely* might.

This, madam, said he, is a risk I cannot run. You would think it strange if I could. And yet, as soon as I knew they had so given out, I thought it proper to apprise you of it, and to take your commands upon it.

Let me hear, said I, willing to try if he had any particular view, what *you* think most advisable?

'Tis very easy to say that, if I durst—*if I might not offend you*—if it were not to *break conditions that shall be inviolable with me.*

Say then, sir, what you *would* say. I can approve or disapprove as I think fit.

Had not the man a fine opportunity here to speak out? He had. And thus he used it.

To waive, madam, what I *would* say till I have more courage to speak out—(*more courage—Mr. Lovelace more courage, my dear!*)—I will only propose what I think will be most agreeable to *you*—suppose, *if you choose not to go to Lady Betty's,* that you take a turn cross the country to Windsor?

Why to Windsor?

Because it is a pleasant place; because it lies in the way either to Berkshire, to Oxford, or to London. *Berkshire,* where Lord M. is at present; *Oxford,* in the neighbourhood of which lives Lady Betty; *London,* whither you may retire at your pleasure; or, if you will *have* it so, whither I may go, you staying at Windsor; and yet be within an easy distance of you, if anything should happen, or if your friends should change their new-taken resolution.

This proposal, however, displeased me not. But I said my only objection was the distance of Windsor from Miss Howe, of whom I should be glad to be always within two or three hours' reach by a messenger, if possible.

A grateful thing then he named to me: to send for my Hannah as soon as I should be fixed.

Upon the whole, I told him that I thought his proposal of Windsor not amiss; I added that the sooner I removed the better; for that then he could have no objection to go to London, or Berkshire, as he pleased; and I should let everybody know my independence.

He again proposed himself, in very polite terms, for my banker. But I, as civilly, declined his offer.

This conversation was to be, all of it, in the main agreeable.

He asked whether I would choose to lodge in the town of Windsor, or out of it?

As near the castle, I said, as possible, for the convenience of going constantly to the public worship; an opportunity I had been long deprived of.

He should be very glad, he told me, if he could procure me accommodations in any one of the canon's houses; which he imagined would be more agreeable to me than any other on many accounts.

I expressed my satisfaction in terms so agreeable to him that he said he found a delight in this early dawning of a better day to him, and in *my* approbation, which he had never received from the success of the most favoured of his pursuits.

Surely, my dear, the man *must* be in earnest. He could not have *said* this, he could not have *thought* it, had he not.

He is gone to Windsor, having left two servants to attend me. He purposes to be back to-morrow.

I have written to my Aunt Hervey to supplicate her interest in my behalf, for my clothes, books, and money; signifying to her, "That, if I may be restored to the favour of my family and allowed a negative only, as to any man who may be proposed to me, and be used like a daughter, a niece, and a sister, I will stand by my offer to live single, and submit as I ought to a negative from my father." Intimating, nevertheless, "That it were perhaps better, after the usage I have received from my brother and sister, that I may be allowed to be distant from them, as well for their sakes as for my own" (meaning, as I suppose it will be taken, at my Dairy-house)—offering "to take my father's directions as to the manner I shall live in, the servants I shall have, and in everything that shall show the dutiful subordination to which I am willing to conform."

I am equally earnest with *her* in *this* letter, as I was with my *sister* in *that* I wrote to *her* to obtain for me a speedy reconciliation, that I may not be further precipitated; intimating, "That by a timely lenity, all may pass for a misunderstanding only, which otherwise will be thought equally disgraceful to them and to me; appealing to her for the necessity I was under to do what I did."

But after all, must it not give me great anguish of mind to

be forced to sanctify, as I may say, by my seeming *after*-approbation, a measure I was so artfully tricked into, and which I was so much resolved not to take?

How one evil brings on another, is sorrowfully witnessed to by

Your ever obliged and affectionate

Clarissa Harlowe.

MR. LOVELACE TO JOHN BELFORD, ESQ.

Friday, April 14.

BUT IS IT NOT a confounded thing that I cannot fasten an obligation upon this proud beauty? I have two motives in endeavouring to prevail upon her to accept of money and raiment from me: one, the real pleasure I should have in the accommodating of the haughty maid; and to think there was something near her, and upon her, that I could call *mine;* the other, in order to abate her severity and humble her a little.

Nothing sooner brings down a proud spirit than a sense of lying under pecuniary obligations.

My charmer has a pride like my own; but she has no *distinction* in her pride; nor knows the pretty fool that there is nothing nobler, nothing more delightful, than for lovers to be conferring and receiving obligations from each other. In this very farm-yard, to give thee a familiar instance, I have more than once seen this remark illustrated. A strutting rascal of a cock have I beheld chuck, chuck, chuck, chucking his mistress to him, when he has found a single barley-corn, taking it up with his bill, and letting it drop five or six times, still repeating his chucking invitation; and when two or three of his feathered ladies strive who shall be the first for it (*O Jack! a cock is a grand signor of a bird!*) he directs the bill of the foremost to it; and, when she has got the dirty pearl, he struts over her with an erected crest, and with an exulting chuck—a chuck-aw-aw-w, circling round her with dropped wings, sweeping the dust in humble courtship; while the obliged she, half-shy, half-willing, by her cowering tail, prepared wings, yet seemingly affrighted eyes, and contracted neck, lets one see that she knows the barley-corn was not all he called her for.

Now, Belford, canst thou imagine what I meant by proposing Hannah, or one of the girls here, for her attendant?

Believing she would certainly propose to have that favourite wench about her as soon as she was a little settled, I had caused the girl to be inquired after, with an intent to make interest, somehow or other, that a month's warning should be insisted on by her master or mistress, or by some other means which I had not determined upon, to prevent her coming to her. But fortune fights for me. The wench is luckily ill; a violent rheumatic disorder, which has obliged her to leave her place, confines her to her chamber.

And so, Jack, *pretending not to know anything of the matter,* I pressed her to send for Hannah.

But it is so discouraging a thing to have my monitress so very good! I protest I know not how to look up at her! Now, as I am thinking, if I could pull her down a little nearer to my own level; that is to say, could prevail upon her to do something that would argue *imperfection,* something *to repent of;* we should jog on much more equally, and be better able to comprehend one another; and so the comfort would be mutual, and the remorse not all on one side.

Miss Howe to Miss Clarissa Harlowe

Saturday, April 15.

Though pretty much pressed in time, and oppressed by my mother's watchfulness, I will write a few lines upon the new light that has broke in upon your gentleman.

His ingenuousness is the thing that staggers me; yet is he cunning enough to know that whoever accuses himself first, blunts the edge of an adversary's accusation.

But this that follows, I think, is the only way to judge of his specious confessions and self-accusations. Does he confess anything that you knew not before, or that you are not likely to find out from others? If nothing else, what does he confess to his own disadvantage? You have heard of his duels; you have heard of his seductions—all the world has. He *owns,* therefore, what it would be to no purpose to *conceal;* and his ingenuousness is a salvo—"Why, this, madam, is no more than Mr. Lovelace *himself* acknowledges."

Well, but what is now to be done? You must make the best

of your situation; and as you say, so say I, I hope that will not be bad; for I like all that he has proposed to you of Windsor, and his canon's house. His readiness to leave you, and go himself in quest of a lodging, likewise looks well. And I think there is nothing can be so properly done as (whether you get to a canon's house or not) that the canon should join you together in wedlock as soon as possible.

Your faithful and affectionate

Anna Howe.

MISS CLARISSA HARLOWE TO MISS HOWE

Sat. Afternoon.

YOU DISHEARTEN me a good deal about Mr. Lovelace. I may be too willing from my sad circumstances to think the best of him. If his pretences to reformation are *but* pretences, what must be his intent? But can the heart of man be so very vile? Can he, *dare* he, mock the Almighty?

But after all, I had rather, much rather, be independent of him and of his family, although I have an high opinion of them; at least till I see what my own may be brought to. Otherwise, I think it were best for me at once to cast myself into Lady Betty's protection. All would then be conducted with decency, and perhaps many mortifications would be spared me. But then I must be *his* at all adventures, and be thought to defy my own family. And shall I not first see the issue of *one* application? And yet I cannot make this till I am settled somewhere, and at a distance from him.

Mrs. Sorlings showed me a letter this morning which she had received from her sister Greme last night; in which Mrs. Greme (hoping I will forgive her forward zeal if her sister thinks fit to show her letter to me) "wishes (and that for all the noble family's sake, and she hopes she may say for my own) that I will be pleased to yield to make his honour, as she calls him, happy." She grounds her *officiousness*, as she calls it, upon what he was so *condescending* (her word also) to say to her yesterday in his way to Windsor, on her *presuming* to ask if she might soon give him joy: "That no man ever loved a woman as he loves me; that no woman ever so well deserved to be beloved; that in every conversation he admires me still more; that he loves me with such a purity as he had never believed himself capable of, or that a mortal creature could have inspired him with; looking upon me as all *soul;* as an angel sent down to save *his*"; and a great deal more of this sort: "but that he apprehends my consent to make him happy is at a greater distance than he wishes. And complained of the too severe restrictions I had laid upon him before I honoured him with my *confidence;* which restrictions *must be as sacred to him as if they were parts of the marriage contract,*" etc.

What, my dear, shall I say to this? How shall I take it? Mrs. Greme is a good woman. Mrs. Sorlings is a good woman. And this letter agrees with the conversation between Mr. Lovelace and me, which I thought, and still think, so agreeable. Yet what means the man by *foregoing the opportunities he has had to declare himself?* What mean his *complaints of my restrictions* to Mrs. Greme? He is not a bashful man.

I am quite petulant, fretful, and peevish with myself at times, to find that I am bound to see the workings of this *subtle,* or this *giddy* spirit; which shall I call it?

How am I punished, as I frequently think, for my vanity in hoping to be an *example* to young persons of my sex! Let me be but a *warning* and I will now be contented.

Forgive me, my dear, and love me as you used to do. For although my fortunes are changed, my heart is not; nor ever will, while it bids my pen tell you that it must cease to beat when it is not as much yours as

Your
Clarissa Harlowe's.

Miss Clarissa Harlowe to Miss Howe

Saturday Evening.

Mr. Lovelace has seen divers apartments at Windsor, but not one, he says, that he thought fit for me, and which at the same time answered my description.

I told him that if Mrs. Sorlings thought me not an encumbrance I would be willing to stay here a little longer; provided he would leave me and go to Lord M.'s or to London, whichever he thought best.

He hoped, he said, that he might suppose me absolutely safe

from the insults or attempts of my brother; and therefore, if it would make me easier, he would obey, for a few days at least.

He again proposed to send for Hannah. I told him I designed to do so, through you. And shall I beg of you, my dear, to cause the honest creature to be sent to?

He hinted to me that he had received a letter from Lady Betty, and another (as I understood him) from one of the Miss Montagues. If they take notice of *me* in them, I wonder that he did not acquaint me with the contents. I am afraid, my dear, that his relations are among those who think I have taken a rash and inexcusable step. It is not to my *credit* to let *even them* know how I have been *frightened out of myself;* and yet perhaps they would hold me unworthy of their alliance if they were to think my flight a voluntary one. O my dear, how uneasy to us are our reflections upon every doubtful occurrence, when we know we have been prevailed upon to do a wrong thing!

Sunday Morning.

Ah! this man, my dear! We have had warmer dialogues than ever yet we have had. At fair argument I find I need not fear him; but he is such a wild, such an ungovernable creature (*he* reformed!), that I am half afraid of him.

He again, on my declaring myself uneasy at his stay with me here, proposed that I would put myself into Lady Betty's protection, assuring me that he thought he could not leave me at Mrs. Sorlings's with safety to myself. And upon my declining to do that he urged me to make a demand of my estate.

He knew it, I told him, to be my resolution not to litigate with my father.

Nor would he put me upon it, he replied, but as the *last* thing. But if my spirit would not permit me to be *obliged,* as I called it, to anybody, and yet if my relations would refuse me my own, he knew not how I could keep up that spirit without being put to inconveniences which would give him infinite concern—unless —unless—unless, he said hesitating, as if afraid to speak out— unless I would take the only method I *could* take to obtain the possession of my own.

What is *that,* sir?

Sure the man saw by my looks, when he came with his creeping *unlesses,* that I guessed what he meant.

Ah, madam! can you be at a loss to know what that method is? They will not dispute with a *man* that right which they would contest with *you.*

Why said he with a *man,* instead of with *him?* Yet he looked as if he wanted to be encouraged to say more.

So, sir, you would have me employ a lawyer, would you, notwithstanding what I have ever declared as to litigating with my papa?

No, I would not, my dearest creature, snatching my hand, and pressing it with his lips—except you would make *me* the lawyer.

Had he said *me* at first, I should have been above the affectation of mentioning a lawyer.

I blushed. The man pursued not the subject so ardently, but that it was more easy as well as more natural to avoid it than to fall into it.

Would to Heaven he might, without offending! But I *so* overawed him! (*Overawed* him—*your* notion, my dear.) And so the overawed, bashful man went off from the subject, repeating his proposal that I would demand my own estate, or empower some man of the law to demand it, if I *would not* (he put in) empower a happier man to demand it. But it could not be amiss, he thought, to acquaint my two trustees that I intended to assume it.

I should know better what to do, I told him, when he was at a distance from me and *known* to be so. I suppose, sir, that if my father propose my return, and engage never to mention Solmes to me, nor any other man, but by *my consent,* and I agree, upon that condition, to think no more of *you,* you will acquiesce.

I was willing to try whether he had the regard to *all* my previous declarations which he pretended to have to *some* of them.

He was struck all of a heap.

What say you, Mr. Lovelace? You know, all you mean is for my good. Surely I am my own mistress; surely I need not ask your leave to make what terms I please for myself, *so long as I break none with you?*

He hemm'd twice or thrice. Why, madam—why, madam, I cannot say—then pausing, and rising from his seat with petulance: I see plainly enough, said he, the reason why none of my proposals can be accepted; at *last* I am to be a sacrifice to your reconciliation with your implacable family.

It has always been your respectful way, Mr. Lovelace, to treat my family in this free manner. But pray, sir, when you call *others* implacable, see that you deserve not the same censure *yourself*.

He must needs say there was no love lost between some of my family and him, but he had not deserved of *them* what they had of *him*.

Yourself being judge, I suppose, sir?

All the world, you yourself, madam, being judge.

Then, sir, let me tell you, had you been less upon your defiances, they would not have been irritated so much against you. But nobody ever heard that avowed despite to the relations of a person was a proper courtship either to that person or to her friends.

Well, madam, all that I know is, that their malice against me is such that, if you determine to sacrifice *me*, you may be reconciled when you please.

And all that I know, sir, is, that if I do give my father the power of a negative, and he will be contented with *that*, it will be but my *duty* to give it him; and if I preserve one to myself, I shall break through no obligation to *you*.

Your duty to your capricious *brother*, not to your *father*, you mean, madam.

If the dispute lay between my brother and me at *first*, surely, sir, a father may choose which party he will take.

He *may*, madam—but that exempts him not from blame for all that, if he take the wrong——

Different people will judge differently, Mr. Lovelace, of the right and the wrong. *You* judge as you please. Shall not others as *they* please? And who has a right to control a father's judgment in his own family, and in relation to his own child?

I know, madam, there is no arguing with you. But nevertheless I had hoped to have made myself some little merit with you, so as that I might not have been the *preliminary sacrifice* to a reconciliation.

Your hopes, sir, had been better grounded if you had had my consent to my abandoning of my father's house——

Always, madam, and for ever to be reminded of the choice you would have made of that damned Solmes—rather than——

Not so hasty! Not so rash, Mr. Lovelace! I am convinced that there was no intention to marry me to that Solmes on Wednesday.

So I am told they now give out, in order to justify themselves at your expense.

Excuse me, *good* Mr. Lovelace (waving my hand and bowing), that I am willing to think the best of my father.

Charming creature! said he, with what a bewitching air is that said!—And with a vehemence in his manner, would have snatched my hand. But I withdrew it, being much offended with him.

I think, madam, my sufferings for your sake might have entitled me to some favour.

My sufferings, sir, for *your* impetuous temper, set against *your* sufferings for *my sake,* I humbly conceive, leave me very little your debtor.

Lord! Madam (assuming a drolling air), what have *you* suffered! Nothing but what you can easily forgive. You have been *only* made a prisoner in your father's house by the way of doing credit to your judgment! You have *only* had an innocent and faithful servant turned out of your service because you loved her. You have *only* had your sister's confident servant set over you, with leave to tease and affront you!

Very well, sir!

You have *only* had an insolent brother take upon him to treat you like a slave, and as insolent a sister to undermine you in everybody's favour, on pretence to keep you out of hands which, if as vile as they vilely report, are not, however, half so vile and cruel as their own!

Go on, sir, if you please!

You have *only* been persecuted in order to oblige you to have a sordid fellow whom you have professed to hate, and whom everybody despises! The licence has been *only* got! The parson has *only* been held in readiness! The day, a near, a *very* near day, has been *only* fixed! And you were *only* to be searched for your correspondences, and still closer confined till the day came, in order to deprive you of all means of escaping the snare laid for you! But all this you can forgive! You can wish you had stood all this, inevitable as the compulsion must have been! And the man who, at the hazard of his life, has delivered you from all these mortifications, is the only person you *cannot* forgive!

Can't you go on, sir? You see I have patience to hear you. Can't you go on, sir?

I can, madam, with *my* sufferings; which I confess ought not to be mentioned, were I at last to be rewarded in the manner I hoped.

Your *sufferings,* then, if you please, sir?

Affrontingly forbidden your father's house, after encouragement given, without any reasons they knew not before, to justify the prohibition; forced upon a rencounter I wished to avoid: the first I ever, so provoked, wished to avoid; and that, because the wretch was your brother!

Wretch, sir!—and my brother! This could be from no man breathing but from him before me!

Pardon me, madam! But oh! how unworthy to be your brother! The quarrel grafted upon an old one when at college; he universally known to be the aggressor; and revived for views equally sordid and injurious both to yourself and me—giving life to him who would have taken away mine!

Your *generosity* THIS, sir, not your sufferings; a little more of your *sufferings,* if you please! I hope you do not repent that you did not murder my brother!

My private life hunted into! My morals decried! Some of the accusers not unfaulty!

That's an aspersion, sir!

Spies set upon my conduct! One hired to bribe my own servant's fidelity, perhaps to have poisoned me at last, if the honest fellow had not——

Facts, Mr. Lovelace! Do you want facts in the display of your sufferings? None of your *perhapses,* I beseech you!

Menaces every day and defiances put into every one's mouth against me! Forced to creep about in disguises—and to watch *all hours*——

And in *all weathers,* I suppose, sir—that, I remember, was once your grievance! *In all weathers,* sir! And all these hardships arising from yourself, not imposed by me.

—Like a thief, or an eavesdropper, proceeded he; and yet neither by birth nor alliances unworthy of *their* relation, whatever I may be and am of their admirable daughter; of whom they, every one of them, are at least *as* unworthy! These, madam, I call sufferings; *justly* call so; if at last I am to be sacrificed to an imperfect reconciliation—*imperfect,* I say; for can you expect to live so much as *tolerably* under the same roof, after all that is passed, with that brother and sister?

O sir, sir! What sufferings have yours been! And all for my sake, I warrant! I can never reward you for them! Never think of me more, I beseech you. How can you have patience with me? Nothing has been owing to your own behaviour, I presume; nothing to your defiances for defiances; nothing to your resolution declared more than once, that you *would* be related to a family which, nevertheless, you would not stoop to ask a relation of; nothing, in short, to courses which everybody blamed you for, you not thinking it worth your while to justify yourself. Had I not thought you used in an ungentlemanly manner, as I have heretofore told you, you had not had my notice by pen and ink. That notice gave you a supposed security, and you generously defied my friends the more for it; and this brought upon me (perhaps not undeservedly) my father's displeasure; without which my brother's private pique and selfish views would have wanted a foundation to build upon; so that all that followed of my treatment, and your redundant *onlys,* I might thank you for principally, as you may yourself for all your *sufferings,* your *mighty* sufferings! And if, voluble sir, you have founded any merit upon them, be so good as to revoke it; and look upon *me,* with my forfeited reputation, as the only sufferer. For what—pray hear me out, sir (for he was going to speak), have you suffered in, but your pride? Your reputation *could not* suffer; *that* it was beneath you to be solicitous about. And had you not been an unmanageable man, I should not have been driven to the extremity I now every hour, as the hour passes, deplore—with this additional reflection upon myself that I ought not to have *begun,* or, having begun, not *continued* a correspondence with one who thought it not worth his while to clear his own character for *my sake,* or to submit to my father for *his own,* in a point wherein every father ought to have an option.

Darkness, light; light, darkness; by my soul!—just as you please to have it. O charmer of my heart! snatching my hand, and pressing it between both his, to his lips, in a strange wild way, take me, take me to yourself; mould me as you please; I am wax in your hands; give me your own impression, and seal me for ever yours. We were born for each other!—you to make me happy, and save a soul—I am all error, all crime. I see what I ought to have done. Include me in your terms; prescribe to me; promise for me as you please; put a halter about my neck and lead me by it, upon condition of forgiveness on that disgraceful penance, and of a prostration as servile, to your father's presence (your brother absent), and I will beg his consent at his feet, and bear anything but spurning from him, because he is your father. But to give you up upon *cold* conditions, d—n me (said the shocking wretch), if I either will or can!

These were his words as near as I can remember them; for his behaviour was so strangely wild and fervent that I was perfectly frighted. I thought he would have devoured my hand.

I told him I by no means approved of his violent temper; he was too boisterous a man for my liking. And with a half-frighted earnestness I desired him to withdraw and leave me to myself.

He obeyed; and that with extreme complaisance in his manner, but with his complexion greatly heightened, and a countenance as greatly dissatisfied.

But on recollecting all that passed, I plainly see that he means not, if he can help it, to leave me to the liberty of refusing him; which I had nevertheless preserved a *right* to do; but looks upon me as *his,* by a strange sort of obligation, for having run away with me *against my will.*

Yet you see he but touches upon the edges of matrimony neither. And that at a time, generally, when he has either excited one's passions or apprehensions; so that one cannot at once descend. But surely this cannot be his design.

I have long been sick of myself; and now I am more and more so. But let me not lose your good opinion. If I do, that loss will complete the misfortunes of

Your
Cl. Harlowe.

Miss Clarissa Harlowe to Miss Howe

Sunday Night (April 16).

Before I could finish my last to you, he sent up twice more to beg admittance.

I have a letter, madam, said he, from Lady Betty Lawrance, and another from my Cousin Charlotte. I came now to make my humble acknowledgments to you, upon the arguments that passed between us so lately.

I was silent, wondering what he was driving at.

I am a most unhappy creature, proceeded he: unhappy from a strange impatiency of spirit which I cannot conquer. It always brings upon me deserved humiliation.

I was still silent.

I have been considering what you proposed to me, madam, that I should acquiesce with such terms as you should think proper to comply with, in order to a reconciliation with your friends.

Well, sir?

And I find all just, all right, on your side; and all impatience, all inconsideration on mine.

Lady Betty in her letter expresses herself in the most obliging manner in relation to me. "She hopes I will not too long delay the ceremony, because that performed will be to her, and to Lord M. and Lady Sarah, a sure pledge of her nephew's merits and good behaviour."

She says "she was always sorry to hear of the hardships I had met with on his account. That he will be the most ungrateful of men if he make not *all up* to me; and that she thinks it incumbent upon all their family to supply to me the lost favour of my own; and for her part, nothing of that kind, she bids him assure me, shall be wanting."

She concludes with "desiring to be informed of our nuptials the moment they are celebrated, that she may be with the earliest in felicitating me on the happy occasion."

But her ladyship gives me no direct invitation to attend her before marriage; which I might have expected from what he had told me.

He then showed me part of Miss Montague's more sprightly letter, "congratulating him upon the honour he had obtained, of the *confidence of so admirable a lady.*" *She* also wishes for his speedy nuptials, and to see her new cousin at M. Hall; as do Lord M., she tells me, and her sister; and in general all the well-wishers of their family.

This young lady says nothing in excuse for not meeting me on the road, or at St. Albans, as he had made me expect she would; yet mentions *her having been indisposed.* Mr. Lovelace had also told me that Lord M. *was ill of the gout,* which Miss Montague's letter confirms.

Miss Clarissa Harlowe to Miss Howe

You may believe, my dear, that these letters put me in good humour with him. He saw it in my countenance and congratulated himself upon it.

He then urged me to go directly to Lady Betty's.

But how, said I, can I do that, were I even out of all hope of a reconciliation with my friends (which yet, however unlikely to be effected, is my duty to *attempt*), as her ladyship has given me no particular invitation?

That, he was sure, was owing to her doubt that it would be accepted—else she had done it with the greatest pleasure in the world.

Then, said I, I thank *you,* sir, I have no clothes fit to go anywhere, or to be seen by anybody.

Oh, I was fit to appear in the drawing-room, were full dress and jewels to be excused, and should make the most amiable (he must mean *extraordinary*) figure there. He was astonished at the elegance of my dress. By what art he knew not, but I appeared to such advantage, as if I had a different suit every day. Besides, his cousins Montague would supply me with all I wanted for the present; and he would write to Miss Charlotte accordingly, if I would give him leave.

Do you think me the jay in the fable? said I. Would you have me visit the owners of the borrowed dresses in their own clothes? Surely, Mr. Lovelace, you think I have either a very low or a very confident mind.

Would I choose to go to London (for a few days only) in order to furnish myself with clothes?

Not at your expense, sir, said I, in an angry tone.

He wished he knew but my mind—that should direct him in his proposals, and it would be his delight to observe it, whatever it were.

My mind is, that you, sir, should leave me out of hand. How often must I tell you so?

You know, Mr. Lovelace, proceeded I, why I am so earnest for your absence. It is that I may appear to the world independent of you; and in hopes, by that means, to find it less difficult to set on foot a reconciliation with my friends.

Charming reasoning! And let him tell me that the assurance I had given him was *all he wished for*. What a happiness to have a woman of honour and generosity to depend upon! Had he, on his first entrance into the world, met with such a one, he had never been other than a man of strict virtue. But all, he hoped, was for the best; since, in that case, he had never perhaps had the happiness he had now in view; because his relations had been always urging him to marry, and that before he had the honour to know me. And now, as he had not been so bad as some people's malice reported him to be, he hoped he should have near as much merit in his repentance as if he had never erred.

This brought on a more serious question or two. You'll see by it what a creature an unmortified libertine is.

I asked him if he knew what he had said alluded to a sentence in the best of books: *That there was more joy in heaven*——

He took the words out of my mouth,

Over one sinner that repenteth, than over ninety-and-nine just persons which need no repentance, were his words.

Yes, madam, I thought of it as soon as I said it, but not before. I have read the story of the Prodigal Son, I'll assure you.

O madam, I have read the Bible as a fine piece of ancient history—but as I hope to be saved, it has for some few years past made me so uneasy when I have popped upon some passages in it, that I have been forced to run to music or company to divert myself.

Poor wretch! lifting up my hands and eyes.

The denunciations come so slap-dash upon one, so unceremoniously, as I may say, without even the by-your-leave of a rude London chairman, that they overturn one, horse and man, as St. Paul was overturned.

O sir, do you want to be complimented into repentance and salvation?

O my beloved creature, shifting his seat, let us call another cause.

Why, sir, don't *I* neither use *ceremony* enough with you?

Dearest madam, forbear for the present: I am but in my noviciate. Your foundation must be laid brick by brick. You'll hinder the progress of the good work you would promote, if you tumble in a whole wagon-load at once upon me.

Lord bless me, thought I, what a character is that of a libertine!

Since I had declined visiting Lady Sarah and Lady Betty, he asked me if I would admit of a visit from his Cousin Montague, and accept of a servant of hers for the present?

That was not, I said, an unacceptable proposal; but I would first see if my friends would send me my clothes, that I might not make such a giddy and runaway appearance to any of his relations.

I remember, my dear, in one of your former letters you mentioned London as the most private place to be in; and I said that since he made such pretences against leaving me here, as showed he had no intention to do so; and since he engaged to go from me, and to leave me to pursue my own measures, if I were elsewhere; and since his presence made these lodgings inconvenient to me, I should not be disinclined to go to London, did I know anybody there.

As he had several times proposed London to me, I expected that he would eagerly have embraced that motion from me. But he took not ready hold of it; yet I thought his eye approved of it.

We are both great watchers of each other's eyes; and indeed seem to be more than half afraid of each other.

He then made a grateful proposal to me, "that I would send for my Norton to attend me."

He saw by my eyes, he said, that he had at last been happy in an expedient which would answer the wishes of us both. Why, says he, did not I think of it before? And snatching my hand: Shall I write, madam? Shall I send? Shall I go and fetch the worthy woman myself?

After a little consideration, I told him that this was *indeed* a grateful motion; but that I apprehended it would put her to a difficulty which she would not be able to get over; as it would make a woman of her known prudence appear to countenance a fugitive daughter in opposition to her parents; and as her coming to me would deprive her of my mother's favour, without its being in my power to make it up to her.

Well, madam, I can only say I would find out some expedient, if I could, that should be agreeable to you. But since I cannot, will you be so good as to tell me what you would *wish* to have done?

This indifference of his to London, I cannot but say, made me incline the more to go thither. I asked him if he could recommend me to any *particular place* in London?

No, he said; none that was fit for me or that I should like. His friend Belford, indeed, had very handsome lodgings near Soho Square, at a relation's, whose wife was a woman of virtue and honour. These, as Mr. Belford was generally in the country, he could borrow till I were better accommodated.

I was resolved to refuse these at the first mention, as I should any other he had named. Nevertheless, I will see, thought I, if he has really thoughts of these for me. If I break off the talk here, and he resume this proposal with earnestness in the morning, I shall apprehend that he is less indifferent than he seems to be about my going to London, and that he has already a lodging in his eye for me—and then I will not go at all.

And so I retired from him. As I do from my pen; hoping for better rest for the few hours that remain of this night than I have had of a long time.

Cl. Harlowe.

MISS CLARISSA HARLOWE TO MISS HOWE

Monday Morning, April 17.

MR. Lovelace, who is an early riser as well as I, joined me in the garden about six, and after the usual salutations, asked me to resume our last night's subject. It was upon lodgings at London, he said.

I think you mentioned one to me, sir—did you not?

Yes, madam, but (watching the turn of my countenance) rather as what you would be welcome to than perhaps approve of.

I believe so too. To go to town upon an *uncertainty,* I own, is not agreeable; but to be obliged to any persons of your acquaintance, when I want to be thought independent of you; and to a person especially to whom my friends are to direct to me, if they vouchsafe to take notice of me at all, is an absurd thing to mention.

We had a good deal of discourse upon the same topic. But at last the result was this: he wrote a letter to one Mr. Doleman, a married man of fortune and character (I excepting to Mr. Belford), desiring him to provide decent apartments ready furnished for a single woman; consisting of a bed-chamber, another for a maidservant, with the use of a dining-room or parlour. This letter he gave me to peruse; and then sealed it up and dispatched it away in my presence by one of his own servants.

I attend the issue of it; holding myself in readiness to set out for London, unless you, my dear, advise the contrary.

MR. LOVELACE TO JOHN BELFORD, ESQ.

Sat., Sunday, Monday.

He gives in several letters the substance of what is containea in the last seven of the lady's.

. . . . . .

I am in the right train now. Every hour, I doubt not, will give me an increasing interest in the affections of this proud beauty. I have just carried *unpoliteness* far enough *to make her afraid of me,* and to show her that I am *no whiner*. Every instance of politeness *now* will give me a double credit with her. My next point will be to make her acknowledge a *lambent* flame, a preference of me to all other men at least; and then my happy hour is not far off. An *acknowledged* love sanctifies every freedom; and one freedom begets another. And if she call me *ungenerous,* I can call her *cruel.* The sex love to be called cruel. Many a time have I complained of cruelty, even in the act of yielding, because I knew it gratified the fair one's pride.

MISS HOWE TO MISS CLARISSA HARLOWE

Tuesday, April 18

YOU HAVE a most implacable family. Another visit from your Uncle Antony has not only confirmed my mother an enemy to our correspondence, but has almost put her upon treading in their steps.

But to other subjects:

You plead generously for Mr. Hickman.

But you ask me if I would treat Mr. Lovelace, were he to be in Mr. Hickman's place, as I do Mr. Hickman? Why really, my dear, I believe I should not. Men must not let us see that we can make fools of them. And I think that *smooth* love; that is to say, a passion without rubs; in other words, a passion without passion; is like a sleepy stream that is hardly seen to give motion to a straw. So that sometimes to make us fear, and even, for a short space, to *hate* the wretch, is productive of the *contrary* extreme.

Your frequent quarrels and reconciliations verify this observation; and I really believe that could Hickman have kept my attention alive after the Lovelace manner, only that he had preserved his morals, I should have married the man by this time.

I am pleased with the contents of these ladies' letters. And the more as I have caused the family to be again sounded, and find that they are all as desirous as ever of your alliance.

They really are (every one of them) your very great admirers. And as for Lord M., he is so much pleased with you, and with the confidence, as he calls it, which you have reposed in his nephew, that he vows he will disinherit him if he reward it not as he ought. You must take care that you lose not both families.

I hear Mrs. Norton is enjoined, as she values the favour of the *other* family, not to correspond either with you or with me.

You really hold this man to his good behaviour with more spirit than I thought you mistress of; especially when I judged of you by that meekness which you always contended for as the proper distinction of the female character; and by the love which (think as you please) you certainly have for him. You may rather be proud of than angry at the imputation; since you are the only woman I ever knew, read, or heard of, whose love was so much governed by her prudence.

I think there can be no objection to your going to London. There, as in the centre, you will be in the way of hearing from everybody and sending to anybody. And then you will put all his sincerity to the test, *as to his promised absence* and such like.

But indeed, my dear, I think you have nothing for it but marriage. You may try (that you may say you *have* tried) what your relations can be brought to; but the moment they refuse your proposals, submit to the yoke and make the best of it. He will be a savage, indeed, if he makes you speak out. Yet it is my opinion that you *must* bend a little; for he cannot bear to be thought slightly of.

All the world, in short, expect you to have this man. They think that you left your father's house for this very purpose. The longer the ceremony is delayed, the worse appearance it will have in the world's eye. And it will not be the fault of some of your relations if a slur be not thrown upon your reputation while you continue unmarried. But hitherto your admirable character has antidoted the poison; the detractor is despised, and every one's indignation raised against him.

Your Hannah cannot attend you. The poor girl left her place about a fortnight ago on account of a rheumatic disorder, which has confined her to her room ever since.

I will own to you that my mother has vexed me a little very lately by some instances of her jealous narrowness. I will mention one of them, though I did not intend it. She wanted to borrow thirty guineas of me; *only* while she changed a note. I said I could lend her but eight or ten. Eight or ten would not do; she thought I was much richer. I could have told her I was much cunninger than to let her know my stock; which, on a review, I find ninety-five guineas, and all of them most heartily at your service.

You must be the less surprised at the inventions of this man, because of his uncommon talents. This therefore is my repeated advice: provoke him not too much against yourself; but unchain him, and let him loose upon your sister's vile Betty, and your brother's Joseph Leman.

Your next, I suppose, will be from London. Pray direct it, and your future letters till further notice, to Mr. Hickman at his own house. He is entirely devoted to you. Don't take so heavily my mother's partiality and prejudices.

Heaven preserve you, and make you as happy as I think you deserve to be, prays

Your ever affectionate
Anna Howe.

Miss Clarissa Harlowe to Miss Howe

Wedn. Morn., April 19.

I am glad, my dear friend, that you approve of my removal to London.

. . . . . .

I am unhappy that I cannot have my worthy Hannah. I am as sorry for the poor creature's illness as for my own disappointment by it. Come, my dear Miss Howe, since you press me to be beholden to you, and would think me proud if I absolutely refused your favour, pray be so good as to send her two guineas in my name.

If I have nothing for it, as you say, but matrimony, it yields a little comfort that his relations do not despise the *fugitive,* as persons of their rank and quality-pride might be supposed to do, for having *been* a fugitive.

MISS CLARISSA HARLOWE TO MISS HOWE

Thursday, April 20.

MR. LOVELACE'S servant is already returned with an answer from his friend Mr. Doleman, who has taken pains in his inquiries and is very particular.

TO ROBERT LOVELACE, ESQ.

Tuesday Night, April 18.

DEAR SIR,—I am extremely rejoiced to hear that we shall so soon have you in town after so long an absence. You will be the more welcome still, if what report says be true; which is that you are *actually married* to the fair lady upon whom we have heard you make such encomiums.

You may have good accommodations in Dover Street, at a widow's, the relict of an officer in the guards, who dying soon after he had purchased his commission she *was obliged to let lodgings.*

She rents two good houses, distant from each other, only joined by a *large handsome passage.*

The apartments she has to let are in the inner house: they are a dining-room, two neat parlours, a withdrawing-room, two or three handsome bed-chambers—one with a pretty light closet in it, which looks into the little garden; all furnished in taste.

I had some knowledge of the colonel, who was always looked upon as a man of honour. His relict I never saw before. I think she has a *masculine air,* and is a *little forbidding at first.*

As we *suppose you married,* but that you have reason, from family differences, to keep it private for the present, I thought it not amiss to hint as much to the widow (but as *uncertainty,* however), and asked her if she could in that case accommodate you and your servants, as well as the lady and hers? She said she could, and wished, by all means, it were to be so; since the circumstance of a person's *being single,* if not as well recommended as this lady, was *one of her usual exceptions.*

I am, my dear Sir,

Your sincere and affectionate friend and servant,

Tho. Doleman.

You will easily guess, my dear, when you have read the letter, *which* lodgings I made choice of.

I fixed upon the widow's; and he has written accordingly to Mr. Doleman, making my compliments to his lady and sister for their kind offer.

. . . . . .

Mr. Lovelace has just now, of his own accord, given me five guineas for poor Hannah. I send them enclosed. Be so good as to cause them to be conveyed to her, and to let her know from whom they came.

He has obliged me much by this little mark of his considerateness. Indeed I have had the better opinion of him ever since he proposed her return to me.

Your ever obliged friend and servant,

Cl. Harlowe.

MR. LOVELACE TO JOHN BELFORD, ESQ.

Thursday, April 20.

HE BEGINS *with communicating to him the letter he wrote to Mr. Doleman; and then gives him a copy of the answer to it.*

Thou knowest the widow; thou knowest her nieces; thou knowest the lodgings. And didst thou ever read a letter more artfully couched than this of Tom Doleman? Every possible objection anticipated! Every accident provided against! Every tittle of it plot-proof!

If thou further objectest that Tom Doleman is too great a dunce to write such a letter in answer to mine—canst thou not imagine that, in order to save honest Tom all this trouble, I, who know the town so well, could send him a copy of what he should write, and leave him nothing to do but transcribe?

Widow SINCLAIR! didst thou not say, Lovelace?

Ay, SINCLAIR, Jack! Remember the name! SINCLAIR, I repeat. She *has* no other. And her features being broad and full-blown, I will suppose her to be of Highland extraction; as her husband the colonel (*mind that too*) was a Scot, as brave, as honest.

MISS HOWE TO MISS CLARISSA HARLOWE

Wednesday, April 19.

I HAVE a piece of intelligence to give you which concerns you much to know.

Your brother having been assured that you are not married, has taken a resolution to find you out, waylay you, and carry you off. A friend of his, a captain of a ship, undertakes to get you on shipboard, and to sail away with you, either to Hull or Leith, in the way to one of your brother's houses.

They are very wicked; for in spite of your virtue they conclude you to be *ruined*. But if they can be assured when they have you that you are not, they will secure you till they can bring you out Mrs. Solmes. Meantime, in order to give Mr. Lovelace full employment, they talk of a prosecution which will be set up against him for some crime they have got a notion of, which they think, if it do not cost him his life, will make him fly his country.

If you can engage Mr. Lovelace to keep his temper upon it, I think you should acquaint him with it. But as it will convince you that there can be no hope of a reconciliation, I wish you were actually married, let the cause for the prosecution hinted at be what it will—short of murder or a rape.

MISS CLARISSA HARLOWE TO MISS HOWE

Friday, April 21.

MR. LOVELACE communicated to me this morning early, from his intelligencer, the news of my brother's scheme.

I asked Mr. Lovelace, seeing him so frank and cool, what he would advise me to do?

Shall I ask *you*, madam, what are your own thoughts? Why I return the question, said he, is because you have been so very earnest that I should leave you as soon as you are in London, that I know not what to propose without offending you.

Inwardly vexed, I told him that he himself had proposed to leave me when I was in town; that I expected he would; and that, when I was known to be absolutely independent, I should consider what to write and what to do; but that while he was with me I neither would nor could.

He would be very sincere with me, he said; this project of my brother's had changed the face of things.

Do you propose, sir, said I, to take up your lodgings in the house where I shall lodge?

He did *not*, he said, as he knew the use I intended to make of his absence, and my punctilio.

The result of all was, to set out on Monday next for town. I hope it will be in a happy hour.

Cl. Harlowe.

MR. LOVELACE TO JOHN BELFORD, ESQ.

Friday, April 21.

AND now, Belford, what will thou say, if, like the fly buzzing about the bright taper, I had like to have singed the silken wings of my liberty? Never was man in greater danger of being caught in his own snares; all my views anticipated; all my schemes untried; the admirable creature not brought to town; nor one effort made to know if she be really angel or woman.

I offered myself to her acceptance with a suddenness, 'tis true, that gave her no time to wrap herself in reserves; and in terms *less tender* than *fervent*, tending to upbraid her for her past indifference, and to remind her of her injunctions; for it was the fear of her brother, not her love of me, that had inclined her to dispense with those injunctions.

I caught hold of her hand, and kneeling at her feet, O my angel, said I (quite destitute of reserve, and hardly knowing the tenor of my own speech; and had a parson been there, I had certainly been a gone man), receive the vows of your faithful Lovelace. Make him yours, and only yours, for ever. Who will dare to form plots and stratagems against my wife? That you are not so is the ground of all their foolish attempts, and of their insolent hopes in Solmes's favour. O be mine!—I beseech you (thus on my knee I *beseech* you) to be mine. We shall then have all the world with us; and everybody will applaud an event that everybody expects.

Was the devil in me! I no more intended all this ecstatic nonsense than I thought the same moment of flying in the air!

Well, but what was the result of this involuntary impulse on my part? Wouldst thou not think I was taken at my offer?—an offer so solemnly made, and on one knee too?

No such thing! The pretty trifler let me off as easily as I could have wished.

Her brother's project; and to find that there were no hopes of a reconciliation for her; and the apprehension she had of the mischiefs that might ensue; these, not *my offer,* nor *love of me,* were the causes to which she ascribed all her sweet confusion—an *ascription* that is high treason against my sovereign pride—to make marriage with *me* but a second-place refuge; and as good as to tell me that her confusion was owing to her concern that there were no hopes that my enemies would accept of her intended offer to renounce a man who had ventured his life for her, and was still ready to run the same risk in her behalf!

I re-urged her to make me happy; but I was to be postponed to her Cousin Morden's arrival.

Miss Clarissa Harlowe to Mrs. Hervey

Thursday, April 20.

Honoured Madam,—Having not had the favour of an answer to a letter I took the liberty to write to you on the 14th, I am in some hopes that it may have miscarried; for I had much rather it should, than to have the mortification to think that my Aunt Hervey deemed me unworthy of the honour of her notice.

If, madam, I were permitted to write to you with the hopes of being answered, I could clear my intention with regard to the step I have taken, although I could not perhaps acquit myself to some of my severest judges of an imprudence previous to it. You, I am sure, would pity me, if you knew all I could say, and how miserable I am in the forfeiture of the good opinion of all my friends.

I flatter myself that *their* favour is yet retrievable. But, whatever be the determination at Harlowe Place, do not *you,* my dearest aunt, deny me the favour of a few lines to inform me if there can be any hope of a reconciliation upon terms less shocking than those heretofore endeavoured to be imposed upon me; or if (which God forbid!) I am to be for ever reprobated.

At least, my dear aunt, procure for me the justice of my wearing apparel, and the little money and other things which I wrote to my sister for; that I may not be destitute of common conveniences, or be under a necessity to owe an obligation for such where (at present, however) I would least of all owe it.

Allow me to say that had I *designed* what happened, I might (as to the money and jewels at least) have saved myself some of the mortifications which I have suffered, and which I still further apprehend, if my request be not complied with.

I am, my dearest aunt,

Your ever dutiful

Cl. Harlowe.

MISS HOWE TO MISS CLARISSA HARLOWE

Sat., April 22.

WHAT A wretch to be so easily answered by your reference to the arrival of your Cousin Morden! But I am afraid that you was too scrupulous; for did he not resent that reference?

Could we have *his* account of the matter, I fancy, my dear, I should think you over-nice, over-delicate.[1] Had you laid hold *your* power as now you seem to be in *his;* you wanted not to be told that the person who had been tricked into such a step as you had taken must of necessity submit to many mortifications.

[1] The reader who has seen his account, which Miss Howe could not have seen when she wrote thus, will observe that it was not possible for a person of her delicacy of mind to act otherwise than she did, to a man so cruelly and so insolently artful.

But were it to *me,* a girl of spirit as I am thought to be, I do assure you, I would in a quarter of an hour know what he drives at; since either he must mean *well* or *ill.* If *ill,* the sooner you know it the better. If *well,* whose modesty is it he distresses but that of his own wife?

And methinks you should endeavour to avoid all exasperating recriminations as to what you have heard of his failure in morals; especially while you are so happy as not to have occasion to speak of them by experience.

I expect nothing from your letter to your aunt. I hope Lovelace will never know the contents of it. In every one of yours I see that he as warmly resents as he dares the little confidence you have in him.

I know you won't demand possession of your estate. But give *him* a right to demand it for you, and that will be still better.

Your ever affectionate and faithful

Anna Howe.

MR. BELFORD TO ROBERT LOVELACE, ESQ.

Friday, April 21.

LAST TIME I was at M. Hall thy noble uncle so earnestly pressed me to use my interest to persuade thee to enter the pale, and gave me so many family reasons for it, that I could not help engaging myself heartily on his side of the question; and the rather as I knew that thy own intentions with regard to this fine woman were then worthy of *her.* And of this I assured his lordship, who was half afraid of thee, because of the ill-usage thou receivedst from her family. But now that the case is altered, let me press the matter home to thee from other considerations.

By what I have heard of this lady's perfections from every mouth, as well as from thine, and from every letter thou hast written, where wilt thou find such another woman? And why shouldst thou tempt her virtue? Why shouldst thou wish to try where there is no reason to doubt?

And let me tell thee, Lovelace, that in this lady's situation the trial is not a fair trial. Thou, a man born for intrigue, full of invention, intrepid, remorseless, able patiently to watch for thy opportunity, not hurried as most men by gusts of violent passion, which often nip a project in the bud, and make the snail that was just putting out its horns to meet the inviter withdraw into its shell—a man who has no regard to his word or oath to the sex; the lady scrupulously strict to *her* word, incapable of art or design, apt therefore to believe well of others—it would be a miracle if she stood such an attempter, such attempts, and such snares as I see will be laid for her.

But let me touch upon thy predominant passion, *revenge;* for *love* is but second to that, as I have often told thee, though it has set thee into raving at me: what poor pretences for revenge are the difficulties thou hadst in getting her off; allowing that she had run a risk of being Solmes's wife had she stayed? If these are other than pretences, why thankest thou not those who threw her into thy power?

That she loves thee, wicked as thou art, and cruel as a panther, there is no reason to doubt. Yet what a command has she over herself, that such a penetrating self-flatterer as thyself art sometimes ready to doubt it! Though persecuted on the one hand as she was by her own family, and attracted on the other by the splendour of thine, every one of whom courts her to rank herself among them!

Thou wilt perhaps think that I have departed from my proposition, and pleaded the *lady's sake* more than *thine* in the above —but no such thing. All that I have written is more in *thy* behalf than in *hers;* since she may make *thee* happy; but it is next to impossible, I should think, if she preserve her delicacy, that thou canst make *her* so.

I plead not for the state from any great liking to it myself. But as thou art the last of thy name; as thy family is of note and figure in thy country; and so as thou thyself thinkest that thou shalt one day marry; is it possible, let me ask thee, that thou canst have such another opportunity as thou now hast, if thou lettest this slip? A woman in her family and fortune not unworthy of thine own; so celebrated for beauty; and so noted at the same time for prudence, for *soul* (I will say, instead of *sense*), and for virtue?

And shall this admirable woman suffer for her generous endeavours to set on foot thy reformation, and for insisting upon proofs of the sincerity of thy professions before she will be thine?

Be honest and be happy.
J. Belford.

Sat. Apr. 22.

Mrs. Hervey to Miss Clarissa Harlowe

Dear Niece,—It would be hard not to write a few lines, so much pressed to write, to one I ever loved. Your former letter I received, yet was not at liberty to answer it. I break my word to answer you now.

You might have given your friends the meeting. If you had *held* your aversion it would have been complied with. As soon as I was entrusted myself with their *intention* to give up the point, I gave you a hint—a dark one, perhaps—but who would have thought—O miss!—such an *artful* flight!—such *cunning* preparation!

It was indeed imagined that you would not have been able to resist your father's entreaties and commands. He was resolved to be all condescension, if anew you had not provoked him. *I love my Clary Harlowe,* said he, but an hour before the killing tidings were brought him; *I love her as my life; I will kneel to her, if nothing else will do, to prevail upon her to oblige me!*

I am sorry for it, but am afraid nothing you ask will be complied with.

You must now make best of your lot. Yet *not* married, it seems!

There may be murder yet, as far as we know. Will the man you are with part willingly with you? If *not,* what may be the consequence? If he *will*—Lord bless me! what shall we think of his reasons for it? I will fly this thought. I know your purity—but, my dear, are you not out of all protection? Are you not unmarried? Have you not (making your daily prayers useless) thrown yourself into temptation? And is not the man the most wicked of plotters?

You have my prayers.

My Dolly knows not that I write.

Your truly afflicted aunt,

D. Hervey.

Friday, April 21.

MISS CLARISSA HARLOWE TO MISS HOWE

Sat. Morn., April 22.

I HAVE just now received the enclosed from my Aunt Hervey. Be pleased, my dear, to keep her secret of having written to the unhappy wretch her niece.

I may go to London, I see, or where I will. No matter what becomes of me.

I was the willinger to suspend my journey thither till I heard from Harlowe Place. I thought if I could be encouraged to hope for a reconciliation, I would let this man see that he should not have me in his power, but upon my own terms, it at all.

But I find I must be *his,* whether I will or not; and perhaps through still greater mortifications than those great ones which I have already met with—and must I be so absolutely thrown upon a man with whom I am not at all satisfied?

And now to know that my father, an hour before he received the tidings of my supposed flight, owned that he loved me as his life; that he would have been all condescension; that he would—Oh! my dear, how tender, how mortifyingly tender, now in him!

There may be murder, my aunt says. This looks as if she knew of Singleton's rash plot. Such an *upshot,* as *she* calls it, of this unhappy affair, Heaven avert!

She flies a thought that I can *less* dwell upon—a *cruel* thought—but she has a poor opinion of the purity she compliments me with, if she thinks that I am not, by GOD's grace, above temptation from this sex. Although I never saw a man, whose *person* I could like, before this man, yet his faulty character allowed me but little merit from the indifference I pretended to on his account. But now I see him *in nearer lights,* I like him less than ever. Unpolite, cruel, insolent! Indeed I never liked him so little as now. Upon my word, I think I could hate him (if I do not already hate him) sooner than any man I ever thought tolerably of—a good reason why: because I have been more disappointed in my expectations of him, although they never we so high *as to have made him my choice in preference to the single life, had that been permitted me.* Still, if the giving him up for ever will make my path to reconciliation easy, and if they will signify as much to me, they shall see that I never will be *his;* for I have the vanity to think my soul his soul's superior.

Cl. Harlowe.

MISS CLARISSA HARLOWE TO MISS HOWE

Saturday Afternoon, April 22.

O MY BEST, my *only* friend! Now indeed is my heart broken! Think not of corresponding with a wretch who now seems absolutely devoted. How can it be otherwise, if a parent's curses have the weight I always attributed to them, and have heard so many instances in confirmation of that weight! Yes, my dear Miss Howe, superadded to all my afflictions, I have the consequences of a father's curse to struggle with!

I have at last a letter from my unrelenting sister.

I am in the depth of vapourish despondency.

Clarissa Harlowe.

TO MISS CLARISSA HARLOWE

Friday, April 21.

IT WAS *expected* you would send again to me or to my Aunt Hervey. You will have no answer from anybody, write to *whom* you will, and as *often* as you will, and *what* you will.

It was designed to bring you back by proper authority, or to send you wither the disgraces you have brought upon us all should be in the likeliest way, after a while, to be forgotten. But I believe that design is over; so you may *range* securely—nobody will think it worth while to give themselves any trouble about you. Yet my mother has obtained leave to send you your clothes of all sorts; but your clothes only. This is a favour you'll see by the within letter not *designed* you; and *now* not granted for *your* sake, but because my poor mother cannot bear in her sight anything you used to wear. Read the enclosed and tremble.

Arabella Harlowe.

To the Most Ungrateful and Undutiful of Daughters

Harlowe Place, April 1[illegible]

Sister that was!—For I know not what name you are *permitted* or *choose* to go by.

You have filled us all with distraction. My father, in the first agitations of his mind, on discovering your wicked, your shameful elopement, imprecated on his knees a fearful curse upon you. Tremble at the recital of it! No less than "that you may meet your punishment, both *here* and *hereafter*, by means of the very wretch in whom you have chosen to place your wicked confidence."

Your clothes will not be sent you.

But does the wretch put you upon writing for your things, for fear you should be too expensive to him? That's it, I suppose.

Was there ever a giddier creature? Yet this is the celebrated, the blazing Clarissa—Clarissa *what? Harlowe*, no doubt!—And Harlowe it will be, to the disgrace of us all!

Your drawings and your pieces are all taken down; as is also you own whole-length picture, in the Vandyke taste, from your late parlour; they are taken down and thrown into your closet, which will be nailed up, as if it were not a part of the house, there to perish together; for who can bear to see them?

My brother vows revenge upon your libertine—for the *family's* sake he vows it; not for *yours!* For he will treat you, he declares, like a common creature, if ever he sees you; and doubts not that this will be your fate.

My Uncle Harlowe renounces you for ever.

So does my Uncle Antony.

So does my Aunt Hervey.

So do *I*, base unworthy creature! the disgrace of a good family, and the property of an infamous rake, as questionless you will soon find yourself, if you are not already.

Your books, since they have not taught you what belongs to your family, to your sex, and to your education, will not be sent you. Your money neither. Nor yet the jewels so undeservedly made yours. For it is wished you may be seen a beggar along London streets.

If all this is heavy, lay your hand to your heart and ask yourself why you have deserved it?

Every man whom your pride taught you to reject with scorn (Mr. Solmes excepted, who, however, has reason to rejoice that he missed you) triumphs in your shameful elopement, and now knows how to account for his being refused.

Everybody, in short, is ashamed of you; but none more than

Arabella Harlowe.

Miss Howe to Miss Clarissa Harlowe

Tuesday, April 25

Be comforted; be not dejected; do not despond, my dearest and best beloved friend. God Almighty is just and gracious, and gives not His assent to rash and inhuman curses.

If you consider this malediction as it ought to be considered, a person of your piety must and will rather pity and pray for your *rash father,* than terrify *yourself* on the occasion. None but God can curse. Parents or others, whoever they be, can only pray to Him to curse; and such prayers can have no weight with a just and all-perfect Being, the motives to which are unreasonable and the end proposed by them cruel.

My mother blames them for this wicked letter of your sister, and she pities you, and, of her own accord, wished me to write to comfort you for this once; for she says, it is pity your heart, which was so noble, should be quite broken.

You will now see that you have nothing left but to overcome all scrupulousness and marry as soon as you have opportunity.

I will give you a motive for it regarding myself. For this I have resolved, and this I have vowed, "That so long as your happiness is in suspense, I will never think of marrying." In justice to the man I shall have, I have vowed this.

I would show Lovelace your sister's abominable letter were it to me. This will enter him, of course, into the subject which now you ought to have most in view.

And let me know your progress with Lovelace, and what he says to this diabolical curse. So far you may enter into this hateful subject. I expect that this will aptly introduce the grand topic between you without needing a mediator.

Come, my dear, when things are at worst they will mend. Good often comes when evil is expected. But if you despond, there can be no hopes of cure. Don't let them break your heart; for that, it is plain to me, is now what some people have in view to do.

How poor to withhold from you your books, your jewels, and your money! As money is all you can at present want, since they will vouchsafe to send your clothes, I send fifty guineas by the bearer, enclosed in single papers in my *Norris's Miscellanies.* I charge you, as you love me, return them not.

Your ever affectionate and faithful

Anna Howe.

Miss Clarissa Harlowe to Miss Howe

Wednesday Morning, April 26.

Your letter, my beloved Miss Howe, gives me great comfort. How sweetly do I experience the truth of the wise man's observation, *That a faithful friend is the medicine of life!*

Your messenger finds me just setting out for London; the chaise at the door.

I received my sister's dreadful letter on Sunday when Mr. Lovelace was out. He saw on his return my *extreme anguish* and *dejection,* and he was told *how much worse I had been;* for I had fainted away more than once.

I think the contents of it have touched my head as well as my heart.

He would fain have seen it. But I would not permit that, because of the threatenings he would have found in it against himself. As it *was,* the effect it had upon me made him break out into execrations and menaces. I was so ill that he himself advised me to delay going to town on Monday, as I proposed to do.

He is extremely regardful and tender of me. All that you supposed *would* follow this violent letter from him *has* followed it. He has offered himself to my acceptance in so unreserved a manner, that I am concerned I have written so freely and so diffidently of him.

I must acquaint you that his kind behaviour and my low-spiritedness, co-operating with your former advice and my unhappy situation, made me think that very Sunday evening *receive unreservedly his declarations;* and now indeed I am more in his power than ever.

Every one is waiting for me. Pardon me, my best, my kindest friend, that I return your Norris. In these more promising prospects I cannot have occasion for your favour. Besides, I have some hope that with my clothes they will send me the money I wrote for, although it is denied me in the letter. If they do not, and if I should have occasion, I can but signify my wants to so ready a friend.

I must acquaint you with one thing more, notwithstanding my hurry, and that is that Mr. Lovelace offered either to attend me to Lord M.'s, or to send for his chaplain, yesterday. He pressed me to consent to this proposal most earnestly, and even seemed desirous rather to have the ceremony pass here than in London; for when there, I had told him, it was time enough to consider of so weighty and important a matter. Now, upon the receipt of your kind, your consolatory letter, methinks I could almost wish it had been *in my power* to comply with his earnest solicitations. But this dreadful letter *has unhinged my whole frame.* Then some *little* punctilio surely is necessary. No preparation made. No articles drawn. No licence ready. Grief so extreme; no pleasure in prospect, nor so much as in wish—oh, my dear, who could think of entering into so solemn an engagement! Who, *so* unprepared, could seem to be *so* ready!

Adieu, my best beloved and kindest friend! Pray for your

Clarissa.

MISS HOWE TO MISS CLARISSA HARLOWE

Thursday, April 27.

I AM SORRY you sent back my Norris. But you must be allowed to do as you please.

You *know best* your *motives* for suspending; but I wish you *could* have taken him at offers so earnest. Why should you not have permitted him to send for Lord M.'s chaplain?

You have now but one point to pursue: that is marriage; let that be solemnized. Leave the rest to Providence, and, to use your own words in a former letter, follow as that leads. You will have a handsome man; a genteel man; he would be a *wise* man if he were not vain of his endowments, and wild and intriguing; but while the eyes of many of our sex, taken by so specious a form and so brilliant a spirit, encourage that vanity, you must be contented to stay till grey hairs and prudence enter upon the stage together. You would not have everything in the same man.

I hope that your next may inform me of your nuptials, although the next to that were to acquaint me that he was the ungratefullest monster on earth; as he must be, if not the kindest husband in it.

Adieu, my dear! I must, I will love you, and love you for ever! So subscribes your

Anna Howe.

MR. LOVELACE TO JOHN BELFORD, ESQ.

Monday, April 24.

FATE is weaving a whimsical web for thy friend, and I see not but I shall be inevitably manacled.

Here have I been at work, dig, dig, dig, like a cunning miner, at one time, and spreading my snares, like an artful fowler, at another, and exulting in my contrivances to get this inimitable creature absolutely into my power. Everything made for me. Her brother and uncle were but my pioneers; her father stormed as I directed him to storm; Mrs. Howe was acted by the springs I set at work; her daughter was moving for me, and yet imagined herself plumb against me; and the dear creature herself had already run her stubborn neck into my gin, and knew not that she was caught; for I had not drawn my sprindges close about her—and just as all this was completed, wouldst thou believe that I should be my own enemy and her friend? That I should be so totally diverted from all my favourite purposes, as to propose to marry her before I went to town, in order to put it out of my own power to resume them?

When thou knowest this, wilt thou not think that my black angel plays me booty, and has taken it into his head to urge me on to the indissoluble tie, that he might be more sure of me (from the complex transgressions to which he will certainly stimulate me, when wedded) than perhaps he thought he could be from the simple sins in which I have so long allowed myself that they seem to have the plea of habit?

Thou wilt be still the more surprised when I tell thee that there seems to be a coalition going forward between the black angels and the white ones; for here has hers induced her in one hour, and by one retrograde accident, to *acknowledge,* what the charming creature never before acknowledged, a preferable favour for me. She even avows an intention to be mine—mine, without reformation conditions! She permits me to talk of love to her: of the irrevocable ceremony: yet, another extraordinary! postpones that ceremony; chooses to set out for London; and even to go to the widow's in town.

This, in short, was the case: While she was refusing all manner of obligation to me, keeping me at haughty distance, in hopes that her Cousin Morden's arrival would soon fix her in a full and absolute independence of me—disgusted likewise at her adorer, for holding himself the reins of his own passions, instead of giving them up to her control—she writes a letter, urging an answer to a letter before sent, for her apparel, her jewels, and some gold, which she had left behind her; all which was to save her pride from obligation, and to promote the independence her heart was set upon. And what followed but a shocking answer, made still more shocking by the communication of a father's curse upon a daughter deserving only blessings? A curse upon the curser's heart, and a double one upon the transmitter's, the spiteful, the envious Arabella!

Absent when it came; on my return I found her recovering from fits, again to fall into stronger fits; and nobody expecting her life; half a dozen messengers dispatched to find me out. Nor wonder at her being so affected; she, whose filial piety gave her dreadful faith in a father's curses; and the curse of this gloomy tyrant extending (to use her own words, when she could speak) *to both worlds*. Oh, that it had turned, in the moment of its utterance, to a mortal quinsey, and, sticking in his gullet, had choked the old execrator, as a warning to all such unnatural fathers!

What a miscreant had I been, not to have endeavoured to bring her back, by all the endearments, by all the vows, by all the offers that I could make her!

I *did* bring her back. More than a father to her; for I have given her a life her unnatural father had well-nigh taken away:

shall I not cherish the fruits of my own benefaction? I was in earnest in my vows to marry; and my ardour to urge the present time was a *real* ardour. But extreme dejection, with a mingled delicacy, that in her dying moments I doubt not she will preserve, have caused her to refuse me the *time,* though not the solemnity; for she has told me that now she must be wholly in my protection (*being destitute of every other!*). More indebted, still, thy friend, as thou seest, to her cruel relations, than to herself for her favour!

Thou takest great pains to convince me, and that from the distresses the lady is reduced to (chiefly by her friends' persecutions and implacableness, I hope thou wilt own, and not from me, as yet) that the proposed trial will not be a fair trial. But let me ask thee, is not calamity the test of virtue? And wouldst thou not have me value this charming creature upon *proof* of her merits? Do I not intend to reward her by marriage if she stand that *proof?*

MR. LOVELACE TO JOHN BELFORD, ESQ.

Tuesday, April 25.

BUT WHY, Belford, why once more puttest thou me in mind that she *may be* overcome? And why is her own reliance on my honour so late and so reluctantly shown?

But after all, so low, so dejected continues she to be, that I am terribly afraid I shall have a vapourish wife, if I *do* marry. I should then be doubly undone. Not that I shall be *much at home with her, perhaps, after the first fortnight or so.* But when a man has been ranging, like the painful bee, from flower to flower, perhaps for a month together, and the thoughts of home and a wife begin to have their charms with him, to be received by a Niobe, who, like a wounded vine, weeps her vitals away, while she but involuntarily curls about him; how shall I be able to bear that?

May Heaven restore my charmer to health and spirits, I hourly pray—that a man may see whether she can love anybody but her father and mother!

It is infinitely better for her and for me that we should not marry. What a delightful manner of life would the life of honour be with such a woman! The fears, the inquietudes, the uneasy days, the restless nights; all arising from doubts of having disobliged me! Every absence dreaded to be an absence for ever! And then how amply rewarded and rewarding, by the rapture-causing return! Such a passion as this keeps love in a continual fervour; makes it all alive. The happy pair, instead of sitting dozing and nodding at each other in opposite chimney-corners in a winter evening, and over a wintry love, always new to each other, and having always something to say.

Mr. Lovelace to John Belford, Esq.

Wedn., Apr. 26.

At last my lucky star has directed us into the desired port, and we are safely landed.

Things already appear with a very different face *now I have got her here*. Already have our mother and her daughters been about me: "Charming lady! What a complexion! What eyes! What majesty in her person! O Mr. Lovelace, you are a happy man! *You owe us such a lady!*" Then they remind me of my revenge, and of my hatred to her whole family.

It would be a miracle, as thou sayest, if this lady can save herself—and having gone so far, how can I recede? Then my revenge upon the Harlowes! To have run away with a daughter of theirs, to make her a Lovelace—to make her one of a family so superior to her own—what a triumph, as I have heretofore observed, to *them!* But to run away with her, and to bring her to my lure in the *other* light, what a mortification of their pride! What a gratification of my own!

Dorcas is a neat creature, both in person and dress; her countenance not vulgar. And I am in hopes, as I hinted above, that her lady will accept of her for her bedfellow in a strange house for a week or so. But I saw she had a dislike to her at her very first appearance: yet I thought the girl behaved very modestly—*overdid* it a little, perhaps—her lady shrunk back, and looked shy upon her.

Know then, that *said* is *done* with me, when I have a mind to have it so; and that we are actually man and wife! Only that consummation has not passed: bound down to the contrary of that by a solemn vow, till a reconciliation with her family take place. The women here are told so. They know it before my beloved knows it; and that, thou wilt say, is odd.

She will insist, I suppose, upon my leaving her, and that I shall not take up my lodgings under the same roof. But circumstances are changed since I first made her that promise. I have taken all the vacant apartments, and must carry this point also.

Miss Clarissa Harlowe to Miss Howe

Wedn. Afternoon, Apr. 26.

At length, my dearest Miss Howe, I am in London, and in my new lodgings. They are neatly furnished, and the situation, for the town, is pleasant. But I think you must not ask me how I like the old gentlewoman. Yet she seems courteous and obliging. Her kinswomen just appeared to welcome me at my alighting. They seem to be genteel young women.

Mr. Lovelace's tender behaviour in the midst of my grief has given him a right, as he seems to think, of addressing me with all the freedom of an approved lover. He has been ever since Sunday last continually complaining of the distance I keep him at; and thinks himself entitled now to call in question my value for him; strengthening his doubts by my former declared readiness to give him up to a reconciliation with my friends; and yet has himself fallen off from that *obsequious tenderness,* if I may couple the words, which drew from me the concessions he builds upon.

. . . . . .

I am exceedingly out of humour with Mr. Lovelace.

He began with letting me know that he had been out to inquire after the character of the widow; which was the more necessary, he said, as he supposed that I would *expect his frequent absence.*

I *did,* I said; and that he would not think of taking up his lodging in the same house with me. But what, said I, is the result of your inquiry?

Why, indeed, the widow's character was, in the main, what he liked well enough. But as it was Miss Howe's opinion, as I had told him, that my brother had not given over his scheme; as the widow lived by letting lodgings; and had others to let in the same part of the house, which might be taken by an enemy; he knew no better way than for him to take them all, as it could not be for a long time—*unless I would think of removing to others.*

So far was well enough: but as it was easy for me to see that he spoke the slighter of the widow in order to have a pretence to lodge here himself, I asked him his intention in that respect. And he frankly owned, that if I chose to stay here, he could not, as matters stood, think of leaving me for six hours together; and he had prepared the widow to expect that we should be here but for a few days; only till we could fix ourselves in a house suitable to our condition; and this, that I might be under the less embarrass if I pleased to remove.

Fix *our*selves in a house, and *we* and *our*, Mr. Lovelace—pray, in what light——

He interrupted me: Why, my dearest life, if you will hear me with patience—yet I am half afraid, that I have been too forward, as I have not consulted you upon it—but as my friends in town, according to what Mr. Doleman has written in the letter you have seen, conclude us to be married——

Surely, sir, you have not presumed——

Hear me out, dearest creature: you have received with favour my addresses; you have made me hope for the honour of your consenting hand: yet, by declining my most fervent tender of myself to you at Mrs. Sorlings's, have given me apprehensions of delay: I would not for the world be thought so ungenerous a wretch, now you have honoured me with your confidence, *as to wish to precipitate you.* Yet your brother's schemes are not given up. If you are *known* to be mine, or if you are but *thought* to be so, there will probably be an end of your brother's contrivances. The widow's character may be as worthy *as it is said to be.* But the worthier she is, the more danger, if your brother's agent should find us out; since she may be persuaded that she ought in conscience to take a parent's part against a child who stands in opposition to them. But if she believes us married, her good character will stand us in stead, and she will be of our party. Then I have taken care to give her a reason why two apartments are requisite to us at the hour of retirement.

I perfectly raved at him. I would have flung from him in resentment; but he would not let me: and what could I do? Whither go, the evening advanced?

I am astonished at you! said I. If you are a man of honour, what need of all this strange obliquity! You delight in crooked ways. Let me know, since I *must* stay in your company (for he held my hand), let me know all you have said to the people below. Indeed, indeed, Mr. Lovelace, you are a very unaccountable man.

My dearest creature, need I to have mentioned anything of this? and could I not have taken up my lodgings in this house unknown to you, if I had not intended to make you the judge of all my proceedings? But *this* is what I have told the widow before her kinswomen, and before your new servant—"That indeed we were privately married at Hertford; but that you had preliminarily bound me under a solemn vow, which I am most religiously resolved to keep, to be contented with separate apartments, and even not to lodge under the same roof, till a certain reconciliation shall take place, which is of high consequence to both." And further, that I might convince you of the purity of my intentions, and that my whole view in this was to prevent mischief, I have acquainted them, "that I have solemnly promised to behave to you before everybody, as if we were only betrothed and not married; not even offering to take any of those innocent freedoms which are not refused in the most punctilious loves."

And then he solemnly vowed to me the strictest observance of the same respectful behaviour to me.

I said that I was not by any means satisfied with the tale he had told, nor with the necessity he wanted to lay me under of appearing what I was not: that every step he took was a wry one, a needless wry one: and since he thought it necessary to tell the people below anything about me, I insisted that he should unsay all he had said and tell them the truth.

What he had told them, he said, was with so many circumstances that he could sooner die than contradict it. And still he insisted upon the propriety of appearing to be married, for the reasons he had given before. And, dearest creature, said he, why this high displeasure with me upon so well-intended an expedient?

'Tis true I should have consulted you first, and had your leave. But since you dislike what I have said, let me implore you, dearest madam, to give the only proper sanction to it, by naming an early day. Would to Heaven that were to be to-morrow! For God's sake, let it be to-morrow! But if not (was it his business, my dear, before I spoke [yet he seemed to be afraid of me] to say, *if not?*), let me beseech you, madam, if my behaviour shall not be to your dislike, that you will not to-morrow at breakfast-time discredit what I have told them. The moment I give you cause to think that I take any advantage of your concession, that moment revoke it, and expose me, as I shall deserve.

What could I say? What could I do? I verily think, that had he urged me again, in a *proper manner,* I should have consented (little satisfied as I am with him) to give him a meeting to-morrow morning at a more solemn place than in the parlour below.

But this I resolve, that he shall not have my consent to stay a night under this roof.

. . . . . .

Alas! my dear, how vain a thing to say what we will or what we will not do, when we have put ourselves into the power of this sex! He went down to the people below, on my desiring to be left to myself; and stayed till their supper was just ready; and then, desiring a moment's *audience,* as he called it, he besought my leave to stay that one night, promising to set out either for Lord M.'s, or for Edgware to his friend Belford's, in the morning after breakfast. But if I were against it, he said, he would not stay supper; and would attend me about eight next day.

I thought, notwithstanding my resolution above-mentioned, that it would seem too punctilious to deny him, under the circumstances he had mentioned: having, besides, no reason to think he would obey me; for he looked as if he were determined

friends, my company on Monday evening at a little collation. Mrs. Sinclair will be present, and she gave him hope of the company of a young lady of very great fortune and merit (Miss *Partington*), an heiress to whom Colonel Sinclair, it seems, in his lifetime was guardian, and who therefore calls Mrs. Sinclair mamma.

I desired to be excused. He had laid me, I said, under a most disagreeable necessity of appearing as a married person; and I would see as few people as possible who were to think me so.

He would not urge it, he said, if I were *much* averse: but they were his select friends; men of birth and fortune, who longed to see me. It was true, he added, that they believed we were married: but they thought him under the restrictions that he had mentioned to the people below.

When he is set upon anything, there is no knowing, as I have said heretofore, what one *can* do. But I will not, if I can help it, be made a show of; especially to men of whose characters and principles I have no good opinion. I am, my dearest friend,

Your ever affectionate

Cl. Harlowe.

Instructions to be observed by John Belford, Richard Mowbray, Thomas Belton, and James Tourville, Esquires of the Body to General Robert Lovelace, on their admission to the presence of his Goddess.

Ye must be sure to let it sink deep into your heavy heads, that there is no such lady in the world as Miss Clarissa Harlowe; and that she is neither more nor less than Mrs. Lovelace, though at present, to my shame be it spoken, a virgin.

Be mindful also, that your old mother's name, after that of *her* mother when a maid, is Sinclair: that her husband was a lieutenant-colonel, and all that *you,* Belford, know from honest Doleman's letter of her, that let your brethren know.

Mowbray and Tourville, the two greatest blunderers of the four, I allow to be acquainted with the widow and nieces, from the knowledge they had of the colonel.

Priscilla Partington (for her looks so innocent, and discretion so deep, yet seeming so softly) may be greatly relied upon. S[illegible]

will accompany the mother, gorgeously dressed, with all her Jew's extravagance flaming out upon her; and first *induce,* then *countenance,* the lady. She has her cue, and I hope will make her acquaintance coveted by my charmer.

Miss Partington's history is this: The daughter of Colonel Sinclair's brother-in-law: that brother-in-law may have been a Turkey merchant, or any merchant, who died confoundedly rich: the colonel one of her guardians (*collateral credit in that to the old one*): whence she always calls Mrs. Sinclair *mamma;* though not succeeding to the trust.

She is just come to pass a day or two, and then to return to her surviving guardian's at Barnet.

Be it principally thy part, Jack, who art a parading fellow, and aimest at wisdom, to keep thy brother-varlets from blundering; for, as thou must have observed from what I have written, we have the most watchful and most penetrating lady in the world to deal with: a lady worth deceiving! but whose eyes will pierce to the bottom of your shallow souls the moment she hears you open. Do thou, therefore, place thyself between Mowbray and Tourville: their toes to be played upon and commanded by thine, if they go wrong: thy elbows to be the ministers of approbation.

Be sure to instruct the rest, and do thou thyself remember not to talk obscenely. You know I never permitted any of you to talk obscenely. Time enough for that when ye grow old, and can ONLY talk. Besides, ye must consider Prisc.'s *affected* character, my goddess's *real* one. Far from obscenity, therefore, do not so much as touch upon the double entendre.

And now, methinks, thou art curious to know what can be my view in risking the displeasure of my fair one, and alarming her fears, after four or five halcyon days have gone over our heads? I'll satisfy thee.

T[illegible] of the two nieces will crowd the house. Beds will be [illegible]ss Partington, a sweet, modest, genteel girl, will be prodigiously taken with my charmer; will want to begin a friendship with her. A share in her bed, for one night only, will be requested. Who knows but on that very Monday night I may be so unhappy as to give *mortal offence* to my beloved? *The shiest birds may be caught napping.* Should she *attempt to fly me* upon it, cannot I *detain her?* Should she *actually fly,* cannot I *bring her back* by authority civil or uncivil, if I have evidence upon evidence that she acknowledged, though but tacitly, her marriage? and *should I,* or *should I not* succeed, and she *forgive me,* or if she but descend to *expostulate,* or if she *bear me in her sight;* then will she be all my own. All delicacy is my charmer. I long to see how such a delicacy, on *any* of these occasions, will behave. And in my situation it behoves me to provide against every accident.

I must take care, knowing what an eel I have to do with, that the little wriggling rogue does not slip through my fingers. How silly should I look, staring after her, when she had shot from me into the muddy river, her family, from which with so much difficulty I have taken her!

Mr. Lovelace to John Belford, Esq.

Sunday.

HAVE been at church, Jack—behaved admirably [illegible] too! Eyes did not much wander. How could they, when the loveliest object, infinitely the loveliest, in the whole church, was in my view?

But let me tell thee what passed between us in my first visit of this morning; and then I will acquaint thee more largely with my good behaviour at church.

I could not be admitted till after eight. I found her ready prepared to go out. I pretended to be ignorant of her intention, having charged Dorcas not to own that she had told me of it.

Going abroad, madam?—with an air of indifference.

Yes, sir; I intend to go to church.

I hope, madam, I shall have the honour to attend you.

No: she designed to take a chair, and go to the next church.

This startled me: a chair to carry her to the next church from Mrs. Sinclair's, her right name not Sinclair, and to bring her back hither, in the face of people who might not think well of the house! There was no permitting that. Yet I was to appear indifferent. But said, I should take it for a favour if she would permit me to attend her in a coach, as there was time [illegible] St. Paul's.

She made objections to the gaiety of my dress; and [illegible] that, if she went to St. Paul's, she could go in a coach without *me.*

I objected Singleton and her brother, and offered to dress in the plainest suit I had.

I beg the favour of attending you, dear madam, said I. I have not been at church a great while: we shall sit in different stalls: and the next time I go, I hope it will be to give myself a title to the greatest blessing I can receive.

She made some further objections: but at last permitted me the honour of attending her.

Sunday Evening.

W[illegible]gether in Mrs. Sinclair's parlour. All *excessively* [illegible] two nieces have topped their parts; Mrs. Sinclai[illegible]ers. Never so easy as now! "She really thought a little oddly of these people at first, she said: Mrs. Sinclair seemed very forbidding! Her nieces were persons with whom she could not wish to be acquainted. But really we should not be too hasty in our censures. Some people improve upon us. The widow seems *tolerable.*" She went no farther than *tolerable.*

I have been letting her into thy character, and into the characters of my other three esquires, in hopes to excite her curiosity to see you to-morrow night.

By her after observations upon each of you, I shall judge what I may or may not do to *obtain* or *keep* her good opinion; what she will *like,* what *not;* and so pursue the one, or avoid the other, as I see proper. So, while she is penetrating into your shallow heads, I shall enter *her* heart, and know what to bid *my own* to hope for.

The house is to be taken in three weeks: all will be over in three weeks, or bad will be my luck! Who knows but in three days? Have I not carried that great point of making her pass for my wife to the people below? And that other great one of fixing myself here night and day? What woman ever escaped me, who lodged under one roof with me? The house too, THE house; the people, people after my own heart: her servants, Will and Dorcas, both *my* servants. *Three days,* did I say! Pho! pho! pho! *Three hours!*

. . . . . .

I have carried my third point; but so extremely to the dislike of my charmer, that I have been threatened, for suffering Miss Partington to be introduced to her without her leave.

To be obliged to appear before my friends as what she was not! She was for insisting that I should acquaint the women here with the truth of the matter; and not go on propagating stories for her to countenance; making her a sharer in my guilt.

But the point thus so much against her will carried, I doubt thou wilt see in her more of a sullen than of an obliging charmer. For when Miss Partington was withdrawn, "What was Miss Partington to her? In her situation she wanted [illegible] acquaintance. And what were my four friends to her [illegible]esent circumstances? She would assure me, if eve[illegible] And there she stopped, with a twirl of her hand.

If you love to see features that glow, though the heart is frozen, and never yet was thawed; if you love fine sense, and adages flowing through teeth of ivory and lips of coral; an eye that penetrates all things; a voice that is harmony itself; an air of grandeur, mingled with a sweetness that cannot be described; a politeness that, if ever equalled, was never excelled—you'll see all these excellences, and ten times more, in this my GLORIANA.

MISS CLARISSA HARLOWE TO MISS HOWE

Sunday Evening, April 30.

I AM STILL well pleased with Mr. Lovelace's behaviour. We have had a good deal of serious discourse together. The man has really just and good notions. He confesses how much he is pleased with this day, and hopes for many such. Nevertheless, he ingenuously warned me that his unlucky vivacity might return: but he doubted not that he should be fixed at last by my example and conversation.

I cannot but call this, my circumstances considered, a happy day to the end of it. Indeed, my dear, I think I could prefer him to all the men I ever knew, were he but to be always what he has been this day. You see how ready I am to own all you have charged me with, when I find myself out. It is a difficult thing, I believe, sometimes, for a young creature that is able to deliberate with herself, to know when she loves, or when she hates: but I am resolved, as much as possible, to be determined both in my hatred and love by *actions*, as *they* make the man worthy or unworthy.

She dates again on Monday, and declares herself highly displeased at Miss Partington's being introduced to her: and still more for being obliged to promise to be present at Mr. Lovelace's collation.

Miss Clarissa Harlowe to Miss Howe

Monday Night, May 1.

I HAVE just escaped from the very disagreeable company I was obliged, so much against my will, to be in.

The names of the gentlemen are Belton, Mowbray, Tourville, and Belford. These four, with Mrs. Sinclair, Miss Partington, the great heiress mentioned in my last, Mr. Lovelace, and myself, made up the company.

I gave you before the favourable side of Miss Partington's character, such as it was given me by Mrs. Sinclair and her nieces. I will now add a few words from my own observation upon her behaviour in *this* company.

In *better* company perhaps she would have appeared to less disadvantage: but, notwithstanding her *innocent looks,* which Mr. Lovelace also highly praised, he is the last person whose judgment I would take upon real modesty. For I observed, that, upon some talk from the gentlemen, not free enough to be openly censured, yet too indecent in its implication to come from well-bred persons, in the company of virtuous people, this young lady was very ready to apprehend; and yet, by smiles and simperings, to encourage, rather than discourage, the culpable freedoms of persons, who, in what they went out of their way to say, must either be guilty of absurdity, meaning *nothing;* or, meaning *something,* of rudeness.

Mr. Belford, it seems, is about seven- or eight-and-twenty. He is the youngest of the five, except Mr. Lovelace: and they are perhaps the wickedest; for they seem to lead the other three as they please. Mr. Belford, as the others, dresses gaily: but has not those advantages of person, nor from his dress, which Mr. Lovelace is too proud of. He has, however, the appearance and air of a gentleman. He is well read in classical authors, and in the best English poets and writers: and, by his means, the conversation took now and then a more agreeable turn: and I, who endeavoured to put the best face I could upon my situation, as I passed for Mrs. Lovelace with them, made shift to join in it, at such times; and received abundance of compliments from all the company, on the observations I made.

How little soever matters in general may be to our liking, we are apt, when hope is strong enough to permit it, to endeavour to make the best we can of the lot we have drawn; and I could not but observe often, how much Mr. Lovelace excelled all his four friends in everything they seemed desirous to excel in. But, as to wit and vivacity, he had no equal there.

He has indeed so many advantages in his person and manner, that what would be inexcusable in another, if one took not great care to watch over one's self, and to distinguish what is the essence of right and wrong, would look becoming in him.

It must, indeed, be confessed, that there is in his whole deportment a natural dignity, which renders all insolent or imperative demeanour as unnecessary as inexcusable. Then that deceiving sweetness which appears in his smiles, in his accent, in his whole aspect and address, when he thinks it worth his while to oblige, or endeavour to attract, how does this show that he was *born* innocent, as I may say; that he was not *naturally* the cruel, the boisterous, the impetuous creature, which the wicked company he may have fallen into have made him! For he has, besides, an open, and, I think, an honest countenance. On all these specious appearances, have I founded my hopes of seeing him a reformed man.

One compliment passed from Mr. Belford to Mr. Lovelace, which hastened my quitting the shocking company—"You are a happy man, Mr. Lovelace," said he, upon some fine speeches made him by Mrs. Sinclair, and assented to by Miss Partington: "You have so much courage, and so much wit, that neither man nor woman can stand before you."

Mr. Belford looked at me when he spoke: yes, my dear, he smilingly looked at me: and he looked upon his complimented friend: and all their *assenting,* and therefore *affronting* eyes, both men's and women's, were turned upon your Clarissa: at least my self-reproaching heart made me think so; for that would hardly permit my eye to look up.

Oh, my dear! were but a woman, who gives reason to the world to think her to be in love with a man (and this must be believed to be my case; or to what can my *supposed* voluntary going off with Mr. Lovelace be imputed?), to reflect one moment on the exaltation she gives *him,* and the disgrace she brings upon *herself;* the low pity, the silent contempt, the insolent sneers and whispers, to which she makes herself obnoxious from a censuring world of both sexes; how would she despise herself!

Miss Clarissa Harlowe to Miss Howe

Monday Midnight.

I am very much vexed and disturbed at an odd incident.

Mrs. Sinclair has just now left me; I believe in displeasure, on my declining to comply with a request she made me: which was to admit Miss Partington to a share in my bed; her house being crowded by her nieces' guests and by their attendants, as well as by those of Miss Partington.

She was loath, she said, that so delicate a young creature and so great a fortune as Miss Partington should be put to lie with Dorcas in a press-bed. She should be very sorry, if she had asked an improper thing. She had never been so put to it before.

I am now out of humour with him, with myself, with all the world, but you. His companions are shocking creatures. Why, again I repeat, should he have been desirous to bring me into such company? Once more, I like him not. Indeed I do not like him!

Miss Clarissa Harlowe to Miss Howe

Tuesday, May 2.

With infinite regret I am obliged to tell you, that I can no longer write to you, or receive letters from you. Your mother has sent me a letter enclosed in a cover to Mr. Lovelace, directed for him at Lord M.'s (and which was brought him just now), reproaching me on this subject in very angry terms, and forbidding me, "as I would not be thought to intend to make her and you unhappy, to write to you without her leave."

This, therefore, is the last you must receive from me, till happier days: and as my prospects are not very bad, I presume we shall soon have leave to write again; and even to see each other: since an alliance with a family so honourable as Mr. Lovelace's is, will not be a disgrace.

Your ever obliged and affectionate,

Clarissa Harlowe.

Miss Howe to Miss Clarissa Harlowe

Wedn., May 3.

I am astonished that my mother should take such a step—purely to exercise an unreasonable act of authority; and to oblige the most remorseless hearts in the world. If I find that I can be of use to you, either by advice or information, do you think I will not give it?

This I will come into, if it will make you easy—I will forbear to write to *you* for a few days, if nothing extraordinary happen; and till the rigour of her prohibition is abated. But be assured that I will not dispense with your writing to *me.*

But how will I help myself? How! Easily enough. For I do assure you that I want but very little further provocation to fly privately to London. And if I do, I will not leave you till I see you either honourably married, or absolutely quit of the wretch: and in this last case, I will take you down with me, in defiance of the whole world: or, if you refuse to go with me, stay with you, and accompany you as your shadow whithersoever you go.

If anything happen to delay your nuptials, I would advise you to remove: but if you marry, perhaps you may think it no great matter to stay where you are till you take possession of your own estate. The knot once tied, and with so resolute a man, it is my opinion your relations will soon resign what they cannot legally hold: and, were even a litigation to follow, you will not be *able,* nor ought you to be *willing,* to help it: for your estate will then be his right; and it will be unjust to wish it to be withheld from him.

I am not displeased with his proposal about the widow lady's house. But if it must be three weeks before you can be certain about it, surely you need not put off his day for that space: and he may bespeak his equipages.

I repeat—continue to write to me. I am, and ever will be,

Your most affectionate

Anna Howe.

MISS CLARISSA HARLOWE TO MISS HOWE

Thursday, May 4.

I FOREGO every other engagement, I suspend every wish, I banish every other fear, to take up my pen, to beg of you that you will not think of being *guilty* of such an act of love as I can never thank you for; but must for ever regret.

If I write, as I find I must, I insist upon *your* forbearing to write. Your silence to *this* shall be the sign to me that you will not think of the rashness you threaten me with; and that you will obey your mother as to *your own* part of the correspondence, however: especially as you can inform or advise me in every weighty case by Mr. Hickman's pen.

My trembling writing will show you, my dear impetuous creature, what a trembling heart you have given to

Your ever obliged,

Or, if you take so rash a step,

Your for ever disobliged,

Clarissa Harlowe.

My clothes were brought to me just now. But you have so much discomposed me, that I have no heart to look into the trunks. Why, why, my dear, will you frighten me with your flaming love?

MR. HICKMAN TO MISS CLARISSA HARLOWE

Friday, May 5.

MADAM,—I have the honour of dear Miss Howe's commands to acquaint you, without knowing the occasion, "That she is excessively concerned for the concern she has given you in her last letter: and that, if you will but write to her, under cover as before, she will have no thoughts of what you are so very apprehensive about." Yet she bid me write,

"That if she has but the *least* imagination that she can *serve* you, and save you," those are her words, "all the censures of the world will be but of second consideration with her."

Your faithful and most obedient servant,

Ch. Hickman.

MR. BELFORD TO ROBERT LOVELACE, ESQ.

Edgware, Tuesday Night, May 2.

WITHOUT staying for the promised letter from you to inform us what the lady says of *us,* I write to tell you that we are all of *one* opinion with regard to *her;* which is, that there is not of her age a finer woman in the world, as to her understanding.

Permit me, dear Lovelace, to be a means of saving this excellent creature from the dangers she hourly runs from the most plotting heart in the world. In a former, I pleaded your own family, Lord M.'s wishes particularly; and then I had not seen her: but now, I join *her* sake, *honour's* sake, motives of justice, generosity, gratitude, and humanity, which are all concerned in the preservation of so fine a woman. Thou knowest not the anguish I should have had (whence arising, I cannot devise), had I not known before I set out this morning, that the incomparable creature had disappointed thee in thy cursed view of getting her to admit the specious Partington for a bedfellow.

I have done nothing but talk of this lady ever since I saw her. There is something *so awful,* and yet *so sweet,* in her aspect, that were I to have the virtues and the graces all drawn in one piece, they should be taken, every one of them, from different airs and attitudes in her. She was born to adorn the age she was given to, and would be an ornament to the first dignity. What a piercing, yet gentle eye; every glance, I thought, mingled with love and fear of you! What a sweet smile darting through the cloud that overspread her fair face; demonstrating that she had more apprehensions and grief at her heart than she cared to express! And wouldst thou make *her* unhappy for her whole life, and *thyself* not happy for a single moment?

Hitherto, it is not too late; and that perhaps is as much as can be said, if thou meanest to preserve her esteem and good opinion, as well as person; for I think it is impossible she can get out of thy hands now she is in this cursed house. Be honest, and marry; and be thankful that she will condescend to have thee.

Thy partial friend,
J. Belford.

MR. LOVELACE TO JOHN BELFORD, ESQ.

Wednesday, May 3.

I OWN with thee, and with the poet, *that sweet are the joys that come with willingness*—but is it to be expected that a *woman of education,* and a *lover of forms,* will yield before she is attacked? And have I so much as summoned this to surrender? I doubt not but I shall meet with difficulty. I must, therefore, make my first effort by surprise. There may possibly be some *cruelty* necessary: but there may be *consent in struggle;* there may be *yielding in resistance.* But the first conflict over, whether the following may not be weaker and weaker, till *willingness* ensue, is the point to be tried. I will illustrate what I have said by the simile of a bird new-caught. We begin, when boys, with birds, and, when grown up, go on to women; and both, perhaps, in turn, experience our sportive cruelty.

Hast thou not observed the charming gradations by which the ensnared volatile has been brought to bear with its new condition? How, at first, refusing all sustenance, it beats and bruises itself against its wires, till it makes its gay plumage fly about, and overspread its well-secured cage. Now it gets out its head; sticking only at its beautiful shoulders: then, with difficulty, drawing back its head, it gasps for breath, and, erectly perched, with meditating eyes, first surveys, and then attempts, its wired canopy. As it gets breath, with renewed rage it beats and bruises again its pretty head and sides, bites the wires, and pecks at the fingers of its delighted tamer. Till at last, finding its efforts ineffectual, quite tired and breathless, it lays itself down and pants at the bottom of the cage, seeming to bemoan its cruel fate and forfeited liberty. And after a few days, its struggles to escape still diminishing as it finds it to no purpose to attempt it, its new habitation becomes familiar; and it hops about from perch to perch, resumes its wonted cheerfulness, and every day sings a song to amuse itself, and reward its keeper.

Now let me tell thee, that I have known a bird actually starve itself, and die with grief, at its being caught and caged. But never did I meet with a woman who was so silly. Yet have I heard the dear souls most vehemently threaten their own lives on such an occasion. But it is saying nothing in a woman's favour, if we do not allow her to have *more sense than a bird*. And yet we must all own, that it is more difficult to catch a *bird* than a *lady*.

To pursue the comparison. If the disappointment of the captivated lady be very great, she will threaten, indeed, as I said: she will even refuse her sustenance for some time, especially if you entreat her much, and she thinks she gives you concern by her refusal. But then the stomach of the dear sullen one will soon return. 'Tis pretty to see how she comes to by degrees: pressed by appetite, she will first steal, perhaps, a weeping morsel by herself; then be brought to piddle and sigh, and sigh and piddle, before you; now and then, if her viands be unsavoury, swallowing with them a relishing tear or two: then she comes to eat and drink, to oblige you: then resolves to live for your sake: her exclamations will, in the next place, be turned into blandishments; her vehement upbraidings into gentle murmurings—How *dare* you, traitor! into How *could* you, dearest! She will draw you to her, instead of pushing you from her: no longer, with unsheathed claws, will she resist you; but, like a pretty, playful, wanton kitten, with gentle paws and concealed talons, tap your cheek, and with intermingled smiles, and tears, and caresses, implore your consideration for her, and your *constancy:* all the favour she then has to ask of you! And this is the time, were it given to man to confine himself to one object, to be happier every day than other.

Now, Belford, were I to go no further than I have gone with my beloved Miss Harlowe, how shall I know the difference between *her* and *another* bird? To let her fly now, what a pretty jest would that be! How do I know, except I try, whether she may not be brought to sing me a fine song, and to be as well contented as I have brought other birds to be, and very shy ones too?

MR. LOVELACE. [*In continuation*]

WELL sayest thou, that mine is the most plotting heart in the world. Thou dost me honour; and I thank thee heartily. Thou art no bad judge.

Then, that she *loves me,* as thou imaginest, by no means appears clear to me. Her conditional offers to renounce me; the little confidence she places in me; entitle me to ask, What merit can she have with a man who won her in spite of herself; and who fairly, in set and obstinate battle, took her prisoner?

As to what thou inferrest from her *eye* when with us, thou knowest nothing of her *heart* from that, if thou imaginest there was one glance of love shot from it. Well did I note her eye, and plainly did I see that it was all but just civil disgust to me and to the company I had brought her into.

Were I to take thy stupid advice and marry, what a figure should I make in rakish annals! The lady in my power: yet not having *intended* to put herself in my power: declaring against love, and a rebel to it: so much open-eyed caution: no confidence in my honour: her family expecting the worst *hath* passed; herself seeming to expect that the worst *will* be attempted: What! wouldst thou not have me act in character?

MR. BELFORD TO ROBERT LOVELACE, ESQ.

Edgware, Thursday, May 4.

IF THOU persistest; if thou wilt avenge thyself on this sweet lamb, which thou hast singled out from a flock thou hatest, for the faults of the dogs who kept it: if thou art not to be moved by beauty, by learning, by prudence, by innocence, all shining out in one charming object; but she must fall, fall by the man whom she has chosen for her protector; I would not for a thousand worlds have thy crime to answer for.

Upon my faith, Lovelace, the subject sticks with me, notwithstanding I find I have not the honour of the lady's good opinion. And the more, when I reflect upon her father's brutal curse, and the villainous hard-heartedness of all her family. But nevertheless, I should be desirous to know (*if thou wilt pro-*

ceed) by what gradations, arts, and contrivances thou effectest thy ingrateful purpose. And, O Lovelace, I conjure thee, if thou art a *man,* let not the specious devils thou hast brought her among be suffered to triumph over her; nor make her the victim of *unmanly artifices.* If she yield to *fair seduction,* if I may so express myself; if thou canst raise a weakness in her by love, or by arts not inhuman; I shall the less pity her: and shall then conclude that there is not a woman in the world who can resist a bold and resolute lover.

J. Belford.

MISS CLARISSA HARLOWE TO MISS HOWE

I THANK YOU and Mr. Hickman for his letter, sent me with such kind expedition; and proceed to obey my dear menacing tyranness.

Mr. Lovelace is constantly accusing me of over-scrupulousness.

Silly and partial encroacher! not to know *to what to attribute the reserve I am forced to treat him with!* But his *pride* has eaten up his *prudence.* It is indeed a dirty low pride, that has swallowed up the *true* pride, which should have set him above the vanity that has overrun him.

Yet he pretends that he has no pride but in obliging me: and is always talking of his reverence and humility, and such sort of stuff: Pride is an infallible sign of weakness; of something wrong in the head or heart. Mr. Lovelace is extremely sunk in my opinion since Monday night; nor can I see before me anything that can afford me a pleasing hope.

I think I mentioned to you that my clothes were brought me on Thursday; but neither my few guineas with them, nor any of my books, except a *Drexelius on Eternity,* the good old *Practice of Piety,* and a *Francis Spira.*

COL. MORDEN TO MISS CLARISSA HARLOWE

Florence, April 13.

I AM EXTREMELY concerned to hear of a difference betwixt the rest of a family so near and dear to me, and *you* still dearer to me than any of the rest.

My Cousin James has acquainted me with the offers you have had, and with your refusals. I wonder not at either.

I know very little of either of the gentlemen; but of Mr. Lovelace I know more than of Mr. Solmes. I wish I could say more to his advantage than I can.

If your parents and you differ in sentiment on this important occasion, let me ask you, my dear cousin, who ought to give way? I own to you, that I should have thought there could not anywhere have been a more suitable match for you than with Mr. Lovelace, had he been a moral man. I should have very little to say against a man, of whose actions I am not to set up myself as a judge, did he not address my cousin.

But as to what may be the consequence respecting yourself, respecting a young lady of your talents, from the preference you are suspected to give to a libertine, I would have you, my dear cousin, consider what that may be. To be agreeable to him, and to hope to preserve an interest in his affections, you must probably be obliged to abandon all your own laudable pursuits. You must enter into his pleasures and distastes. You must give up your own virtuous companions for his profligate ones—perhaps be forsaken by yours, because of the scandal he daily gives.

A libertine, my dear cousin, a *plotting*, an *intriguing* libertine, must be generally *remorseless—unjust* he must always be. He has great contempt for your sex. He believes no woman chaste, because he is a profligate. Every woman who *favours him, confirms him* in his wicked incredulity.

You have an opportunity offered you to give the highest instance that can be given of filial duty. Embrace it. It is worthy of you. It is expected *from* you; however, for your inclination sake, we may be sorry that you are called upon to give it.

Your most affectionate and faithful servant,

Wm. Morden.

MISS CLARISSA HARLOWE TO MISS HOWE

Sunday Night, May 7.

WHEN YOU REFLECT upon my unhappy situation, which is attended with so many indelicate and even shocking circumstances, some of which my pride will not let me think of with patience; all aggravated by the contents of my cousin's affecting letter; you will not wonder that the vapourishness which has laid hold of my heart should rise to my pen.

Now, my dear, I cannot bear the life I live. I would be glad at my heart to be out of his reach.

What I am thinking of, is this: "Suppose Mr. Hickman, whose good character has gained him everybody's respect, should put himself in my Uncle Harlowe's way? And (as if from your knowledge of the state of things between Mr. Lovelace and me) assure him not only of the above particulars, but that I am under no obligations that shall hinder me from taking his directions?"

I submit the whole to your discretion, whether to pursue it at all, or in what manner. But if it *be* pursued, and if my uncle refuses to interest himself in my favour upon Mr. Hickman's application as from you I can then have no hope; and my next step, in the mind I am in, shall be to throw myself into the protection of the ladies of his family.

The lady dates again on Monday, to let Miss Howe know that Mr. Lovelace, on observing her uneasiness, had introduced to her Mr. Mennell, Mrs. Fretchville's kinsman, who managed all her affairs. She calls him a young officer of sense and politeness, who gave her an account of the house and furniture; as also of the melancholy way Mrs. Fretchville is in.

She tells Miss Howe how extremely urgent Mr. Lovelace was with the gentleman, to get his spouse (as he now always calls her before company) a sight of the house: and that Mr. Mennell undertook that very afternoon to show her all of it, except the apartment Mrs. Fretchville should be in when she went. But that she chose not to take another step till she knew how she approved of her scheme to have her uncle sounded; and with what success, if tried, it would be attended.

Mr. Lovelace gives his friend an account of the lady's pee-

vishness and dejection, on receiving a letter with her clothes. He regrets that he has lost her confidence; which he attributes to his bringing her into the company of his four companions.

Mentioning his introducing Mr. Mennell to her,

Now, Jack, *says he,* was it not very kind of Mr. Mennell (*Captain* Mennell I sometimes called him; for among the military men there is no such officer, thou knowest, as a *lieutenant,* or an *ensign*--was it not very kind in him) to come along with me so readily as he did, to satisfy my beloved about the vapourish lady and the house?

But who is Captain Mennell?

Knowest thou not young Newcomb, honest Doleman's nephew?

But Mennell, now he has seen this angel of a woman, has qualms; that's the devil! At times I have confounded qualms myself. But say not a word of them to the confraternity: nor laugh at me for them thyself.

This perverse lady keeps me at such distance, that I am sure something is going on between her and Miss Howe, notwithstanding the prohibition from Mrs. Howe to both.

He then, in apprehension that something is meditating between the two ladies, or that something may be set on foot to get Miss Harlowe out of his hands, relates several of his contrivances, and boasts of his instructions given in writing to Dorcas and to his servant Will Summers; and says that he has provided against every possible accident, even to bring her back *if she should escape, or in case she should go abroad, and then* refuse to return; *and hopes so to manage, as that, should he make an attempt, whether he succeed in it or not, he may have a pretence to detain her.*

He then proceeds as follows:

I have ordered Dorcas to cultivate by all means her lady's favour; to lament her incapacity as to writing and reading. I have moreover given the wench an ivory-leafed pocket-book, with a silver pencil, that she may make memoranda on occasion.

. . . . . .

I gave thee just now some of *my* contrivances. Dorcas, who is ever attentive to all her lady's motions, has given me some instances of her *mistress's* precautions. She wafers her letters, it seems, in two places; pricks the wafers; and then seals upon them. No doubt but the same care is taken with regard to those brought to her; for she always examines the seals of the latter before she opens them.

I must, I must come at them.

Mr. Lovelace to John Belford, Esq.

Tuesday, May 9.

I am a very unhappy man. This lady is said to be one of the sweetest-tempered creatures in the world: and so I thought her. But to *me,* she is one of the most perverse. I imagined, for a long while, that we were born to make each other happy: but, quite the contrary; we really seem to be sent to plague each other.

I had been out. On my return, meeting Dorcas on the stairs —Your lady in her chamber, Dorcas? In the dining-room, sir: and if ever you hope for an opportunity to come at a letter, it must be now. For at her feet I saw one lie, which, as may be seen by its open folds, she has been reading, with a little parcel of others she is now busied with—all pulled out of her pocket, as I believe: so, sir, you'll know where to find them another time.

I was ready to leap for joy, and entering into the dining-room with an air of transport, I boldly clasped my arms about her, as she sat; she huddling up her papers in her handkerchief all the time; the dropped paper unseen. Oh, my dearest life, a lucky expedient have Mr. Mennell and I hit upon just now. In order to hasten Mrs. Fretchville to quit the house, I have agreed, if you approve of it, to entertain her cook, her housemaid and two menservants, till you are provided to your mind.

Thus will you have a charming house entirely ready to receive you. Some of the ladies of my family will soon be with you: they will not permit you long to suspend my happy day. And that nothing may be wanting to gratify your utmost punctilio, I will till then consent to stay here at Mrs. Sinclair's, while you reside at your new house; and leave the rest to your own generosity. O my beloved creature, will not this be agreeable to you? I am sure it will—it must—and clasping her closer to me, I gave her a more fervent kiss than ever I had dared to give her before. I permitted not my ardour to overcome my discretion, however; for I took care to set my foot upon the letter, and scraped it farther from her, as it were behind her chair.

She was in a passion at the liberty I took. Bowing low, I begged her pardon; and stooping still lower, in the same motion, took up the letter, and whipped it into my bosom.

The letter being unfolded, I could not put it into my bosom without alarming her ears, as my sudden motion did her eyes. Up she flew in a moment: Traitor! Judas! her eyes flashing lightning, and a perturbation in her eager countenance, so charming! What have you taken up? And then, what for both my ears I durst not to have done to her, she made no scruple to seize the stolen letter, though in my bosom.

I clasped her hand, which had hold of the ravished paper, between mine: O my beloved creature! said I, can you think I have not *some* curiosity?

Let go my hand!—stamping with her pretty foot. How dare you, sir! At this rate, I see—too plainly I see—and more she could not say: but, gasping, was ready to faint with passion and affright; the devil a bit of her accustomed gentleness to be seen in her charming face, or to be heard in her musical voice.

Once more I got hold of the rumpled-up letter! *Impudent man!* were her words: stamping again. *For God's sake,* then it was. I let go my prize, lest she should faint away: but had the pleasure first to find my hand within both hers, she trying to open my reluctant fingers.

When she had got it in her possession, she flew to the door. I threw myself in her way, shut it, and, in the humblest manner, besought her to forgive me. Pushing me rudely from the door, as if I had been nothing, she gaining that force through passion, which I had lost through fear, out she shot to her own apartment (thank my stars she could fly no farther!); and as soon as she entered it, in a passion still, she double-locked and double-bolted herself in.

Miss Howe to Miss Clarissa Harlowe

Wednesday, May 10.

I much approve of your resolution to leave this wretch, if you can make up with your uncle.

I hate the man—most heartily do I hate him. May you have encouragement to fly the foolish wretch!

I have other reasons to wish you may: for I have just made an acquaintance with one who knows a vast deal of his private history. The man is really a villain, my dear! an execrable one! if all be true that I have heard!

I will have your uncle sounded, as you desire, and that out of hand. But yet I am afraid of the success; and this for several reasons.

I am sorry to tell you that I have reason to think that your brother has not laid aside his foolish plot. A sunburnt, sailor-looking fellow was with me just now, pretending great service to you from Captain Singleton, could he be admitted to your speech. I pleaded ignorance as to the place of your abode. The fellow was too well instructed for me to get anything out of him.[1]

Miss Clarissa Harlowe to Miss Howe

Friday, May 12.

I am sorry you have reason to think Singleton's projects are not at an end. But who knows what the sailor had to propose? Yet had any good been intended me, this method would hardly have been fallen upon.

I have made a handle of Mr. Lovelace's bold attempt and freedom, as I told you I would, to keep him ever since at distance, that I may have an opportunity to see the success of the application to my uncle, and to be at liberty to embrace any favourable overtures that may arise from it. Yet he has been very importunate, and twice brought Mr. Mennell from Mrs. Fretchville to talk about the house. *If I should be obliged to make up with him again, I shall think I am always doing myself a spite.*

[1] An agent of Lovelace.

Sunday, May 14.

I have not been able to avoid a short debate with Mr. Lovelace. I had ordered a coach to the door. When I had notice that it was come, I went out of my chamber to go to it; but met him dressed on the stairs head, with a book in his hand, but without his hat and sword. He asked with an air very solemn, yet respectful, if I were going abroad. I told him I was. He desired leave to attend me, if I were going to church. I refused him. And then he complained heavily of my treatment of him; and declared that he would not live such another week as the past, for the world.

I owned to him very frankly, that I had made an application to my friends; and that I was resolved to keep myself to myself till I knew the issue of it.

He coloured, and seemed surprised. But checking himself in something he was going to say, he pleaded my danger from Singleton, and again desired to attend me.

And then he told me that Mrs. Fretchville had desired to continue a fortnight longer in the house. This, madam, has been an unhappy week; for had I not stood upon such bad terms with you, *you might have been now mistress of that house;* and probably had my Cousin Montague, if not Lady Betty, actually with you.

And so, sir, taking all you say for granted, your Cousin Montague cannot come to Mrs. Sinclair's? What, pray, is her objection to Mrs. Sinclair's? Is this house fit for me to live in a month or two, and not fit for any of your relations for a few days? Then, pushing by him, I hurried downstairs.

He called to Dorcas to bring him his sword and hat; and following me down into the passage, placed himself between me and the door; and again desired leave to attend me.

Then turning to him, I asked if he kept me there his prisoner?

Dorcas just then bringing him his sword and hat, he opened the street door, and taking my reluctant hand, led me, in a very obsequious manner, to the coach.

He was very full of assiduities all the way; while I was as reserved as possible: and when I returned, dined, as I had done the greatest part of the week, by myself.

Clarissa Harlowe.

Miss Howe to Mrs. Judith Norton

Thursday, May 11.

Good Mrs. Norton,—Cannot you, without naming *me* as an adviser, who am hated by the family, contrive a way to let Mrs. Harlowe know, that in an accidental conversation with me, you had been assured that my beloved friend pines after a reconciliation with her relations?

Pray acquaint me by a line of the result of your interposition. If it prove not such as may be reasonably hoped for, our dear friend shall know nothing of this step from me; and pray let her not from you.

Your true friend,
Anna Howe.

Mrs. Norton to Miss Howe

Saturday, May 13.

Dear Madam,—My heart is almost broken to be obliged to let you know, that such is the situation of things in the family of my ever dear Miss Harlowe, that there can be at present no success expected from any application in her favour.

I hope in God that my beloved young lady has preserved her honour inviolate. I hope there is not a man breathing who could attempt a sacrilege so detestable. If it be not, adieu to all the comforts this life can give: since none will it be able to afford to the poor

Judith Norton.

Miss Howe to Mrs. Judith Norton

Saturday Evening, May 13.

Dear good Woman,—Your beloved's honour is inviolate! *Must* be inviolate! And *will* be so, in spite of men and devils. Could I have had hope of a reconciliation, all my view was, that she should not have had this man. All that can be said now is, she must run the risk of a bad husband: she of whom no man living is worthy!

I hate tyrants in every form and shape: but paternal and maternal tyrants are the worst of all: for they can have no bowels.

I repeat, that I pity *none* of them. Our beloved friend *only* deserves pity. She had never been in the hands of this man, but for them. She is quite blameless.

Your sincere friend and servant,

Anna Howe.

Miss Howe to Miss Clarissa Harlowe

Sunday, May 14.

How it is now, my dear, between you and Mr. Lovelace, I cannot tell. But wicked as the man is, I am afraid he must be your lord and master.

Were you once married, I should think you cannot be *very* unhappy, though you may not be so happy with him as you deserve to be. The stake he has in his country, and his reversions; the care he takes of his affairs; his freedom from obligation; nay, his pride, with your merit, must be a tolerable security for you, I should think.

By the time you have read to this place, you will have no doubt of what has been the issue of the conference between the *two gentlemen.* I am equally shocked, and enraged against them all. Against them *all,* I say; for I have tried your good Norton's weight with your mother (though at first I did not intend to tell you so), to the same purpose as the gentleman sounded your uncle. Never were there such determined brutes in the world! Why should I mince the matter? Yet would I fain, methinks, make an exception for your mother.

Your uncle will have it that you are ruined.

My dearest soul! resolve to assert your right. Claim your own, and go and live upon it, as you ought. Then, if you marry not, how will the wretches creep to you for your reversionary dispositions!

Upon the whole, it is now evident to me, and so it must be to you, when you read this letter, that you must be his. And the sooner you are so, the better. Shall we suppose that marriage is not in your power? I cannot have patience to suppose that.

I am concerned, methinks, to know how you will do to condescend (now you see you must be his), after you have kept him at such distance; and for the revenge his pride may put him upon taking for it. But let me tell you, that if my going up, and sharing fortunes with you, will prevent such a noble creature from stooping too low; much more, were it likely to prevent your ruin; I would not hesitate a moment about it. I am exasperated against your foolish, your *low-vanitied* Lovelace. But let us stoop to take the wretch as he is, and make the best of him, since you are destined to stoop, to keep grovellers and worldlings in countenance.

Give him the day. Let it be a short one. It would be derogating from your own merit, and *honour* too, let me tell you, even although he should *not* be so explicit as he ought to be, to seem but to doubt his meaning; and to wait for that explanation for which I should for ever despise him, if he makes it necessary. Twice already have you, my dear, if not oftener, *modestied* away such opportunities as you ought not to have slipped.

Adieu, my dearest friend.

Anna Howe.

MISS CLARISSA HARLOWE TO MISS HOWE

Monday Afternoon, May 15.

Now indeed it is evident, my best, my only friend, that I have but one choice to make. And now do I find that I have carried my resentment against this man too far; since now I am to appear as if under an obligation to his patience with me for a conduct which perhaps he will think (if not humoursome and childish) plainly demonstrative of my little esteem of him; of but a *secondary* esteem at least, where before, his pride rather than his merit, had made him expect a *first.* O my dear! to be cast upon a man that is not a *generous* man; that is indeed a *cruel* man! A man that is capable of creating a distress to a young creature, who by her evil destiny is thrown into his power; and then of *enjoying* it, as I may say! (I verily think I may say so, of this savage!)

You give me, my dear, good advice as to the peremptory manner in which I ought to treat him: but do you consider to *whom* it is that you give it? What, *I* to challenge a man for a husband! *I* to exert myself to quicken the delayer in his resolutions! And having, as you think, lost an opportunity, to begin to try to recall it, as *from myself,* and *for myself!* To *threaten* him, as I may say, into the marriage state! O my dear! if this be right to be done, how difficult is it, where modesty and self (or where pride, if you please) is concerned, to do that right?

Well, but now to look forward, you are of opinion that I must be his: and that I cannot leave him with reputation to myself, whether with or without his consent. I must, if so, make the best of the bad matter.

Miss Clarissa Harlowe to Miss Howe

Tuesday, May 16.

I THINK once more we seem to be in a kind of train; but through a storm.

I heard him in the dining-room at five in the morning. I had rested very ill, and was up too. But opened not my door till six: when Dorcas brought me his request for my company.

He approached me, and taking my hand as I entered the dining-room, I went not to bed, madam, till two, said he; yet slept not a wink. For God's sake, torment me not, as you have done for a week past.

He paused.

I was silent.

At first, proceeded he, I thought your resentment of a curiosity, in which I had been disappointed, could not be deep; and that it would go off of itself: but when I found it was to be kept up till you knew the success of some new overtures which you had made, and which, complied with, might have deprived me of you for ever, how, madam, could I support myself under the thoughts of having, with such a union of interests, made so little impression upon your mind in my favour?

He paused again. I was still silent. He went on.

I acknowledged that I have a *proud heart*, madam. I cannot but hope for some instances of previous and preferable favour from the lady I am ambitious to call mine; and that her choice of me should not appear, not *flagrantly* appear, directed by the perverseness of her selfish persecutors, who are my irreconcilable enemies.

Every one of these instances, said I, convinces me of your *pride* indeed, sir, but not of your *merit*. I confess that I have as much *pride* as you can have, although I hope it is of another kind than that you so *readily avow*. But if, sir, you have the least mixture in yours, of that pride which may be expected, and thought laudable, in a man of your birth, alliances, and fortune, you should rather wish, I will presume to say, to promote what you call my pride, than either to suppress it or to regret that I have it. It is *this* my acknowledged pride, proceeded I, that induces me to tell you, sir, that I think it beneath me to disown what have been my motives for declining, for some days past, any conversation with you, or visit from Mr. Mennell, that might lead to points out of my power to determine upon, until I heard from my Uncle Harlowe.

I know not, said he, what those terms were. But I can but too well guess at them; and that I was to have been the preliminary sacrifice. This, madam, after the persecutions of those relations! After what you have suffered! After what you have made me hope! Let me, my dearest creature, ask you, What sort of pride must *his* be, which can dispense with inclination and preference in the lady whom he adores? What must be that love——

Love, sir! who talks of *love?* Have *I* ever professed, have *I* ever required of *you* professions of a passion of that nature? But there is no end of these debatings; each *so* faultless,——

I do not think myself *faultless,* madam—but——

But what, sir! Would you evermore argue with me, as if you were a child? Seeking palliations, and making promises? Promises of what, sir? Of being in future the man it is a shame a gentleman is not? Of being the man——

Good God! interrupted he, with eyes lifted up, if *thou* wert to be thus severe——

Well, well, sir (impatiently), I need only to observe, that all this vast difference in sentiments shows how unpaired our minds are—so let us——

Let us *what,* madam! And he looked so wildly, that I was a good deal terrified. Let us *what,* madam——

Why, sir, let us resolve to quit every regard for each other—nay, flame not out—I am a poor weak-minded creature in some things: but—let us resolve to quit every regard for each other that is more than civil. *This* you may depend upon: I will never marry any other man. I have seen enough of your sex; at least of *you*. A single life shall ever be *my* choice—while I will leave you at liberty to pursue *your own*.

Indifference, worse than indifference! said he, in a passion——

Interrupting him: Indifference let it be—you have not deserved that it should be other: if you have in *your own*, you have cause (at least your *pride* has) to hate me for misjudging you.

Dearest, dearest creature! snatching my hand with fierceness, let me beseech you to be *uniformly* noble! *Civil regards*, madam! *Civil regards!* Can you so expect to narrow and confine such a passion as mine!

Such a passion as yours, Mr. Lovelace, *deserves* to be narrowed and confined. It is either the passion *you* do not think it, or *I* do not. Lift up your hands and your eyes, sir, in silent wonder, if you please: but what does that wonder convince me of, but that we are not born for one another?

By my soul, said he, and grasped my hand with an eagerness that hurt it, we *were* born for one another: you *must* be mine—you *shall* be mine (and put his other arm round me), although my damnation were to be the purchase!

I was still more terrified. Let me leave you, Mr. Lovelace, said I; or do you be gone from me.

You must not go, madam! You must not leave me in anger——

I will return—I will return—when you can be less violent—less shocking.

And he let me go.

The man quite frighted me; insomuch that when I got into my chamber, I found a sudden flow of tears a great relief to me.

In half an hour, he sent a little billet, expressing his concern for the vehemence of his behaviour, and praying to see me.

I went. Because I could not help myself, I went.

He was full of his excuses.

It was very possible for him now, he said, to account for the workings of a beginning frenzy. For his part, he was near distraction. All last week to suffer as he had suffered; and now to talk of *civil regards* only, when he had hoped from the nobleness of my mind——

Hope what you will, interrupted I; I must insist upon it, that our minds are by no means suited to each other. You have brought me into difficulties. I am deserted by every friend but Miss Howe. My true sentiments I will not conceal. It is against my will that I must submit to owe protection from a brother's projects, which Miss Howe thinks are not given over, to you, who have brought me into these straits—*not* with my own concurrence brought me into them; remember that——

I do remember that, madam! So often reminded, how can I forget it?

I presume, madam, replied he, from what you have said, that your application to Harlowe Place has proved unsuccessful: I therefore hope that you will now give me leave to mention the terms in the nature of settlements, which I have long intended to propose to you; and which having till now delayed to do, through accidents not proceeding from myself, I had thoughts of urging to you *the moment you entered upon your new house;* and upon your finding yourself as independent in *appearance* as you are in *fact*. Permit me, madam, to propose these matters to you—not with an expectation of your *immediate answer;* but for your *consideration.*

He urged on upon my silence: he would call God to witness to the justice, nay to the *generosity* of his intentions to me, if I would be so good as to hear what he had to propose to me as to settlements.

In this way are we now: a sort of calm, as I said, succeeding a storm. What may happen next, whether a storm or a calm, with such a spirit as I have to deal with, who can tell?

Although circumstances have so offered that I could not take your advice as to the *manner* of dealing with him; yet you gave me so much courage by it, as has enabled me to conduct things to this issue; as well as determined me against leaving him: which, *before,* I was thinking to do, at all adventures.

I am, my dearest friend,

Your ever obliged
Clarissa Harlowe.

Miss Clarissa Harlowe to Miss Howe

Tuesday Night, May 16.

Mr. Lovelace has sent me, by Dorcas, his proposals, as follows:

"In the first place, madam, I offer to settle upon you, by way of jointure, your whole estate: and moreover to vest in trustees such a part of mine in Lancashire, as shall produce a clear four hundred pounds a year, to be paid to your sole and separate use quarterly.

"My own estate is a clear not nominal £2,000 *per annum.*

"If, as your own estate is at present in your father's hands, you rather choose that I should make a jointure out of mine, tantamount to yours, be it what it will, it shall be done.

"To show the beloved daughter the consideration I have for her, I will consent that she shall prescribe the terms of agreement in relation to the large sums, which must be in her father's hands, arising from her grandfather's estate.

"I will only add, that if I have omitted anything that would have given you further satisfaction; or if the above terms be short of what you would wish; you will be pleased to supply them as you think fit.

"You will now, dearest madam, judge how far all the rest depends upon yourself."

I shall now judge how far all the rest depends upon myself! So coldly concludes he such warm, and, in the main, unobjectionable proposals! Would you not, as you read, have supposed, that the paper would conclude with the most earnest demand of a day?

But you say there is no help. I must perhaps make *further* sacrifices. All delicacy it seems is to be at an end with me!

I will consider this paper; and write to it, if I am able: for it seems now, *all the rest depends upon myself.*

Miss Clarissa Harlowe to Miss Howe

Wednesday Morning, May 17

Mr. Lovelace would fain have engaged me last night. I desired to be excused seeing him till morning; and the rather, as there is hardly any getting from him in tolerable time over-night.

Accordingly, about seven o'clock we met in the dining-room.

I find he was full of expectation that I should meet him with a very favourable, who knows but with a *thankful* aspect? And I immediately found by his sullen countenance, that he was under no small disappointment that I did not.

My dearest love, are you well? Why look you so solemn upon me? Will your indifference never be over? If I have proposed terms in any respect *short* of your expectation——

Thus far, I told him, I could say, that my principal point was peace and reconciliation with my relations.

He asked me if I would so far permit him to touch upon the happy day, as to request the presence of Lord M. on the occasion, and to be my father.

Father had a sweet and venerable sound with it, I said. I should be glad to have a father who would own me!

Mr. Lovelace I thought seemed a little affected at the *manner* of my speaking, and perhaps at the sad reflection.

For his own part, he said, as Lord M. was so subject to the gout, he was afraid that the compliment he had just proposed to make him, might, if made, occasion a *longer suspension* than he could bear to think of: and if it did, it would vex him to the heart that he had made it.

I could not say a single word to this, you know, my dear. But you will guess at my thoughts of what he said—so much passionate love, *lip-deep!* So prudent, and so dutifully patient *at heart* to a relation he had till now so undutifully despised!

He hesitated, as if contending with himself; and after taking a turn or two about the room, he was at a great loss what to determine upon, he said, because he had not the honour of knowing when he was to be made the happiest of men. Would to God it might that very instant be resolved upon!

He stopped a moment or two, staring, in his usual confident way, in my downcast face: but if he could not, so *soon* as he wished, procure my consent to a day; in *that* case, he thought the compliment might *as well be* made to Lord M. *as not* (*see, my dear!*): since the settlements might be drawn and engrossed in the intervenient time, which would pacify his impatience, *as no time would be lost.*

You will suppose how *I* was affected by this speech, by repeating the substance of what *he* said upon it; as follows:

But, by his soul, he knew not, so much was I upon the reserve, and so much latent meaning did my eye import, whether, when he most hoped to please me, he was not farthest from doing so. Would I vouchsafe to say, whether I approved of his compliment to Lord M. or not?

To leave it to me, to choose whether the speedy day he ought to have urged for with earnestness, should be accelerated or suspended! Miss Howe, thought I, at that moment, says, I must *not* run away from this man!

To be sure, Mr. Lovelace, if this matter be *ever to be,* it must be agreeable to me to have the full approbation of *one* side, since I cannot have that of the *other.*

If this matter be ever to be! Good God! what words are those at this time of day! And full *approbation* of one side! Why that word *approbation*? when the greatest pride of all my family is that of having the honour of so dear a creature for their relation? Would to Heaven, my dearest life, added he, that, without complimenting *any*body, to-morrow might be the happiest day of my life! What say you, my angel? with a trembling impatience, that *seemed* not affected. What say you for *to-morrow?*

I was silent.

Next day, madam, if not to-morrow?

Had he given me *time* to answer, it could not have been in the affirmative, you must think—but, *in the same breath,* he went on: Or the *day after that?* And taking both my hands in his, he stared me into a half-confusion.

No, no, said I, as calmly as possible, you cannot think that I should imagine there can be reason for such a hurry. It will be most agreeable, to be sure, for my lord to be present.

I am all obedience and resignation, returned the wretch, with a self-pluming air, as if he had acquiesced to a proposal *made by me,* and had complimented me with a great piece of *self-denial.*

Is it not plain, my dear, that he designs to vex and tease me?

But when he would have *rewarded himself,* as he had heretofore called it, for this self-supposed concession, with a kiss, I repulsed him with a just and very sincere disdain.

He plainly said, that he thought our situation would entitle him to such an innocent freedom: and he was both amazed and grieved to be thus scornfully repulsed.

I abruptly broke from him. I recollect, as I passed by one of the pier-glasses, that I saw in it his clenched hand offered in wrath to his forehead: the words, *Indifference, by his soul, next to hatred,* I heard him speak: and something of *ice* he mentioned: I heard not what.

Miss Howe to Miss Clarissa Harlowe

Thursday, May 18.

I HAVE neither time nor patience, my dear friend, to answer every material article in your last letters just now received. Mr. Lovelace's proposals are all I like of him.

He, to suggest delay from a compliment to be made to Lord M. and to give time for settlements! *He,* a part of whose character it is, not to know what complaisance to his relations is—I have no patience with him! But, upon my word, were I to have been that moment in your situation, and been so treated, I would have torn his eyes out, and left it to his own heart, when I had done, to furnish the reason for it.

Would to Heaven to-morrow, without complimenting anybody, might be his happy day! Villain! After he had himself suggested the compliment! And I think he accuses YOU of delaying! Fellow, that he is!

His clenched fist offered to his forehead—I wish it had been a pole-axe, and in the hand of his worst enemy.

I will endeavour to think of some method, of some scheme, to get you from him, and to fix you safely somewhere till your Cousin Morden arrives—a scheme to lie by you, and to be pursued as occasion may be given. You are sure that you can go abroad when you please? and that our correspondence is safe? I cannot, however (for the reasons heretofore mentioned respecting your own reputation), wish you to leave him while he gives you not cause to suspect his honour.

Your ever affectionate and faithful

Anna Howe.

MR. LOVELACE TO JOHN BELFORD, ESQ.

BUT HOW stands it between thyself and the lady, methinks thou askest, since her abrupt departure from thee, and undutiful repulse of Wednesday morning?

Why, pretty well in the main. Nay, *very* well. For why? The dear saucy-face knows not how to help herself. Can fly to no other protection. And has, besides, overheard a conversation (who would have thought she had been so near?) which passed between Mrs. Sinclair, Miss Martin, and myself, that very Wednesday afternoon; which has set her heart at ease with respect to several doubtful points.

Such as, particularly, "Mrs. Fretchville's unhappy state of mind—most humanely pitied by Miss Martin, who knows her very well—the husband she has lost, and herself (as Sally says) lovers from their cradles.

"My Lord M.'s gout his only hindrance from visiting my spouse. Lady Betty and Miss Montague soon expected in town.

"My earnest desire signified to have my spouse receive those ladies in her own house, if Mrs. Fretchville would but know her own mind; and I pathetically lamented the delay occasioned by her not knowing it.

"My intention to stay at Mrs. Sinclair's, *as I said I had told them before,* while my spouse resides in her own house, in order to gratify her utmost punctilio.

"My passion for my beloved (which, as I told them in a high and fervent accent, was the truest that man could have for woman) I boasted of. It was, in short, I said, of the *true platonic kind;* or I had no notion of what platonic love was.

"Sally and Mrs. Sinclair next praised, *but not grossly,* my beloved. Sally particularly admired her purity; called it exemplary; yet (to avoid suspicion) expressed her thoughts that she was *rather over-nice,* if she might presume to say so *before me*. But nevertheless she applauded me for the strict observation I made of my vow.

"I more freely blamed her reserves to me; called her cruel; inveighed against her relations; doubted her love. Every favour I asked of her denied me. Yet my behaviour to her as pure and delicate when alone, as when before them—hinted at something that had passed between us that very day, that showed her indifference to me in so strong a light, that I could not bear it. But that I would ask her for her company to the play of *Venice Preserved,* given out for Saturday night as a benefit play; the prime actors to be in it; and this, to see if I were to be denied every favour. Yet, for my own part, I loved not *tragedies;* though she did, for the sake of the instruction, the warning, and the example generally given in them.

"Sally, meantime, objected Singleton, that *I* might answer the objection, and save my beloved the trouble of making it, or debating the point with me; and on this occasion I regretted that her brother's projects were not laid aside; since, if they had been given up, I would have gone in person to bring up the ladies of my family to attend my spouse.

"I then, from a letter just before received from one of her father's family, warned them of a person who had undertaken to find us out, and whom I thus in writing (having called for pen and ink) described, that they might arm all the family against him: 'A sun-burnt, pock-fretten sailor, ill-looking, big-boned; his stature about six foot; an heavy eye, an overhanging brow, a deck-treading stride in his walk; a couteau generally by his side; lips parched from his gums, as if by staring at the sun in hot climates; a brown coat; a coloured handkerchief about his neck; an oaken plant in his hand, near as long as himself, and proportionably thick.'

"No questions asked by this fellow must be answered. They should call *me* to him. But not let my beloved know a tittle of this, so long as it could be helped. And I added, that if her brother or Singleton came, and if they behaved civilly, I would, for *her sake,* be civil to *them*: and in this case, she had nothing to do but to own her marriage, and there could be no pretence for violence on either side. But most fervently I swore, that if she were *conveyed away,* either by *persuasion* or *force,* I would directly, *on missing her but one day,* go to demand her at Harlowe Place, whether she were there or not; and if I recovered not a sister, I would have a brother; and should find out a captain of a ship as well as he."

Thursday we were very happy. All the morning *extremely* happy. I kissed her charming hand—*fifty* times kissed her hand, I believe; once her cheek, intending her lip, but so rapturously, that she could not help seeming angry.

Had she not thus kept me at arm's length; had she not denied me those innocent liberties which our sex, from step to step, aspire to; could I but have gained access to her in her hours of heedlessness and dishabille; we had been familiarized to each other long ago. But keep her up ever so late; meet her ever so early; by breakfasttime she is dressed for the day; and at her *earliest hour,* as nice as others dressed.

Thursday morning, as I said, we were extremely happy. About *noon,* she numbered the hours she had been with me; all of them to me but as one minute; and desired to be left to herself. I was loath to comply: but observing the sunshine begin to shut in, I yielded.

I dined out. Returning, I talked of the house, and of Mrs. Fretchville—had seen Mennell—had pressed him to get the widow to quit: she pitied Mrs. Fretchville—had written to Lord M.; expected an answer soon from him. I was admitted to sup with her. I urged for her approbation or correction of my written terms. She again promised an answer as soon as she had heard from Miss Howe.

Then I pressed for her company to the play on Saturday night. She made objections, as I had foreseen: her brother's projects, warmth of the weather, etc; but in such a manner, as if half afraid to disoblige me. I soon got over these, therefore; and she consented to favour me.

Friday passed as the day before.

Here were two happy days to both. Why cannot I make every day equally happy? It looks *as if it were in my power to do so.* Strange, I should thus delight in teasing a woman I so dearly love! But I could not do thus by such an angel as this, did I not believe that, after her probation time shall be expired, and if she be not to be brought to *cohabitation* (my darling view) I shall reward her as she wishes.

Saturday is half over. We are equally happy—preparing for the play. Polly has offered her company, and is accepted. I have directed her where to weep: and this not only to show her humanity, but to have a pretence to hide her face with her fan or handkerchief.

The woes of others, so well represented as those of Belvidera particularly will be, must, I hope, unlock and open my charmer's heart.

Indeed, I have no hope of such an effect here; but I have more than one end to answer by getting her to a play. To name but one—Dorcas has a *master-key*, as I have told thee.

R. Lovelace.

MISS CLARISSA HARLOWE TO MISS HOWE

Friday, May 19.

LET ME tell you, my dear, that I have known four-and-twenty hours together not unhappy ones, my situation considered.

Let me give you my *reflections* on my more hopeful prospects.

I am now, in the first place, better able to account for the delays about the house than I was before. Poor Mrs. Fretchville! Next, it looks well, that he had apprised the women (before this conversation with them) of his intention to stay in this house, after I was removed to the other. By the tone of his voice he seemed concerned for the appearance this new delay would have with me.

So handsomely did Miss Martin express herself of me, that I am sorry, methinks, that I judged so hardly of her, when I first came hither.

His reason for declining to go in person to bring up the ladies of his family, while my brother and Singleton continue their machinations, carries no bad face with it; and one may the rather allow for *their* expectations, that so proud a spirit as his should attend them for this purpose, as he speaks of them sometimes as persons of punctilio.

Other reasons I will mention for my being easier in my mind than I was before I overheard this conversation.

Such as the advice he has received in relation to Singleton's mate; which agrees but too well with what you, my dear, wrote to me in yours of May the 10th.

His not intending to acquaint *me* with it.

His cautions to the servants about the sailor, if he should come and make inquiries about us.

His resolution to avoid violence, were he to fall in either with my brother or this Singleton; and the easy method he has chalked out, in this case, to prevent mischief; since I need only *not to deny* my being his. But yet I should be exceedingly unhappy in my own opinion, to be driven into such a tacit acknowledgment to any new persons, till I am so, although I have been led (so much against my liking) to give countenance to the belief of the persons below that we are married.

I think myself obliged, from what passed between Mr. Lovelace and me on Wednesday, and from what I overheard him say, to consent to go with him to the play; and the rather, as he had the discretion to propose one of the nieces to accompany me.

I cannot but acknowledge that I am pleased to find that he has actually written to Lord M.

I have promised to give Mr. Lovelace an answer to his proposals as soon as I have heard from you, my dear, on the subject.

I hope, that in the trial which you hint may happen between *me* and *myself* (as you express it), if he should so behave as to oblige me to leave him, I shall be able to act in such a manner as to bring no discredit upon myself in your eye; and that is all now that I have to wish for. But if I value him so much as you are pleased to suppose I do, the trial, which you imagine will be so difficult to me, will not, I conceive, be upon getting from him, when the means to effect my escape are lent me; but how I shall behave when got from him; and if, like the Israelites of old, I shall be so weak as to wish to return to my Egyptian bondage.

I think it will not be amiss, notwithstanding the present favourable appearances, that you should perfect the scheme (whatever it be) which you tell me you have thought of, in order to procure for me an asylum, in case of necessity. Mr. Lovelace is certainly a deep and dangerous man; and it is therefore but prudence to be watchful, and to be provided against the worst.

I am certain that your letters are safe.

Mr. Lovelace will never be out of my company by his good-will; otherwise I have no doubt that I am mistress of my goings-out and comings-in; and did I think it needful, and were I not afraid of my brother, and Captain Singleton, I would oftener put it to trial.

Miss Howe to Miss Clarissa Harlowe

Saturday, May 20.

I did not know, my dear, that you deferred giving an answer to Mr. Lovelace's proposals till you had my opinion of them.

The scheme I think of is this:

There is a person whom I believe you have seen with me, her name Townsend, who is a great dealer in Indian silks, Brussels and French laces, cambrics, linen, and other valuable goods; which she has a way of coming at duty-free; and has a great vend for them in the private families of the gentry round us.

She has her days of being in town, and then is at a chamber she rents at an inn in Southwark. But her place of residence, and where she has her principal warehouse, is at Deptford, for the opportunity of getting her goods on shore.

She was first brought to me by my mother, to whom she was recommended on the supposal of my speedy marriage, that I might have an opportunity to be as fine as a princess, was my mother's expression, at a moderate expense.

Now, my dear, I must own that I do not love to encourage these contraband traders.

But, however, Mrs. Townsend and I, though I have not yet had dealings with her, are upon a very good foot of understanding. She is a sensible woman; she has been abroad, and often goes abroad in the way of her business; and gives very entertaining accounts of all she has seen. And having applied to me to recommend her to you, I am sure I can engage her to give you protection at her house at Deptford; which she says is a populous village, and one of the last, I should think, in which you would be sought for. She is not much there, you will believe, by the course of her dealings; but, no doubt, must have somebody on the spot, in whom she can confide: and there perhaps you might be safe till your cousin comes. And I should not think it amiss that you write to him out of hand. I cannot suggest to you *what* you should write. That must be left to your own discretion.

But notwithstanding all this, and were I sure of getting you safely out of his hands, I will nevertheless forgive you, were you to make all up with him, and marry to-morrow. Yet I will proceed with my projected scheme in relation to Mrs. Townsend; though I hope there will be no occasion to prosecute it, since your prospects seem to be changed, and since you have had *twenty-four not unhappy hours together*. How my indignation rises for this poor consolation in the courtship (*courtship* must I call it?) of such a woman!

Mrs. Townsend, as I have recollected, has two brothers, each a master of a vessel; and who knows, as she and they have concerns together, but that, in case of need, you may have a whole ship's crew at your devotion? If Lovelace give you cause to leave him, take no thought for the people at Harlowe Place. Let *them* take care of one another. The law will help to secure *them*. The wretch is no assassin, no night-murderer. He is an *open*, because a *fearless* enemy; and should he attempt anything that would make him obnoxious to the laws of society, you might have a fair riddance of him either by flight or the gallows; no matter which.

But, my dear, let the articles be drawn up, and engrossed; and solemnize upon them; and there's no more to be said.

May your prospects be still more and more happy, prays

Your own

Anna Howe

MR. LOVELACE TO JOHN BELFORD, ESQ.

Sunday, May 21.

I AM TOO MUCH disturbed in my mind to think of anything but revenge; or I did intend to give thee an account of Miss Harlowe's observations on the play. *Miss Harlowe's* I say. Thou knowest that I hate the name of *Harlowe;* and I am exceedingly out of humour with her, and with her saucy friend.

What's the matter *now,* thou'lt ask?

Matter enough; for while we were at the play, Dorcas, who had her orders, and a key to her lady's chamber, as well as a master-key to her drawers and mahogany chest, closet key and all, found means to come at some of Miss Howe's last written letters.

And here, just now, is another letter brought from the same little virulent devil. I hope to procure transcripts from that too, very speedily, if it be put to the rest; for the saucy fair one is resolved to go to church this morning; not so much from a spirit of devotion, I have reason to think, as to try whether she can go out without check, control, or my attendance.

. . . . . .

She is gone. Slipped down before I was aware. She had ordered a chair, on purpose to exclude my personal attendance. But I had taken proper precautions. Will attended her by consent; Peter, the house-servant, was within Will's call.

I had, by Dorcas, represented her danger from Singleton, in order to dissuade her from going at all, unless she allowed me to attend her; but I was answered, with her usual saucy smartness, that if there were no cause of fear of being met with at the playhouse, when there were but *two* playhouses, surely there was less at church, when there were so *many* churches. The chairmen were ordered to carry her to St. James's Church.

But she would not be so careless of obliging me, if she knew what I have already come at, and how the women urge me on; for they are continually complaining of *the restraint they lie under,* in their behaviour: in their attendance; *neglecting all their concerns in the front house;* and *keeping this elegant back one entirely free from company,* that she may have no suspicion of them. They doubt not my generosity, they say: but *why* for my own sake, in Lord M.'s style, *should I make so long a harvest of so little corn?*

Women, ye reason well. I think I will begin my operations the moment she comes in.

. . . . . .

I have come at the letter brought her from Miss Howe to-day. Plot, conjuration, sorcery, witchcraft, all going forward! I shall not be able to see this *Miss Harlowe* with patience. As the nymphs below ask, so do I, Why is *night* necessary? And Sally and Polly upbraidingly remind me of my first attempts upon themselves. Yet *force* answers not my end—and yet it may, if there be truth in that part of the libertine's creed, *That once subdued, is always subdued!*

[Through his agents, Dorcas and Sally, Mr. Lovelace procures copies of Miss Howe's letters, and writes to Mr. Belford a long vituperation of Miss Howe. Ed.]

Miss Clarissa Harlowe to Miss Howe

Sunday Morning, Seven o'clock.

I was at the play last night with Mr. Lovelace and Miss Horton.

His behaviour, on this occasion, and on our return, was unexceptionable; only that he would oblige me to stay to supper with the women below, when we came back, and to sit up with him and them till near one o'clock this morning. I was resolved to be even with him; and indeed I am not very sorry to have the pretence; for I love to pass the Sundays by myself.

To have the better excuse to avoid his teasing, I am ready dressed to go to church this morning. I will go only to St. James's Church, and in a *chair;* that I may be sure I can go out and come in when I please, without being intruded upon by him, as I was twice before.

Near Nine o'clock

I have your kind letter of yesterday. He knows I have. And I shall expect, that he will be inquisitive next time I see him after your opinion of his proposals.

He is very importunate to see me. He has desired to attend me to church. He is angry that I have declined to breakfast with him. I bid Dorcas tell him, that I desired to have this day to myself. I would see him in the morning, as early as he pleased.

He has sent again in a peremptory manner. He warns me of Singleton. I sent him word, that if *he* was not afraid of Singleton at the playhouse last night, *I* need not at church to-day: so many churches to *one* playhouse. I have accepted of his servant's proposed attendance. But he is quite displeased, it seems. I don't care. I will not be perpetually at his insolent beck. The chair waits. He won't stop me, sure, as I go down to it.

. . . . . .

He was very earnest to dine with me. But I was resolved to carry this one small point; and so denied to dine myself. And indeed I was endeavouring to write to my Cousin Morden; and had begun three different times, without being able to please myself.

He afterwards *demanded,* as I may say, to be admitted to afternoon tea with me. However, I repeated my promise to meet him as early as he pleased in the morning, or to breakfast with him.

Dorcas says, he raved: I heard him loud, and I heard his servant fly from him, as I thought.

. . . . . .

He has just sent me word, that he insists upon supping with me. As we had been in a good train for several days past, I thought it not prudent to break with him for little matters. Yet to be, in a manner, threatened into his will, I know not how to bear that.

. . . . . .

While I was considering, he came up, and, tapping at my door, told me, in a very angry tone, he must see me this night. He could not rest till he had been told what he had done to deserve the treatment I gave him.

Treatment I give him! A wretch! Yet perhaps he has nothing new to say to me. I shall be very angry with him.

As the lady could not know what Mr. Lovelace's designs were, nor the cause of his ill-humour, it will not be improper to pursue the subject from this letter.

Having described his angry manner of demanding, in person, her company at supper; he proceeds as follows:

'Tis hard, answered the fair perverse, that I am to be so little my own mistress. I will meet you in the dining-room half an hour hence.

I went down to wait that half-hour. All the women set me hard to give her cause for this tyranny. They demonstrated, as well from the nature of the *sex,* as of the *case,* that I had nothing to hope for from my tameness, and could meet with no worse treatment, were I to be guilty of the last offence. They urged me vehemently to *try* at least what effect some greater familiarities than I had ever taken with her, would have: and their arguments being strengthened by my just resentments on the discoveries I had made, I was resolved to take *some liberties,* and, as *they* were received, to take *still greater,* and lay all the fault upon her *tyranny*. In this humour I went up, and never had paralytic so little command of his joints, as I had, as I walked about the dining-room, attending her motions.

Let me ask you, madam, I beseech you tell me, what I have done to deserve this distant treatment?

And let me ask *you,* Mr. Lovelace, why are my retirements to be thus invaded? What can you have to say to me since last night, that I went with you so much against my will to the play? And after sitting up with you, equally against my will, till a very late hour?

This I have to say, madam, that I cannot bear to be kept at this distance from you under the same roof.

Under the same roof, sir! How came you——

Hear me out, madam (letting go her trembling hands, and snatching them back again with an eagerness that made her start)—I have a thousand things to say, to talk of, relating to our present and future prospects; but when I want to open my whole soul to you, you are always contriving to keep me at a distance. You make me inconsistent with myself. Your heart is set upon delays. You must have views that you will not own. Tell me, madam, I conjure you to tell me, this moment, without subterfuge or reserve, in what light am I to appear to you in future? I cannot bear this distance. The suspense you hold me in I cannot bear.

In what light, Mr. Lovelace! (visibly terrified). In no bad light, I hope. Pray, Mr. Lovelace, do not grasp my hands so hard (endeavouring to withdraw them). Pray let me go.

You *hate* me, madam.

I hate nobody, sir.

You *hate* me, madam, repeated I.

Instigated and resolved, as I came up, I wanted some new provocation.

You come up in no good temper, I see, Mr. Lovelace—but

pray be not violent—*I have done you no hurt*—pray be not violent——

Sweet creature! And I clasped one arm about her, holding one hand in my other. *You have done me no hurt!* I could have devoured her—but restraining myself—You have done me the greatest hurt! In what have I deserved the distance you keep me at?

She struggled to disengage herself. Pray, Mr. Lovelace, let me withdraw. I know not why this is. I know not what I have done to offend you. I see you are come with a *design to quarrel with me*. If you would not terrify me by the ill-humour you are in, permit me to withdraw. I will hear all you have to say another time—to-morrow morning, as I sent you word—but indeed you frighten me. I beseech you, if you have any value for me, permit me to withdraw.

I kissed her hand with a fervour, as if I would have left my lips upon it. Withdraw then, dearest and ever-dear creature. Indeed I entered in a very ill-humour. I cannot bear the distance at which you so causelessly keep me. Withdraw, madam, since it is your will to withdraw; and judge me generously; judge me but as I deserve to be judged; and let me hope to meet you to-morrow morning early, in such temper as becomes our present situation, and my future hopes.

And so saying, I conducted her to the door, and left her there. But instead of going down to the women, I went into my own chamber, and locked myself in; ashamed of being awed by her majestic loveliness, and apprehensive virtue, into so great a change of purpose, notwithstanding I had such just provocations from the letters of her saucy friend, founded on her own representations of facts and situations between herself and me.

The lady (*dating Sunday night*) *thus describes her terrors, and Mr. Lovelace's behaviour, on the occasion*:

On my entering the dining-room, he took my hands in his, in such a humour, as I saw plainly he was resolved to quarrel with me. *And for what? What had I done to him?* I never in my life beheld in anybody such wild, such angry, such impatient airs. I was terrified; and instead of being as angry as I intended to be, I was forced to be all mildness. I can hardly remember what were his first words, I was so frightened. But, *You hate me, madam! You hate me, madam!* were some of them—with such a fierceness—I wished myself a thousand miles distant from him. I hate nobody, said I; I thank God I hate nobody. You terrify me, Mr. Lovelace—let me leave you. The man, my dear, looked *quite ugly*—I never saw a man look so ugly as passion made him look. *And for what?* And he so grasped my hands! fierce creature! He so grasped my hands! In short, he seemed by his looks, and by his words (once putting his arms about me), to wish me to provoke him. So that I had nothing to do but to beg of him (which I did repeatedly) to permit me to withdraw; and to promise to meet him at his own time in the morning.

It was with a very ill grace that he complied, on that condition; and at parting he kissed my hand with such a savageness, that a redness remains upon it still.

Do you not think, my dear, that I have reason to be incensed at him, my situation considered? What pleasure can I propose to myself in meeting such a wretch?

Perfect for me, my dearest Miss Howe, perfect for me, I beseech you, your kind scheme with Mrs. Townsend; and I will then leave this man.

My temper, I believe, is changed. No wonder if it be. I question whether ever it will be what it was. But I cannot make *him* half so uneasy by the change as I am *myself*. See you not how, from step to step, he grows upon me? I tremble to look back upon his encroachments. And now to give me cause to apprehend *more evil from him, than indignation will permit me to express!* O my dear, perfect your scheme, and let me fly from so strange a wretch!

. . . . . .

I was so disgusted with him, as well as frightened by him, that, on my return to my chamber, in a fit of passionate despair, I tore almost in two the answer I had written to his proposals.

I will see him in the morning, because I promised I would. But I will go out, and that without him, or any attendant. If he account not tolerably for his sudden change of behaviour, and a proper opportunity offer of a private lodging in some creditable house, I will not any more return to this: at present I think so. And there will I either attend the perfecting of your scheme; or, by your epistolary mediation, make my own terms with the wretch; since it is your opinion, that I must be his, and cannot help myself: or, perhaps, take a resolution to throw myself at once into Lady Betty's protection; and this will hinder him from making his insolently threatened visit to Harlowe Place.

Your
Clarissa Harlowe.

The lady writes again on Monday evening; and gives her friend an account of all that passed between herself and Mr. Lovelace that day; and of her being terrified out of her purpose of going out: but Mr. Lovelace's next letters giving a more ample account of all, hers are omitted.

MR. LOVELACE TO JOHN BELFORD, ESQ.

Monday Morn., May 22.

I WAS in the dining-room before six, expecting her. She opened not her door. I went upstairs and down; and hemmed; and called Will; called Dorcas; threw the doors hard to; but still she opened not her door. Thus till half an hour after eight, fooled I away my time; and then (breakfast ready) I sent Dorcas to request her company.

But I was astonished when I saw her enter dressed all but her gloves, and those and her fan in her hand; in the same moment bidding Dorcas direct Will to get her a chair to the door.

Cruel creature, thought I, to expose me thus to the derision of the women below!

Going abroad, madam?

I am, sir.

You will breakfast first, I hope, madam; in a very humble strain; yet with a hundred tenter hooks in my heart.

Yes, she would drink one dish; and then laid her gloves and fan in the window just by.

I was perfectly disconcerted. I hemmed, and was going to speak several times; but knew not in what key.

She a dish—I a dish.

Sip, her eyes her own, she; like a haughty and imperious sovereign, conscious of dignity, every look a favour.

Sip, like her vassal, I; lips and hands trembling, and not knowing that I sipped or tasted.

I was—I was—I sipped—(drawing in my breath and the liquor together, though I scalded my mouth with it) I was in hopes, madam—

Dorcas came in just then. Dorcas, said she, is a chair gone for?

William is gone for one, madam.

This cost me a minute's silence before I could begin again. And then it was with my hopes, and my hopes, and my hopes, and my hopes, that I should have been early admitted to——

What weather is it, Dorcas? said she, as regardless of me as if I had not been present.

A little lowering, madam. The sun is gone in. It was very fine half an hour ago.

I had no patience. Up I rose. Down went the tea-cup, saucer and all. Confound the weather, the sunshine, and the wench! Begone for a devil, when I am speaking to your lady.

Up rose the saucy-face, half-frightened; and snatched from the window her gloves and fan.

You must not go, madam!—seizing her hand—by my soul you must not——

Must not, sir! But I must. You can curse your maid in my absence, as well as if I were present—except—except—you intend for *me,* what you direct to *her.*

Dearest creature, you must not go—you must not leave me. Such determined scorn! Such contempts! Questions asked your servant of no meaning but to break in upon me—I cannot bear it!

Detain me not (struggling). I will not be withheld. I like you not, nor your ways. You sought to quarrel with me yesterday, *for no reason in the world I can think of, but because I was too obliging*. You are an ungrateful man; and I hate you with my whole heart, Mr. Lovelace.

Do not make me desperate, madam. Permit me to say, that you shall not leave me in this humour. Wherever you go, I will attend you. Had Miss Howe been my friend, I had not been thus treated. It is but too plain to whom my difficulties are owing. I have long observed, that every letter you receive from *her,* makes an alteration in your behaviour to *me.*

This startled her.

But recollecting herself, Miss Howe, said she, is a friend to virtue, and to good men. If she like not you, it is because you are not one of those.

Yes, madam; and therefore to speak of Mr. Hickman and myself, as you both, I suppose, think of each, she treats *him* as she would not treat a *Lovelace.* I challenge you, madam, to show me but one of the many letters you have received from her, where I am mentioned.

Miss Howe is just; Miss Howe is good, replied she. She writes, she speaks, of everybody as they deserve.

She would have flung from me: I will *not* be detained, Mr. Lovelace. I *will* go out.

Indeed you must not, madam, in this humour. And I placed myself between her and the door. And then, fanning, she threw herself into a chair, her sweet face all crimsoned over with passion.

I cast myself at her feet. Begone, Mr. Lovelace, said she, with a rejecting motion, her fan in her hand; for your own sake leave me! My soul is above thee, man! with both her hands pushing me from her! Urge me not to tell thee, how sincerely I think my soul above thee! Leave me, and leave me for ever! Thou hast a proud heart to contend with!

Her air, her manner, her voice, were bewitchingly noble, though her words were so severe.

Let me worship an angel, said I, no woman. Forgive me, dearest creature! Forgive my inequalities! Pity my infirmities! Who is equal to my Clarissa?

I trembled between admiration and love; and wrapped my arms about her knees, as she sat. She tried to rise at the moment; but my clasping round her thus ardently, drew her down again; and never was woman more frightened. But free as my clasping emotion might appear to her apprehensive heart, I had not, at the instant, any thought but what reverence inspired. And till she had actually withdrawn (which I permitted under promise of a speedy return. and on her consent to dismiss the chair) all the motions of my heart were as pure as her own.

She kept not her word. An hour I waited before I sent to claim her promise. She could not possibly see me yet, was the answer. As soon as she could, she would.

Dorcas says she still excessively trembled; and ordered her to give her hartshorn and water.

A strange apprehensve creature! Her terror is too great for the occasion.

Dear creature! Did she never romp? Did she never, from girlhood to now, hoyden? The *innocent* kinds of freedom taken and allowed on these occasions, would have familiarized her to greater. Sacrilege but to touch the hem of her garment! Excess of delicacy! Oh, the consecrated beauty! how can she think to be a wife!

But how do I know till I try, whether she may not by a less alarming treatment be prevailed upon, or whether (*day,* I have done with thee!) she may not yield to *nightly surprises?* This is still the burden of my song, I can marry her when I will.

Monday, Two o'clock.

Not yet visible! My beloved is not well. What *expectations* had she from my ardent admiration of her! More rudeness than revenge apprehended. Yet, how my soul thirsts for revenge upon both these ladies! I must have recourse to my *masterstrokes.* This cursed project of Miss Howe and her Mrs. Townsend (if I cannot contrive to render it abortive) will be always a sword hanging over my head. Upon every little disobligation my beloved will be for taking wing; and the pains I have taken to deprive her of every other refuge or protection in order to make her absolutely dependent upon me, will be all thrown away. But perhaps I shall find out a smuggler to counterplot Miss Howe.

Monday Evening.

At my repeated request she condescended to meet me in the dining-room to afternoon tea, and not before.

She entered with bashfulness, as I thought; in a pretty confusion, for having carried her apprehensions too far. Sullen and slow moved she towards the tea-table. Dorcas present, busy in tea-cup preparations. I took her reluctant hand, and pressed it to my lips. Dearest, loveliest of creatures, why this distance? How can you thus torture the faithfullest heart in the world?

I urged her to speak; to look up at me; to bless me with an eye more favourable.

I had reason, she told me, for my complaint of her indifference. She saw nothing in my mind that was generous. My strange behaviour to her since Saturday night, *for no cause at all that she knew of,* convinced her of this. Whatever hopes she had conceived of me, were utterly dissipated: all my ways were disgustful to her.

This cut me to the heart.

I bespoke her patience, while I took the liberty to account for this change on my part. Marriage, I said, was a state that was not to be entered upon with indifference on either side.

It is insolence, interrupted she, it is presumption, sir, to expect tokens of value, without resolving to *deserve* them. You have no whining creature before you, Mr. Lovelace, overcome by weak motives, to love where there is no merit.

And what are my prospects with you, at the very best? My indignation rises against you, Mr. Lovelace, while I speak to you, when I recollect the many instances, equally ungenerous and impolite, of your behaviour to one whom you have brought into distress—and I can hardly bear you in my sight.

She turned from me, standing up; and lifting up her folded hands, and charming eyes swimming in tears, O my father, said the inimitable creature, you might have spared your heavy curse, had you known how I have been punished, ever since my swerving feet led me out of your garden doors to meet this man! Then sinking into her chair, a burst of passionate tears forced their way down her glowing cheeks.

My dearest life, taking her still folded hands in mine, who can bear an invocation so affecting, though so passionate?

And, as I hope to live, my nose tingled, as I once, when a boy, remember it did just before some tears came into my eyes; and I durst hardly trust my face in view of hers.

What have I done to deserve this impatient exclamation?

Have I, at any time, by word, by deeds, by looks, given you cause to doubt my honour, my reverence, my *adoration,* I may call it, of your virtues? Give me but hope, that you hate me not; that you do not *despise me.*

O Mr. Lovelace, we have been long enough together to be tired of each other's humours and ways; ways and humours so different, that perhaps you ought to dislike *me,* as much as I do *you.* I think, I think, that I cannot make an answerable return to the value you profess for me. My temper is utterly ruined. You have given me an ill opinion of all mankind; of yourself in particular: and withal so bad a one of myself, that I shall never be able to look up, having utterly and for ever lost all that self-complacency, and conscious pride, which are so necessary to carry a woman through this life with tolerable satisfaction to herself.

She paused. I was silent. By my soul, thought I, this sweet creature will at last undo me!

She proceeded. What now remains, but that you pronounce me free of all obligation to you?

Again she paused. I was still silent; meditating whether to renounce all further designs upon her; whether I had not received sufficient evidence of a virtue, and of a greatness of soul, that could not be questioned or impeached.

She went on: Propitious to me be your silence, Mr. Lovleace! Tell me that I am free of all obligation to you. You know I never made *you* promises. You know that you are not under any to *me.* My broken fortunes I matter not——

My dearest life, said I, I have been all this time, though you fill me with doubts of your favour, busy in the nuptial preparations. I am actually in treaty for equipage.

Equipage, sir! Trappings, tinsel! What is equipage; what is life; what is anything; to a creature sunk so low as I am in my own opinion! Labouring under a father's curse! Unable to look backward without reproach, or forward without terror!

I had not a word to say for myself. Such a war in my mind had I never known. Gratitude, and admiration of the excellent creature before me, combating with villainous habit, with resolutions so premeditately made, and with views so much gloried in! I had certainly been a lost man, had not Dorcas come seasonably in with a letter. On the superscription written, *Be pleased, sir, to open it now.*

I retired to the window—opened it. It was from Dorcas herself. These the contents, "Be pleased to detain my lady: a paper of importance to transcribe. I will cough when I have done."

I put the paper in my pocket, and turned to my charmer, less disconcerted, as she, by that time, had also a little recovered herself. One favour, dearest creature, Let me but know whether Miss Howe approves or disapproves of my proposals? I know her to be my enemy. And now, dearest creature, let me know, I once more ask you, what is Miss Howe's opinion of my proposals?

Were I disposed to debate with you, Mr. Lovelace, I could very easily answer your fine harangue. But at present, I shall only say, that your ways have been very unaccountable.

Curse upon the heart of the little devil, said I, who instigates you to think so hardly of the faithfullest heart in the world!

How dare you, sir? And there she stopped; having almost overshot herself; as I designed she should.

How dare I *what*, madam? And I looked with meaning. How dare I *what*?

Vile man! And do you——and there again she stopped.

Do I *what,* madam? And why *vile man?*

How dare you to curse *anybody* in my presence?

O the sweet receder! But that was not to go off so with a Lovelace.

Why then, dearest creature, is there *anybody* that instigates you? If there be, again I curse them, be they whom they will.

She was in a charming pretty passion. And this was the first time that I had the odds in my favour.

Artful wretch! And is it thus you would entrap me? Miss Howe likes some of your ways as little as I do; for I have set everything before her. Yet she is thus far *your* enemy, as she is *mine*—she thinks I should not refuse your offers; but endeavour to make the best of my lot. And now you have the truth. Would to Heaven you were capable of dealing with equal sincerity!

I *am,* madam. And here, on my knee, I renew my vows, and my supplication, that you will make me yours—yours for ever.

Rise, sir, from your too-ready knees; and mock me not.

Too-ready knees, thought I!

Mock you, madam! And I arose, and re-urged her for the day. I blamed myself at the same time, for the invitation I had given to Lord M., as it might subject me to delay from his infirmities: but told her, that I would write to him to excuse me, if she had no objection; or to give him the day she would give me, and not wait for him, if he could not come in time.

My day, sir, said she, is never. Be not surprised. A person of politeness judging between us, would not be surprised that I say so. But indeed, Mr. Lovelace (and wept through impatience), you either know not how to treat with a mind of the least degree of delicacy, notwithstanding your birth and education, or you are an ungrateful man; and (after a pause) a *worse* than ungrateful one. But I will retire. I will see you again to-morrow. I cannot before. I think I hate you—you *may* look—indeed I think I hate you. And if, upon a re-examination of my own heart, I find I do, I would not for the world that matters should go on farther between us.

But I see, I see, she does not *hate* me!

I was, however, too much vexed, disconcerted, mortified, to hinder her from retiring—and yet she had not gone, if Dorcas had not coughed.

The wench came in, as soon as her lady had retired, and gave me the copy she had taken. And what should it be but of the answer the truly admirable creature had intended to give to my written proposals in relation to settlements?

I have but just dipped into this affecting paper. Were I to read it attentively, not a wink should I sleep this night. To-morrow it shall obtain my serious consideration.

MR. LOVELACE TO JOHN BELFORD, ESQ.

Tuesday Morning, May 23.

THE dear creature desires to be excused seeing me till evening. She is not very well, as Dorcas tells me.

It is impossible that I should proceed with my project against this admirable woman, were it not that I am resolved, after a few trials more, if as nobly sustained as those she has already passed through, to make her (if she really hate me not) legally mine.

To Mr. Lovelace

"When a woman is married, that supreme earthly obligation requires that in all instances where her husband's real honour is concerned, she should yield her own will to his. But, beforehand, I could be glad, comformably to what I have always signified, to have the most explicit assurances, that every possible way should be tried to avoid litigation with my father. Time and patience will subdue all things. My prospects of happiness are extremely contracted. A husband's right will be always the same. In my life-time I could wish nothing to be done of this sort.

"This article, then, I urge to your serious consideration, as what lies next my heart. I enter not here minutely into the fatal misunderstanding between them and you: the fault may be in both.

"Let it be remembered, that, in *their* eye, you have robbed them of a daughter they doted upon; and that their resentments on this occasion rise but in proportion to their love and their disappointment. You, sir, who will judge everybody as you please, and will let nobody judge you, in *your own* particular, must not be *their* judge. It may therefore be expected that they will stand out.

"As for *myself,* sir, I must leave it (so seems it to be destined) to your justice, to treat me as you shall think I deserve: but if your future behaviour to *them* is not governed by that harsh-sounding implacableness, which you charge upon some of *their* tempers, the splendour of your family, and the excellent character of *some* of them (of *all* indeed, unless your own conscience furnishes you with one *only* exception) will, on better consideration, do everything with them: for they *may* be overcome; perhaps, however, with the more difficulty, as the greatly prosperous less bear control and disappointment than others: for I will own to you, that I have often in secret lamented that their great acquirements have been a snare to them; perhaps as great a snare as some *other* accidentals have been to you; which being less immediately your own gifts, you have still less reason than they to value yourself upon them.

"Let me only, on this subject, further observe, that condescension is not meanness. There is a glory in yielding, that hardly any violent spirit can judge of. My brother perhaps is no more sensible of *this* than you. But as you have talents which he has not (who, however, has, as I hope, that regard for morals, the want of which makes one of his objections to you), I could wish it may not be owing to *you,* that your mutual dislikes to each other do not subside; for it is my earnest hope, that in time you may see each other without exciting the fears of a wife and a sister for the consequence.

"As to clothes, I have particularly two suits, which, having been only in a manner tried on, would answer for any present occasion. Jewels I have of my grandmother's, which want only new setting: another set I have, which on particular days I used to wear. Although these are not sent me, I have no doubt, being merely personals, but they will, when I send for them in *another name:* till when I should not choose to wear any.

"As to your complaints of my diffidences, and the like, I appeal to your own heart, if it be possible for you to make my case your own for one moment, and to retrospect some parts of your behaviour, words, and actions, whether I am not rather to be justified than censured: and whether, of all men in the world, *avowing what you avow,* you ought not to think so. If you do not, let me admonish you, sir, from the very great *mismatch* that then must appear to be in our minds, never to seek, nor so much as wish, to bring about the *most intimate* union of interests between yourself and

"*May* 20." *Clarissa Harlowe.*

The original of this charming paper, as Dorcas tells me, was torn almost in two. In one of her pets, I suppose! What business have the sex, whose principal glory is meekness, and patience, and resignation, to be in a passion, I trow? Will not she, who allows herself such liberties as a maiden, take greater when married?

I had better not to have had a copy of it, as far as I know: for, determined as I was before upon my operations, it instantly turned all my resolutions in her favour.

But, after all, I am sorry, *almost* sorry that I cannot, until I have made further trials, resolve upon wedlock.

I have just read over again this intended answer to my proposals: and how I adore her for it!

But yet; another *yet!* She has not given it or sent it to me. It is not therefore *her* answer. It is not written *for* me, though *to* me.

My cursed character was against me at setting out—yet is she not a *woman?* Cannot I find one yielding or but half-yielding moment, if she do not absolutely hate me?

What can be done to make such a matchless creature get over the first tests, in order to put her to the grand proof, *whether once overcome, she will not be always overcome?*

Our mother and her nymphs say, I am a perfect Craven, and no Lovelace: and so I think. But this is no simpering, smiling charmer, as I have found others to be.

And must, think I, O creature so divinely excellent, and so beloved of my soul, those arms, those encircling arms, that would make a monarch happy, be used to repel brutal force; all their strength, unavailingly perhaps, exerted to repel it, and to defend a person so delicately framed? Can violence enter into the heart of a wretch, who might entitle himself to all thy willing, yet virtuous love, and make the blessings I aspire after, her *duty* to confer? And I am then ready to throw myself at her feet, to confess my villainous designs, to avow my repentance, and to put it out of my power to act unworthily by such an excellence.

Robert Lovelace.

MR. LOVELACE TO JOHN BELFORD, ESQ.

Tuesday, May 23.

WELL DID I, and but just in time, conclude to have done with Mrs. Fretchville and the house: for here Mennell has declared, that he cannot in conscience and honour go any farther.

Mennell has, however, though with some reluctance, consented to write me a letter, provided I will allow it to be the last step he shall take in this affair.

This letter is directed, *To Robert Lovelace, Esq.; or, in his absence, to his lady*. She had refused dining with me, or seeing me; and I was out when it came.

I came in to dinner. She sent me down the letter, desiring my excuse for opening it. Did it before she was aware.

I requested to see her upon it that moment. But she desires to suspend our interview till morning.

Did I tell thee that I wrote a letter to my Cousin Montague, wondering that I heard not from Lord M. as the subject was so very interesting?

I have received just now an answer from Charlotte.

M. Hall, May 22.

DEAR COUSIN,—We have been in daily hope for a long time, I must call it, of hearing that the happy knot was tied. My lord has been very much out of order: and yet nothing would serve him, but he would himself write an answer to your letter.

Indeed, Mr. Lovelace, his worthy heart is wrapped up in you. I wish you loved yourself but half as well. But I believe too, that if all the family loved you less, you would love yourself more.

As for myself, I am not at all well, and have not been for some weeks past, with my old stomach disorder. I had certainly else before now have done myself the honour you wonder I have *not* done myself. Lady Betty, who would have accompanied me (for we had laid it all out), has been exceedingly busy in her law affair; her antagonist, who is actually on the spot, having been making proposals for an accommodation. But you may assure yourself, that when our dear relation-elect shall be entered upon the new habitation you tell me of, we will do ourselves the honour of visiting her; and if any delay arises from the dear lady's want of courage (which, considering her man, let me tell you, may very well be), we will endeavour to inspire her with it, and be sponsors for you; for, cousin, I believe you have need to be christened over again before you are entitled to so great a blessing. What think you?

My best compliments, and sister's, to the most deserving lady in the world conclude me

Your affectionate cousin and servant,

Charl. Montague.

The lady in her next letter gives Miss Howe an account of what has passed between Mr. Lovelace and herself. She resents his behaviour with her usual dignity: but when she comes to mention Mr. Mennell's letter, she re-urges Miss Howe to perfect her scheme for her deliverance; being resolved to leave him. But, dating again, on his sending up to her Miss Montague's letter, she alters her mind, and desires her to suspend for the present her application to Mrs. Townsend.

Mr. Lovelace to John Belford, Esq.

May 24

The devil take this uncle of mine! He has at last sent me a letter which I cannot show, without exposing the head of our family for a fool. A confounded parcel of pop-guns has he let off upon me.

All that makes for me in it, I will transcribe for her. Yet hang it, she shall have the letter, and my soul with it, for one consenting kiss.

. . . . . .

She has got the letter from me without the reward. Deuce take me, if I had the courage to propose the condition. A new character this of bashfulness in thy friend. I see *that a truly modest woman may make even a confident man keep his distance.*

Lord M. to Robert Lovelace, Esq.

Tuesday, May 23.

It is *a long lane that has no turning.* Do not despise me for my proverbs. You know I was always fond of them; and if you had been so too, it would have been the better for you, let me tell you. I dare swear, the fine lady you are so likely to be soon happy with, will be far from despising them; for I am told that she writes well, and that all her letters are full of sentences. God convert you! for nobody but He and this lady can.

I have no manner of doubt now but that you will marry, as your father, and all your ancestors, did before you: else you would have had no title to be my heir; nor can your descendants have any title to be yours, unless they are legitimate; that's worth your remembrance, sir! *No man is always a fool, every man sometimes*. But your follies, I hope, are now at an end.

I know you have vowed revenge against this fine lady's family: but no more of that, now. You must look upon them all as your relations; and forgive and forget. And when they see you make a good husband and a good father (which God send, for all our sakes!) they will wonder at their nonsensical antipathy, and beg your pardon: but while they think you a vile fellow, and a rake, how can they either love you, or excuse their daughter?

Pray let her know as that I will present HER (not *you*) either my Lancashire seat, or *The Lawn* in Hertfordshire; and settle upon her a thousand pounds a year penny-rents; to show her that we are not a family to take base advantages: and you may have writings drawn, and settle as you will.

I am still very bad with my gout; but will come in a litter, as soon as the day is fixed: it would be the joy of my heart to join your hands. And, let me tell you, if you do not make the best of husbands to so good a young lady, and one who has had so much courage for your sake, I will renounce you; and settle all I can upon her and hers by you, and leave you out of the question.

And when the Harlowes know all this, let us see whether they are able to blush, and take shame to themselves.

For your part, you will not want a place, as some others do, to piece up their broken fortunes. If you can now live reputably upon two thousand pounds a year, it will be hard if you cannot hereafter live upon seven or eight—less you will not have, if you oblige me; as now by marrying so fine a lady, very much you will—and all this, over and above Lady Betty's and Lady Sarah's favours! What, in the name of wonder, could possibly possess the proud Harlowes! That son, that son of theirs! But, for his dear sister's sake, I will say no more of him.

My nieces Montague, and Lady Sarah and Lady Betty, join in compliments to my niece that is to be. If she would choose to have the knot tied among us, pray tell her that we shall see it *securely done:* and we will make all the country ring and blaze for a week together.

Your most affectionate uncle,

M.

MR. LOVELACE TO JOHN BELFORD, ESQ.

Thursday, May 25.

THOU SEEST, Belford, how we now drive before the wind. The dear creature now comes almost at the first word, whenever I desire the honour of her company. I told her last night, that I was determined to leave it to my lord to make his compliments in his own way; and had actually that afternoon put my writings into the hands of a very eminent lawyer, Counsellor Williams, with directions for him to draw up settlements.

I have actually deposited these writings with Counsellor Williams; and I expect the drafts in a week at furthest. So shall be doubly armed.

Everything of this nature, the dear creature answered (with a downcast eye, and a blushing cheek), she left to me.

I proposed my lord's chapel for the celebration, where we might have the presence of Lady Betty, Lady Sarah, and my two cousins Montague.

She seemed not to favour a public celebration; and waived this subject for the present.

I do assure thee, Belford, I was in earnest in all this. My whole estate is nothing to me, put in competition with her hoped-for favour.

She then told me that she had put into writing her opinion of my general proposals; and there had expressed her mind as to clothes and jewels: but on my strange behavior to her (*for no cause that she knew of*) on Sunday night, she had torn the paper in two.

I earnestly pressed her to let me be favoured with a sight of this paper, torn as it was. And after some hesitation, she withdrew, and sent it to me by Dorcas.

I perused it again. It was in a manner new to me, though I had read it so lately: and, by my soul, I could hardly stand it. A hundred admirable creatures I called her to myself.

You may easily suppose, when I was re-admitted to her presence, that I ran over in her praises, and in vows of gratitude, and everlasting love. But here's the devil; she still receives all I say with reserve; or if it be not with reserve, she receives it so much *as her due,* that she is not at all raised by it.

My beloved, in her torn paper, mentions but two hundred pounds a year, for her separate use. I insisted upon her naming a larger sum. She said it might then be three; and I, for fear she should suspect very large offers, named only five; but added the entire disposal of all arrears in her father's hands, for the benefit of Mrs. Norton or whom she pleased.

She said that the good woman would be uneasy if anything more than a competency were done for her.

Here's prudence! Here's judgment in so young a creature! How do I hate the Harlowes for producing such an angel! O why, why, did she refuse my sincere address to tie the knot before we came to this house!

But yet, what mortifies my pride is, that this exalted creature, if I *were* to marry her, would not be governed in her behaviour to me by love, but by generosity merely, or by blind duty; and had rather live single, than be mine.

I cannot bear this. I would have the woman whom I honour with my name, if ever I confer this honour upon any, forego even her *superior duties* for me. I would have her look after me when I go out, as far as she can see me, as my Rosebud after her Johnny; and meet me at my return with rapture.

. . . . . .

Another agreeable conversation. The Day of days the subject. As to fixing a particular one, that need not be done, my charmer says, till the settlements are completed. As to marrying at my lord's chapel, the ladies of my family present, that would be making a public affair of it; and the dear creature observed with regret, that it seemed to be my lord's intention to make it so.

I cannot, said she, endure the thoughts of a public day. It will carry with it an air of insult upon my whole family. And, for my part, if my lord will not take it amiss (and perhaps he will not, as the motion came not from himself, but from you, Mr. Lovelace), I will very willingly dispense with his lordship's presence; the rather, as dress and appearance then will be unnecessary; for I cannot bear to think of decking my person while my parents are in tears.

I withdrew, and wrote directly to my lord.

"That I was much obliged to his lordship for his intended goodness to me, on an occasion the most solemn of my life. That the admirable lady, whom he so justly praised, thought his lordship's proposals in her favour too high. That she chose not to make a public appearance, if, without disobliging my friends, she could avoid it, till a reconciliation with her own could be effected.

"That the Lawn will be most acceptable to us both to retire to; and the rather, as it is so to his lordship."

Lord M. never in his life received so handsome a letter as this from his nephew

LOVELACE.

The lady, after having given to Miss Howe the particulars contained in Mr. Lovelace's last letter, thus expresses herself:

A principal consolation arising from these favourable appearances, is, that I, who have now but one only friend, shall most probably, and, if it be not my own fault, have as many new ones as there are persons in Mr. Lovelace's family; and this whether Mr. Lovelace treat me kindly or not. And who knows, but that by degrees, those new friends, by their rank and merit, may have weight enough to get me restored to the favour of my relations? Till which can be effected, I shall not be tolerably easy. Happy I never expect to be. Mr. Lovelace's mind and mine are vastly different; different in *essentials*.

Clarissa Harlowe.

MR. LOVELACE TO JOHN BELFORD, ESQ.

AND NOW, Belford, what dost think?

I shall be very sick to-morrow.

Sick! Why sick? What a-devil shouldst thou be sick for?

For more good reasons than one, Jack.

I should be glad to hear but one. Of all thy roguish inventions I should not have thought of this.

Perhaps thou thinkest my view to be, to draw the lady to my bedside: that's a trick of three or four thousand years old; and I should find it much more to my purpose, if I could get to hers.

I am excessively disturbed about this smuggling scheme of Miss Howe. I have no doubt that my fair one, were I to make an attempt, and miscarry, will fly from me, if she can.

I don't intend to be so very bad as Dorcas shall represent me to be. But yet I know I shall reach confoundedly, and bring up some clotted blood. To be sure, I shall break a vessel: there's no doubt of that: and a bottle of Eaton's Styptic shall be sent for; but no doctor. If she has *humanity,* she will be concerned. But if she has *love,* let it have been pushed ever so far back, it will, on this occasion, come forward and show itself; not only in her eye, but in every line of her sweet face.

Now, Belford, if she be not much concerned at the broken vessel, which, in one so fiery in his temper as I have the *reputation* to be thought, may be very dangerous; a malady that I shall calmly attribute to the harasses and doubts under which I have laboured for some time past; and this will be a further proof of my love, and will demand a grateful return.

And what then, thou egregious contriver?

Why then I shall have the *less remorse,* if I am to use a little violence: for can *she* deserve compassion, who shows none?

And what if she show a *great deal of concern?*

Then shall I be in hope of *building on a good foundation.* Love, when acknowledged, authorizes freedom; and freedom begets freedom; and I shall then see how far I can go.

Well but, Lovelace, how the deuce wilt thou, with that full health and vigour of constitution, and with that bloom in thy face, make anybody believe thou art sick?

How! Why, take a few grains of ipecacuanha; enough to make me reach like a fury.

Good! But how wilt thou manage to bring up blood, and not hurt thyself?

Foolish fellow! Are there not pigeons and chickens in every poulterer's shop?

Mr. Lovelace to John Belford, Esq.

Friday Evening

Just returned from an airing with my charmer, complied with after great importunity. She was attended by the two nymphs.

I am mad with love—yet eternal will be the distance, at the rate I go on: now fire, now ice, my soul is continually upon the *hiss,* as I may say. In vain, however, is the trial to quench—what, after all, is unquenchable.

Did I not tell thee, not that I am *sick* of love, but that I am *mad* with it! Why brought I such an angel into such a house, into such company? And why do I not stop my ears to the sirens, who, knowing my aversion to wedlock, are perpetually touching that string?

Mr. Lovelace to John Belford, Esq.

Cocoa-Tree, Saturday, May 27.

This ipecacuanha is a most disagreeable medicine.

It has done it: for, with violent reachings, having taken enough to make me sick, and not enough water to carry it off, I presently looked as if I had kept my bed a fortnight.

Two hours it held me. I had forbid Dorcas to let her lady know anything of the matter; out of tenderness to her; being willing, when she knew my prohibition, to let her see that I *expected* her to be concerned for me.

Well, but Dorcas was nevertheless a *woman,* and she can *whisper* to her lady the secret she is enjoined to keep!

What's the matter, Dorcas?

Nothing, madam.

My beloved wonders she has not seen me this morning, no doubt; but is too shy to say she wonders. Repeated What's the matter, however, as Dorcas runs up and downstairs by her door, bring on, O madam, my master! my poor master!

What! How! When!—and all the monosyllables of surprise.

I must not tell you, madam. My master ordered me not to tell you—but he is in a worse way than he thinks for! But he would not have *you* frightened.

High concern took possession of every sweet feature. She pitied me! By my soul, she pitied me!

Where is he?

Too much in a hurry for good manners, I cannot stay to answer questions, cries the wench.

At last, O Lord! let Mrs. Lovelace know! There is danger, to be sure! whispered one nymph to another; but at the door, and so loud, that my listening fair one might hear.

Out she darts. As how! as how, Dorcas!

O madam, a vomiting of blood! A vessel broke, to be sure!

Down she hastens; finds every one as busy over my blood in the entry, as if it were that of the Neapolitan saint.

In steps my charmer, with a face of sweet concern.

How do you, Mr. Lovelace?

O my best love! Very well! Very well! Nothing at all! Nothing of consequence! I shall be well in an instant! Straining again! for I was indeed plaguy sick, though no more blood came.

In short, Belford, I have gained my end. I see the dear soul loves me. I see she forgives me all that's past. I see I have credit for a new score.

Miss Howe, I defy thee, my dear. Mrs. Townsend! Who the devil are you? Troop away with your contrabands. No smuggling! Nor smuggler, but myself! Nor will the choicest of my fair one's favours be long prohibited goods to me!

Miss Clarissa Harlowe to Miss Howe

Saturday, May 27.

Mr. Lovelace, my dear, has been very ill. Suddenly taken. With a vomiting of blood in great quantities. Some vessel broken. He complained of a disorder in his stomach over-night.

I was the more affected with it, *as I am afraid it was occasioned by the violent contentions between us*. But was I in fault?

How lately did I think I hated him! But hatred and anger, I see, are but temporary passions with me. One cannot, my dear, hate people in danger of death, or who are in distress or affliction. My heart, I find, is not proof against kindness, and acknowledgment of errors committed.

He took great care to have his illness concealed from me as long as he could. So tender in the violence of his disorder! So desirous to make the best of it! I wish he had not been ill in my sight. I was too much affected—everybody alarming me with his danger. The poor man, from such high health, so *suddenly* taken!—and so unprepared!

He is gone out in a chair. I advised him to do so. I fear that my advice was wrong; since quiet in such a disorder must needs be best.

I am really very uneasy. For I have, I doubt, exposed myself to him, and to the women below. *They* indeed will excuse me, as they think us married. But if he be not generous, I shall have cause to regret this surprise; which (as I had reason to think myself unaccountably treated by him) has taught me more than I knew of myself.

Nevertheless let me tell you that if again he give me cause to resume distance and reserve, I hope my reason will gather strength enough from his imperfections to enable me to keep my passions under. What can we do more than govern ourselves by the temporary lights lent us?

But I will not add another word, after I have assured you, that I will look still more narrowly into myself: and that I am

Your equally sincere and affectionate,

Cl. Harlowe.

[Still pursuing his love of intrigue and contriving, Mr. Lovelace engages the services of one M'Donald, a rogue, who, under the name of Captain Tomlinson, comes into the story posing as a friend of Mr. John Harlowe, Clarissa's eldest uncle. Tomlinson's role is to convince Clarissa that, once married to Mr. Lovelace, her Uncle Harlowe hopes to arrange a reconciliation with her family. The scenes in which Tomlinson appears seem artificial and forced, and in the rest of the story his scenes and his machinations directed by Lovelace are for the most part omitted. Ed.]

MR. LOVELACE TO JOHN BELFORD, ESQ.

Monday, May 29.

WHEN I returned from attending the captain downstairs, which I did to the outward door, my beloved met me as I entered the dining-room; complacency reigning in every lovely feature.

"You see me already, *said she,* another creature. You know not, Mr. Lovelace, how near my heart this hoped-for reconciliation is. I am now willing to banish every disagreeable remembrance. You know not, sir, how much you have obliged me. And oh, Mr. Lovelace, how happy shall I be, when my heart is lightened from the all-sinking weight of a father's curse! When my dear mamma (you don't know, sir, half the excellences of my dear mamma! and what a kind heart she has, when it is left to follow its own impulses—when this blessed mamma) shall once more fold me to her indulgent bosom! When I shall again have uncles and aunts, and a brother and sister, all striving who shall show most kindness and favour to the poor outcast, then *no more* an outcast! And you, Mr. Lovelace, to behold all this, and to be received into a family so dear to me, with welcome—What though a little cold at first? when they come to know you better, and to see you oftener, no fresh causes of disgust occurring, and you, as I hope, having entered upon a new course, all will be warmer and warmer love on both sides, till every one perhaps will wonder how they came to set themselves against you."

Then drying her tears with her handkerchief, after a few moments pausing, on a sudden, as if recollecting that she had been led by her joy to an expression of it which she had not intended I should see, she retired to her chamber with precipitation; leaving me almost as unable to stand it as herself.

In short, I was—I want words to say how I was. My nose had been made to tingle before; my eyes have before been made to glisten by this soul-moving beauty; but so *very* much affected,

I never was—for, trying to check my sensibility, it was too strong for me, and I even sobbed. Yes, by my soul, I *audibly* sobbed, and was forced to turn from her before she had well finished her affecting speech.

I want, methinks, now I have owned the odd sensation, to describe it to thee—the thing was so strange to me—something choking, as it were, in my throat—I know not how—yet, I must needs say, though I am out of countenance upon the recollection, that there was something very pretty in it; and I wish I could know it again, that I might have a more perfect idea of it, and be better able to describe it to thee.

MR. LOVELACE TO JOHN BELFORD, ESQ.

Friday, June 2.

NOTWITHSTANDING my studied-for politeness and complaisance for some days past; and though I have wanted courage to throw the mask quite aside; yet I have made the dear creature more than once look about her, by the warm, though decent expression of my passion. I have brought her to own that I am *more* than indifferent with her: but as to LOVE, which I pressed her to acknowledge, *what need of acknowledgments of that sort, when a woman consents to marry?* And once repulsing me with displeasure, *the proof of the true love I was vowing for her was* RESPECT, *not* FREEDOM. And offering to defend myself, she told me that all the conception she had been able to form of a faulty passion was that it must demonstrate itself as mine sought to do.

I endeavoured to justify my passion by laying over-delicacy at her door. Over-delicacy, she said, was not *my* fault, if it were *hers*. She must plainly tell me that I appeared to her incapable of distinguishing what were the requisites of a pure mind. Perhaps, had the *libertine* presumption to imagine that there was no difference in *heart,* nor any but what proceeded from *education* and *custom,* between the pure and the impure. And yet custom *alone,* as she observed, if I *did* so think, would make a second nature, as well in *good* as in *bad* habits.

I have just now been called to account for some innocent liberties which I thought myself entitled to take before the women; as they suppose us to be married, and now within view of consummation.

I took the lecture very hardly; and with impatience wished for the happy day and hour when I might call her all my own, and meet with no check from a niceness that had no example.

She looked at me with a bashful kind of contempt. I thought it *contempt,* and required the reason for it; not being conscious of offence, as I told her.

This is not the first time, Mr. Lovelace, said she, that I have had cause to be displeased with you, when *you,* perhaps, have not thought yourself exceptionable. But, sir, let me tell you that the married state, in my eye, is a state of purity, and (I *think* she told me) not of *licentiousness;* so, at least, I understood her.

The dear creature now considers herself as my wife-elect. The *unsaddened* heart, no longer prudish, will not now, I hope, give the sable turn to every address of the man she dislikes not. And yet she must keep up so much reserve as will justify past inflexibilities. "Many and many a pretty soul would yield, were she not afraid that the man she favoured would think the worse of her for it." This is also a part of the rake's creed. But should she resent ever so strongly, she cannot now break with me; since, if she does, there will be an end of the family reconciliation; and that in a way highly discreditable to herself.

MR. LOVELACE TO JOHN BELFORD, ESQ.

Monday, June 5.

HIGH DISPLEASURE! followed by an abrupt departure.

I sat down by her. I took both her hands in mine. I would *have* it so. All gentle my voice. Her father mentioned with respect. Her mother with reverence. Even her brother amicably spoken of. I never thought I could have wished so ardently, as I told her I did wish, for a reconciliation with her family.

A sweet and grateful flush then overspread her fair face; a gentle sigh now and then heaved her handkerchief.

I perfectly longed to hear from Captain Tomlinson. It was impossible for her uncle to find fault with the draft of the settlements. I would not, however, be understood, by sending them down, that I intended to put it in her uncle's power to delay my happy day. When, when was it to be?

I would hasten again to the Commons; and would not return without the licence.

The Lawn I proposed to retire to as soon as the happy ceremony was over. This day and that day I proposed.

It was time enough to name the day when the settlements were completed and the licence obtained. Happy should she be, could the kind Captain Tomlinson obtain her *uncle's presence privately*.

No new delays, for Heaven's sake, I besought her; and reproached her gently for the past. Name but the day (an *early* day, I hoped it would be, in the following week).

My cheek reclined on her shoulder—kissing her hands by turns. Rather bashfully than angrily reluctant, her hands sought to be withdrawn; her shoulder avoiding my reclined cheek—apparently loath, and more loath, to quarrel with me; her downcast eye confessing more than her lips could utter. Now surely, thought I, is my time to try if she can forgive a still bolder freedom than I had ever yet taken.

I then gave her struggling hands liberty. I put one arm round her waist: I imprinted a kiss on her sweet lips, with a *Be quiet* only, and an averted face, as if she feared another.

Encouraged by so gentle a repulse, the tenderest things I said; and then, with my other hand, drew aside the handkerchief that concealed the beauty of beauties, and pressed with my burning lips the most charming breast that ever my ravished eyes beheld.

A very contrary passion to that which gave her bosom so delightful a swell immediately took place. She struggled out of my encircling arms with indignation. I detained her reluctant hand. Let me go, said she. *I see there is no keeping terms with you.* Base encroacher! Is this the design of your flattering speeches? Far as matters have gone, I will for ever renounce you. You have an odious heart. Let me go, I tell you.

I was forced to obey, and she flung from me, repeating *base*, and adding *flattering*, encroacher.

In vain have I urged by Dorcas for the promised favour of dining with her. She would not dine *at all*. She *could not*.

But why makes she every inch of her person thus sacred? So near the time, too, that she must suppose that all will be my own by deed of purchase and settlement?

Let me perish, Belford, if I would not forego the brightest diadem in the world for the pleasure of seeing a twin Lovelace at each charming breast, drawing from it his first sustenance; the pious task, for physical reasons, continued for one month and no more!

I now, methinks, behold this most charming of women in this sweet office: her conscious eye now dropped on one, now on the other, with sigh of maternal tenderness; and then raised up to my delighted eye, full of wishes, for the sake of the pretty varlets, and for her own sake, that I would deign to legitimate; that I would condescend to put on the nuptial fetters.

MR. BELFORD TO ROBERT LOVELACE, ESQ.

Tuesday, June 6.

UNSUCCESSFUL as hitherto my application to you has been, I cannot for the heart fo me forbear writing once more in behalf of this admirable woman: and yet am unable to account for the zeal which impels me to take her part with an earnestness so sincere.

If thou proceedest, I have no doubt that this affair will end tragically, one way or other. It *must*. Such a woman must interest both gods and men in her cause.

'Tis a seriously sad thing, after all, that so fine a creature should have fallen into such vile and remorseless hands: for, from thy cradle, as I have heard thee own, thou ever delightedst to sport with and torment the animal, whether bird or beast, that thou lovedst and hadst a power over.

But let me beg of thee, once more, my dear Lovelace, if thou hast any regard for thine own honour, for the honour of thy family, for thy future peace, or for my opinion of thee (who yet pretend not to be so much moved by principle, as by that dazzling merit which ought still more to attract *thee*), to be prevailed upon—to be—to be *humane*, that's all—only, that thou wouldest not disgrace our common humanity!

I conclude with recommending to your serious consideration all I have written, as proceeding from the heart and soul of

Your assured friend,

John Belford.

MR. LOVELACE TO JOHN BELFORD, ESQ.

Wednesday Night 11 o'clock.

FAITH, Jack, thou hadst half undone me with thy nonsense, though I would not own it in my yesterday's letter: my conscience of thy party before. But I think I am my own man again.

So near to execution my plot; so near springing my mine; all agreed upon between the women and me; or I believe thou hadst overthrown me.

I have time for a few lines preparative to what is to happen in an hour or two; and I love to write to the *moment*.

We have been extremely happy. How many agreeable days have we known together! What may the next two hours produce!

MR. LOVELACE TO JOHN BELFORD, ESQ.

Thursday Morning, Five o'clock (June 8).

NOW IS my reformation secured; for I never shall love any other woman! Oh, she is all variety! *Imagination* cannot form; much less can the pencil paint; nor can the soul of painting, *poetry,* describe an angel so exquisitely, so elegantly lovely! Although the subject is too hallowed for profane contemplation, yet shalt thou have the *whole* before thee as it passed: and this not from a spirit wantoning in description upon so rich a subject; but with a design to put a bound to thy roving thoughts.

At a little after two, when the whole house was still, or seemed to be so, and, as it proved, my Clarissa in bed and fast asleep; I also in a manner undressed (as indeed I was for an hour before), and in my gown and slippers, though, to oblige thee, writing on; I was alarmed by a trampling noise overhead, and a confused buzz of mixed voices, some louder than others, like scolding, and little short of screaming. While I was wondering what could be the matter, downstairs ran Dorcas, and at my door, in an accent rather frightedly and hoarsely inward, than shrilly clamorous, she cried out: Fire! Fire! And this the more alarmed me, as she seemed to endeavour to cry out louder, but could not.

My pen dropped from my fingers; and up started I; and making but three steps to the door, opening it, I cried out, Where? Where? almost as much terrified as the wench: while she, more than half-undressed, her petticoats in her hand, unable to speak distinctly, pointed upstairs.

I was there in a moment, and found all owing to the carelessness of Mrs. Sinclair's cook-maid, who, having sat up to read when she should have been in bed, had set fire to an old pair of calico window-curtains.

She had had the presence of mind, in her fright, to tear down the half-burnt valance, as well as curtains, and had got them, though blazing, into the chimney, by the time I came up; so that I had the satisfaction to find the danger happily over.

Meantime Dorcas, after she had directed me upstairs, not knowing the worst was over, and expecting every minute the house would be in a blaze, out of tender regard for her lady, ran to her door, and rapping loudly at it, in a recovered voice cried out, with a shrillness equal to her love: *Fire! Fire! The house is on fire! Rise, madam!—this instant rise—if you would not be burnt in your bed!*

No sooner had she made this dreadful outcry, but I heard her lady's door, with hasty violence, unbar, unbolt, unlock, and open, and my charmer's voice sounding like that of one going into a fit.

I trembled with concern for her, and hastened down faster than the alarm of fire had made me run up, in order to satisfy her that all the danger was over.

When I had *flown down* to her chamber door, there I beheld the most charming creature in the world, supporting herself on the arm of the gasping Dorcas, sighing, trembling, and ready to faint, with nothing on but an under-petticoat, her lovely bosom half open, and her feet just slipped into her shoes. As soon as she saw me she panted, and struggled to speak; but could only say, O Mr. Lovelace! and down was ready to sink.

I clasped her in my arms with an ardour she never felt before: My dearest life! fear nothing: I have been up—the danger is over—the fire is got under.

O Jack! how her sweet bosom, as I clasped her to mine, heaved and panted! I could even distinguish her dear heart flutter, flutter, flutter against mine; and for a few minutes I feared she would go into fits.

Lest the half-lifeless charmer should catch cold in this undress, I lifted her to her bed, and sat down by her upon the side of it, endeavouring with the utmost tenderness, as well of action as expression, to dissipate her terrors.

But, far from being affected, as I wished, by an address so fervent (although from a man for whom she had so lately owned a regard, and with whom, but an hour or two before, she had parted with so much satisfaction), I never saw a bitterer, or more moving grief, when she came fully to herself.

She conjured me, in the most solemn and affecting manner, by turns threatening and soothing, to quit her apartment and permit her to hide herself from the light, and from every human eye.

I besought her pardon; yet could not avoid offending; and repeatedly vowed that the next morning's sun should witness our espousals: but taking, I suppose, all my protestations of this kind as an indication that I intended to proceed to the last extremity, she would hear nothing that I said; but, redoubling her struggles to get from me, in broken accents, and exclamations the most vehement, she protested that she would not survive what she called a treatment so disgraceful and villainous; and, looking all wildly round her, as if for some instrument of mischief, she espied a pair of sharp-pointed scissors on a chair by the bedside, and endeavoured to catch them up, with design to make her words good on the spot.

Seeing her desperation, I begged her to be pacified; that she would hear me speak but one word; declaring that I intended no dishonour to her: and having seized the scissors, I threw them into the chimney; and she still insisting vehemently upon my distance, I permitted her to take the chair.

But, oh, the sweet discomposure! Her bared shoulders and arms, so inimitably fair and lovely: her spread hands crossed over her charming neck; yet not half concealing its glossy beauties: the scanty coat, as she rose from me, giving the whole of her admirable shape, and fine-turned limbs: her eyes running over, yet seeming to threaten future vengeance: and at last her lips uttering what every indignant look and glowing feature portended; exclaiming as if I had done the worst I could do, and vowing never to forgive me; wilt thou wonder if I resumed the incensed, the already too much provoked fair one?

I did; and clasped her once more to my bosom: but, considering the delicacy of her frame, her force was amazing, and showed how much in earnest she was in her resentment; for it was with the utmost difficulty that I was able to hold her: nor could I prevent her sliding through my arms, to fall upon her knees: which she did at my feet: and there, in the anguish of her soul, her streaming eyes lifted up to my face with supplicating softness, hands folded, dishevelled hair; for her night head-dress having fallen off in her struggling, her charming tresses fell down in naturally shining ringlets, as if officious to conceal the dazzling beauties of her neck and shoulders; her lovely bosom too heaving with sighs and broken sobs, as if to aid her quivering lips in pleading for her—in this manner, but when her grief gave way to her speech, in words pronounced with that emphatical propriety which distinguishes this admirable creature in her elocution from all the women I ever heard speak, did she implore my compassion and my honour.

"Consider me, *dear* Lovelace" (*dear* was her charming word!), "on my knees I beg you to consider me, as a poor creature who has no protector but you; who has no defence but your honour: by that honour! by your humanity! by all you have vowed! I conjure you not to make me abhor myself!—not to make me vile in my own eyes!"

I mentioned the morrow as the happiest day of my life.

Tell me not of to-morrow. If indeed you mean me honourably, *now,* this very instant NOW! you must show it, and be gone! You can never in a whole long life repair the evils you may NOW make me suffer.

Wicked wretch! Insolent villain!—Yes, she called me insolent villain, although so much in my power! And for what?—

only for kissing (*with passion indeed*) her inimitable neck, her lips, her cheeks, her forehead, and her streaming eyes, as this assemblage of beauties offered itself at once to my ravished sight; she continuing kneeling at my feet, as I sat.

If I *am* a villain, madam—And then my grasping, but trembling hand—I hope I did not hurt the tenderest and loveliest of all her beauties—If I *am* a villain, madam——

She tore my ruffle, shrunk from my happy hand with amazing force and agility, as with my other arm I would have encircled her waist.

Indeed you are! The worst of villians! Help! dear blessed people! and screamed. No help for a poor creature!

Am I then a villain, madam? *Am* I then a villain, say you? and clasped both my arms about her, offering to raise her to my bounding heart.

Oh, no!—and yet you are! And again I was her *dear* Lovelace!—her hands again clasped over her charming bosom. Kill me! kill me! if I am odious enough in your eyes to deserve this treatment; and I will thank you! Too long, much too long, has my life been a burden to me! Or (wildly looking all around her), give me but the means, and I will instantly convince you that my honour is dearer to me than my life!

Then, with still folded hands, and fresh-streaming eyes, I was her *blessed* Lovelace; and she would thank me with her latest breath if I would permit her to make that preference, or free her from further indignities.

Still, however, close clasping her to my bosom, as I had raised her from her knees, she again slid through my arms and dropped upon them:

"See, Mr. Lovelace!—Good God! that I should live to see this hour, and to bear this treatment!—See at your feet a poor creature, imploring your pity, who, for your sake, is abandoned of all the world! Let not my father's curse thus dreadfully operate! Be not *you* the inflicter, who have been the *cause* of it: but spare me, I beseech you, spare me! For how have I deserved this treatment from you? For *your own sake,* if not for *my sake,* and as you would that God Almighty, in your last hour, should have mercy upon *you,* spare me!"

I would again have raised the dear suppliant from her knees; but she would not be raised, till my softened mind, she said, had yielded to her prayer, and bid her rise to be innocent.

Rise then, my angel! Rise, and be what you are, and all you wish to be! Only pronounce me pardoned for what has passed.

God Almighty, said she, hear your prayers in your most arduous moments, as you have heard mine! And now leave me, this moment leave me to my own recollection: in *that* you will leave me to misery enough, and more than you ought to wish to your bitterest enemy.

Impute not everything, my best beloved, to design; for design it was not——

O Mr. Lovelace!

Upon my soul, madam, the fire was real. (*And so it was, Jack!*) The house, my dearest life, might have been consumed by it, as you will be convinced in the morning by ocular demonstration.

O Mr. Lovelace!

Let my passion for you, madam, and the unexpected meeting of you at your chamber door, in an attitude so charming——

Leave me, leave me, this moment! I beseech you, leave me; looking wildly and in confusion about her, and upon herself.

Excuse me, dearest creature, for those liberties which, innocent as they were, your too great delicacy may make you take amiss——

No more! no more! Leave me, I beseech you! Again looking upon herself, and around her, in a sweet confusion. Begone! Begone!

Then weeping, she struggled vehemently to withdraw her hands, which all the while I held between mine. Her struggles! Oh, what additional charms, as I now reflect, did her struggles give to every feature, every limb, of a person so sweetly elegant and lovely!

Impossible, my dearest life, till you pronounce my pardon! Say but you forgive me!—say but you forgive me!

I beseech you, begone! Leave me to myself, that I may think what I *can* do, and what I *ought* to do.

That, my dearest creature, is not enough. You must tell me

that I am forgiven; that you will see me to-morrow as if nothing had happened.

And then I clasped her again in my arms, hoping she would not forgive me.

I will—I do forgive you—wretch that you are!

Nay, my Clarissa! And is it such a reluctant pardon, mingled with a word so upbraiding, that I am to be put off with, when you are thus (clasping her close to me) in my power?

I do, I *do* forgive you!

Heartily?

Yes, heartily!

And freely?

Freely!

And will you look upon me to-morrow as if nothing had passed?

Yes, yes!

I cannot take these peevish affirmatives, so much like intentional negatives! Say you will, upon your honour.

Upon my honour, then. Oh, now begone! begone! And never—never——

What, never, my angel! Is this forgiveness?

Never, said she, let what has passed be remembered more!

I insisted upon one kiss to seal my pardon—and retired like a fool, a woman's fool, as I was! I sneakingly retired! Couldst thou have believed it?

But I had no sooner entered my own apartment than, reflecting upon the opportunity I had lost, and that all I had gained was but an increase of my own difficulties; and upon the ridicule I should meet with below upon a weakness so much out of my usual character; I repented, and hastened back, in hope that through the distress of mind which I left her in, she had not so soon fastened her door; and I was fully resolved to execute all my purposes, be the consequence what it would; for, thought I, I have already sinned beyond *cordial* forgiveness, I doubt; and if fits and desperation ensue, I can but marry at last, and then I shall make her amends.

But I was justly punished; for her door was fast: and hearing her sigh and sob, as if her heart would burst: My beloved creature, said I, rapping gently (her sobbings then ceasing), I want but to say three words to you, which must be the most acceptable you ever heard from me. Let me see you but for one moment.

I thought I heard her coming to open the door, and my heart leaped in that hope; but it was only to draw another bolt, to make it still the faster; and she either could not or would not answer me, but retired to the farther end of her apartment, to her closet probably: and more like a fool than before, again I sneaked away.

MR. LOVELACE TO JOHN BELFORD, ESQ.

Thursday Morning, Eight o'clock.

HER chamber door has not yet been opened. I must not expect she will breakfast with me. Nor dine with me, I doubt. A little silly soul, what troubles does she make to herself by her over-niceness! All I have done to her would have been looked upon as a *frolic* only, a *romping-bout,* and laughed off by nine parts in ten of the sex accordingly. The more she makes of it, the more painful to herself, as well as to me.

. . . . . .

By my troth, Jack, I am half as much ashamed to see the women below, as my fair one can be to see me. I have not yet opened my door, that I may not be obtruded upon by them.

For thou canst not imagine how even Sally Martin rejoiced last night in the thought that the lady's hour was approaching.

Past Ten o'clock.

I never longed in my life for anything with so much impatience as to see my charmer. She has been stirring, it seems, these two hours.

Dorcas just now tapped at her door, to take her morning commands.

She had none for her, was the answer.

She desired to know if she would not breakfast?

A sullen and low-voiced *negative* received Dorcas.

I will go myself.

. . . . . .

Three different times tapped I at the door; but had no answer.

Permit me, dearest creature, to inquire after your health. As you have not been seen to-day, I am impatient to know how you do?

Not a word of answer; but a deep sigh, even to sobbing.

Let me beg of you, madam, to accompany me up another pair of stairs—you'll rejoice to see what a happy escape we have all had.

A happy escape indeed, Jack! For the fire had scorched the window-board, singed the hangings, and burnt through the slit-deal lining of the window-jambs.

No answer, madam! Am I not worthy of one word? Is it thus you keep your promise with me? Shall I not have the favour of your company for two minutes in the dining-room?

Ahem! and a deep sigh! were all the answer.

Answer me but how you do! Answer me but that you are well! Is this the forgiveness that was the condition of my obedience?

Then, in a faintish, but angry voice: Begone from my door! Wretch, inhuman, barbarous, and all that is base and treacherous! begone from my door! Nor tease thus a poor creature, entitled to protection, not outrage.

I see, madam, how you keep your word with me! *If* a sudden impulse, the effects of an unthought-of accident, cannot be forgiven——

Oh, the dreadful weight of a father's curse, thus in the very letter of it——

And then her voice dying away in murmurs inarticulate, I looked through the keyhole, and saw her on her knees, her face, though not towards me, lifted up, as well as hands, and these folded, deprecating, I suppose, that gloomy tyrant's curse.

I could not help being moved.

My dearest life! admit me to your presence but for two minutes, and confirm your promised pardon; and may lightning blast me on the spot if I offer anything but my penitence at a shrine so sacred! I will afterwards leave you for the whole day; and till to-morrow morning; and then attend you with writings, all ready to sign, a licence obtained, or, if it cannot, a minister without one. This once believe me! When you see the reality of the danger that gave occasion for this your unhappy resentment, you will think less hardly of me. And let me beseech you to perform a promise on which I made a reliance not altogether ungenerous.

I cannot see you! Would to Heaven I never had! If I write, that's all I can do.

Let your writing then, my dearest life, confirm your promise: and I will withdraw in expectation of it.

Past Eleven o'clock.

She rung her bell for Dorcas; and, with her door in her hand, only half opened, gave her a billet for me.

How did the dear creature look, Dorcas?

She was dressed. She turned her face quite from me; and sighed, as if her heart would break.

Sweet creature! I kissed the wet wafer, and drew it from the paper with my breath.

These are the contents. No inscriptive Sir! No Mr. Lovelace!

I cannot see you: nor will I, if I can help it. Words cannot express the anguish of my soul on your baseness and ingratitude.

If the circumstances of things are such, that I can have no way for reconciliation with those who would have been my natural protectors from such outrages, but through *you* (the only inducement I can have to stay a moment longer in your knowledge), pen and ink must be, at present, the only means of communication between us.

Vilest of men! and most detestable of plotters! how have I deserved from you the shocking indignities—But no more—only for your own sake, wish not, at least for a week to come, to see

The undeservedly injured and insulted
Clarissa Harlowe.

But not to see her for a week! Dear pretty soul! how she anticipates me in everything! The counsellor will have finished the writings to-day or to-morrow, at furthest: the licence with the parson, or the parson without the licence, must be also procured within the next four-and-twenty hours. *Yet not to see her for a week!* Dear sweet soul! Her good angel is gone a journey: is truanting at least. But nevertheless, in thy week's time, or in much less, my charmer, I doubt not to complete my triumph!

But what vexes me of all things is, that such an excellent creature should break her word. But nobody is absolutely perfect! *'Tis human to err,* but *not to persevere*—I hope my charmer cannot be inhuman!

MR. LOVELACE TO JOHN BELFORD, ESQ.

King's Arms, Pallmall, Thursday, Two o'clock.

SEVERAL billets passed between us before I went out, by the *internuncioship* of Dorcas: for which reason mine are superscribed by her married name. She would not open her door to receive them; lest I should be near it, I suppose: so Dorcas was forced to put them under the door (after copying them for thee); and thence to take the answers.

TO MRS. LOVELACE

INDEED, my dearest life, you carry this matter too far. What will the people below, who suppose us one as to the ceremony, think of so great a niceness?

Most sincerely do I repent the offence given to your delicacy. But must I, for so accidental an occurrence, be branded by such shocking names? *Vilest of men,* and *most detestable of plotters,* are hard words!

I beg your presence in the dining-room for one quarter of an hour, and I will then leave you for the day. I am,

My dearest life,
Your ever-adoring and truly penitent,
Lovelace.

TO MR. LOVELACE

I WILL not see you. I cannot see you. I have no directions to give you. Let Providence decide for me as it pleases.

'Tis grievous to me to write, or even to *think* of you at present. Urge me no more then. Once more, I will *not* see you. Nor care I, now you have made me vile to myself, what other people think of me.

To Mrs. Lovelace

Again, madam, I remind you of your promise: and beg leave to say, I insist upon the performance of it.

I cannot reproach myself with anything that deserves this high resentment.

I own that the violence of my passion for you might have carried me beyond fit bounds.

For Heaven's sake, favour me with your presence for a few minutes: and I will leave you for the day.

Your truly contrite and afflicted

Lovelace.

To Mr. Lovelace

The more you tease me, the worse will it be for you.

At *present,* it is my sincere wish that I may never more see your face.

All that can afford you the least shadow of favour from me, arises from the hoped-for reconciliation with my *real* friends, not my *Judas*-protector.

To Mrs. Lovelace

Madam,—I will go to the Commons, and proceed in every particular as if I had not the misfortune to be under your displeasure.

I hope to find you in a kinder and, I will say, *juster* disposition on my return. Whether I get the licence or not, let me beg of you to make the *soon* you have been pleased to bid me hope for, to-morrow morning.

The settlements are ready to sign, or will be by night.

For Heaven's sake, madam, do not carry your resentment into a displeasure so disproportionate to the offence.

As I have no hope to be permitted to dine with you, I shall

not return till evening: and then, I presume to say, I *expect* (your *promise* authorizes me to use the word) to find you disposed to bless, by your consent for to-morrow,

Your adoring
Lovelace.

I looked through the keyhole at my going by her door, and saw her on her knees, at her bed's feet, her head and bosom on the bed, her arms extended (*sweet creature, how I adore her!*); and in an agony she seemed to be, sobbing, as I heard at that distance, as if her heart would break.

MR. LOVELACE TO JOHN BELFORD, ESQ.

Thursday Evening, June 8.

OH, FOR A CURSE to kill with! Ruined! Undone! Outwitted! Tricked! Zounds, man, the lady is gone off! Absolutely gone off! Escaped!

The little hypocrite, who knows not a soul in this town (*I thought I was sure of her at any time*), such an inexperienced traitress; giving me hope too, in her first billet, that her expectation of the family-reconciliation would withold her from taking such a step as this. Curse upon her contrivances! I thought that it was owing to her bashfulness, to her modesty, that, after a few innocent freedoms, she could not look me in the face; when, all the while, she was impudently (yes, I say, *impudently,* though she be Clarissa Harlowe) contriving to rob me of the dearest property I had ever purchased. Purchased by a painful servitude of many months; fighting through the wild beasts of her family for her, and combating with a wild-mill virtue, which hath cost me millions of perjuries only to attempt; and which now, with its damned air-fans, has tossed me a mile and an half beyond hope! And this, just as I had arrived within view of the consummation of all my wishes!

. . . .

How she could effect this her wicked escape, is my astonishment; the whole sisterhood having charge of her: for, as yet, I have not had patience enough to inquire into the particulars, nor to let a soul of them approach me.

To what purpose brought I this angel (angel I must yet call her) to this hellish house? And was I not meditating to do her deserved honour? By my soul, Belford, I was resolved. But thou knowest what I had *conditionally* resolved. And now, who can tell into what hands she may have fallen?

I am mad, stark mad, by Jupiter, at the thoughts of this! Unprovided, destitute, unacquainted—some villain, worse than myself, who adores her not as I adore her, may have seized her, and taken advantage of her distress! Let me perish, Belford, if a whole hecatomb of *innocents,* as the little plagues are called, shall atone for the broken promise and wicked artifices of this *cruel creature.*

. . . . . .

Going home, as I did, with resolutions favourable to her, judge thou of my distraction, when her escape was first hinted to me, although but in broken sentences. I knew not what I said, nor what I did. I wanted to kill somebody. I flew out of one room into another, while all avoided me but the veteran Betty Carberry, who broke the matter to me. I charged bribery and corruption, in my first fury, upon all; and threatened destruction to old and young, as they should come in my way.

This is the substance of the old wretch's[1] account.

She told me, "That I had no sooner left the vile house than Dorcas acquainted the siren" with it; and that I had left word that I was gone to Doctors' Commons.

"She sent Will with a letter to Wilson's, directed to Miss Howe, ordering him to inquire if there were not one for her.

"He only pretended to go, and brought word there was none; and put her letter in his pocket for me.

"She then ordered him to carry another (which she gave him) to the Horn Tavern to me. All this done without any seeming hurry; yet she appeared to be very solemn; and put her handkerchief frequently to her eyes.

"Will went out, pretending to bring the letter to me; but

[1] Mrs. Sinclair.

quickly returned; his heart still misgiving him, on recollecting my frequent cautions.

"But it must have been in this little interval that she escaped; for soon after his return they made fast the street door and hatch, the mother and the two nymphs taking a little turn into the garden; Dorcas going upstairs, and Will (to avoid being seen by his lady, or his voice heard) down into the kitchen.

"About half an hour after, Dorcas, who had planted herself where she could see her lady's door open, had the curiosity to go to look through the keyhole, having a misgiving, as she said, that her lady might offer some violence to herself, in the mood she had been in all day; and finding the key in the door, which was not very unusual, she tapped at it three or four times, and having no answer, opened it, with Madam, madam, did you call? Supposing her in her closet.

"Having no answer she stepped forward, and was astonished to find she was not there. She hastily ran into the dining-room, then into my apartments, searched every closet; dreading all the time to behold some sad catastrophe.

"Not finding her anywhere, she ran down to the old creature and her nymphs, with a Have you seen my lady?—Then she's gone! She's nowhere above!

"The whole house was in an uproar in an instant; some running upstairs, some down, from the upper rooms to the lower; and all screaming, How should they look *me* in the face!

"Will cried out, he was a dead man; *he* blamed *them; they him;* and every one was an *accuser,* and an *excuser,* at the same time.

"When they had searched the whole house, and every closet in it, ten times over, to no purpose, they took it into their heads to send to all the porters, chairmen, and hackney-coachmen, that had been near the house for two hours past, to inquire if any of them saw such a young lady; describing her.

"This brought them some light: the only dawning for hope that I can have, and which keeps me from absolute despair. One of the chairmen gave them this account: That he saw such a one come out of the house a little before four (in a great hurry, and as if frighted) with a little parcel tied up in an handkerchief, in her hand: that he took notice to his fellow, who plied her without her answering, that she was a fine young lady: that he'd warrant she had either a bad husband, or very cross parents; for that her eyes seemed swelled with crying. Upon which, a third fellow replied that it might be a doe escaped from Mother *Damnable's* park.

"From these appearances the fellow who gave this information had the curiosity to follow her, unperceived. She often looked back. Everybody who passed her, turned to look after her; passing their verdicts upon her tears, her hurry, and her charming person; till coming to a stand of coaches, a coachman plied her; was accepted; alighted; opened the coach door in a hurry, seeing *her* hurry; and in it she stumbled for haste; and, as the fellow believed, hurt her shins with the stumble.

"The fellow heard her say, Drive fast! Very fast! Where, madam? To Holborn Bars, answered she; repeating, Drive very fast! And up she pulled both the windows: and he lost sight of the coach in a minute.

"Will, as soon as he had this intelligence, speeded away in hopes to trace her out; declaring, that he would never think of seeing me till he had heard some tidings of his lady."

And now, Belford, all my hope is, that this fellow (who attended us in our airing to Hampstead, to Highgate, to Muswell Hill, to Kentish Town) will hear of her at some one or other of those places. And on this I the rather build, as I remember she was once, after our return, very inquisitive about the stages, and their prices; praising the convenience to passengers in their going off every hour; and this in Will's hearing, who was then in attendance. Woe be to the villain, if he recollect not this!

. . . . . .

But now that I have heard the mother's story, and contemplated the dawning hopes given by the chairman's information, I am a good deal easier, and can make cooler reflections.

If ever——

Here Mr. Lovelace lays himself under a curse, too shocking to be repeated, if he revenge not himself upon the lady, should he once more get her into his hands.

Again going into her chamber, because it *was* hers, and sighing over the bed, and every piece of furniture in it, I cast my eye towards the drawers of the dressing-glass, and saw peep out, as it were, in one of the half-drawn drawers, the corner of a letter. I snatched it out, and found it superscribed by her, *To Mr. Lovelace.* The sight of it made my heart leap, and I trembled so, that I could hardly open the seal.

How does this damned love unman me! But nobody ever loved as I love! It is even increased by her unworthy flight, and my disappointment. Ungrateful creature, to fly from a passion thus ardently flaming!

But wouldst thou think that this *haughty promise-breaker* could resolve as she does, absolutely and for ever to renounce me for what passed last night? That she could resolve to forego all her opening prospects of reconciliation; that reconciliation with a worthless family, on which she had set her whole heart? Yet she does! She acquits me of all obligation to her, and herself of all expectations from me—and for what? O that indeed I had given her real cause! Damned confounded niceness, prudery, affectation, or pretty ignorance, if not affectation! By my soul, Belford, I told thee all—I was more indebted to her struggles, than to my own forwardness. I cannot support my own reflections upon a decency so ill-requited. She could not, she would not have been so much a Harlowe in her resentment, had I deserved, as I *ought* to have done, her resentment. All she feared, had then been over; and her own good sense, and even modesty, would have taught her to make the best of it.

But if ever again I get her into my hands, *art,* and more *art,* and *compulsion* too, if she make it necessary (*and 'tis plain that nothing else will do*), shall she experience from the man whose fear *of* her has been above even his passion *for* her; and whose gentleness and forbearance she has thus *perfidiously* triumphed over.

MR. LOVELACE TO JOHN BELFORD, ESQ.

A LETTER is put into my hands by Wilson himself.

A letter from Miss Howe to her cruel friend! I made no scruple to open it.

It is a miracle that I fell not into fits at the reading of it; and at the thought of what *might* have been the consequence had it come into the hands of *this Clarissa Harlowe.*

Thus wilt see the margin of this cursed letter crowded with indices [*]. I put them to mark the places which call for vengeance upon the vixen writer, or which require animadversion. Return thou it to me the moment thou hast perused it.

To Miss Lætitia Beaumont

Wednesday, June 7.

My dearest Friend,—You will perhaps think that I have been too long silent. But I had begun two letters at different times since my last, and written a great deal each time, and with spirit enough I assure you, incensed as I was against *the abominable wretch you are with, particularly on reading yours of the twenty-first of the past month.

* The *first* I intended to keep open till I could give you some account of my proceedings with Mrs. Townsend. It was some days before I saw her; and this intervenient space giving me time to reperuse what I had written, I thought it proper to lay that aside and to write in a style a little less fervent, for you *would have blamed me, I know, for the freedom of some of my *expressions (*execrations,* if you please). And when I had gone a good way in the *second,* the change in your prospects, on his communicating to you Miss Montague's letter, and his better behaviour, occasioning a change in your mind, I laid that aside also. And in this uncertainty thought I would wait to see the issue of affairs between you before I wrote again, believing all would soon be decided one way or other.

I had still, perhaps, held this resolution (as every appearance, according to your letters, was more and more promising), had not the two passed days furnished me with intelligence which it highly imports you to know.

The women of the house where you are—O my dear—the women of the house—but you never thought highly of them, so it cannot be very surprising—nor would you have *stayed so* **long with them, had not the notion of removing to one of your own,* made you less uneasy, and less curious about their char-

*acters and behaviour. Yet I could *now* wish that you had been less reserved among them—but I tease you. In short, my dear, *you are certainly in a devilish house! Be assured that the woman is one of the vilest of women—nor does she go to you by her right name.—Very true! Her name is *not* Sinclair, nor is the street she lives in, Dover Street. Did you never go out by yourself and discharge the coach or chair, and return by an- *other coach or chair? If you did you would never have found your way to the vile house, either by the woman's name, *Sinclair,* or by the street's name mentioned by that Doleman in his letter about the lodgings.

The wretch might indeed have held out these false lights a little more excusably had the house been an honest house, and had his end only been to prevent mischief from your brother. But this contrivance was antecedent, as I think, to your brother's project; so that no excuse can be made for his intentions at the *time*—the man, whatever he may *now* intend, *was certainly then, even *then,* a villain in his heart!

* Upon my life, my dear, this man is a vile, a contemptible villain—I must speak out!

I will tell you how I came by my intelligence. *That* being *a *fact* and requiring the less attention, I will try to account to you for *that.*

Thus then it came about: "Miss Lardner saw you at St. James's Church on Sunday was fortnight. She kept you in her eye during the whole time, but could not once obtain the notice of yours, though she curtsied to you twice. She thought to pay her compliments to you when the service was over, for *she doubted not but you were married; and for an odd reason —*Because you came to church by yourself.* Every eye was upon you; and this seeming to give you hurry, and you being nearer the door than she, you slid out before she could get to you. But she ordered her servant to follow you till you were housed. This servant saw you step into a chair which waited for you, and you ordered the men to carry you to the place where they took you up.

"The next day Miss Lardner sent the same servant, out of mere curiosity, to make private inquiry whether Mr. Lovelace were, or were not, with you there. And this inquiry brought out, from *different* people, that the house was suspected to be one of those genteel wicked houses which receive and accommodate *fashionable people* of both sexes.

"Miss Lardner, confounded at this strange intelligence, made further inquiry, enjoining secrecy to the servant she had sent, as well as to the gentleman whom she employed; who had it confirmed from a rakish friend who knew the house, and told him that there were two houses; the one *in which all decent appearances were preserved, and guests rarely admitted;* the other, the receptacle of those who were absolutely engaged, and broken to the vile yoke."

* Say, my dear creature, say, shall I not execrate the wretch?

"Miss Lardner kept this to herself some days, not knowing what to do; for she loves you, and admires you of all women. At last she revealed it, but in confidence, to Miss Biddulph by letter. Miss Biddulph, in like confidence, being afraid it would distract *me* were I to know it, communicated it to Miss Lloyd; and so, like a whispered scandal, it passed through several canals; and then it came to me."

I thought I should have fainted upon the surprising communication. But rage taking place, it blew away the sudden illness. I besought Miss Lloyd to re-enjoin secrecy to every one. I told her that I would not for the world that my mother, *or any of your family, should know it. And I instantly caused a trusty friend to make what inquiries he could about Tomlinson.

* I had thoughts to have done it before I had this intelligence; but not imagining it to be needful, and little thinking that you could be in such a house, and as you were pleased with your *changed prospects, I forbore. And the rather forbore, as the matter is so laid, that Mrs. Hodges is supposed to know nothing of the projected treaty of accommodation; but, on the contrary, that it was designed to be a secret to her, and to everybody but immediate parties, and it was Mrs. Hodges that I had proposed to sound by a *second* hand.

* Now, my dear, it is certain, without applying to that too much favoured housekeeper, that there is not such a man within ten miles of your uncle.

* Yet, methinks, the story is so plausible; Tomlinson, as you

describe him, is so good a man, and so much of a gentleman; the end to be answered by his being an impostor, so much *more than necessary* if Lovelace has villainy in his head; and as you are in such a house—your wretch's behaviour to him was so petulant and lordly; and Tomlinson's answer so full of spirit and circumstance; and then what he communicated to you of Mr. Hickman's application to your uncle, and of Mrs. Norton's to your mother (some of which particulars, I am satisfied, his vile agent Joseph Leman could not reveal to his viler employer); his pressing on the marriage-day, in the name of your uncle, which it could not answer any *wicked* purpose for him to do; and what he writes of your uncle's proposal, to have it thought that you were married from the time that you have lived in one house together; and that to be made to agree with the time of Mr. Hickman's visit to your uncle; the insisting on a trusty person's being present at the ceremony, at that uncle's nomination—*These things make me willing to try for a tolerable construction to be made of all;* though I am so much puzzled by what occurs on both sides of the question, that I cannot but abhor the devilish wretch, whose inventions and contrivances are for ever employing an inquisitive head, as mine is, without affording the means of absolute detection.

But this is what I am ready to conjecture, that Tomlinson, specious as he is, is a machine of Lovelace; and that he is employed for some end, which has not yet been answered. This is certain, that not only Tomlinson, but Mennell, who, I think, attended you more than once at this vile house, must know it to *be* a vile house.

What can you then think of Tomlinson's declaring himself in *favour* of it, upon inquiry?

Lovelace too must know it to be so; if not before he brought you to it, soon after.

Perhaps the *company he found there* may be the most probable way of accounting for his bearing with the house, and for his strange suspensions of marriage, when it was in his power to call such an angel of a woman his.

O my dear, the man is a villain! the greatest of villains, in every light! And this Doleman must be another of his implements!

* There are so many wretches who think *that* to be no sin, which is one of the greatest and the most ungrateful of all sins, to ruin young creatures of our sex who place their confidence in them; that the wonder is less than the shame, that people of figure, of *appearance* at least, are found to promote the horrid purposes of profligates of fortune and interest!

* But can I think (you will ask with indignant astonishment) that Lovelace can have designs upon your honour?

* That such designs he *has had,* if he *still* hold them not, I can have no doubt, now that I know the house he has brought you to, to be a vile one.

Allow me a brief retrospection of it all.

* We both know that pride, revenge, and a delight to tread in unbeaten paths, are principal ingredients in the character of this finished libertine.

* He hates all your family, yourself excepted; and I have several times thought that I have seen him stung and mortified *that love has obliged him to kneel at your footstool, because you are a *Harlowe*. Yet is this wretch a savage in love. Love that humanizes the fiercest spirits has not been able to *subdue his. His *pride,* and the credit which a few *plausible* *qualities, sprinkled among his *odious ones,* have given him, have secured him too good a reception from our eye-judging, our undistinguishing, our self-flattering, our too-confiding sex, to make assiduity and obsequiousness, and a conquest of his unruly passions, any part of his study.

* He has some reason for his animosity to *all* the men, and to *one* woman of your family. He has always shown you, and *his own family too, that he prefers his pride to his interest. He is a declared marriage-hater; a notorious intriguer; full of his inventions, and glorying in them. He never could draw you into declarations of love; nor till your *wise* relations persecuted you as they did, to receive his addresses as a lover. *He knew that you professedly disliked him for his immoralities; he could not therefore justly blame you for the coldness and indifference of your behaviour to him.

* The prevention of mischief was your first main view in the correspondence he drew you into. He ought not, then, to have wondered that you declared your preference of the *single life*

to *any* matrimonial engagement. He knew that this was *always* your preference, and *that* before he tricked you away *so artfully. What was his conduct to you afterwards, that you should of a sudden change it?

Thus was your whole behaviour regular, consistent, and dutiful to those to whom by birth you owed duty; and neither prudish, coquettish, nor tyrannical to him.

* He had *agreed* to go on with you upon those your own terms, and to rely only on his *own merits* and *future reformation* for your favour.

* It was plain to me, indeed, to whom you communicated all that *you knew* of your own heart, though not all of it that *I found out*, that love had pretty early gained footing in it. And this you yourself would have discovered sooner than you *did, had not his alarming, his unpolite, his rough conduct, kept it under.

* I knew by experience that love is a fire that is not to be played with without burning one's fingers; I knew it to be a dangerous thing for two single persons of different sexes to *enter into familiarity and correspondence with each other; since, as to the latter, must not a person be capable of premeditated art who can sit down to write, and not write from the heart?

* As this man's vanity had made him imagine that no woman could be proof against love, when his address was honourable, no wonder that he struggled, like a lion held in toils, against a passion that he thought not returned. And how could you, *at first,* show a return in love to so fierce a spirit, and who had seduced you away by vile artifices, but to the approval of those artifices?

* Hence, perhaps, it is not difficult to believe that it became possible for such a wretch as this to give way to his old prejudices against marriage, and to that revenge which had always been a first passion with him.

This is the only way, I think, to account for his horrid views in bringing you to a vile house.

And now may not all the rest be naturally accounted for? His delays—his teasing ways—his bringing you to bear with his lodging in the same house—his making you pass to the people of it as his wife; *though restrictively so,* yet with hope, *no doubt (vilest of villains as he is!), to take you at advantage *—his bringing you into the company of his libertine companions—the attempt of imposing upon you that Miss Partington for a bedfellow, very probably his own invention for the worst of purposes—his terrifying you at many different times—his obtruding himself upon you when you went out to church, no doubt to prevent your finding out what the people of the house were—the advantages he made of your brother's foolish project with Singleton.

* See how the monster, whom I thought, and so often called a *fool, comes out to have been all the time one of the greatest villains in the world!

* But now, my dear, do I apprehend that you are in greater danger than ever yet you have been in; if you are not married in a week; and yet stay in this abominable house. For were you out of it, I own I should not be much afraid for you.

These are my thoughts, on the most deliberate considera- *tion: "That he is now convinced that he has not been able to draw off your guard; that therefore, if he can obtain no new advantage over you as he goes along, he is resolved to do you all the *poor justice* that it is in the power of such a wretch as he to do you. He is the rather induced to this, as he sees that all his own family have warmly engaged themselves in *your cause; and that it is his *highest interest* to be just to you. Then the horrid wretch loves you (as well he may) above all women. I have no doubt of this; with *such* a love as such a *wretch is capable of; with *such* a love as Herod loved his Mariamne. He is now therefore, very probably, at last, in earnest."

I took time for inquiries of different natures, as I knew by the train you are in, that whatever his designs are, they *cannot ripen either for good or evil till something shall result from this new device of his about Tomlinson and your uncle.

* And yet I find it to be true that Counsellor Williams (whom Mr. Hickman knows to be a man of eminence in his profes- *sion) has actually as good as finished the settlements; that two drafts of them have been made; one avowedly to be sent to

one Captain Tomlinson, as the clerk says:—and I find that a licence has actually been more than once endeavoured to be obtained! and that difficulties have hitherto been made, *equally to Lovelace's vexation and disappointment. My mother's proctor, who is very intimate with the proctor applied to by the wretch, has come at this information in confidence; and hints that, as Mr. Lovelace is a man of high fortunes, these difficulties will probably be got over.

* His sudden (and as suddenly recovered) illness has given him an opportunity to find out that you love him. (*Alas, my dear, I knew you loved him!*) He is, as you relate, every hour *more and more an encroacher upon it. He has seemed to change his nature, and is all love and gentleness. The wolf has put on the sheep's clothing; yet more than once has shown his *teeth and his hardly sheathed claws.

* What then have you to do but to fly this house, this infernal house! O that your heart would let you fly the *man!*

* If you should be disposed so to do, Mrs. Townsend shall be ready at your command. But if you meet with no impediments, no new causes of doubt, I think your reputation in the eye of the world, though not your happiness, is concerned, that *you should be his. And yet I cannot bear that these libertines should be rewarded for their villainy with the best of the sex, when the worst of it are too good for them.

But if you meet with the least ground for suspicion; if he would detain you at the odious house, or wish you to stay, *now you know what the people are; fly *him,* whatever your prospects are, as well as *them.*

In one of your next airings, if you have no other way, refuse *to return with him. Name *me* for your intelligencer, that you are in a bad house.

But suppose you desire to go out of town for the air, this sultry weather, and insist upon it? You may plead your health *for so doing. Your brother's foolish scheme, I am told, is certainly given up; so you need not be afraid on that account.

If you do not fly the house upon reading of this, I shall judge of his power over you, by the little you will have over either him or yourself.

* One of my informants has made slight inquiries concerning

Mrs. Fretchville. Did he ever name to you the street or square she lived in?—I don't remember that you, in any of yours, *mentioned the place of her abode to me. No such person or house can be found, near any of the new streets or squares, where the lights I had from your letters led me to imagine her *house might be. Ask him what street the house is in, if he has not told you; and let me know. If he make a difficulty of that *circumstance, it will amount to a detection.

I shall send this long letter by Collins, who changes his day to oblige me; and that he may try to get it into your own hands. If he cannot, he will leave it at Wilson's. As none of our letters by that conveyance have miscarried when you have been in more *apparently* disagreeable situations than you are in at present, I hope that this will go safe.

* One word more. Command me up, if I can be of the least service or pleasure to you. I value not fame; I value not censure; nor even life itself, I verily think, as I do your honour and your friendship—for is not your honour my honour? And is not your friendship the pride of my life?

May Heaven preserve you, my dearest creature, in honour and safety, is the prayer, the hourly prayer, of

Your ever faithful and affectionate

Anna Howe.

Thursday Morn. 5. I have written all night.

[Mr. Lovelace forged this letter, using much the same language, but turning it to his own advantage, and gave it to Clarissa. Ed.]

To Miss Howe

My dearest Creature,—How you have shocked, confounded, surprised, astonished me, by your dreadful communication! My *heart is too weak* to bear up against such a stroke as this!—But can there be such villainy in men as in this vile principal, and equally vile agent?

I am really ill—very ill. Grief and surprise, and *now* I will say despair, have overcome me!

O that your mother would have the goodness to permit me the presence of the only comforter that my afflicted, my half-broken heart, could be raised by! But I charge you, think not of coming up without her indulgent permission. I am too ill at present, my dear, to think of combating with this dreadful man; and of flying from this horrid house! But my illness will be my present security, should he indeed have meditated villainy. Forgive, O forgive me, my dearest friend, the trouble I have given you!

Clarissa Harlowe.

Well, Jack!

Shall I send this letter? Thou seest I have left room, if I fail in the exact imitation of so charming a hand, to avoid too strict a scrutiny. Do they not both deserve it of me?

But the principal reason that withholds me is, for fear of being utterly blown up, if I should not be quick enough with my letter, or if Miss Howe should deliberate on setting out, or try her mother's consent first; in which time a letter from my frighted beauty might reach her; for I have no doubt, wherever she has refuged, but her first work was to write to her vixen friend. I will therefore go on patiently, and take my revenge upon the little fury at my leisure.

I am always careful to open covers cautiously, and to preserve seals entire.

MISS CLARISSA HARLOWE TO MISS HOWE

Thursday Evening, June 8.

O MY DEAREST friend, the man has at last proved himself to be a villain!

It was with the utmost difficulty last night that I preserved myself from the vilest dishonour. He extorted from me a promise of forgiveness, and that I would see him next day as if nothing had happened; but if it were possible to escape from a wretch, who, as I have too much reason to believe, formed a plot to fire the house, to frighten me, almost naked, into his arms, how could I see him next day?

I have escaped—And have now no other concern than that

I fly from the only hope that could have made such an husband tolerable to me; the reconciliation with my friends, so agreeably undertaken by my uncle.

All my present hope is to find some reputable family, or person of my own sex, who is obliged to go beyond sea, or who lives abroad; I care not whither; but if I might choose, in some one of our American colonies—never to be heard of more by my relations, whom I have so grievously offended.

Nor let your generous heart be moved at what I write. If I can escape the dreadfullest part of my father's malediction (for the temporary part is already in a manner fulfilled, which makes me tremble in apprehension of the other), I shall think the wreck of my worldly fortunes a happy composition.

Neither is there need of the renewal of your so often tendered goodness to me; for I have with me rings and other valuables, that were sent me with my clothes.

Then as to the envied estate, which has been the original cause of all my misfortunes, it shall never be mine upon litigated terms. If my father will be pleased to pay two annuities out of it, one to my dear Mrs. Norton; the other of fifty pounds *per annum*, to the same good woman, for the use of *my poor* concerning whom she knows all my mind; that so as few as possible may suffer by the consequences of my error; God bless them, and give them heart's ease and content, with the rest!

This wicked man knows I have no friend in the world but you; your neighbourhood therefore would be the first he would seek for me in, were you to think it possible for me to be concealed in it.

From my Cousin Morden, were he to come, I could not hope protection; since by his letter to me it is evident that my brother has engaged him in his party; nor would I, by any means, subject so worthy a man to danger; as might be the case, from the violence of this ungovernable spirit.

I am at present at one Mrs. Moore's at Hampstead. My heart misgave me at coming to this village, because I had been here with him more than once; but the coach hither was so ready a conveniency that I knew not what to do better. Then I shall stay here no longer than till I can receive your answer to this; in which you will be pleased to let me know if I cannot be hid, according to your former contrivance, by Mrs. Townsend's assistance, till the heat of the search be over. The Deptford road, I imagine, will be the right direction to hear of a passage and to get safely aboard.

This letter will enable you to account for a line or two, which I sent to Wilson's to be carried to you, only for a feint to get his servant out of the way. He seemed to be left, as I thought, for a spy upon me. But he returning too soon, I was forced to write a few lines for him to carry to his master, to a tavern near Doctors' Commons, with the same view; and this happily answered my end.

I wrote early in the morning a bitter letter to the wretch, which I left for him obvious enough; and I suppose he has it by this time. I shall recollect the contents, and give you the particulars of all, at more leisure.

I am sure you will approve of my escape—the rather, as the people of the house must be very vile; for they, and that Dorcas too, did hear me cry out for help; if the fire had been other than a villainous plot (although in the morning, to blind them, I pretended to think it otherwise) they would have been alarmed as much as I; and have run in, hearing me scream, to *comfort me* supposing my terror was the fire; to *relieve me,* supposing it were anything else. But the vile Dorcas went away as soon as she saw the wretch throw his arms about me!—Bless me, my dear, I had only my slippers and an under-petticoat on. I was frighted out of my bed by her cries of fire; and that I should be burnt to ashes in a moment—and she to go away, and never to return, nor anybody else! And yet I heard women's voices in the next room; indeed I did.

My terror is not yet over; I can hardly think myself safe; every well-dressed man I see from my windows I think to be him.

I know you will expedite an answer. A man and horse will be procured me to-morrow early, to carry this. To be sure, you cannot return an answer by the same man, because you must see Mrs. Townsend first; nevertheless, I shall wait with impatience till you *can;* having no friend but you to apply to; and being such a stranger to this part of the world, that I know not which way to turn myself; whither to go; nor what to do.

Mrs. Moore, at whose house I am, is a widow and of good character; and of this, one of her neighbours, of whom I bought a handkerchief, purposely to make inquiry before I would venture, informed me.

I will not set foot out of doors till I have your direction; and I am the more secure, having dropped words to the people of the house where the coach set me down, as if I expected a chariot to meet me in my way to Hendon, a village a little distance from this. And when I left their house, I walked backward and forward upon the hill; at first, not knowing what to do; and afterwards, to be certain that I was not watched before I ventured to inquire after a lodging.

You will direct for me, my dear, by the name of Mrs. Harriot Lucas.

For fear I should not get away at my first effort, I had apprised him that I would not set eye upon him under a week, in order to gain myself time for it in different ways; and were I so to have been watched as to have made it necessary, I would, after such an instance of the connivance of the women of the house, have run out into the street and thrown myself into the next house I could have entered, or claimed protection from the first person I had met.

Your unhappy, but ever affectionate
Clarissa Harlowe.

Mr. Lovelace to John Belford, Esq.

Friday Morning, past Two o'clock.

Io Triumphe! Io Clarissa, sing!—Once more, what a happy man thy friend!—A silly dear novice, to be heard to tell the coachman whither to carry her!—And to go to *Hampstead,* of all the villages about London!—The place where we had been together more than once!

But thou wilt be impatient to know how I came by my lights. Read the enclosed here.

Honnored Sur,—This is to sertifie your Honner, as how I am here at Hamestet, wher I have found out my lady to be in logins at one Mrs. Moore's, near upon Hamestet Hethe. And I have so ordered matters, that her ladiship cannot stur but I must have notice of her goins and comins.

My lady knows nothing of my being hereaway. But I thoute it best not to leve the plase, because she has tacken the logins but for a fue nites.

If your Honner come to the Upper Flax, I will be in site all the day about the tapp-house or the Hethe.

The tow inner letters I had from my lady, before she went off the prems's. One was to be for Miss Howe. The next was to be for your Honner. Miss How's I only made belief to her ladiship as I carred it, and sed as how there was nothing left for hur, as shee wished to knoe; so here they be bothe.

I am, may it plese your Honner,
Your Honner's most dutiful,
and, wonce more, happy sarvant,
Wm. Summers.

The two *inner* letters, as Will calls them, 'tis plain, were wrote for no other purpose, but to send him out of the way with them, and one of them to amuse me. That directed to Miss Howe is only this:

Thursday, June 8.

I WRITE this, my dear Miss Howe, only for a feint, and to see if it will go current. I shall write at large very soon, if not miserably prevented!!!

Cl. H.

This is my dear juggler's letter to me; the other *inner* letter sent by Will.

Thursday, June 8.

MR. LOVELACE,—Do not give me cause to dread your return. If you would not that I should hate you for ever, send me half a line by the bearer, to assure me that you will not attempt to see me for a week to come. I cannot look you in the face without equal confusion and indignation. The obliging me in this is but a poor atonement for your last night's vile behaviour.

You may pass this time in a journey to Lord M.'s; and I cannot doubt, if the ladies of your family are as favourable to me as you have assured me they are, but that you will have interest enough to prevail with one of them to oblige me with her company. After your baseness of last night, you will not wonder that I insist upon this proof of your future honour.

If Captain Tomlinson comes meantime, I can hear what he has to say, and send you an account of it.

But in less than a week, if you see me, it must be owing to a fresh act of violence, of which you know not the consequence.

Send me the requested line, if ever you expect to have the forgiveness confirmed, the promise of which you extorted from

The unhappy

Cl. H.

Suffice it at present to tell thee, in the first place, that *she is determined never to be my wife.*

I have *ruined* her, she says!—Now that's a fib, take it in her own way—if I had, she would not perhaps have run away from me.

She is *thrown upon the wide world!*—Now I own that Hampstead Heath affords very pretty and very *extensive* prospects; but 'tis not the *wide world* neither; and suppose *that* to be her grievance, I hope soon to restore her to a *narrower.*

She talks of her *father's curse;* but have I not repaid him for it a hundred-fold in the same coin? But why must the faults of other people be laid at my door?

A gentleman to speak with me, Dorcas?

Captain Tomlinson, sayest thou!

Let but the chariot come, and he shall accompany me in it to the bottom of the hill, that I may hear all he has to say, and tell him all my mind, and lose no time.

Dear captain, I rejoice to see you—just in the nick of time.

Strange news since I saw you, captain! Poor mistaken lady! But you have too much goodness, I know, to reveal to her Uncle Harlowe the errors of this capricious beauty. It will all turn out for the best. You must accompany me part of the way. I know the delight you take in composing differences.

And now, dressed like a bridegroom, my heart elated beyond that of the most desiring one, I am already at Hampstead!

MR. LOVELACE TO JOHN BELFORD, ESQ.

Upper Flask, Hampstead, Friday morn. 7 o'clock (June 9).

I AM NOW here, and here have been this hour and half.

All Will's account, from the lady's flight to his finding her again, all the accounts of the people of the house, the coachman's information to Will, and so forth, collected together, stand thus.

"The Hampstead coach, when the dear fugitive came to it, had but two passengers in it. But she made the fellow go off directly, paying for the vacant places.

"The two passengers directing the coachman to set them down at the Upper Flask, she bid him set her down there also.

"They took leave of her and she went into the house and asked if she could not have a dish of tea, and a room to herself for half an hour.

"They showed her up to the very room where I am now. She sat at the very table I now write upon; and, I believe, the chair I sit in was hers.

"She made no inquiry about a lodging, though by the sequel, thou'lt observe, that she seemed to intend to go no farther that night than Hampstead. But after she had drank two dishes, and put a biscuit in her pocket (sweet soul, to serve for her supper perhaps), she laid down half a crown; and refusing change, sighing, took leave, saying she would proceed towards Hendon, the distance to which had been one of her questions.

"They offered to send to know if a Hampstead coach were not to go to Hendon that evening.

"No matter, she said—perhaps she might meet the chariot.

"All these things put together, excited their curiosity; and they engaged a *peery* servant, as they called a footman who was drinking with Kit the hostler at the tap-house, to watch all her motions.

"She indeed went towards Hendon, passing by the sign of the

Castle on the Heath; then, stopping, looked about her, and down into the valley before her.

"Then, continuing on a few paces, she stopped again; and, as if disliking her road, directed her course back towards Hampstead.

"She then saw a coach-and-four driving towards her empty. She crossed the path she was in, as if to meet it; and seemed to intend to speak to the coachman, had he stopped or spoke first.

"The lady as well as the coachman, in short, seemed to want resolution; the horses kept on and the distance soon lengthened beyond recall. With a wistful eye she looked after him; sighed and wept; as the servant who then slyly passed her observed.

"By this time she had reached the houses. She looked up at every one as she passed; now and then breathing upon her bared hand, and applying it to her swelled eyes, to abate the redness and dry the tears. At last, seeing a bill up for letting lodgings, she walked backwards and forwards half a dozen times, as if unable to determine what to do. And then went further into the town; and there the fellow, being spoken to by one of his familiars, lost her for a few minutes; but he soon saw her come out of a linen-drapery shop, attended with a servant-maid, having, as he believed, bought some little matters, and, as it proved, got that maidservant to go with her to the house she is now at.

"The fellow, after waiting about an hour, and not seeing her come out, returned, concluding that she had taken lodgings there."

ACT II

SCENE.—*Hampstead Heath, continued.*

Enter my Rascal.

It is necessary that I give thee the particulars of Will's tale—and I have a little time upon my hands; for the maid of the house, who had been out of an errand, tells us that she saw Mrs. Moore go into the house of a young gentleman, within a few doors of her, who has a maiden sister, Miss Rawlins by name, *so notified* for prudence, that none of her acquaintance undertake anything of consequence without consulting her.

Meanwhile my honest coachman is walking about Miss Rawlins's door, in order to bring me notice of Mrs. Moore's return to her own house.

Will told them, before I came, "That his lady was but lately married to one of the finest gentlemen in the world. But that, he being very gay and lively, she was *mortal* jealous of him; and in a fit of that sort, had eloped from him."

When I came, my person and dress having answered Will's description, the people were ready to worship me.

Here, landlord; one word with you. My servant, I find, has acquainted you with the reason of my coming this way. An unhappy affair, landlord! But never was there a more virtuous woman.

So, sir, she seems to be. A thousand pities her ladyship has such ways—and to so good-humoured a gentleman as you seem to be, sir.

Mother-spoilt, landlord! Mother-spoilt!—that's the thing! But (sighing) I must make the best of it. What I want *you* to do for me, is to lend me a great-coat. I care not what it is. If my spouse should see me at a distance, she would make it very difficult for me to get at her speech. A great-coat with a cape, if you have one. I must come upon her before she is aware.

I am afraid, sir, I have none fit for such a gentleman as you.

Oh, anything will do!—the worse the better.

Exit Landlord. Re-enter with two great-coats.

Ay, landlord, this will be best; for I can button the cape over the lower part of my face. Don't I look devilishly down and concerned, landlord?

And as thou knowest that I am not a bad mimic, I took a cane, which I borrowed of the landlord, and stooped in the shoulders to a quarter of a foot of less height, and stumped away cross to the bowling-green, to practise a little the hobbling gait of a gouty man.

And now I am going to try if I can't agree with goody Moore for lodgings and other conveniences for my sick wife.

"Wife, Lovelace!" methinks thou interrogatest.

Yes, *wife;* for who knows what cautions the dear fugitive may have given in apprehension of me?

MR. LOVELACE TO JOHN BELFORD, ESQ.

Hampstead, Friday Night, June 9.

Now, Belford, for the narrative of narratives.

Although grievously afflicted with the gout, I alighted out of my chariot (leaning very hard on my cane with one hand, and on my new servant's shoulder with the other) the same instant almost that he had knocked at the door, that I might be sure of admission into the house.

The maid came to the door. I asked for her mistress. She showed me into one of the parlours; and I sat down with a gouty Oh!

Enter Goody Moore

Your servant, madam—but you must excuse me; I cannot well stand. I find by the bill at the door, that you have lodgings to let (mumbling my words); be pleased to inform me what they are; for I like your situation—and I will tell you my family—I have a wife, a good old woman—older than myself, by the way, a pretty deal. She is in a bad state of health, and is advised into the Hampstead air. She will have two maid-servants and a footman.

When, sir, shall you want to come in?

I will take them from this very day; and if convenient, will bring my wife in the afternoon.

Perhaps, sir, you would board, as well as lodge?

That as you please.

We have a single lady, who will be gone in two or three days. She has one of the best apartments; that will then be at liberty.

You have one or two good ones meantime, I presume, madam, just to receive my wife; for we have lost time.

You shall see what accommodations I have, if you please, sir. But I doubt you are too lame to walk up stairs.

I can make shift to hobble up now I have rested a little. I'll just look upon the apartment my wife is to have.

She led the way; and I, helping myself by the banisters, made shift to get up with less fatigue than I expected from ankles so weak.

There were three rooms on a floor; two of them handsome; and the third, she said, still handsomer; but the lady was in it.

I saw, I saw she was! for as I hobbled up, crying out upon my weak ankles, in the hoarse mumbling voice I had assumed, I beheld a little piece of her as she just cast an eye (with the door ajar, as they call it) to observe who was coming up; and seeing such an old clumsy fellow, great-coated in weather so warm, slouched and muffled up, she withdrew, shutting the door without any emotion. But it was not so with me; for thou canst not imagine how my heart danced to my mouth at the very glimpse of her, so that I was afraid the thump, thump, thumping villain, which had so lately thumped as much to no purpose, would have choked me.

But, madam, cannot a body just peep into the other apartment, that I may be more particular to my wife in the furniture of it?

The lady desires to be private, sir—but—and was going to ask her leave.

I caught hold of her hand. However, stay, stay, madam; it mayn't be proper, if the lady loves to be private. Don't let me intrude upon the lady——

No intrusion, sir, I dare say; the lady is good-humoured. She will be so kind as to step down into the parlour, I dare say. As she stays so little a while, I am sure she will not wish to stand in my way.

No, madam, that's true, if she be good-humoured, as you say, —Has she been with you long, madam?

She came but yesterday, sir——

I believe I just now saw the glimpse of her. She seems to be an elderly lady.

No, sir; you're mistaken. She's a young lady, and one of the handsomest I ever saw.

There's no casting an eye upon her, is there, without her notice?

I will go ask if I may show a gentleman the apartment, sir;

and as you are a married gentleman, and not *over*-young, she'll perhaps make the less scruple.

What may be her story then, I pray?

She is pretty reserved in her story; but to tell you my thoughts, I believe *love* is in the case; she is always in tears, and does not much care for company.

Nay, madam, it becomes not me to dive into ladies' secrets; I want not to pry into other people's affairs. But, pray, how does she employ herself?—Yet she came but yesterday; so you can't tell.

Writing continually, sir.

To be brief, she went in; and after a little while came out again. The lady, sir, is retired to her closet. So you may go in and look at the room.

I hobbled in, and stumped about, and liked it very much; and was sure my wife would. I begged excuse for sitting down, and asked, Who was the minister of the place? If he were a good preacher?

But I keep the lady in her closet. My gout makes me rude.

O Belford! to be so near my angel, think what a painful constraint I was under!

I was resolved to fetch her out, if possible: and pretending to be going—You can't agree as to any *time,* Mrs. Moore, when we can have this third room, can you?

Mrs. Moore, says my charmer, you may acquaint the gentleman that I shall stay here only for two or three days at most, till I receive an answer to a letter I have written into the country; and rather than be your hindrance, I will take up with any apartment a pair of stairs higher.

Not for the world! Not for the world, young lady! cried I. My wife, well as I love her, should lie in a garret, rather than put such a considerate lady, as you seem to be, to the least inconveniency.

She opened not the door yet; and I said, But since you have so much goodness, madam, if I could but just look into the closet as I stand, I could tell my wife whether it is large enough to hold a cabinet she much values, and will have with her wherever she goes.

Then my charmer opened the door, and blazed upon me, as it

were, in a flood of light, like what one might imagine would strike a man, who, born blind, had by some propitious power been blessed with his sight, all at once, in a meridian sun.

Upon my soul, I never was so strangely affected before. I had much ado to forbear discovering myself that instant: but hesitatingly, and in great disorder, I said, looking into the closet and around it, There is room, I see, for my wife's cabinet; and it has many jewels in it of high price; but, upon my soul (for I could not forbear swearing, like a puppy: habit is a cursed thing, Jack—), nothing so valuable as the lady I see, can be brought into it.

She started, and looked at me with terror. The truth of the compliment, as far as I know, had taken dissimulation from my accent.

I saw it was impossible to conceal myself longer from her, any more than (from the violent impulses of my passion) to forbear manifesting myself. I unbuttoned therefore my cape, I pulled off my flapped, slouched hat; I threw open my great-coat, and, like the devil in Milton (an odd comparison though!)

> I started up in my own form divine,
> Touch'd by the beam of her celestial eye,
> More potent than Ithuriel's spear!—

She no sooner saw who it was, than she gave three violent screams; and, before I could catch her in my arms (as I was about to do the moment I discovered myself), down she sunk at my feet, in a fit; which made me curse my indiscretion for so suddenly, and with so much emotion, revealing myself.

The gentlewoman, seeing so strange an alteration in my person and features, and voice, and dress, cried out, Murder, help! murder, help! by turns, for half a dozen times running. This alarmed the house, and up ran two servant-maids, and *my* servant after them. I cried out for water and hartshorn, and every one flew a different way, one of the maids as fast down as she came up; while the gentlewoman ran out of one room into another, and by turns up and down the apartment we were in, without meaning or end, wringing her foolish hands, and not knowing what she did.

Up then came running a gentleman and his sister, fetched, and brought in by the maid who had run down; and who having let in a cursed crabbed old wretch, hobbling with his gout, and mumbling with his hoarse broken-toothed voice was metamorphosed all at once into a lively gay young fellow, with a clear accent, and all his teeth; and she would have it, that I was neither more nor less than the devil, and could not keep her eye from my foot; expecting, no doubt, every minute to see it discover itself to be cloven.

For my part, I was so intent upon restoring my angel, that I regarded nobody else. And at last, she slowly recovering motion, with bitter sighs and sobs (only the whites of her eyes however appearing for some moments), I called upon her in the tenderest accent, as I kneeled by her, my arm supporting her head; My angel! My charmer! My Clarissa! Look upon me, my dearest life! I am not angry with you! I will forgive you, my best beloved!

The gentleman and his sister knew not what to make of all this: and the less, when my fair one, recovering her sight, snatched another look at me; and then again groaned, and fainted away.

I threw up the closet sash for air, and then left her to the care of the young gentlewoman, the same notable Miss Rawlins, whom I had heard of at the Flask; and to that of Mrs. Moore; who by this time had recovered herself; and then retiring to one corner of the room, I made my servant pull off my gouty stockings, brush my hat, and loop it up into the usual smart cock.

I then stepped to the closet to Mr. Rawlins, whom, in the general confusion, I had not much minded before. Sir, said I, you have an uncommon scene before you. The lady is my wife, and no gentleman's presence is necessary here but my own.

I beg pardon, sir; *if* the lady be your wife, I have no business here. *But*, sir, by her concern at seeing you——

Pray, sir, none of your *ifs* and *buts*, I beseech you: nor *your* concern about the *lady's* concern. You are a very unqualified judge in this cause; and I beg of you, sir, to oblige me with your absence.

'Tis well he made not another word: for I found my choler begin to rise.

I withdrew once more from the closet, finding her beginning to recover, lest the sight of me too soon should throw her back again.

The first words she said, looking round her with great emotion, were, Oh! hide me, hide me! Is he gone? Oh! hide me! Is he gone?

Sir, said Miss Rawlins, coming to me with an air both peremptory and assured, this is some surprising case. The lady cannot bear the sight of you. What you have done is best known to yourself. But another such fit will probably be her last. It would be but kind therefore for you to retire.

The dear creature, said I, may *well* be concerned to see me. If *you,* madam, had a husband who loved you as I love her, you would not, I am confident, fly from him, and expose yourself to hazards, as she does whenever she has not all her way—and yet with a mind not capable of intentional evil—but mother-spoilt!

They promised to keep her quiet; and I withdrew into the next room; ordering every one down but Mrs. Moore and Miss Rawlins.

They preached patience and quietness to her; and would have had her to lie down; but she refused; sinking, however, into an easy chair; for she trembled so, she could not stand.

By this time I hoped that she was enough recovered to bear a presence that it behoved me to make her bear; and fearing she would throw out something in her exclamations that would still more disconcert me, I went into the room again.

Base man! said the violent lady, I have no wishes, but never to behold you more! Why must I be thus pursued and haunted? Have you not made me miserable enough already? Despoiled of all succour and help, and of every friend, I am contented to be poor, low, and miserable, so I may be free from your persecutions.

But this is not a time—I have a letter from Captain Tomlinson—here it is—offering it to her——

I will receive nothing from your hands—tell me not of Captain Tomlinson—tell me not of anybody—you have no *right* to invade me thus—once more leave me to my fate—have you not made me miserable enough?

However, you must permit me to insist on your reading this letter; and on your seeing Captain Tomlinson, and hearing what he has to say from your uncle.

Don't trifle with me, said she, in an imperious tone. Do as you offer. I will not receive any letter from your hands. If I see Captain Tomlinson, it shall be on his *own* account; not on *yours*.

One word only, madam, repeated I—The captain, you know, has reported our *marriage* to two different persons. It is come to your brother's ears. My own relations have also heard of it. Letters were brought me from town this morning, from Lady Betty Lawrance and Miss Montague. Here they are.

Begone from me, man! Begone from me with thy letters! What pretence hast thou for tormenting me thus?

For your own mind's sake, frustrate not Captain Tomlinson's negotiation. That worthy gentleman will be here in the afternoon. Lady Betty will be in town, with my Cousin Montague, in a day or two. They will be your visitors. I beseech you do not carry this misunderstanding so far, as that Lord M. and Lady Betty and Lady Sarah may know it. (*How considerable this made me look to the women!*) Lady Betty will not let you rest till you consent to accompany her to her own seat, and to that lady may you safely entrust your cause.

Again, upon my pausing a moment, she was going to break out. I liked not the turn of her countenance, nor the tone of her voice—"And thinkest thou, base wretch," were the words she *did* utter. I again raised my voice and drowned hers. *Base wretch,* madam! You knew that I have not deserved the violent names you have called me. Words so opprobrious! from a mind so gentle! But this treatment is from *you,* madam!—From *you,* whom I love more than my own soul. By that soul, I swear that I do. Nevertheless, I must say that you have carried matters too far for the occasion. I see you hate me——

She was just going to speak—If we are to *separate for ever,* in a strong and solemn voice, proceeded I, this island shall not long be troubled with me. Meantime, only be pleased to give these letters a perusal, and consider what is to be said to your uncle's friend; and what he is to say to your uncle. Anything will I come into (renounce me if you will) that shall make for *your* peace, and for the reconciliation *your heart was so lately set upon*. But I humbly conceive that it is necessary that you should come into better temper with me, were it but to give a favourable appearance to what *has passed*, and weight to any *future application* to your friends, in whatever way you shall think proper to make it.

I then put the letters into her lap, and retired into the next apartment with a low bow and a very solemn air.

[Mr. Lovelace then tells Mrs. Moore and Miss Rawlins the story of himself and his "wife," all to his own credit, and engages their help to restore Clarissa to him. He also sets his servant Will as a spy on all messengers to and from Clarissa. He forges a letter from Captain Tomlinson bearing upon that gentleman's negotiations for a reconciliation with her family through the intercession of his "friend," Clarissa's uncle John Harlowe. Ed.]

I told the women that what I had mentioned to my spouse of Lady Betty's coming to town with her Niece Montague, and of their intention to visit my beloved, whom they had never seen, nor she them, was real; and that I expected news of their arrival every hour. I then showed them copies of the other two letters which I had left with *her;* the one from Lady Betty, the other from my Cousin Montague. And here thou mayest read them if thou wilt.

[Lovelace forges letters from his aunt, Lady Betty Lawrance, and his Cousin Montague which he shows to Mrs. Moore and Miss Rawlins to engage their aid further. He also forges a letter from Lord M. Ed.]

To Robert Lovelace, Esq.

Wedn. Morn. June 7.

Dear Nephew,—I understand that at length all our wishes are answered in your happy marriage. My brother had set his heart upon giving to you the wife we have all so long wished you to have. But if you were actually married at the time you made him that request (*supposing, perhaps, that his gout would not let him attend you*), it is but like *you.* If your lady had *her* reasons to wish it to be private while the differences between her family and self continue, you might nevertheless have communicated it to us with *that* restriction; and we should have forborne the public manifestations of our joy, upon an event we have so long desired.

The distant way we have come to know it, is by my steward; who is acquainted with a friend of Captain Tomlinson, to whom that gentleman revealed it: and he, it seems, had it from yourself and lady, with such circumstances as leave it not to be doubted.

I am, indeed, very much disobliged with you: so is Lady Sarah. But I shall have a very speedy opportunity to tell you so in person; being obliged to go to town on my old Chancery affair. My Cousin Leeson, who is, it seems, removed to Albemarle Street, has notice of it. I shall be at *her* house, where I bespeak your attendance on Sunday night. I have written to my Cousin Charlotte for either her, or her sister, to meet me at Reading, and accompany me to town. I shall stay but a few days; my business being matter of form only. On my return I shall pop upon Lord M. at M. Hall, to see in what way his last fit has left him.

Meantime, having told you my mind on your negligence, I cannot help congratulating you both upon the occasion. Your fair lady particularly, upon her entrance into a family which is prepared to admire and love her.

My principal intention of writing to you (dispensing with the necessary punctilio) is that you may acquaint my dear new niece that I will not be denied the honour of her company down with me into Oxfordshire.

Lady Sarah, who has not been out of her own house for months, will oblige me with her company for a week, in honour of a niece so dearly beloved, as I am sure she will be of us all.

Being but in lodgings in town, neither you nor your lady can require much preparation.

Some time on Monday I hope to attend the dear young lady, to make her my compliments; and to receive *her* apology for *your* negligence: which, and her going down with me, as I said before, shall be full satisfaction. Meantime, God bless *her* for her courage (tell her I say so): and bless you *both* in each other; and that will be happiness to us all—particularly to

Your truly affectionate aunt,

Eliz. Lawrance.

To ROBERT LOVELACE, ESQ.

DEAR COUSIN,—At last, as we understand, there is some hope of you. Now does my good lord run over his bead-roll of proverbs; of *black oxen, wild oats, long lanes,* and so forth.

Now, cousin, say I, is your time come; and you will be no longer, I hope, an infidel either to the power or excellence of the sex you have pretended hitherto so much to undervalue; nor a ridiculer or scoffer at an institution which all sober people reverence, and all rakes, sooner or later, are brought to reverence, or to wish they had.

His lordship is very much displeased that you have not written him word of the day, the hour, the manner, and everything.

I have a letter from Lady Betty. She commands either my attendance or my sister's at Reading, to proceed with her to town, to Cousin Leeson's. She puts Lord M. in hopes that she shall certainly bring down with her our lovely new relation; for she says she will not be denied. His lordship is the willinger to let *me* be the person, as I am in a manner wild to see her; my sister having two years ago had that honour at Sir Robert Biddulph's. So get ready to accompany us in our return; except your lady has objections strong enough to satisfy us all.

I shall soon, I hope, pay my compliments to the dear lady in person: so have nothing to add, but that I am

Your old mad playfellow and cousin,

Charlotte Montague.

To ROBERT LOVELACE, ESQ.

M. Hall, Wedn. June 7.

COUSIN LOVELACE,—I think you might have found time to let us know of your nuptials being actually solemnized.

I might have expected this piece of civility from you. But perhaps the ceremony was performed at the very time that you asked me to be your lady's father—but I shall be angry if I proceed in my guesses—and *little said is soon amended.*

But I can tell you that Lady Betty Lawrance, whatever Lady Sarah does, will not so soon forgive you as I have done. I have before now said, that I will disinherit you and settle all I can upon her, if you prove not a good husband to her.

May this marriage be crowned with a great many fine boys (I desire no girls) to build up again a family so ancient!

Lady Betty and Niece Charlotte will be in town about business *before you know where you are.* They long to pay their compliments to your fair bride. I suppose you will hardly be at the Lawn when they get to town: because Greme informs me you have sent no orders there for your lady's accommodation.

Pritchard has all things in readiness for signing. I will take no advantage of your slights.

One reason for Lady Betty's going up, as I may tell you *under the rose,* is to buy some suitable presents for Lady Sarah and all of us to make on this agreeable occasion.

My most affectionate compliments and congratulations to my new niece, conclude me, for the present, in violent pains, that with all your heroicalness would make you mad,

Your truly affectionate uncle,

M.

This letter clenched the nail.

They began to intercede for my spouse (so nicely had I turned the tables); and that I would not go abroad, and disappoint a reconciliation so much wished for on one side, and such desirable prospects on the other in my own family.

MR. LOVELACE TO JOHN BELFORD, ESQ.

I WILL NOW give thee the substance of the dialogue that passed between the two women and the lady.

Mrs. Moore was to be the messenger; but Miss Rawlins began the dialogue.

Your SPOUSE, madam——

Cl. My *spouse,* madam——

Miss R. Mr. Lovelace, madam, avers that you are married to him; and begs admittance, of your company in the dining-room, to talk upon the subject of the letters he left with you.

Cl. He is a poor wicked wretch. Let me beg of you, madam, to favour me with your company as often as possible while he is hereabouts, and I remain here.

Miss R. I shall with pleasure attend you, madam. But, methinks, I could wish you would *see* the gentleman, and hear what he has to say on the subject of the letters.

Cl. My case is a hard, a very hard one—I am quite bewildered!—I know not what to do! I have not a friend in the world that can or will help me! Yet had none *but* friends till I knew *that man!*

Miss R. The gentleman neither looks nor talks like a bad man.—Not a *very* bad man; as men go.

Cl. O madam, you know him not! He can put on the appearance of an angel of light; but has a black, a very black heart! As to the letters he has left with me, I know not what to say to *them:* but am resolved never to have anything to say to *him.*

Miss R. If, madam, I may be allowed to say so, I think you carry matters very far.

Cl. Has he been making a bad cause a good one with you, madam? That he can do with those who know him not. Indeed I heard him talking, though not what he said, and am indifferent about it. But what account does he give of himself?

Miss R. He says, madam, that he could not prevail for marriage, till he had consented, under a solemn oath, to separate beds, while your family remained unreconciled.

Cl. Oh, the wretch! What can be still in his head, to endeavour to pass these stories upon strangers?

Miss R. He has owned that an accidental fire had frightened you very much on Wednesday night, and that—and that—and that—an accidental fire had frightened you—very much frightened you—last Wednesday night!

Cl. You have heard *his* story. Mine, as I told you before, is too long, and too melancholy; my disorder on seeing the wretch is too great; and my time here is too short, for me to enter upon it. And if he has any end to serve by his own vindication, in which I shall not be a *personal* sufferer, let him make himself appear as white as an angel; with all my heart.

My love for her, and the excellent character I gave her, were then pleaded.

Cl. Specious seducer! Only tell me if I cannot get away from him by some back way?

Mrs. Moore then came to me; and I, being afraid that something would pass meantime between the other two, which I should not like, took the letters and entered the room.

Can I have no retirement uninvaded, sir? said she, with indignation. What business have you here, or with me? You have your letters; have you not?

Lovel. I have, my dear; and let me beg of you to consider what you are about. I every moment expect Captain Tomlinson here. Upon my soul, I do. He has promised to keep from your uncle what has happened: but what will he think if he find you hold in this strange humour?

Cl. I will endeavour, sir, to have patience with you for a moment or two, while I ask you a few questions before this lady, and before Mrs. Moore (who just then came in), both of whom you have prejudiced in your favour by your specious stories:—Will you say, sir, that we are married together? Lay your hand upon your heart, and answer me, am I your wedded wife?

I am gone too far, thought I, to give up for such a push as this, home one as it is.

My dearest soul! how can you put such a question? Is it either for *your* honour or *my own*, that it should be doubted? Surely, surely, madam, you cannot have attended to the contents of Captain Tomlinson's letter.

You and I! *Vilest of men*——

My name is Lovelace, madam——

Therefore it is that I call you the *vilest of men. You* and *I* know the truth, the *whole* truth. I want not to clear up my reputation with these gentlewomen: that is already lost with every one I had most reason to value: but let me have this *new* specimen of what you are capable of—say, wretch (say,

Lovelace, if thou hadst rather), art thou really and truly my wedded husband? Say! answer without hesitation.

She trembled with impatient indignation; but had a wildness in her manner, which I took some advantage of, in order to parry this cursed thrust.

Lovel. What *makes a marriage,* we all know. If it be the union of two hearts, to my utmost grief, I must say we are *not;* since now I see you hate me. If it be the completion of marriage, to my confusion and regret, I must own we are *not.* But my dear, will you be pleased to consider what answer half a dozen people whence you came could give to your question? And do not now, in *the disorder of your mind,* and in the height of passion, bring into question before these gentlewomen a point you have acknowledged before those who know us better.

I own no marriage with thee!—Bear witness, ladies, I do not. I resume my former language: you have no right to pursue me: you *know* you have not: begone, then; and leave me to make the best of my hard lot. O my dear cruel father! said she, in a violent fit of grief (falling upon her knees, and clasping her uplifted hands together), thy heavy curse is completed upon thy devoted daughter! I am *punished,* dreadfully punished, *by the very wretch in whom I had placed my wicked confidence!*

For Heaven's sake, madam, for a soul's sake, which it is in your power to save from perdition, forgive me the past offence. I am the greatest villain on earth, if it was a premeditated one. Yet I presume not to excuse myself. On your mercy I throw myself. I will not offer any plea, but that of penitence. See but Captain Tomlinson. See but Lady Betty and my cousin; let *them* plead for me; let *them* be guarantees for my honour.

If Captain Tomlinson come while I stay here, I may see *him.*

I went down with the women to dinner. Mrs. Moore sent her fair boarder up a plate; but she only ate a little bit of bread, and drank a glass of water.

MR. LOVELACE. [*In continuation*]

WE HAD at dinner, besides Miss Rawlins, a young widow-niece of Mrs. Moore, who is come to stay a month with her aunt—*Bevis* her name; very forward, very lively, and a great admirer of *me,* I assure you; hanging smirkingly upon all I said; and prepared to approve of every word before I spoke: and who, by the time we had half dined (by the help of what she had collected before), was as much acquainted with our story as either of the other two.

We had hardly dined, when my coachman, who kept a look-out for Captain Tomlinson, conducted hither that worthy gentleman, attended by one servant, *both* on horseback. I went out to meet him at the door.

I led him in to the parlour, and presented him to the women, and them to him. I thought it highly imported me (as they might still have some diffidences about our marriage, from my fair one's home-pushed questions on that head) to convince them entirely of the truth of all I had asserted.

It was now high time to acquaint my spouse that Captain Tomlinson was come. And the rather, as the maid told us that the lady had asked her if such a gentleman was not in the parlour?

Mrs. Moore went up, and requested, in my name, that she would give us audience.

But she returned, reporting my beloved's desire that Captain Tomlinson would excuse her for the present. She was very ill.

I was vexed, and at first extremely disconcerted. The captain was vexed too. And my concern, thou mayest believe, was the greater on *his account.*

It was indeed very inconvenient for him, he said, to return in the morning; but he was willing to do all in his power to heal this breach, and that as well for the sakes of me and my lady, as for that of his dear friend Mr. John Harlowe; who must not know how far this misunderstanding had gone. He would therefore only drink one dish of tea with the ladies and me.

And accordingly, after he had done so, and I had had a little private conversation with him, he hurried away.

I had hardly taken leave of the captain, and sat down again with the women, when Will came; and calling me out, "Sir, sir," said he, grinning with a familiarity in his looks as if what he had to say entitled him to take liberties; "I have got the fellow down! I have got old Grimes—Hah, hah, hah, hah!—He is at the Lower Flask—almost in the condition of *David's sow,* and please your honour—(the dog himself not much better) here is his letter—from—from Miss Howe—Ha, ha, ha, ha!" laughed the varlet; holding it fast, as if to make conditions with me, and to excite my praises as well as my impatience.

I could have knocked him down; but he would have his *say* out—"Old Grimes knows not that I have the letter—I must get back to him before he misses it—I only made a pretence to go out for a few minutes—but—but"—and then the dog laughed again—"he *must* stay—old Grimes *must* stay—till I go back to pay the reckoning."

I was once thinking to rumple up this billet till I had broken the seal. *Young* families (Miss Howe's is not an ancient one) love ostentatious sealings: and it might have been supposed to have been squeezed in pieces in old Grimes's breeches pocket. But I was glad to be *saved* the guilt as well as suspicion of having a hand in so dirty a trick; for thus much of the contents (enough for my purpose) I was enabled to scratch out in character without it; the folds depriving me only of a few connecting words; which I have supplied between hooks.

"I CONGRATULATE YOU, my dear, with all my heart and soul, upon (your escape) from the villain. (I long) for the particulars of all. (My mother) is out: but, expecting her return every minute, I dispatched (your) messenger instantly. (I will endeavour to come at) Mrs. Townsend without loss of time; and will write at large in a day or two, if in that time I can see her. (Meantime I) am excessively uneasy for a letter I sent you yesterday by Collins, (who must have left it at) Wilson's after you got away. (It is of very) great importance. (I hope the) villain has it not. I would not for the world (that he should.) Immediately send for it, if, by so doing, the place you are at (will not be) discovered. If he has it, let me know it by some way (out of) hand. If not, you need not send.

"Ever, ever yours,

"*June 9.* *A. H.*"

[The letter put into Clarissa's hand is Lovelace's forgery of Miss Howe's letter addressed to Clarissa under her assumed name, Miss Lætitia Beaumont. Though Clarissa is put on her guard, she is still unaware of the depth of Lovelace's machinations. Ed.]

O Jack, what heart's-ease does this *interception* give me! I sent the rascal back with the letter to old Grimes, and charged him to drink no deeper.

In a quarter of an hour came old Grimes on horseback, waving to his saddle-bow, now on this side, now on that; his head, at others, joining to that of his more sober beast.

It looked very well to the women, that I made no effort to speak to old Grimes (though I wished *before them,* that I knew the contents of what he brought); but, on the contrary, desired that they would instantly let my spouse know that her messenger was returned.

Down she flew, violently as she had the headache!

She took the letter from old Grimes with her own hands, and retired to an inner parlour to read it.

She presently came out again to the fellow, who had much ado to sit his horse. Here is your money, friend. I thought you long. But what shall I do to get somebody to go to town immediately for me? I see *you* cannot.

Old Grimes took his money; let fall his hat in doffing it; had it given him; and rode away; his eyes isinglass, and set in his head, as I saw through the window; and in a manner speechless; all his language hiccoughs.

The lady applied to Mrs. Moore: she mattered not the price. Could a man and horse be engaged for her? Only to go for a letter left for her, at one Mr. Wilson's in Pall Mall.

A poor neighbour was hired. A horse procured for him. He had his directions.

In vain did I endeavour to engage my beloved when she was below. Her headache, I suppose, returned. She, like the rest of her sex, can be ill or well when she pleases.

Up she went, expressing great impatience about the letter she had sent for; and desired Mrs. Moore to let her know if I offered to send any of my servants to town—to get at the letter, I suppose, was her fear: but she might have been quite easy on that head; and yet perhaps would not, had she known that the worthy Captain Tomlinson (who will be in town before her messenger) will leave there the important letter: which I hope will help to pacify her, and to reconcile her to me.

. . . . . .

I WENT up to my new-taken apartment, and fell to writing in character, as usual. I thought I had made good my quarters. But the cruel creature, understanding that I intended to take up my lodgings there, declared with so much violence against it, that I was obliged to submit, and to accept of another lodging, about twelve doors off, which Mrs. Moore recommended. And all the advantage I could obtain was, that Will, unknown to my spouse, and for fear of a freak, should lie in the house.

The second fellow came back from town about nine o'clock, with Miss Howe's letter of Wednesday last.

She took the letter with great eagerness, opened it in a hurry (I am glad she did: yet, I believe, all was right) before Mrs. Moore and Mrs. Bevis (Miss Rawlins was gone home); and said, She would not for the world that I should have had that letter, for the sake of her dear friend the writer; who had written to her very uneasily about it.

I knew thou wouldst be uneasy for me: but did not I tell thee that I had provided for everything? That I always took care to keeps seals entire, and to preserve covers? Was it not easy then, thinkest thou, to contrive a shorter letter out of a longer; and to copy the very words?

If thou art capable of taking in all my *providences,* in this letter, thou wilt admire my sagacity and contrivance almost as much as I do myself.

Miss Howe might well be anxious about the letter she wrote. Her sweet friend, from what I have let pass of hers, has reason to rejoice in the thought that it fell not into my hands.

And now must all my contrivances be set at work, to intercept the expected letter from Miss Howe; which is, as I suppose, to direct her to a place of safety, and out of my knowledge. I hope the *villain,* as I am so frequently called between these two girls, will be able to manage this point.

MR. LOVELACE TO JOHN BELFORD, ESQ.

Saturday, 6 o'clock, June 10.

THE LADY gave Will's sweetheart a letter last night to be carried to the post-house as this morning, directed for Miss Howe, under cover to Hickman. I dare say neither cover nor letter will be seen to have been opened.

Now, Belford, I thought it would be but kind in me to save Miss Howe's concern on these alarming hints; since the curiosity of such a spirit must have been prodigiously excited by them. Having therefore so good a copy to imitate, I wrote; and, taking out that of my beloved, put under the same cover the following short billet; inscriptive and conclusive parts of it in her own words.

Hampstead, Tuesday Evening.

MY EVER DEAR MISS HOWE,—A few lines only, till calmer spirits and quieter fingers be granted me, and till I can get over the shock which your intelligence has given me—to acquaint you—that your kind long letter of Wednesday, and, as I may say, of Thursday morning, is come safe to my hands. On receipt of yours by my messenger to you, I sent for it from Wilson's. There, thank Heaven! it lay. May that Heaven reward you for all your past, and for all your *intended* goodness to

Your for ever obliged

Cl. Harlowe.

I took great pains in writing this. It cannot, I hope, be suspected. Her hand is so *very* delicate. Yet hers is written less beautifully than she usually writes: and I hope Miss Howe will allow somewhat for *hurry of spirits,* and *unsteady fingers.*

[In a long scene here omitted, Clarissa is completely taken in by Tomlinson's acting and is consequently more deeply ensnared. Ed.]

MR. LOVELACE TO JOHN BELFORD, ESQ.

Sunday Morning.

I HAVE HAD the honour of my charmer's company for two complete hours. We met before six in Mrs. Moore's garden.

The sedateness of her aspect, and her kind compliance in this meeting, gave me hopes. And all that either the captain or I had urged yesterday to obtain a full and free pardon, that re-urged I; and I told her, besides, that Captain Tomlinson was gone down with hopes to prevail upon her Uncle Harlowe to come up in person, in order to present to me the greatest blessing that man ever received.

But the utmost I could obtain was, that she would take no resolution in my favour till she received Miss Howe's next letter.

She besought me to give over all thoughts of her. Sometimes, she said, she thought herself cruelly treated by her nearest and dearest relations: at *such* times, a spirit of repining, and even of resentment, took place; and the reconciliation, at other times so desirable, was not then so much the favourite wish of her heart, as was the scheme she had formerly planned—of taking her good Norton for her directress and guide, and living upon her own estate in the manner her grandfather had intended she should live.

She frankly owned that she had once thought of embarking *out of all our ways* for some one of our American colonies; but now that she had been *compelled* to see me (which had been her greatest dread, and which she would have given her life to avoid), she thought she might be happiest in the resumption of her former favourite scheme, if Miss Howe could find her a reputable and private asylum, till her Cousin Morden could come. But if he came not soon, and if she had a difficulty to get to a place of refuge, whether from her brother or from *anybody else* (meaning me, I suppose), she might yet perhaps go abroad: for, to say the truth, she could not think of returning to her father's house; since her brother's rage, her sister's upbraidings, her father's anger, her mother's still more affecting sorrowings, and her own consciousness under them all, would be insupportable to her.

O Jack! I am sick to death, I pine, I die for Miss Howe's next letter! I would bind, gag, strip, rob, and do anything but murder, to intercept it.

But, determined as she seems to be, it was evident to me, nevertheless, that she has still some tenderness for me.

She often wept as she talked, and much oftener sighed. She looked at me twice with an eye of *undoubted* gentleness, and three times with an eye *tending* to compassion and softness: but its benign rays were as often *snatched* back, as I may say, and her face averted, as if her sweet eyes were not to be trusted, and could not stand against my eager eyes; seeking, as they did, for a lost heart in hers, and endeavouring to penetrate to her very soul.

More than once I took her hand. She struggled not *much* against the freedom. I pressed it once with my lips. She was not *very* angry. A frown indeed; but a frown that had more distress in it than indignation.

I hoped, I said, that she would admit of the intended visit, which I had so often mentioned, of the two ladies.

She was *here*. She had seen *me*. She could not help herself at present. She ever had the highest regard for the ladies of my family, because of their worthy characters. There she turned away her sweet face, and vanquished a half-risen sigh.

I kneeled to her then. It was upon a verdant cushion; for we were upon the grasswalk. I caught her hand. I besought her with an earnestness that called up, as I could feel, my heart to my eyes, to make me, by her forgiveness and example, more worthy of them, and of her own kind and generous wishes. By my soul, madam, said I, you stab me with your goodness, your undeserved goodness! and I cannot bear it!

Divine creature! (as I *thought* her) I *called* her. I acknowledged the superiority of her mind; and was proceeding—but she interrupted me. All human excellence, said she, is comparative only. My mind, I believe, is indeed superior to yours, debased as yours is by evil habits: but I had not known it to be so, if you had not *taken pains* to convince me of the inferiority of yours.

How great, how sublimely great, this creature! By my soul, I cannot forgive her for her virtues! There is no bearing the consciousness of the infinite inferiority she charged me with. But why will she break from me, when good resolutions are taking place? The red-hot iron she refuses to strike—Oh, why will she suffer the yielding wax to harden?

And now, Belford, thou perceivest that all my reliance is upon the mediation of Lady Betty and Miss Montague; and upon the hope of intercepting Miss Howe's next letter.

MR. LOVELACE TO JOHN BELFORD, ESQ.

Sunday Afternoon.

O BELFORD! what a hair's-breadth escape have I had! Such an one, that I tremble between terror and joy at the thoughts of what *might* have happened, and did not.

But not to keep thee in suspense; I have, within this half-hour, obtained possession of the expected letter from Miss Howe.

[Lovelace induced the widow Bevis to feign illness and to impersonate Clarissa. The ruse works, and Lovelace gets hold of Miss Howe's letter, addressed under the name Mrs. Harriot Lucas. Ed.]

TO MRS. HARRIOT LUCAS, AT MRS. MOORE'S, AT HAMPSTEAD

AFTER the discoveries I had made of the villainous machinations of the *most abandoned of men,* particularized in my long letter of Wednesday last, you will believe, my dearest friend, that my surprise upon perusing yours of Thursday evening from Hampstead was not so great as my indignation. Had the *villain* attempted to fire a city instead of a house, I should not have wondered at it. All that I am amazed at is, that he (whose boast, as I am told, it is, *that no woman shall keep him out of her bedchamber, when he has made a resolution to be in it*) did not discover *his foot* before. And it is as strange to me, that, having got you at such a shocking advantage, and in such a horrid house, you could, at the time, *escape dishonour,* and afterwards get from such a set of *infernals.*

I gave you, in my long letter of Wednesday and Thursday last, reasons why you ought to mistrust that specious Tomlinson. That man, my dear, must be a solemn villain. *May lightning from Heaven blast the wretch who has set him, and the rest of his* REMORSELESS GANG, *at work, to endeavour to destroy the most consummate virtue!* Heaven be praised! you have escaped from all their snares, and *now are out of danger*. So I will not trouble you at present with the particulars that I have further collected relating to this abominable imposture.

The whole story of Mrs. Fretchville, and her house, I have no doubt to *pronounce,* likewise, an absolute fiction. *Fellow! How my soul spurns the villain!*

Your thought of going abroad, and your reasons for so doing, most sensibly affect me. But, be comforted, my dear; I hope you will not be under a necessity of quitting your native country. Were I sure that that must be the cruel case, I would abandon all my own better prospects, and soon be with you.

Sat. Afternoon.

I have just parted with Mrs. Townsend. I thought you had once seen her with me: but she says she never had the honour to be personally known to you. She has a *manlike spirit*. She knows the world. And her two brothers being in town, she is sure she can engage *them* in so good a cause, and (if there should be occasion) *both their ships' crews,* in your service.

Give your consent, my dear; and the *horrid villain* shall be repaid with *broken bones, at least,* for all his vileness!

The misfortune is, Mrs. Townsend cannot be with you till *Thursday next, or Wednesday at soonest*. Are you sure you can be safe where you are till then? I think you are too near London; and perhaps you had better be *in it*. If you remove, let me, the very moment, know *whither*.

Mrs. Townsend will in person attend you—she *hopes,* on Wednesday. Her brothers, and some of their people, will scatteringly, and as if they knew nothing of you (so we have contrived), see you safe not only to London, but to her house at Deptford.

She has a kinswoman, who will take your commands there, if she herself be obliged to leave you. And there you may stay, till the wretch's fury on losing you, and his search, are over.

He will very soon. 'tis likely, enter upon some *new villainy,* which may engross him: and it may be given out that you are gone to lay claim to the protection of your Cousin Morden at Florence.

After a while, I can procure you a lodging in one of our neighbouring villages; where I may have the happiness to be your daily visitor. And if this Hickman be not silly and apish, and if my mother do not do unaccountable things, I may the sooner think of marrying, that I may, without control, receive and entertain the darling of my heart.

As to your estate, since you are resolved not to litigate for it, we will be patient, either till Colonel Morden arrives, or till shame compels some people to be just.

Upon the whole, I cannot but think your prospects *now* much happier than they could have been, had you been actually married to such a man as this. I must, therefore, congratulate you upon your escape, not only from a *horrid libertine,* but from *so vile a husband,* as he *must* have made to any woman; but more especially to a person of your virtue and delicacy.

You hate him, heartily hate him, I hope, my dear—I am *sure* you do.

In your letter before me, you mention one written to me for a *feint*. I have not received any such. Depend upon it, therefore, that he must have it. And if he has, it is a wonder that he did not likewise get my long one of the 7th. Heaven be praised that he did not; *and that it came safe to your hands!*

I send this by a young fellow, whose father is one of our tenants, with command to deliver it to no other hands but yours.

So shall conclude with my prayers, that Heaven will direct and protect my dearest creature, and make your future days happy!

Anna Howe.

And now, Jack, I will suppose, that thou hast read this cursed letter.

But as to her sordid menace—To *repay the horrid villain,* as she calls me, *for all my vileness* by BROKEN BONES! Broken bones, Belford! Who can bear this porterly threatening! Broken bones, Jack! Damn the little vulgar—Give me a name for her—but I banish all *furious* resentment. If I get these two girls into my power, Heaven forbid that I should be a second Phalaris, who turned his bull upon the artist! No bones of theirs will I break! They shall come off with me upon much lighter terms!

This, however, is my triumphant hope, that at the very time that these ragamuffins will be at Hampstead (looking for us), my dear Miss Harlowe and I shall be fast asleep in each other's arms in town.

Mr. Lovelace to John Belford, Esq.

Sunday Night—Monday Morning.

I went down with revenge in my *heart,* the contents of Miss Howe's letter almost engrossing me.

When we were in the garden, I poured my whole soul into her attentive ear; and besought her returning favour.

The captain, I told her, was rid down post, in a manner, to forward my wishes with her uncle. Lady Betty and Miss Montague were undoubtedly arrived in town by this time. I would set out early in the morning to attend them. They adored her. They longed to see her. They *would* see her. They would not be denied her company into Oxfordshire.

And now may I go to town with hopes at my return to find thee, dearest, where I shall leave thee.

This that follows is my new argument—

Should she fail in the trial; should I succeed; and should she refuse to go on with me; and even resolve not to marry me (of which I can have no notion); and should she disdain to be obliged to me for the handsome provision I should be proud to make for her, even to the *half of my estate;* yet cannot she be altogether unhappy. Is she not entitled to an independent fortune? Will not Colonel Morden, as her trustee, put her in possession of it? And did she not in our former conference point out the *way of life,* that she always preferred to the *married life* —to wit, "To take her good Norton for her directress and guide, and to live upon her own estate in the manner her grandfather desired she should live?"

She piques herself, thou knowest, and makes it matter of reproach to me, that she went not off with me by her own consent; but was tricked out of herself.

Nor upbraid thou me upon the meditated breach of vows so repeatedly made. She will not, thou seest, *permit* me to fulfil them. And if she *would,* this I have to say, that at the time I made the most solemn of them, I was fully determined to keep them.

Thou seest at bottom that I am not an abandoned fellow; and that there is a mixture of gravity in me. This, as I grow older, may increase; and when my active capacity begins to abate, I may sit down with the preacher, and resolve all my past life into vanity and vexation of spirit.

This is certain, that I shall never find a woman so well suited to my taste as Miss Clarissa Harlowe. I only wish that I may have such a lady as her to comfort and adorn my setting sun. I have often thought it very unhappy for us both, that so excellent a creature sprang up a little too late for my *setting-out,* and a little too early in my *progress,* before I can think of *returning.* And yet, as I have picked up the sweet traveller in my way, I cannot help wishing that she would bear me company in the *rest* of my journey, although she were to step out of her own path to oblige me. And then, perhaps, we could put up in the *evening* at the same *inn;* and be very happy in each other's conversation; recounting the difficulties and dangers we had passed in our way to it.

MR. LOVELACE TO JOHN BELFORD, ESQ.

Monday, June 12.

DIDST EVER see a license, Jack?

Edmund, by Divine permission, Lord Bishop of London, to our well-beloved in Christ, Robert Lovelace, of the parish of St. Martin's in the Fields, bachelor, and Clarissa Harlowe, of the same parish, spinster, sendeth greeting. WHEREAS ye are, as is alleged, determined to enter into the holy state of Matrimony (This is only alleged, thou observest), *by and with the consent of, etc. etc. etc.*

And determined to marry I would be, were it not for this consideration, that once married, and I am married for life.

That's the plague of it! Could a man do as the birds do, change every Valentine's Day (a *natural* appointment! for birds have not the *sense,* forsooth, to fetter themselves, as we wiseacre men take great and solemn pains to do), there would be nothing at all in it.

I remember I proved, to a demonstration, that such a change would be a means of annihilating, absolutely annihilating, four or five very atrocious and capital sins. *Rapes,* vulgarly so called; adultery, and fornication; nor would *polygamy* be panted after. Frequently would it prevent *murders* and *duelling:* hardly any such thing as *jealousy* (the cause of shocking violences) would be heard of: and hypocrisy between man and wife be banished the bosoms of each. Nor, probably, would the reproach of *barrenness* rest, as now it too often does, where it is least deserved. Nor would there possibly be such a person as a barren woman.

Moreover, what a multitude of domestic quarrels would be avoided, were such a scheme carried into execution? Since both sexes would bear with each other, in the view that they could help themselves in a few months.

And then what a charming subject for conversation would be the gallant and generous last partings between man and wife! Each, perhaps, a new mate in eye, and rejoicing secretly in the manumission, could *afford* to be complaisantly sorrowful in appearance. "He presented *her* with this jewel, it will be said by the reporter, for *example* sake: she *him* with that. How *he* wept! How *she* sobbed! How they looked after one another!" Yet, that's the jest of it, neither of them wishing to stand another twelvemonth's trial.

And if giddy fellows, or giddy girls, misbehave in a first marriage, whether from *noviceship,* having expected to find more in the matter than can be found; or from *perverseness* on *her* part, or *positiveness* on *his,* each being mistaken in the other (a mighty difference, Jack, in the same person, an *inmate,* or a *visitor*); what a fine opportunity will each have, by this scheme, of recovering a lost character, and of setting all right in the next adventure?

And, O Jack! with what joy, with what rapture, would the *changelings* (or *changeables,* if thou like that word better) number the weeks, the days, the hours, as the annual obligation approached to its desirable period!

As for the spleen or vapours, no such malady would be known or heard of. The physical tribe would, indeed, be the sufferers, and the only sufferers; since fresh health and fresh spirits, the consequences of sweet blood and sweet humours (the mind and body continually pleased with each other), would perpetually flow in; and the joys of *expectation,* the highest of all our joys, would invigorate and keep all alive.

Every one would be married a dozen times at least. Both men and women would be careful of their characters, and polite in their behaviour, as well as delicate in their *persons,* and elegant in their *dress* (a great matter each of these, let me tell thee, to keep passion alive), either to induce a *renewal* with the *old love,* or to recommend themselves to a *new.* While the newspapers would be crowded with paragraphs; all the world their readers, as all the world would be concerned to see *who and who's together*—

Then would not the distinction be very pretty, Jack? as in flowers; such a gentleman, or such a lady, is an ANNUAL—such a one a PERENNIAL.

[Lovelace procures the services of two of Mrs. Sinclair's women to impersonate Lady Betty and Cousin Charlotte Montague. They come to Hampstead and Clarissa is duped by them. Believing they are taking her to their cousin Leeson's in London and placing her under the protection of the Lovelace family, Clarissa is carried back, and by the vilest of contrivances and deceits, finds herself again a prisoner in Mrs. Sinclair's house. Ed.]

MR. LOVELACE TO JOHN BELFORD, ESQ.

WELL, but now my plots thicken; and my employment of writing to thee on this subject will soon come to a conclusion. For now, having got the licence; and Mrs. Townsend with her tars being to come to Hampstead next Wednesday or Thursday; and another letter possibly or message from Miss Howe, to express her wonder that she has not heard from her in answer to hers on her escape; I must soon blow up the lady, or be blown up myself. And so I am preparing, with Lady Betty and my Cousin Montague, to wait upon my beloved with a coach and four, or a set.

MR. LOVELACE TO JOHN BELFORD, ESQ.

At Mrs. Sinclair's, Monday Afternoon.

ALL'S RIGHT, as heart can wish! In spite of all objection—in spite of a reluctance next to fainting—in spite of all foresight, vigilance, suspicion—once more is the charmer of my soul in her old lodgings!

Now indeed, said she, am I a lost creature! O the poor Clarissa Harlowe!

She tore off her head-clothes; inquired where I was: and in she came, her shining tresses flowing about her neck; her ruffles torn, and hanging in tatters about her snowy hands; with her arms spread out; her eyes wildly turned, as if starting from their orbits. Down sunk she at my feet, as soon as she approached me; her charming bosom heaving to her uplifted face; and clasping her arms about my knees, Dear Lovelace, said she, if ever—if ever—if ever—and, unable to speak another word, quitting her clasping hold, down prostrate on the floor sunk she, neither in a fit nor out of one.

I was quite astonished. All my purposes suspended for a few moments, I knew neither what to say, nor what to do. But, recollecting myself, Am I *again,* thought I, in a way to be overcome, and made a fool of! If I now recede, I am gone for ever.

I raised her: but down she sunk, as if quite disjointed; her limbs failing her—yet not in a fit neither. I never heard of or saw such a dear unaccountable: almost lifeless, and speechless too for a few moments. What must her apprehensions be at that moment! And for what?

Never having met with so sincere, so unquestionable a repugnance, I was staggered—I was confounded. Yet how should I know that it would be so till I tried? And how, having proceeded thus far, could I stop, were I *not* to have had the women to goad me on, and to make light of circumstances, which they pretended to be better judges of than I?

I lifted her, however, into a chair; and in words of disordered passion, told her, all her fears were needless: wondered at them: begged of her to be pacified: besought her reliance on my faith and honour: and revowed all my old vows, and poured forth new ones.

At last, with a heart-breaking sob, I see, I see, Mr. Lovelace, in broken sentences she spoke, I see, I see—that at last—at last—I am ruined! Ruined, if *your* pity—let me implore your pity! And down on her bosom, like a half-broken-stalked lily, top-heavy with the overcharging dews of the morning, sunk her head, with a sigh that went to my heart.

All I could think of to reassure her, when a little recovered, I said.

Let her go to Lady Betty's lodgings, then; *directly* go; if the person I called Lady Betty was really Lady Betty.

IF, my dear! Good Heaven! What a villain does that IF show you believe me to be!

Then assuming a more resolute spirit—I will go! I will inquire my way! I will go by myself! And would have rushed by me.

I folded my arms about her to detain her.

She would order a coach and go in it to Hampstead, late as it was; and all alone; so much the better: for in the house of *people* of whom Lady Betty, upon inquiry, had heard a bad character she was resolved not to stay another night.

Dreading what might happen as to her intellects, and being very apprehensive that she might possibly go through a great deal before morning (though more violent she could not well be with the worst she dreaded), I humoured her, and ordered Will to endeavour to get a coach directly, to carry us to Hampstead; I cared not at what price.

Robbers, with whom I would have terrified her, she feared not—*I* was all her fear, I found; and this house her terror: for I saw plainly that she now believed that Lady Betty and Miss Montague were both impostors.

O Jack, the rage of love, the rage of revenge, is upon me! By turns they tear me! The progress already made—the women's instigations—the power I shall have to try her to the utmost, and still to marry her, if she be not to be brought to cohabitation—let me perish, Belford, if she escape me now!

. . . . . .

Will is this moment returned. No coach to be got, either *for love or money*.

Once more she urges—To Mrs. Leeson's let me go, Lovelace! Good Lovelace, let me go to Mrs. Leeson's! For the Almighty's sake, Mr. Lovelace!—her hands clasped.

O my angel! What a wildness is this! Do you know, do you see, my dearest life, what appearances your causeless apprehensions have given you? Do you know it is past eleven o'clock?

Twelve, one, two, three, four—any hour—I care not. If you mean me honourably, let me go out of this hated house!

Just as she had repeated the last words, in came Mrs. Sinclair, in a great ferment. And what, pray, madam, has *this house* done to you? Mr. Lovelace, you have known me some time; and, if I have not the niceness of this lady, I hope I do not deserve to be treated thus!

She set her huge arms akembo: *Hoh!* madam, let me tell you, I am amazed at your freedoms with my character! And, Mr. Lovelace (holding up, and violently shaking, her head), if you are a gentleman, and a man of honour——

Having never before seen anything but obsequiousness in this woman, little as she liked her, she was frighted at her masculine air, and fierce look—God help me! cried she—what will become of me now! Then, turning her head hither and thither, in a wild kind of amaze, What will become of me now!

I will be your protector, my dearest love! But indeed you are uncharitably severe upon poor Mrs. Sinclair! She is a gentlewoman born, and the relict of a man of honour; and though left in such circumstances as oblige her to let lodgings, yet would she scorn to be guilty of a wilful baseness.

I hope so—it may be so—I may be mistaken—but—but there is no crime, I presume, no treason, to say I don't like her house.

The old dragon straddled up to her, with her arms kemboed again, her eyebrows erect, like the bristles upon a hog's back, and, scowling over her shortened nose, more than half hid her ferret eyes. Her mouth was distorted. She pouted out her blubber-lips, as if to bellows up wind and sputter into her horse-nostrils; and her chin was curdled, and more than usually prominent with passion.

With two *hoh-madams* she accosted the frighted fair one; who, terrified, caught hold of my sleeve.

I feared she would fall into fits; and with a look of indignation, told Mrs. Sinclair that these apartments were mine; and I could not imagine what she meant, either by listening to what passed between me and my spouse, or to come in uninvited; and still more I wondered at her giving herself these strange liberties.

The old beldam, throwing herself into a chair, fell a blubbering and exclaiming. And the pacifying of her, and endeavouring to reconcile the lady to her, took up till near one o'clock.

And thus, between terror, and the late hour, and what followed, she was diverted from the thoughts of getting out of the house to Mrs. Leeson's, or anywhere else.

MR. LOVELACE TO JOHN BELFORD, ESQ.

Tuesday Morn., June 13.

AND NOW, Belford, I can go no farther. The affair is over. Clarissa lives. And I am

Your humble servant,

R. Lovelace.

The whole of this black transaction is given by the injured lady to Miss Howe, in her subsequent letters, dated Thursday, July 6.

MR. BELFORD TO ROBERT LOVELACE, ESQ.

Watford, Wedn., June 14.

O THOU savage-hearted monster! What work hast thou made in *one guilty hour,* for a *whole age* of repentance!

I am inexpressibly concerned at the fate of this matchless lady!

I had written a great part of another long letter, to try to soften thy flinty heart in her favour; for I thought it but too likely that thou shouldst succeed in getting her back again to the accursed woman's. But I find it would have been too late, had I finished it, and sent it away. Yet cannot I forbear writing, to urge thee to make the *only* amends thou now canst make her, by a proper use of the licence thou hast obtained.

Poor, poor lady! It is a pain to me that I ever saw her.

CLARISSA LIVES, thou sayest. That she does is my wonder; and these words show that thou thyself (though thou couldst, nevertheless, proceed) hardly expectedst she would have survived the outrage. What must have been the poor lady's distress (watchful as she had been over her honour) when dreadful certainty took place of cruel apprehension! And yet a man may guess what it must have been, by that which thou paintest, when she suspected herself tricked, deserted, and betrayed, by the pretended ladies.

That thou couldst behold her frenzy on this occasion, and her half-speechless, half-fainting prostration at thy feet, and yet retain thy evil purposes, will hardly be thought credible, even by those who know *thee,* if they have seen *her.*

O LOVELACE! LOVELACE! *had I doubted it before, I should now be convinced that there must be a* WORLD AFTER THIS, *to do justice to injured merit, and to punish barbarous perfidy!* Could the divine SOCRATES, and the divine CLARISSA, otherwise have suffered?

Belford.

MR. LOVELACE TO JOHN BELFORD, ESQ.

Thursday, June 15.

LET ME ALONE, you great dog, you!

So say I to thee, on occasion of thy severity to thy poor friend, who, as thou ownest, has furnished thee with the weapons thou brandishest so fearfully against him. And to what purpose, when the mischief is done? when, of consequence, the affair is irretrievable? and when a CLARISSA could not move me?

But people's extravagant notions of things alter not *facts,* Belford: and, when all's done, Miss Clarissa Harlowe has but run the fate of a thousand others of her sex—only that they did not set such a romantic value upon what they call their *honour;* that's all.

And yet I will allow thee this—That if a person sets a high value upon anything, be it ever such a trifle in itself, or in the eye of others, the robbing of that person of it is *not* a trifle to *him.* Take the matter in this light, I own I have done wrong, great wrong, to this admirable creature.

To thy urgent supplication then, that I will do her grateful justice by marriage, let me answer in Matt Prior's two lines on his hoped-for auditorship; as put into the mouths of his St. John and Harley;

——Let that be done, which Matt doth say.
YEA, quoth the Earl—BUT NOT TO-DAY.

Thou seest, Jack, that I make no resolutions, however, against doing her, one time or other, the wished-for justice, even were I to succeed in my principal view, *cohabitation.* And of this I do assure thee, that, if I ever marry, it must, it shall be Miss Clarissa Harlowe.

But what shall I do with this admirable creature the while? Hang me, if I know! For, if I stir, the venomous spider of this habitation will want to set upon the charming fly, whose silken wings are already so entangled in my enormous web, that she cannot move hand or foot: for so much has grief stupefied her, that she is at present as destitute of will as she always seemed to be of desire.

MR. LOVELACE TO JOHN BELFORD, ESQ.

I HAVE just now had a specimen of what the resentment of this dear creature will be when quite recovered: an affecting one!

She seemed about to call down vengeance upon me; when, happily, the leaden god, in pity to her trembling Lovelace, waved over her half-drowned eyes his somniferous wand, and laid asleep the fair exclaimer, before she could go half through her intended imprecation.

Thou wilt guess, by what I have written, that some *little* art has been made use of: but it was with a *generous* design (if thou'lt allow me the word on such an occasion) in order to lessen the too quick sense she was likely to have of what she was to suffer. A contrivance I never had occasion for before, and had not thought of now, if Mrs. Sinclair had not proposed it to me: to whom I left the management of it: and I have done nothing but curse her ever since, lest the quantity should have for ever damped her charming intellects.

[Mrs. Sinclair had given Clarissa some kind of narcotic. Ed.]

MR. LOVELACE TO JOHN BELFORD, ESQ.

Friday, June 16.

JUST NOW Dorcas tells me that what she writes she tears, and throws the paper in fragments under the table, either as not knowing what she does, or disliking it: then gets up, wrings her hands, weeps, and shifts her seat all round the room: then returns to her table, sits down, and writes again.

. . . . . .

One odd letter, as I may call it, Dorcas has this moment given me from her. *Carry this,* said she, *to the vilest of men.* Dorcas, a toad, brought it, without any further direction, to *me.*

By the first thou'lt guess that I have told her that Miss Howe is very ill, and can't write; that she may account the better for not having received the letter designed for her.

PAPER I. (*Torn in two pieces.*)

MY DEAREST MISS HOWE,—O what dreadful, dreadful things have I to tell you! But yet I cannot tell you neither. But say, are you really ill, as a vile, vile creature informs me you are?

But he never yet told me truth, and I hope has not in this: and yet, if it were not true, surely I should have heard from you before now! But what have I to do to upbraid? You may well be tired of me! And if you are, I can forgive you; for I am tired of myself: and all my own relations were tired of me long before you were.

How good you have always been to me, mine own dear Anna Howe! But how I ramble!

I sat down to say a great deal—my heart was full—I did not know what to say first—and thought, and grief, and confusion, and (O my poor head!) I cannot tell what—and thought, and grief, and confusion, came crowding so thick upon me; *one* would be first, *another* would be first, *all would* be first; so I can write nothing at all. Only that, whatever they have done to me, I cannot tell; but I am no longer what I was in any one thing. In any one thing did I say? Yes, but I am; for I am still, and I ever will be,

Your true——

PAPER II. (*Scratched through, and thrown under the table.*)

—AND CAN you, my dear honoured papa, resolve for ever to reprobate your poor child? But I am sure you would not, if you knew what she has suffered since her unhappy—And will nobody plead for your poor suffering girl? I don't presume to think you should receive me—no, indeed! My name is—I don't know what my name is! I never dare to wish to come into your family again! But your heavy curse, my papa—yes, I *will* call you papa, and help yourself as you can—for you are my own dear papa, whether you will or not—and though I am an unworthy child—yet I *am* your child——

PAPER III

REJOICE NOT now, my Bella, my sister, my friend; but pity the humbled creature, whose foolish heart you used to say you beheld through the thin veil of humility which covered it.

I must have been so! My fall had not else been permitted.

You penetrated my proud heart with the jealousy of an elder sister's searching eye.

You knew me better than I knew myself.

I thought, poor proud wretch that I was, that what you said was owing to your envy.

PAPER IV

THOU PERNICIOUS caterpillar, that preyest upon the fair leaf of virgin fame, and poisonest those leaves which thou canst not devour!

Thou fell blight, thou eastern blast, thou overspreading mildew, that destroyest the early promises of the shining year! that mockest the laborious toil, and blastest the joyful hopes, of the painful husbandman!

Thou fretting moth, that corruptest the fairest garment!

Thou eating canker-worm, that preyest upon the opening bud, and turnest the damask rose into livid yellowness!

If, as religion teaches us, God will judge us, in a great measure, by our benevolent or evil actions to one another—O wretch! bethink thee, in time bethink thee, how great must be thy condemnation!

PAPER V

AT FIRST, I saw something in your air and person that displeased me not. Your birth and fortunes were no small advantages to you. You acted not ignobly by my passionate brother. Everybody said you were brave: everybody said you were generous. A *brave* man, I thought, could not be a *base* man: a *generous* man could not, I believed, be *ungenerous*, where he acknowledged *obligation*. Thus prepossessed, all the rest that my soul loved and wished for in your reformation, I hoped! I knew not, but by report, any flagrant instances of your vileness. You seemed frank as well as generous: frankness and generosity ever attracted me: whoever kept up those appearances, I judged of their hearts by my own; and whatever qualities *I wished* to find in them, I was *ready* to find; and, *when* found, I believed them to be natives of the soil.

My fortunes, my rank, my character, I thought a further security. I was in none of those respects unworthy of being the niece of Lord M. and of his two noble sisters. Your vows, your imprecations—But, oh! you have barbarously and basely conspired against that honour, which you ought to have protected: and now you have made me—what is it of vile that you have *not* made me?

PAPER VI

Death only can be dreadful to the Bad:
To Innocence 'tis like a bugbear dress'd
To frighten children. Pull but off the mask,
And he'll appear a friend.
I could a Tale unfold—
Would harrow up thy soul!——
O my Miss Howe! if thou hast friendship, help me,
And speak the words of peace to my divided Soul,
That wars within me,
And raises ev'ry sense to my confusion.
I'm tott'ring on the brink
Of peace; and thou art all the hold I've left!
Assist me—in the pangs of my affliction!

When Honour's lost, 'tis a relief to die:
Death's but a sure retreat from infamy.

But, in the letter she wrote to me, there are yet greater extravagances. The reading of it affected me ten times more than the severest reproaches of a regular mind could do.

To Mr. Lovelace

I never intended to write another line to you. I would not see you, if I could help it. O that I never had!

But tell me of a truth, is Miss Howe really and truly ill? Very ill? And is not her illness poison? And don't *you* know who gave it her?

What you, or Mrs. Sinclair, or somebody (I cannot tell who) have done to my poor head, you best know: but I shall never be what I was. I have wept away all my brain, I believe; for I can weep no more.

But, good now, Lovelace, don't set Mrs. Sinclair upon me again. I never did her any harm. She *so* affrights me, when I see her! Ever since—when was it? I cannot tell.

Yet she may be a very good woman——

What would I say! I forget what I was going to say.

For I never will be Lovelace—let my uncle take it as he pleases.

Well, but now I remember what I was going to say.

Alas! you have killed my head among you—I don't say who did it! God forgive you all! But had it not been better to have put me out of all your ways at once? You might safely have done it! For nobody would require me at your hands—no, not a soul—except, indeed, Miss Howe would have said, when she should see you, What, Lovelace, have you done with Clarissa Harlowe? And then you could have given any slight gay answer —Sent her beyond sea; or, She has run away from me, as she did from her parents.

But this is nothing to what I wanted to say. Now I have it!

I must needs be both a trouble and an expense to you. And here my Uncle Harlowe, when he knows how I am, will never wish any man to have me: no, not even *you,* who have been the occasion of it—barbarous and ungrateful! A less complicated villainy cost a Tarquin—but I forget what I would say again——

Then *this* is it—I never shall be myself again: I have been a very wicked creature—a vain, proud, poor creature—full of secret pride—which I carried off under an humble guise, and deceived everybody—my sister says so—and now I am punished. So let me be carried out of this house, and out of your sight; and let me be put into that Bedlam privately, which once I saw: but it was a sad sight to me then! Little as I thought what I should come to *myself!* That is all I would say: this is all I have to wish for—then I shall be out of all your ways; and I shall be taken care of; and bread and water, without your tormentings, will be dainties; and my straw bed the easiest I have lain in—for—I cannot tell how long!

My clothes will sell for what will keep me there, perhaps, as long as I shall live. But, Lovelace, *dear* Lovelace, I will call you; for you have cost me enough, I'm sure!—don't let me be made a show of, for my *family's* sake; nay, for your *own sake,* don't do that.

So, suppose, instead of Bedlam, it were a private madhouse, where nobody comes! That will be better a great deal.

But, another thing, Lovelace: don't let them use me cruelly when I am there—*you* have used me cruelly enough, you know!

The miserably abused
Clarissa Harlowe.

. . . . . .

Will is just returned from an errand to Hampstead; and acquaints me that Mrs. Townsend was yesterday at Mrs. Moore's, accompanied by three or four rough fellows; a greater number (as supposed) at a distance. She was strangely surprised at the news that my spouse and I are entirely reconciled; and that two fine ladies, my relations, came to visit her, and went to town with her: where she is very happy with me.

Now, since my fair one can neither receive, nor send away letters, I am pretty easy as to this Mrs. Townsend and her employer.

MR. LOVELACE TO JOHN BELFORD, ESQ.

Sunday Night.

I WILL NOT anticipate—only to tell thee that I am too much awakened by her to think of sleep, were I to go to bed; and so shall have nothing to do, but to write an account of our odd conversation, while it is so strong upon my mind that I can think of nothing else.

She was dressed in a white damask night-gown, with less negligence than for some days past.

She entered with such dignity in her manner, as struck me with great awe, and prepared me for the poor figure I made in the subsequent conversation.

You see before you, sir, the wretch whose preference of you to all your sex you have rewarded—as it indeed *deserved* to be rewarded.

Hear me out, guilty wretch! abandoned man! *Man*, did I say? Yet what name else can I? since the mortal worryings of the fiercest beast would have been more natural, and infinitely more welcome, than what you have acted by me; and that with a premeditation and contrivance worthy only of that single heart which now, *base* as well as ungrateful as thou art, seems to quake within thee.

But tell me, since I am a prisoner, as I find, in the vilest of houses, and have not a friend to protect or save me, what thou intendest shall become of the remnant of a life not worth the keeping? Say, if thou hast courage to speak out to her whom thou hast ruined, tell me what *further* I am to suffer from thy barbarity?

O thou truly despicable wretch! Then, lifting up her eyes—Good Heaven! who shall pity the creature who could fall by so base a mind! Yet—and then she looked indignantly upon me—yet, I hate thee not (base and low-souled as thou art!) half so much as I hate myself, that I saw thee not sooner in thy proper colours!

As soon, madam—as soon—as—as soon as your uncle—or—not waiting——

Thou wouldst tell me, I suppose—I know what thou wouldst tell me—but thinkest thou that *marriage will satisfy for a guilt like thine?* Destitute as thou hast made me both of friends and fortune, I too much despise the wretch *who could rob himself of his wife's virtue,* to endure the thoughts of thee in the light thou seemest to hope I will accept thee in!

I hesitated an interruption: but my meaning died away upon my trembling lips. I could only pronounce the word *marriage*—and thus she proceeded:

Let me therefore know whether I am to be controlled in the future disposal of myself? Whether, in a country of liberty, as *this,* where the *sovereign* of it must be guilty of *your* wickedness; and where *you* neither durst have attempted it, had I one friend or relation to look upon me; I am to be kept here a prisoner, to sustain fresh injuries? Whether, in a word, you intend to hinder me from going whither my destiny shall lead me?

After a pause; for I was still silent:

Can you not answer me this plain question? I quit all claim, all expectation, upon you—what right have you to detain me here?

I could not speak. What could I say to such a question?

O wretch! wringing her uplifted hands, had I not been robbed of my senses, and that in the *basest* manner—you best know how—had I been able to account for myself, and your proceedings, or to have known but how the days passed; a whole week should not have gone over my head, as I find it has done, before I had told you, what I now tell you, *That the man who has been the villain to me you have been, shall never make me his wife.* I repeat, therefore, Am I *now* at liberty to dispose of myself as I please?

Now comes the fool, the miscreant again, hesitating his broken answer: My dearest love, I am confounded, quite confounded, at the thought of what—of what has been done; and at the thought of—to whom. I see, I see, there is no withstanding your eloquence! Such irresistible proofs of the love of virtue *for its own sake*—did I never hear of, nor meet with, in all my reading. And if you can forgive a repentant villain, who thus on his knees implores your forgiveness (then down I dropped, absolutely in earnest in all I said), I vow by all that's sacred and just (and may a thunderbolt strike me dead at your feet, if I am not sincere!) that I will by marriage, before to-morrow noon, without waiting for your uncle, or anybody, do you all the justice I now *can* do you.

Hadst thou not sinned beyond the *possibility of forgiveness,* interrupted she; and this had been the first time that thus thou solemnly promisest and invokest the vengeance thou hast as often defied; the desperateness of my condition might have induced me to think of taking a wretched chance with a man so profligate. But, *after what I have suffered by thee,* it would be *criminal* in me to wish to bind my soul in covenant to a man so nearly allied to perdition.

And, saying this, she flung from me; leaving me absolutely shocked and confounded at her part of a conversation, which she began with such uncommon, however severe composure, and concluded with so much sincere and unaffected indignation.

Monday morn. past three.

MR. LOVELACE TO JOHN BELFORD, ESQ.

Monday Morn. 5 o'clock (June 19)

IT IS NOW near six. The sun, for two hours past, has been illuminating everything about me: for that impartial orb shines upon mother Sinclair's house, as well as upon any other: but nothing within me can it illuminate.

At day-dawn I looked through the keyhole of my beloved's door. She had declared she would not put off her clothes any more in this house. There I beheld her in a sweet slumber, which I hope will prove refreshing to her disturbed senses; sitting in her elbow-chair, her apron over her head; her head supported by one sweet hand, the other hand hanging down upon her side, in a sleepy lifelessness; half of one pretty foot only visible.

See the difference in our cases, thought I! She, the charming injured, can sweetly sleep, while the varlet injurer cannot close his eyes; and has been trying to no purpose the whole night to divert his melancholy, and to fly from himself!

Six o'clock.

Just now Dorcas tells me that her lady is preparing openly, and without disguise, to be gone. Very probable. The humour she flew away from me in last night has given me expectation of such an enterprise.

Now, Jack, to be thus hated and despised! And if I *have* sinned beyond forgiveness——

. . . . . .

But she has sent me a message by Dorcas, that she will meet me in the dining-room; and desires (odd enough!) that the wench may be present at the conversation that shall pass between us. This message gives me hope.

Nine o'clock.

Confounded art, cunning villainy! By my soul, she had like to have slipped through my fingers. She meant nothing by her message but to get Dorcas out of the way, and a clear coast.

Had she been in the fore-house, and no passage to go through to get at the street door, she had certainly been gone. But her haste betrayed her: for Sally Martin happening to be in the fore-parlour, and hearing a swifter motion than usual, and a rustling of silks, as if from somebody in a hurry, looked out; and seeing who it was, stepped between her and the door, and set her back against it.

You must not go, madam. Indeed you must not.

By what right? And how dare you? While Sally called out for her aunt; and half a dozen voices joined instantly in the cry, for me to hasten down, to hasten down in a moment.

And down I flew. And there was the charming creature, the sweet deceiver, panting for breath, her back against the partition, a parcel in her hand (women make no excursions without their parcels), Sally, Polly (but Polly obligingly pleading for her), the mother, Mabel, and Peter (the footman of the house) about her; all, however, keeping their distance; the mother and Sally between her and the door—in her soft rage the dear soul repeating, I *will* go! Nobody has a right—I *will* go! If you kill me, women, I won't go up again!

As soon as she saw me, she stepped a pace or two towards me; Mr. Lovelace, I *will* go! said she. Do you authorize these women—What right have they, or *you* either, to stop me?

Is this, my dear, preparative to the conversation you led me to expect in the dining-room? And do you think I can part with you thus? Do you think I will?

And am I, sir, to be thus beset! Surrounded thus? What have these women to do with me?

I desired them to leave us, all but Dorcas, who was down as soon as I. I then thought it right to assume an air of resolution, having found my tameness so greatly triumphed over. And now, my dear, said I (urging her reluctant feet), be pleased to walk into the fore-parlour. Hence, since you will not go upstairs, here we may *hold our parley;* and Dorcas *be witness to it.* And now, madam, seating her, and sticking my hands in my sides, your pleasure!

Insolent villain! said the furious lady. And, rising, ran to the window, and threw up the sash (she knew not, I suppose, that there were iron rails before the windows). And, when she found she could not get out into the street, clasping her uplifted hands together, having dropped her parcel—For the love of God, good honest man! For the love of God, mistress (to two passers-by), a poor, poor creature, said she, ruined——

I clasped her in my arms, people beginning to gather about the window: and then she cried out, Murder! Help! Help! and carried her up to the dining-room, in spite of her little plotting heart (as I may now call it), although she violently struggled, catching hold of the banisters here and there, as she could. I would have seated her there; but she sunk down half-motionless, pale as ashes. And a violent burst of tears happily relieved her.

Dorcas wept over her. The wench was actually moved for her!

Violent hysterics succeeded. I left her to Mabel, Dorcas, and Polly; the latter the most supportable to her of the sisterhood.

This attempt, so resolutely made, alarmed me not a little.

Mrs. Sinclair and her nymphs are much more concerned; because of the reputation of their house, as they call it, having received some insults (broken windows threatened) to make them produce the young creature who cried out.

While the mobbish inquisitors were in the height of their office, the women came running up to me, to know what they should do; a constable being actually fetched.

Get the constable into the parlour, said I, with three or four of the forwardest of the mob, and produce one of the nymphs, onion-eyed, in a moment, with disordered head-dress and handkerchief, and let her own herself the person: the occasion, a female skirmish; but satisfied with the justice done her. Then give a dram or two to each fellow, and all will be well.

Eleven o'clock.

I thought to have had one trial (having gone so far) for *cohabitation*. But what hope can there be of succeeding? She in invincible! *Against all my notions, against all my conceptions* (thinking of her as a woman, and in the very bloom of her charms), *she is absolutely invincible*. My whole view, at the present, is to do her legal justice, if I can but once more get her out of her altitudes.

The *consent* of such a woman must make her ever new, ever charming. But, astonishing! Can the want of a church ceremony make such a difference!

She *owes* me her consent; for hitherto I have had nothing to boast of. All, of my side, has been *deep remorse, anguish of mind,* and *love increased* rather *than abated.*

But I am overmatched, egregiously overmatched, by this woman. What to do with her, or without her, I know not.

MR. LOVELACE TO JOHN BELFORD, ESQ.

I HAVE this moment intelligence from Simon Parsons, one of Lord M.'s stewards, that his lordship is very ill. Simon, who is my obsequious servant, in virtue of my presumptive heirship, gives me a hint in his letter that my presence at M. Hall will not be amiss. So I must accelerate, whatever be the course I shall be allowed or compelled to take.

. . . . . .

But now, at last, am I to be admitted to the presence of my angry fair one: after three denials, nevertheless; and a *peremptory* from me, by Dorcas, that I must see her in her chamber, if I cannot see her in the dining-room.

Dorcas has hinted to her my lord's illness, as a piece of intelligence that dropped in conversation from me.

But here I stop. My beloved, pursuant to my peremptory message, is just gone up into the dining-room.

MR. LOVELACE TO JOHN BELFORD, ESQ.

Monday Afternoon.

SHE BEGAN with me like a true woman the moment I entered the dining-room: not the least apology, not the least excuse, for the uproar she had made, and the trouble she had given me.

I come, said she, into thy detested presence, because I cannot help it. But why am I to be imprisoned here?

Dearest madam, interrupted I, give not way to so much violence. You must know that your detention is entirely owing to the desire I have to make you all the amends that is in my power to make you.

Surely, madam, if I may be permitted to call you *legally* mine, I might have but anticip——

Wretch, that thou art! Say not another word upon this subject. When thou vowedst, when thou promisedst at Hampstead, I had begun to think that I must be thine. If I had consented, at the request of those I thought thy relations, this would have been a principal inducement, that I could then have brought thee, what was *most* wanted, an unsullied honour in dowry, to a wretch destitute of all honour; and could have met the gratulations of a family to which thy life has been one continued disgrace, with a consciousness of *deserving* their gratulations. But thinkest thou that I will give a harlot niece to thy honourable uncle, and to thy *real* aunts; and a cousin to thy cousins from a brothel?

Then, turning towards me, who knew neither what to say *to* her, nor *for* myself, I renounce thee for ever, Lovelace! Abhorred of my soul! for ever I renounce thee! Seek thy fortunes wheresoever thou wilt! Only now, that thou hast already ruined me——

Ruined you, madam—the world need not—I knew not what to say.

Ruined me in my *own* eyes; and that is the same to me as if *al' the world* knew it. Hinder me not from going whither my mysterious destiny shall lead me.

Why hesitate you, sir? What right have you to stop me, as you lately did; and to bring me up by force, my hands and arms bruised with your violence?

I am cut to the heart, madam, with invectives so violent. I am but too sensible of the wrong I have done you, or I could not *bear* your reproaches. Yet, if you think yourself in my power, I would caution you, madam, not to make me desperate. For you *shall* be mine, or my life shall be the forfeit! Nor is life worth having without you!

Be *thine!* I be *thine!* said the passionate beauty.

Yes, madam, be *mine!* I repeat, you *shall* be mine! My very crime is your glory. My love, my admiration of you is increased by what has passed: *and so it ought*.

I never, never will be yours! said she, clasping her hands together, and lifting up her eyes.

Only forgive me, my dearest life, this *one* time! A virtue so invincible! What further view *can* I have against you? Have I attempted any further outrage? If you will be mine, your injuries will be injuries done to myself. You have too well guessed at the unnatural arts that have been used. But can a greater testimony be given of your virtue? And now I have only to hope, that although I cannot make you *complete* amends, yet that you will permit me to make you *all* the amends that can possibly be made.

Hear me out, I beseech you, madam; for she was going to speak with an aspect unpacifiedly angry: the God, whom you serve, requires but repentance and amendment: imitate *Him,* my dearest love, and bless me with the *means* of reforming a course of life that begins to be hateful to me. And let to-morrow's sun witness to our espousals.

I cannot judge thee, said she; but the God to whom thou so boldly referrest can; and assure thyself *He* will.

Tell me is there any reality in the treaty thou hast pretended to be on foot between my uncle and Captain Tomlinson, and thyself?

That was a cursed thrust. What could I say? But was I not obliged to proceed as I had begun?

In short, I solemnly averred that there was! How one crime, as the good folks say, brings on another!

Let me ask thee next, said she whether those women be *really* Lady Betty Lawrance and thy Cousin Montague?

Let me, my dearest love, be enabled to-morrow to call you lawfully mine, and we will set out the next day, if you please, to Berkshire, to my Lord M.'s, where they both are at this time; and you shall convince yourself by your own eyes, and by your own ears.

Now, Belford, I swore to it (*lover's oaths, Jack*) that they were really and truly Lady Betty Lawrance and my Cousin Montague.

She lifted up her hands and eyes—What can I think!—What *can* I think!

You *think* me a devil, madam; a very devil! or you could not, after you have put these questions to me, seem to doubt the truth of answers so solemnly sworn to.

I thought she had now reason to be satisfied; and I begged her to allow me to talk to her of to-morrow, as of the happiest day of my life. We have the licence, madam—and you *must* excuse me, that I cannot let you go hence till I have tried every way I *can* try to obtain your forgiveness.

And am I then (with a kind of frantic wildness) to be detained a prisoner in this horrid house? Am I, sir? Take care! Take care! holding up her hand, menacing, how you make me desperate! If I fall, though by my own hand, inquisition will be made for my blood: and be not out in thy plot, Lovelace, if it *should* be so—make *sure* work, I charge thee: dig a hole deep enough to cram in and conceal this unhappy body: for, depend upon it, that some of those who will not stir to protect me living, will move heaven and earth to avenge me dead!

A horrid dear creature! By my soul, she made me shudder!

MR. LOVELACE TO JOHN BELFORD, ESQ.

THERE IS certainly a good deal in the observation, *That it costs a man ten times more pains to be wicked, than it would cost him to be good.*

But to proceed with my narrative.

The dear creature resumed the topic her heart was so firmly fixed upon; and insisted upon quitting the *odious house,* and that in very high terms.

I urged her to meet me the next day at the altar in either of the two churches mentioned in the licence.

And canst thou, Lovelace, be so *mean*—as to wish to make a wife of the creature thou hast insulted, dishonoured, and abused, as thou hast me? Was it necessary to humble me down to the low level of thy baseness, before I could be a wife meet for thee? Thou hadst a father, who was a man of honour: a mother, who deserved a better son. Thou hast an uncle, who is no dishonour to the peerage of a kingdom, whose peers are more respectable than the nobility of any other country. Thou hast other relations also, who may be *thy* boast, though thou canst not be *theirs*—and canst thou not imagine that thou hearest them calling upon thee; the dead from their monuments: the living from their laudable pride; not to dishonour thy ancient and splendid house, by entering into wedlock with a creature whom thou hast levelled with the dirt of the street, and classed with the vilest of her sex?

I extolled her greatness of soul, and her virtue. I execrated myself for my guilt: and told her, how grateful to the *manes* of my ancestors, as well as to the wishes of the living, the honour I supplicated for would be.

But still she insisted upon being a free agent; of seeing herself in other lodgings before she would give what I urged the *least* consideration. Nor would she promise me favour even then, or to permit my visits. How then, as I asked her, could I comply, without resolving to lose her for ever?

She put her hand to her forehead often as she talked; and at last, pleading disorder in her head, retired; neither of us satisfied with the other.

Monday Night.

How determined is this lady! Again had she like to have escaped us! What a fixed resentment! She only, I find, assumed a little calm, in order to quiet suspicion. She was got down, and actually had unbolted the street door, before I could get to her, alarmed as I was by Mrs. Sinclair's cookmaid, who was the only one that saw her fly through the passage: yet lightning was not quicker than I.

Again I brought her back to the dining-room, with infinite reluctance on her part. And before her face, ordered a servant to be placed constantly at the bottom of the stairs for the future.

She seemed even choked with grief and disappointment.

Dorcas was exceedingly assiduous about her; and confidently gave it as her own opinion, that the dear lady should be permitted to go to another lodging, since *this* was so disagreeable to her: were she to be killed for saying so, she would say it. And was *good* Dorcas for this afterwards.

But for some time the dear creature was all passion and violence.

I see, I see, said she, when I had brought her up, what I am to expect from your new professions, O vilest of men!

Have I offered to you, my beloved creature, anything that can justify this impatience after a more hopeful calm?

She wrung her hands. She disordered her head-dress. She tore her ruffles. She was in a perfect frenzy.

I dreaded her returning malady: but entreaty rather exasperating, I affected an angry air. I bid her expect the worst she had to fear—and was menacing on, in hopes to intimidate her, when dropping down at my feet,

'Twill be a mercy, said she, the highest act of mercy you can do, to kill me outright upon this spot—this happy spot, as I will, in my last moments, call it! Then, baring, with a still more frantic violence, part of her enchanting neck, Here, here, said the soul-harrowing beauty, let thy pointed mercy enter! And I will thank thee, and forgive thee for all the dreadful past! With my lastest gasp will I forgive and thank thee! Or help *me* to the means, and I will myself put out of thy way so miserable a wretch! And bless thee for those means!

Why all this extravagant passion? Why all these exclamations? Have I offered any new injury to you, my dearest life? What a frenzy is this! Am I not ready to make you all the reparation that I *can* make you? Had I not reason to hope——

No, no, no, no—half a dozen times, as fast as she could speak.

Had I not reason to hope that you were meditating upon the means of making me happy, and yourself not miserable, rather than upon a flight so causeless and so precipitate?

No, no, no, no, as before, shaking her head with wild impatience, as resolved not to attend to what I said.

My resolutions are so honourable, if you will permit them to take effect, that I need not be solicitous whither you go, if you will but permit my visits, and receive my vows. And God is my witness that I bring you not back from the door with any view to your dishonour, but the contrary: and this moment I will send for a minister to put an end to all your doubts and fears.

Say this, and say a thousand times more, and bind every word with a solemn appeal to that God whom thou art accustomed to invoke to the truth of the vilest falsehoods, and all will still be short of what thou *hast* vowed and promised to me. And, were *not* my heart to abhor thee, and to rise against thee, for thy *perjuries,* as it *does,* I would not, I tell thee once more, I would not, bind my soul in covenant with such a man, for a thousand worlds!

Compose yourself, however, madam; for *your own sake,* compose yourself. Permit me to raise you up; *abhorred* as I am of your soul!

Nay, if I must not touch you; for she wildly slapped my hands; but with such a sweet passionate air, her bosom heaving and throbbing as she looked up to me, that although I was most sincerely enraged, I could with transport have pressed her to mine.

If I must not touch you, I will not. But depend upon it (and I assumed the sternest air I could assume, to try what *that* would do), depend upon it, madam, that this is not the way to avoid the evils you dread. Let me do what I will, I cannot be used worse! Dorcas, be gone!

She arose, Dorcas being about to withdraw; and wildly caught hold of her arm: O Dorcas! If thou art of mine own sex, leave me not, I charge thee! Then quitting Dorcas, down she threw herself upon her knees, in the furthermost corner of the room, clasping a chair with her face laid upon the bottom of it! O where can I be safe? Where, where can I be safe, from this man of violence?

This gave Dorcas an opportunity to confirm herself in her lady's confidence: the wench threw herself at my feet, while I seemed in violent wrath; and, embracing my knees, Kill me, sir, kill me, sir, if you please! I must throw myself in your way, to save my lady. I beg your pardon, sir—but you must be set on! God forgive the mischief-makers! But your own heart, if left to itself, would not permit these things! Spare, however, sir! spare my lady, I beseech you! bustling on her knees about me, as if I were intending to approach her lady, had I not been restrained by her.

This, humoured by me, Begone, devil! Officious devil, begone! startled the dear creature; who, snatching up hastily her head from the chair, and as hastily popping it down again in terror, hit her nose, I suppose, against the edge of the chair; and it gushed out with blood, running in a stream down her bosom; she herself too much affrighted to heed it!

Never was mortal man in such terror and agitation as I; for I instantly concluded that she had stabbed herself with some concealed instrument.

I ran to her in a wild agony, for Dorcas was frighted out of all her mock interposition.

What have you done! O what have you done! Look up to me, my dearest life! Sweet injured innocence, look up to me! What have you done! Long will I not survive you! And I was upon the point of drawing my sword to dispatch myself, when I discovered (what an unmanly blockhead does this charming creature make me at her pleasure!) that all I apprehended was but a bloody nose, which, as far as I know (for it could not be stopped in a quarter of an hour), may have saved her head and her intellects.

But I see by this scene, that the sweet creature is but a pretty coward at bottom; and that I can terrify her out of her virulence against me, whenever I put on a sterness and anger: but then, as a qualifier to the advantage this gives me over her, I find myself to be a coward too, which I had not before suspected, since I was capable of being so easily terrified by the apprehensions of her offering violence to herself.

MR. LOVELACE TO JOHN BELFORD, ESQ.

AS MUCH of my heart, as I know of it myself, will I tell thee. When I am *from* her, I cannot still help hesitating about marriage; and I even frequently resolve against it, and determine to press my favourite scheme for cohabitation. But when I am *with* her, I am ready to say, to swear, and to do, whatever I think will be most acceptable to her: and were a parson at hand, I should plunge at once, no doubt of it, into the state.

A wife at any time, I used to say. I had ever confidence and vanity enough to think that no woman breathing could deny her hand when I held out mine. I am confoundedly mortified to find that this lady is able to hold me at bay, and to refuse all my *honest* vows.

The lady tells Dorcas that her heart is broken; and that she shall live but a little while. I think nothing of that, if we marry.

And for what should her heart be broken? Her will is unviolated:—at *present,* however, her will is unviolated.

What nonsense, then, to suppose that such a mere *notional*

violation as she has suffered, should be able to cut asunder the strings of life?

Her religion, married, or not married, will set her above making such a trifling accident, such an *involuntary* suffering, fatal to her.

O Jack! had I an imperial diadem, I swear to thee that I would give it up, even to my *enemy,* to have one charming boy by this lady. And should she *escape me,* and no such effect follow, my revenge on her family, and, in *such* a case, on herself, would be incomplete, and I should reproach myself as long as I lived.

[Aware of what an intriguer she has to deal with in Lovelace, Clarissa begins her own contrivances to escape from this vile house and from Lovelace. She writes a promissory note to pay Dorcas £20 a year if Dorcas (who is Lovelace's agent) will help her to escape. Dorcas shows the document to Lovelace and this challenges him to further and more elaborate intrigues. His plot is to aid Clarissa, with Dorcas's help, to find refuge with a dowager lady. This impostor is Mrs. Sinclair's sister. Once in that house, Lovelace was to appear and try again for cohabitation. Lovelace has seen to it that Clarissa sees his forged letter from Tomlinson saying that her uncle Harlowe will be at Kentish Town on Wed. June 29 and will be present at the marriage. At the last moment Clarissa's complete distrust of Lovelace and Dorcas prevents her from trying to escape in the chariot all ready at the street corner, and Lovelace's plot collapses. Ed.]

MR. LOVELACE TO JOHN BELFORD, ESQ.

Wednesday Night.

A MAN IS just now arrived from M. Hall, who tells me that my lord is in a very dangerous way. The gout is in his stomach to an extreme degree, occasioned by drinking a great quantity of lemonade.

A man of £8,000 a year to prefer his appetite to his health! He deserves to die!

The man says that his lordship was so bad when he came away that the family began to talk of sending for me in post-haste. As I know the old peer has a good deal of cash by him, of which he seldom keeps account, it behoves me to go down as soon as I can. But what shall I do with this dear creature the while? To-morrow over, I shall, perhaps, be able to answer my own question. I am afraid she will make me desperate.

For here have I sent to implore her company, and am denied with scorn.

MR. LOVELACE TO JOHN BELFORD, ESQ.

Thursday Noon, June 22.

LET ME perish if I know what to make either of myself, or of this surprising creature—now calm, now tempestuous—but I know thou lovest not anticipation any more than I.

At my repeated requests, she met me at six this morning. She was ready dressed; for she has not had her clothes off ever since she declared that they never more should be off in this house. And charmingly she looked, with all the disadvantages of a three hours' violent stomach-ache (for Dorcas told me that she had been really ill), no rest, and eyes red, and swelled with weeping.

She looked not favourably upon me. A cloud hung upon her brow at her entrance: but as she was going to answer me, a still greater solemnity took possession of her charming features.

It is easy for me, Mr. Lovelace, to see that further violences are intended me, if I comply not with your purposes; whatever they are, I will suppose them to be what you so solemnly profess they are. But I have told you, as solemnly, my mind, that I never *will*, that I never *can*, be yours; nor, if so, any man's upon earth. All vengeance, nevertheless, for the wrongs you have done me, I disclaim. The desire lately so near my heart, of a reconciliation with my friends, is much abated. They shall not receive me *now*, if they would. Sunk in mine own eyes, I now think myself unworthy of their favour. In the anguish of my soul, therefore, I conjure you, Lovelace (tears in her eyes), to leave me to my fate.

Whither, my dearest life——

No matter whither. I will leave to Providence, when I am out of this house, the direction of my future steps. I am sensible enough of my destitute condition. I know that I have not now a friend in the world. Even Miss Howe has given me up—

or you are—but I would fain keep my temper! By your means I have lost them all—and you have been a barbarous enemy to me.

She paused.

I could not speak.

The evils I have suffered, proceeded she (turning from me), however irreparable, are but *temporary* evils. Leave me to my hopes of being enabled to obtain the Divine forgiveness for the offence I have been drawn in to give to my parents, and to virtue; that so I may avoid the evils that are *more than temporary*. This is now all I have to wish for. And what is it that I demand, that I have not a right to, and from which it is an illegal violence to withhold me?

It was impossible for me, I told her plainly, to comply. I besought her to give me her hand as this very day. I could not live without her. I communicated to her my lord's illness, as a reason why I wished not to stay for her uncle's anniversary. I besought her to bless me with her consent; and, after the ceremony was passed, to accompany me down to Berks. And thus, my dearest life, said I, will you be freed from a house to which you have conceived so great an antipathy.

She hesitated, and looked down, as if irresolute. And this set my heart up at my mouth. And, believe me, I had instantly popped in upon me, in imagination, an old spectacled parson, with a white surplice thrown over a black habit (a fit emblem of the halcyon office, which, under a benign appearance, often introduces a life of storms and tempests), whining and snuffling through his nose the irrevocable ceremony.

I hope now, my dearest life, said I, snatching her hand, and pressing it to my lips, that your silence bodes me good. Let me, my beloved creature, have but your *tacit* consent; and this moment I will step out and engage a minister—and then I promised how much my whole future life should be devoted to her commands, and that I would make her the best and tenderest of husbands.

At last, turning to me, I have told you my mind, Mr. Lovelace, said she. Think you that I could thus solemnly—there she stopped—I am too much in your power, proceeded she; your prisoner, rather than a person free to choose for myself, or to say what I will *do* or *be*—but, as a testimony that you mean me well, let me instantly quit this house; and I will then give you such an answer in writing, as best befits my unhappy circumstances.

I have no patience, said she, to find myself a slave, a prisoner, in a vile house. Tell me, sir, in so many words tell me, whether it be, or be not, your intention to permit me to quit it? To permit me the freedom which is my birthright as an English subject?

Will not the consequence of your departure hence be, that I shall lose you for ever, madam?

She flung from me. My soul disdains to hold parley with thee, were her violent words—but I threw myself at her feet, and took hold of her reluctant hand, and began to imprecate, to vow, to promise—but thus the passionate beauty, interrupting me, went on:

I am sick of thee, MAN! One continued string of vows, oaths, and protestations, varied only by time and place, fills thy mouth! My heart rises against thee, O thou *cruel implement of my brother's causeless vengeance*. All I beg of thee is, that thou wilt remit me the *future* part of my father's dreadful curse! The *temporary* part, base and ungrateful as thou art! thou hast completed!

I was speechless; Well I might! Her *brother's* implement! *James Harlowe's* implement! Zounds, Jack! what words were these!

I let go her struggling hand. She took two or three turns across the room, her whole haughty soul in her air. Then approaching me, but in silence, turning from me, and again to me, in a milder voice—I see thy confusion, Lovelace. Or is it thy remorse? I have but one request to make thee—the request so often repeated: that thou wilt this moment permit me to quit this house.

And saying this, away she flung, leaving me in a confusion so great, that I knew not what to think, say, or do.

But Dorcas soon roused me. Do you know, sir, running in hastily, that my lady is gone downstairs!

No, sure! And down I flew, and found her once more at the street door, contending with Polly Horton to get out.

She rushed by me into the fore parlour, and flew to the window, and attempted once more to throw up the sash. Good people! Good people! cried she.

I caught her in my arms and lifted her from the window. But being afraid of hurting the charming creature (charming in her very rage), she slid through my arms on the floor:—Let me die here! Let me die here! were her words; remaining jointless and immovable till Sally and Mrs. Sinclair hurried in.

She was visibly terrified at the sight of the old wretch; while I (sincerely affected) appealed, Bear witness, Mrs. Sinclair! Bear witness, Miss Martin! Miss Horton! Every one bear witness, that I offer not violence to this beloved creature!

She then found her feet. O house (looking towards the windows, and all round her, O house) contrived on purpose for my ruin! said she—but let not that woman come into my presence—nor that Miss Horton neither, who would not have dared to control me, had she not been a base one!

Hoh, sir! Hoh, madam! vociferated the old dragon, her arms kemboed, and flourishing with one foot to the extent of her petticoats—What ado's here about nothing! I never knew such work in my life, between a chicken of a gentleman and a tiger of a lady!

She was visibly affrighted: and upstairs she hastened.

I followed her up. She rushed by her own apartment into the dining-room: no terror can make her forget her punctilio.

To recite what passed there of invective, exclamations, threatenings, even of her own life, on one side; of expostulations, supplications, and sometimes menaces, on the other, would be too affecting; and, after my particularity in like scenes, these things may as well be imagined as expressed.

I will therefore only mention, that, at length, I extorted a concession from her. She had reason[1] to think it would have

[1] The lady mentions, in her memorandum-book, that she had no other way, as she apprehended, to save herself from instant dishonour, but by making this concession. Her only hope now, she says, if she cannot escape by Dorcas's connivance (whom, nevertheless, she suspects), is to find a way to engage the protection of her uncle, and even of the civil magistrate, on Thursday next, if necessary. "He shall see," says she, "tame and timid as he has thought me, what I dare to do to avoid so hated a compulsion, and a man capable of a baseness so premeditatedly vile and inhuman."

been worse for her on the spot, if she had not made it. It was, *That she would endeavour to make herself easy, till she saw what next Thursday, her uncle's birthday would produce.* But oh, that it were not a sin, she passionately exclaimed on making this poor concession, to put an end to her own life, rather than yield to give me but *that* assurance!

This however, shows me, that she is aware that the reluctantly given assurance may be fairly construed into a matrimonial expectation on my side. And if she will *now,* even *now,* look forward, I think, from my heart, that I will put on her livery, and wear it for life.

What a situation am I in, with all my cursed inventions? I am puzzled, confounded, and ashamed of myself, upon the whole. Nevertheless, she had best take care that she carries not her obstinacy much further. She knows not what revenge for slighted love will make me do.

MR. LOVELACE TO JOHN BELFORD, ESQ.

Thursday Night.

CONFOUNDEDLY out of humour with this perverse woman! Nor wilt thou blame me, if thou art my friend. She regards the concession she made, as a concession extorted from her: and we are but just where we were before she made it.

With great difficulty I prevailed upon her to favour me with her company for one half-hour this evening. The necessity I was under to go down to M. Hall was the subject I wanted to talk upon.

I told her, that as she had been so good as to promise that she would endeavour to make herself easy till she saw the Thursday in next week over, I hoped that she would not scruple to oblige me with her word, that I should find her here at my return from M. Hall.

Indeed she would make me no such promise. Nothing of *this house* was mentioned to me, said she: you know it was not. And do you think that I would have given *my consent to my imprisonment in it?*

Have you, madam, any reliance upon my honour?

Still silent.

You hate me, madam! You despise me more than you do the most odious of God's creatures!

You ought to despise *me,* if I did not.

You say, madam, you are in a *bad* house. You have *no reliance* upon my honour—you believe you *cannot avoid me*——

She arose. I beseech you, let me withdraw.

I snatched her hand, rising, and pressed it first to my lips, and then to my heart, in wild disorder. She might have felt the bounding mischief ready to burst its bars. You *shall* go—to your own apartment, if you please—but, by the great God of Heaven, I will accompany you thither!

She trembled. Pray, pray, Mr. Lovelace, don't terrify me so!

Be seated, madam! I beseech you, be seated!

I will sit down——

Do then, madam—do then—all my soul in my eyes, and my heart's blood throbbing at my finger-ends.

I will, I will—you hurt me—pray, Mr. Lovelace, don't—don't frighten me so—and down she sat, trembling; my hand still grasping hers.

I hung over her throbbing bosom, and putting my other arm round her waist—And you say you hate me, madam—and you say you despise me—and you say you promised me nothing——

Yes, yes, I *did* promise you—let me not be held down thus—you see I sat down when you bid me. Why (struggling) need you hold me down thus? I did promise *to endeavour to be easy till Thursday was over!* But you won't let me! How can I be easy? Pray, let me not be thus terrified.

And what, madam, *meant* you by your promise? Did you mean anything in my favour? You designed that I should, at the time, *think* you did. Did you mean anything in my favour, madam? Did you intend that I should *think* you did?

Let go my hand, sir—take away your arm from about me (struggling, yet trembling). *Why do you gaze upon me so?*

Answer me, madam. Did you mean anything in my favour by your promise?

Let me not be thus constrained to answer.

Say only, dearest creature, say only, *may* I trust to your favour, if you go to Hampstead?

How *dare* you, sir, if I *must* speak out, expect a promise of favour from me? What a mean creature must you think me, after your ungrateful baseness to me, were I to give you such a promise?

Then standing up, Thou hast made me, O vilest of men! (her hands clasped, and a face crimsoned over with indignation) an inmate of the vilest of houses—nevertheless, while I am in it, I shall have a heart incapable of anything but abhorrence of *that* and of *thee!*

I dare to die, Lovelace—and she who fears not death is not to be intimidated into a meanness unworthy of her heart and principles!

As a mark of my submission to your will, you shall, *if you please,* withdraw. But I will not go to M. Hall—live or die my Lord M. I will not go to M. Hall—but will attend the effect of your promise. Remember, madam, you have promised *to endeavour to make yourself easy, till you see the event of next Thursday*. Next Thursday, remember, your uncle comes up to see us married—*that's the event*. You think ill of your Lovelace —do not, madam, suffer your own morals to be degraded by the *infection,* as you called it, of his example.

Away flew the charmer with this half-permission—and no doubt thought that she had an escape—nor without reason.

[Clarissa has demanded to remove from the vile house to Hampstead. Lovelace, who must leave at once to attend Lord M. who is dangerously ill, accedes—no new cause arising. He arranges a new cause by producing Clarissa's promissory note to Dorcas. The "culprit" Dorcas is arraigned by Lovelace and Mrs. Sinclair and her nymphs, whereupon Clarissa, who had locked herself in her chamber, appears, and one of the fine scenes of the story follows. Ed.]

As you please, madam.

And then (the servants being withdrawn) I urged her again for the assurance that she would meet me at the altar on Thursday next. But to no purpose. May she not thank herself for all that may follow?

One favour, however, I would not be denied; to be admitted to pass the evening with her.

All sweetness and obsequiousness will I be on this occasion. My whole soul shall be poured out to move her to forgive me. If she will not, and if the promissory note should fall in my way, my revenge will doubtless take total possession of me.

A few hours will now decide all.

Meantime I am in strange agitations. I must suppress them, if possible, before I venture into her presence. My heart bounces my bosom from the table. I will lay down my pen, and wholly resign to its impulses.

Just then, we heard the lady's door unbar, unlock, unbolt—

Now, Belford, see us all sitting in judgment, resolved to punish the fair briberess—I, and the mother, the hitherto *dreaded* mother, the nieces Sally, Polly, the traitress Dorcas, and Mabel, a guard, as it were, over Dorcas, that she might not run away, and hide herself: all predetermined, and of *necessity* predetermined, from the journey I was going to take, and my precarious situation with her—and hear her *unbolt, unlock, unbar* the door; then, as it proved afterwards, put the key into the lock on the outside, lock the door, and put it in her pocket—and then *hear* her step towards us, and instantly *see* her enter among us, confiding in her own innocence; and with a majesty in her person and manner, that is *natural* to her; but which then shone out in all its glory! Every tongue silent, every eye awed, every heart quaking, mine, in a particular manner, sunk, throbless, and twice below its usual region, to once at my throat—a shameful recreant! She silent too, looking round her, first on me; then on the mother, as no longer fearing her; then on Sally, Polly, and the culprit Dorcas! Such the glorious power of innocence exerted at that awful moment!

She would have spoken, but could not, looking down my guilt into confusion. A mouse might have been heard passing over the floor; her own light feet and rustling silks could not have prevented it; for she seemed to tread air, and to be all soul. She passed to the door, and back towards me, two or three times, before speech could get the better of indignation; and at last, after twice or thrice hemming, to recover her articulate voice:

"O thou contemptible and abandoned Lovelace, thinkest thou that I see not through this poor villainous plot of thine, and of these thy wicked accomplices?

"Thou, woman (looking at the mother), once my terror! always my dislike! but now my detestation! shouldst once more (for thine perhaps was the preparation) have provided for me intoxicating potions, to rob me of my senses——

"And then (*turning to me*), thou, wretch, mightest more securely have depended upon such a low contrivance as this!

"And ye, vile women, who perhaps have been the ruin, body and soul, of hundreds of innocents (you show me *how,* in full assembly), know that I am not married—ruined as I am, by your help, I bless God, I am *not* married to this miscreant. And I have friends that will demand my honour at your hands! And to whose authority I will apply; for none has this man over me. Look to it then, what further insults you offer me, or incite him to offer me. I am a person, though thus vilely betrayed, of rank and fortune. I never will be his; and, to your utter ruin, will find friends to pursue you: and now I have this full proof of your detestable wickedness, and have heard your base incitements, will have no mercy upon you!"

They could not laugh at the poor figure I made.

"And as for thee, thou vile Dorcas! Thou *double* deceiver! whining out thy pretended love for me! Begone, wretch! Nobody will hurt thee! Begone, I say! Thou hast too well acted thy part to be blamed by *any* here but myself—thou art safe: thy guilt is thy security in such a house as this! Thy shameful, thy poor part, thou hast as well acted as the low farce could give thee to act! As well as they each of them (thy superiors, though not thy betters), thou seest, can act theirs. Steal away into darkness! No inquiry after this will be made, whose the first advances, thine or mine."

And, as I hope to live, the wench, confoundedly frightened, slunk away; so did her sentinel Mabel; though I, endeavouring to rally, cried out for Dorcas to stay—but I believe the devil could not have stopped her, when an angel bid her begone.

Madam, said I, let me tell you; and was advancing towards her, with a fierce aspect, most cursedly vexed, and ashamed too.

But she turned to me; "Stop where thou art, O vilest and most abandoned of men! Stop where thou art! Nor, with that determined face, offer to touch me, if thou wouldst not that I should be a corpse at thy feet!"

To my astonishment, she held forth a penknife in her hand, the point to her own bosom, grasping resolutely the whole handle, so that there was no offering to take it from her.

"I offer not mischief to anybody but myself. You, sir, and ye women, are safe from every violence of mine. The LAW shall be all my resource: the LAW" and she spoke the word with emphasis, that to such people carries natural terror with it, and now struck a panic into them.

"The LAW only shall be my refuge!"——

The infamous mother whispered me that it were better to *make terms* with this *strange* lady, and let her go.

Sally, nothwithstanding all her impudent bravery at other times, said, *If* Mr. Lovelace had told *them* what was *not true* of her being his wife——

And Polly Horton, That she must *needs* say, the lady, if she were *not* my wife, had been very much injured; that was all.

That is not now a matter to be disputed, cried I: you and I know, madam.——

"We do, said she; and I thank God, I am *not* thine—*once more,* I thank God for it—I have no doubt of the further baseness that thou hadst intended me, by this vile and low trick: but I have my SENSES, Lovelace: and from my heart I despise thee, thou very poor Lovelace! How canst thou stand in my presence! Thou, that——"

Madam, madam, madam—these are insults not to be borne —and was approaching her.

She withdrew to the door, and set her back against it, holding the pointed knife to her heaving bosom; while the women held me, beseeching me not to provoke the violent lady—for their *house's* sake, and be cursed to them, they besought me—and all three hung upon me—while the truly heroic lady braved me at that distance:

"Approach me, Lovelace, with resentment, if thou wilt. I dare die. It is in defence of my honour. God will be merciful to my poor soul! I expect no mercy from thee! I have gained this distance, and two steps nearer me, and thou shalt see what I dare do!"

Leave me, women, to myself, and to my angel! They retired at a distance. O my beloved creature, how you terrify me! Holding out my arms, and kneeling on one knee—Not a step, not a step further, except to receive the death myself at that injured hand that threatens its own. I am a villain! the blackest of villains! Say you will sheathe your knife in the injurer's, not the injured's, heart; and then will I indeed approach you, but not else.

The mother twanged her damned nose; and Sally and Polly pulled out their handkerchiefs, and turned from us. They never in their lives, they told me afterwards, beheld such a scene.——

Innocence so triumphant: villainy so debased, they must mean!

Unawares to myself, I had moved onward to my angel. "And dost thou, dost thou, *still* disclaiming, *still* advancing, dost thou, dost thou, *still* insidiously move towards me?" (and her hand was extended). "I dare—I dare—not rashly neither —my heart from *principle* abhors the act, which *thou* makest *necessary!* God, in Thy mercy! (lifting up her eyes and hands) God, in Thy mercy!"

I threw myself to the further end of the room. An ejaculation, a silent ejaculation, employing her thoughts that moment; Polly says the whites of her lovely eyes were only visible: and, in the instant that she extended her hand, *assuredly* to strike the fatal blow (how the very recital terrifies me!), she cast her eye towards me, and saw me at the utmost distance the room would allow, and heard my broken voice—my voice was utterly broken; nor knew I what I said, or whether to the purpose or not—and her charming cheeks, that were all in a glow before, turned pale, as if terrified at her own purpose; and lifting up her eyes—"Thank God!—Thank God! said the angel—delivered *for the present;* for the *present* delivered—from myself! Keep, sir, keep that distance" (looking down towards me, who was prostrate on the floor). "That distance has saved a life; to what reserved, the Almighty only knows!"

To *be* happy, madam; and to *make* happy! And oh, let me

but hope for your favour for to-morrow—I will put off my journey till then—and may God——

Swear not, sir!—with an awful and piercing aspect. You have too, too often sworn! God's eye is upon us!—His more *immediate* eye; and looked wildly. But the women looked up to the ceiling, as if *afraid* of God's eye, and trembled. And well they might; and *I* too, who so very lately had each of us the devil in our hearts.

If not to-morrow, madam, say but next Thursday, your uncle's birthday; say but next Thursday!

"This I say, of this you may assure yourself, I never, never *will* be yours. And let me hope that I may be entitled to the performance of your promise, to be permitted to leave this *innocent* house, as one called it (but long have my ears been accustomed to such inversions of words), as soon as the day breaks."

Did my perdition depend upon it, that you cannot, madam, but upon terms. And I hope you will not terrify me—still dreading the accursed knife.

"Nothing less than an attempt upon my honour shall make me desperate. I have no view, but to defend my honour: with such a view only I entered into treaty with your infamous agent below. The resolution you have seen, I trust, God will give me again, upon the same occasion. But for a *less,* I wish not for it. Only take notice, women, that I am no wife of *this man:* basely as he has used me, I am not his wife. He has no authority over me. If he go away by and by, and you act by his authority to detain me, look to it."

Then, taking one of the lights, she turned from us; and away she went, unmolested. Not a soul was *able* to molest her.

Mabel saw her, tremblingly, and in a hurry, take the key of her chamber door out of her pocket, and unlock it; and, as soon as she entered, heard her double lock, bar, and bolt it.

By her taking out her key, when she came out of her chamber to us, she no doubt suspected my design: which was, to have carried her in my arms thither, if she made such force necessary, after I had intimidated her; and to have been her companion for that night.

She was to have had several bedchamber women to assist to

undress her upon occasion: but, from the moment she entered the dining-room with so much intrepidity, it was absolutely impossible to think of prosecuting my villainous designs against her.

. . . . . .

But for the lady, by my soul I love her, I admire her, more than ever! I *must* have her. I *will* have her still—*with* honour, or *without*, as I have often vowed. Had she threatened ME, I should soon have been master of *one* arm, and *in both!* But for so sincere a virtue to threaten *herself*, and not offer to intimidate *any other*, and with so much presence of mind, as to distinguish, in the very passionate intention, the necessity of the act, in defence of her *honour*, and so *fairly* to disavow *lesser* occasions; showed such a deliberation, such a choice, such a principle; and then keeping me so watchfully at a distance, that I could not seize her hand so soon as she could have given the fatal blow; how impossible not to be subdued by so *true* and so *discreet* a magnanimity!

But she is not *gone*. She shall not go. I will press her with letters for the Thursday. She shall yet be mine, legally mine. For, as to cohabitation, there is now no such thing to be thought of.

The captain shall give her away, as proxy for her uncle. My lord will die. My fortune will help my *will*, and set me above everything and everybody.

But here is the curse—she despises me, Jack! What man, as I have heretofore said, can bear to be despised, especially by his wife? O Lord! O Lord! What a hand, what a cursed hand, have I made of this plot!

It goes against me to say,

God bless the lady!

Near 5, Sat. Morn.

MR. LOVELACE TO MISS CLARISSA HARLOWE
[*Superscribed to Mrs. Lovelace*]

M. Hall, Sat. Night, June 24.

MY DEAREST LIFE,—If you do not impute to love, and to terror raised by love, the poor figure I made before you last night, you will not do me justice. I thought I would try to the very last moment, if, by complying with you in *everything*, I could prevail upon you to promise to be mine on Thursday next, since you refused me an earlier day. Could I have been so happy, you had not been hindered going to Hampstead, or wherever else you pleased. But when I could not prevail upon you to give me this assurance, what room had I (my demerit so great) to suppose that your going thither would not be to lose you for ever?

I will not offer to defend myself, for *wishing you to remain where you are,* till either you give me your word to meet me at the altar on Thursday; or till I have the honour of attending you, preparative to the solemnity which will make that day the happiest of my life.

The orders I have given to the people of the house are: "That you shall be obeyed in every particular that is consistent with my expectations of finding you there on my return to town on Wednesday next: that Mrs. Sinclair, and her nieces shall not, without your orders, come into your presence: that neither shall Dorcas, till she has fully cleared her conduct to your satisfaction, be permitted to attend you: but Mabel, in her place; of whom you seemed some time ago to express some liking. Will I have left behind me to attend your commands. But, as to letters which may be sent you, or any which you may have to send, I must humbly entreat that none such pass *from* or *to* you, for the few days that I shall be absent." But I do assure you, madam, that the seals of both sorts shall be sacred: and the letters, if such be sent, shall be given into your own hands the moment the ceremony is performed, or before, if you require it.

I send this by a special messenger, who will wait your pleasure in relation to the impatiently wished-for Thursday: which I humbly hope will be signified by a line.

Lady Sarah and Lady Betty have also their tokens of respect ready to court your acceptance: but may Heaven incline you to give the opportunity of receiving their personal compliments, and those of my Cousins Montague, before the next week be out!

His lordship is exceeding ill. Dr. S. has no hopes of him. The only consolation I can have for the death of a relation who loves me so well, if he *do* die, must arise from the additional power it will put into my hands of showing how much I am,

My dearest life,

Your ever affectionate and faithful

Lovelace.

Mr. Lovelace to Miss Clarissa Harlowe

[*Superscribed to Mrs. Lovelace*]

M. Hall, Sunday Night, June 25.

My dearest Love,—I cannot find words to express how much I am mortified at the return of my messenger without a line from you.

Thursday is so near, that I will send messenger after messenger every four hours, till I have a favourable answer.

Your love, madam, I neither expect, nor ask for; nor will, till my future behaviour gives you cause to think I deserve it. All I at present presume to wish, is to have it in my power to do you all the justice I can now do you: and to your generosity will I leave it, to reward me, as I shall merit, with your affection.

At present, revolving my poor behaviour of Friday night before you, I think I should sooner choose to go to my last audit, unprepared for it as I am, than to appear in your presence, unless you give me some hope that I shall be received as your elected husband, rather than (however deserved) as a detested criminal.

Let me, therefore, propose an expedient, in order to spare my own confusion; and to spare you the necessity for that soul-harrowing recrimination, which I cannot stand, and which must be disagreeable to yourself—to name the church, and I will have everything in readiness; so that our next interview will be, in a manner, at the very altar; and then you will have the kind husband to forgive for the faults of the ungrateful lover. If your resentment be still too high to write more, let it only be in your own dear hand, these words, *St. Martin's Church, Thursday*—or these, *St. Giles's Church, Thursday;* nor will I insist upon any inscription or subscription, or so much as the initials of your name. This shall be all the favour I will expect, till the dear hand itself is given to mine, in presence of that Being whom I invoke as a witness of the inviolable faith and honour of

Your adoring,

Lovelace.

MR. LOVELACE TO MISS CLARISSA HARLOWE

[*Superscribed to Mrs. Lovelace*]

M. Hall, Monday, June 26.

ONCE MORE, my dearest love, do I conjure you to send me the four requested words. Hitherto all that has passed is between you and me only; but, after Thursday, if my wishes are unanswered, the whole will be before the world.

My lord is extremely ill, and endures not to have me out of his sight for one half-hour. But this shall not have the least weight with me if you be pleased to hold out the olive-branch to me in the four requested words.

I have the following intelligence from Captain Tomlinson:

"All your family are at your Uncle Harlowe's. Your uncle finds he cannot go up; and names Captain Tomlinson for his proxy. He proposes to keep all your family with him till the captain assures him that the ceremony is over.

"Already he has begun, with hope of success, to try to reconcile your mother to you."

My Lord M. but just now has told me how happy he should think himself to have an opportunity, before he dies, to salute you as his niece. I have put him in hopes that he shall see you; and have told him, that I will go to town on Wednesday, in order to prevail upon you to accompany me down on Thursday or Friday. I have ordered a set to be in readiness to carry me up; and, were not my lord so very ill, my Cousin Montague tells me she would offer *her* attendance on you. If you please, therefore, we can set out for this place the moment the solemnity is performed.

Do not, dearest creature, dissipate all these promising appearances, and, by refusing to save your own and your family's reputation in the eye of the world, use yourself worse than the ungratefullest wretch on earth has used you. For, if we are married, all the disgrace you imagine you have suffered while a single lady, will be my own; and only known to ourselves.

In a letter sent, I have desired that my friend, Mr. Belford, who is your very great admirer, and who knows all the secrets of my heart, will wait upon you, to know what I am to depend upon as to the chosen day.

If I have not an answer to this, either from your own goodness, or through Mr. Belford's intercession, it will be too late for me to set out.

Relieve, I beseech you, dearest madam, by the four requested words, or by Mr. Belford, the anxiety of

Your ever affectionate and obliged

Lovelace.

MR. BELFORD TO ROBERT LOVELACE, ESQ.

Thursday, June 29.

THOU HAST HEARD the news. Bad or good, I know not which thou'lt deem it.

But to my narrative; for I suppose thou expectest all particulars from me.

"The noble exertion of spirit she had made on Friday night, had, it seems, greatly disordered her; insomuch that she was not visible till Saturday evening; when Mabel saw her; and she seemed to be very ill: but on Sunday morning, having dressed herself, as if designing to go to church, she ordered Mabel to get her a coach to the door.

"The wench told her she was to obey her in everything but the calling of a coach or chair, or in relation to letters.

"She sent for Will, and gave him the same command.

"He pleaded his master's orders to the contrary, and desired to be excused.

"Upon this, down she went herself, and would have gone out without observation: but finding the street door double locked, and the key not in the lock, she stepped into the street parlour, and would have thrown up the sash to call out to the people passing by, as they doubted not: but that, since her last attempt of the same nature, had been fastened down.

"Hereupon she resolutely stepped into Mrs. Sinclair's parlour in the back house; where were the old devil and her two partners; and demanded the key of the street door, or to have it opened for her.

"They were all surprised; but desired to be excused, and pleaded your orders.

"She asserted that you had no authority over her; and never should have any: that their present refusal was their own act and deed: she saw the intent of their back house, and the reason of putting her there: she pleaded her condition and fortune; and said they had no way to avoid utter ruin, but by opening their doors to her, or by murdering her, and burying her in their garden or cellar, too deep for detection: that already what had been done to her was punishable by death: and bid them at their peril detain her.

"They answered that Mr. Lovelace could prove his marriage and would indemnify them. And they all would have vindicated their behaviour on Friday night, and the reputation of their house: but refusing to hear them on that topic, she flung from them, threatening.

"She then went up a half a dozen stairs in her way to her own apartment: but, as if she had bethought herself, down she stepped again, and proceeded towards the street parlour; saying, as she passed by the infamous Dorcas, I'll make myself protectors, though the windows suffer: but that wench, of her own head, on the lady's going out of that parlour to Mrs. Sinclair's, had locked the door, and taken out the key: so that finding herself disappointed, she burst into tears, and went menacing and sobbing upstairs again.

"She made no other attempt till the effectual one.

"The women, in pursuance of your orders, offered not to obtrude themselves upon her; and Dorcas also kept out of her sight all the rest of Sunday; also on Monday and Tuesday. But by the lady's condescension (even to familiarity) to Mabel, they imagined that she must be working in her mind all that time to get away: they therefore redoubled their cautions to the wench: who told them so faithfully all that passed between her lady and her, that they had no doubt of her fidelity to her wicked trust.

" 'Tis probable she might have been contriving something all this time; but saw no room for perfecting any scheme: the contrivance by which she effected her escape seems to me not to have been fallen upon till the very day: since it depended partly upon the *weather,* as it proved. But it is evident she hoped something from Mabel's simplicity, or gratitude, or compassion, by cultivating all the time her civility to her.

"Polly waited on her early on Wednesday morning; and met with a better reception than she had *reason* to expect. She complained however with warmth of her confinement. Polly said there would be a happy end to it (if it *were* a confinement) next day, she presumed. She absolutely declared to the contrary, in the way Polly meant it; and said, That Mr. Lovelace on his *return* (*which looked as if she intended to wait for it*), should have reason to repent the orders he had given, as *they all should* their observance of them: let him send twenty letters, she would not answer one, be the consequence what it would; nor give him hope of the least favour, while she was in that house. She had given Mrs. Sinclair and themselves fair warning, she said: no orders of another ought to make them detain a free person: but having made an open attempt to *go,* and been detained by them, she was the calmer, she told Polly; let *them* look to the consequence.

"But yet she spoke this with temper; and Polly gave it as her opinion (with apprehension for their own safety) that, having so good a handle to punish them all, she would not go away if she might. And what, inferred Polly, is the indemnity of a man who has committed the vilest of rapes on a person of condition; and must himself, if prosecuted for it, either fly or be hanged?

"Sinclair, upon this representation of Polly, foresaw, she said, *the ruin of her poor house* is the issue of this *strange* business; and the infamous Sally and Dorcas bore their parts in the apprehension: and this put them upon thinking it advisable for the future, that the street door should generally in the daytime be only left upon a bolt-latch, as they called it, which anybody might open on the inside; and that the key should be kept in the door; that their numerous *comers* and *goers,* as they called their guests, should be able to give evidence *that she might have gone out if she would:* not forgetting, however, to renew their orders to Will, to Dorcas, to Mabel, and the rest, to redouble their vigilance on this occasion, to prevent her escape:

none of them doubting, at the same time, that her love of a man so considerable in *their* eyes, and the prospect of what was to happen, as she had reason to believe, on Thursday, her uncle's birthday, would (though perhaps not till the *last hour*, for her *pride's sake*, was their word) engage her to change her temper.

"They believe that she discovered the key to be left in the door; for she was down more than once to walk in the little garden, and seemed to cast her eye each time to the street door.

"About eight yesterday morning, an hour after Polly had left her, she told Mabel she was sure she should not live long; and having a good many suits of apparel, which after her death would be of no use to anybody she valued, she would give her a brown lustring gown, which, with some alterations, to make it more suitable to her degree, would a great while serve her for a Sunday wear; for that she (Mabel) was the only person in that house of whom she could think without terror or antipathy.

"Mabel expressing her gratitude upon the occasion, the lady said she had nothing to employ herself about; and if she could get a workwoman directly, she would look over her things then, and give her what she intended for her.

"Her mistress's mantua-maker, the maid replied, lived but a little way off; and she doubted not that she could procure *her*, or one of her journey-women, to alter the gown out of hand.

"I will give you also, said she, a quilted coat, which will require but little alteration, if any; for you are much about my stature: but the gown I will give directions about, because the sleeves and the robings and facings must be altered for your wear, being, I believe, above your station: and try, said she, if you can get the workwoman, and we'll advise about it. If she cannot come now, let her come in the afternoon; but I had rather now, because it will amuse me to give you a lift.

"Then stepping to the window, It rains, said she: slip on the hood and short cloak I have seen you wear, and come to me when you are ready to go out, because you shall bring me in something that I want.

"Mabel equipped herself accordingly, and received her commands to buy her some trifles, and then left her; but, in her way out, stepped into the back parlour, where Dorcas was with Mrs. Sinclair, telling her where she was going, and on what account, bidding Dorcas look out till she came back.

"Mrs. Sinclair commended her; Dorcas envied her, and took her cue: and Mabel soon returned with the mantua-maker's journey-woman; and then Dorcas went off guard.

"The lady looked out the gown and petticoat, and before the workwoman caused Mabel to try it on; and, that it might fit the better, made the willing wench pull off her upper petticoat, and put on that she gave her. Then she bid them go into Mr. Lovelace's apartment, and contrive about it before the pier-glass there, and stay till she came to them, to give them her opinion.

"Mabel would have taken her own clothes, and hood, and short cloak with her: but her lady said, No matter; you may put them on again here, when we have considered about the alterations: there's no occasion to litter the other room.

"They went; and instantly, as it is supposed, she slipped on Mabel's gown and petticoat over her own, which was white damask, and put on the wench's hood, short cloak, and ordinary apron, and down she went.

"Hearing somebody tripping along the passage, both Will and Dorcas whipped to the inner hall door, and saw her; but, taking her for Mabel, Are you going far, Mabel, cried Will?

"Without turning her face, or answering, she held out her hand, pointing to the stairs; which they construed as a caution for them to look out in her absence; and supposing she would not be long gone, as she had not in form repeated her caution to them, up went Will, tarrying at the stairs-head in expectation of the supposed Mabel's return.

"Mabel and the workwoman waited a good while, amusing themselves not disagreeably, the one with contriving in the way of her business, the other delighting herself with her fine gown and coat: but at last, wondering the lady did not come in to them, Mabel tiptoed it to her door, and tapping, and not being answered, stepped into the chamber.

"Will at that instant, from his station at the stairs-head, seeing Mabel in her *lady's* clothes; for he had been told of the present, was very much surprised, having, as he thought, just seen her go out in *her own;* and stepping up, met her at the door. How the devil can this be? said he. Just now you went out in your own dress! How came you here in this? And how could you pass me unseen? But nevertheless, kissing her, said he would now brag he had kissed his lady, or one in her clothes.

"I am glad, Mr. William, cried Mabel, to see you here so diligently. But know you where my lady is?

"In my master's apartment, answered Will. Is she not? Was she not talking with you this moment?

"No, that's Mrs. Dolins's journey-woman.

"They both stood aghast, as they said; Will again recollecting he had seen Mabel, as he thought, go out in her own clothes. And while they were debating and wondering, up comes Dorcas; and seeing Mabel dressed out (whom she had likewise beheld a little before, as she supposed, in her common clothes) she joined in the wonder; till Mabel, re-entering the lady's apartment, missed her own clothes; and then suspecting what had happened, and letting the others into the ground of her suspicion, they all agreed that she had certainly escaped. And then followed such an uproar of mutual accusation, and *You should have done this,* and *You should have done that,* as alarmed the whole house; every apartment in both houses giving up its devil, to the number of fourteen or fifteen, including the mother and her partners.

"Will told them *his* story; and then ran out, as on the like occasion formerly, to make inquiry whether the lady was seen by any of the coachmen, chairmen, or porters, plying in that neighbourhood: while Dorcas cleared herself immediately, and that at the poor Mabel's expense, who made a figure as guilty as awkward, having on the suspected price of her treachery; which Dorcas, out of envy, was ready to tear from her back.

"Hereupon all the pack opened at the poor wench, while the mother, foaming at the mouth, bellowed out her orders for seizing the suspected offender; who could neither be heard in her own defence, nor, *had* she been heard, would have been believed.

"The poor Mabel, frightened out of her wits, expected every moment to be torn in pieces, having half a score open-clawed paws upon her all at once. She promised to confess all. But that all, when she had obtained a hearing, was nothing; for *nothing* had she to confess.

"The wench went upstairs; and whipped on another gown, and sliding downstairs, escaped to her relations. And this flight, which was certainly more owing to *terror* than *guilt,* was, in the true Old Bailey construction, made a confirmation of the latter."

Thy sincere friend,
J. Belford.

P.S. Mabel's clothes were thrown into the passage this morning; nobody knows by whom.

MR. LOVELACE TO JOHN BELFORD, ESQ.

Friday, June 30.

I AM RUINED, undone, blown up, destroyed, and worse than annihilated, that's certain!

It is certainly as much my misfortune to have fallen in with Miss Clarissa Harlowe, were I to have valued my reputation or ease, as it is that of Miss Harlowe to have been acquainted with me. And, after all, what have I done more than prosecute the maxims by which thou and I and every rake are governed, and which, before I knew this lady, we have pursued from pretty girl to pretty girl, as fast as we had set one down, taking another up; just as the fellows do with the flying coaches and flying horses at a country fair, with a *Who rides next! Who rides next!*

. . . . . .

But alas, Jack, all this is but a copy of my countenance, drawn to evade thy malice! Though it answer thy unfriendly purpose to own it, I cannot forbear to own it, that I am stung to the very soul with this unhappy—*accident,* must I call it? Have I nobody whose throat, either for carelessness or treachery, I ought to cut in order to pacify my vengeance?

One thing I will nevertheless add, to show the sincerity of my contrition: 'Tis this, that if thou canst by any means find her out within these three days, or any time before she has discovered the stories relating to Captain Tomlinson and her uncle to be what they are; and if thou canst prevail upon her to consent; I will actually, in thy presence and his (he to represent her uncle), marry her.

I am still in hopes it may be so—she cannot be long concealed—I have already set all engines at work to find her out; and if I do, what *indifferent* persons (and no one of her *friends,* as thou observest, will look upon her) will care to embroil themselves with a man of my figure, fortune, and resolution? Show her this part then, or any other part, of this letter, at thy own discretion, if thou *canst* find her: for, after all, methinks I would be glad that this affair, which is bad enough in itself, should go off without worse personal consequences to anybody else; and yet it runs in my mind, I know not why, that sooner or later it will draw a few drops of blood after it; except she and I can make it up between ourselves.

Lovelace.

. . . . . .

Miss Clarissa Harlowe to Miss Howe

Wednesday Night, June 28.

O my dearest Miss Howe!—Once more have I escaped—but, alas! *I,* my *best self,* have *not* escaped! Oh, your poor Clarissa Harlowe! *You* also will hate me, I fear! Yet you won't, when you know all!

But no more of myself! my *lost* self.

. . . . . .

Forgive. Oh, forgive my rambling. My peace is destroyed. My intellects are touched.

O my best, my dearest, my *only* friend! What a tale have I to unfold! But still upon *self,* this vile, this hated *self!* I will shake it off, if possible; and why should I not, since I think, except one wretch, I hate nothing so much? Self, then, be banished from *self* one moment (for I doubt it *will* for no longer), to inquire after a *dearer* object, my beloved Anna Howe!—whose mind, all robed in spotless white, charms and irradiates—but what would I say?——

. . . . . .

And how, my dearest friend, after this rhapsody, which, on reperusal, I would not let go, but to show you what a distracted mind dictates to my trembling pen; *how do you?* You have been very ill, it seems. That you are *recovered,* my dear, let me hear. That your mother is well, pray let me hear, and hear quickly.

. . . . . .

And what is all this wild incoherence for? It is only to beg to know how you have been, and how you now do, by a line directed for Mrs. Rachel Clark, at Mr. Smith's, a glove shop in King Street, Covent Garden; which (although my abode is a secret to everybody else) will reach the hands of—*your unhappy* —but that's not enough——

Your miserable
Clarissa Harlowe.

MRS. HOWE TO MISS CLARISSA HARLOWE

[*Superscribed as directed in the preceding.*]

Friday, June 30.

MISS CLARISSA HARLOWE,—You will wonder to receive a letter from me. I am sorry for the great distress you seem to be in. Such a hopeful young lady as you were! But see what comes of disobedience to parents!

But pray, miss, don't make my Nancy guilty of your fault; which is that of disobedience. I have charged her over and over not to correspond with one who has made such a giddy step. It is not to her reputation, I am sure. You *knew* that I so charged her; yet you go on corresponding together, to my very great vexation; for she has been very perverse upon it more than once. *Evil communication,* miss—you know the rest.

Here, people cannot be unhappy by themselves, but they must involve their friends and acquaintance, whose discretion has kept them clear of their errors, into near as much unhappiness as if they had run into the like of their own heads! Thus my poor daughter is always in tears and grief. And she has postponed her own felicity, truly, because *you* are unhappy!

I write a long letter, where I proposed to say but a few words;

and those to forbid you writing to my Nancy: and this as well because of the false step you have made, as because it will grieve her poor heart, and do you no good. If you love her, therefore, write not to her. Your sad letter came into my hands, Nancy being abroad, and I shall not show it her: for there would be no comfort for her, if she saw it, nor for me whose delight she is—as you once was to your parents.

Your compassionating well-wisher,
Annabella Howe.

MISS CLARISSA HARLOWE TO MRS. HOWE

Saturday, July 1.

PERMIT ME, madam, to trouble you with a few lines, were it only to thank you for your reproofs; which have, nevertheless, drawn fresh streams of blood from a bleeding heart.

My story is a dismal story. It has circumstances in it that would engage pity, and possibly a judgment not altogether unfavourable, were those circumstances known. But it is my business, and shall be *all* my business, to repent of my failings, and not endeavour to extenuate them.

Nor will I seek to distress your worthy mind. If *I cannot suffer alone,* I will make as few parties as I can in my sufferings. And indeed, I took up my pen with this resolution when I wrote the letter which has fallen into your hands. It was only to know, and that for a very particular reason, as well as for affection unbounded, if my dear Miss Howe, from whom I had not heard of a long time, were ill; as I had been told she was; and if so, how she now does. But my injuries being recent, and my distresses having been exceeding great, *self* would crowd into my letter.

Miss Howe being abroad when my letter came, I flatter myself that she is recovered. But it would be some satisfaction to me to be informed if she *has been ill.* Another line from *your* hand would be too great a favour: but, if you will be pleased to direct any servant to answer *yes,* or *no,* to that question, I will not be further troublesome.

Nevertheless, I must declare that my Miss Howe's friendship was all the comfort I had or expected to have in this world; and a line from her would have been a cordial to my fainting heart.

Judge then, dearest madam, how reluctantly I must obey your prohibition—but yet I will endeavour to obey it; although I should have hoped, as well from the tenor of all that has passed between Miss Howe and me, as from *her* established virtue, that she could not be tainted by *evil communication,* had one or two letters been permitted. This, however, I ask not for, since I think I have nothing to do, but to beg of God (who, I hope, has not yet withdrawn His grace from me, although He is pleased to let loose His justice upon my faults) to give me a truly broken spirit, if it be not already broken enough, and then to take to His mercy

The unhappy
Clarissa Harlowe.

Two favours, good madam, I have to beg of you. The first that you will not let any of my relations know that you have heard from me. The other, that no living creature be apprised where I am to be heard of, or directed to.

Miss Clarissa Harlowe to Hannah Burton

Thursday, June 29

My good Hannah,—Strange things have happened to me since you were dismissed my service.

How do you, my Hannah? Are you recovered of your illness? If you are, do you choose to come and be with me? Or *can* you conveniently?

Living or dying, I will endeavour to make it worth your while, my Hannah.

If you are recovered, as I hope, and if you have a good place, it may be they would bear with your absence, and suffer somebody in your room *for a month or so:* and, by that time, I hope to be provided for, and you may then return to your place.

Don't let any of my friends know of this my desire; whether you can come or not.

I am at Mr. Smith's, a hosier's and glove shop, in King Street, Covent Garden.

You must direct to me by the name of Rachel Clark.

I send this to your mother at St. Albans, not knowing where

to direct to you. Return me a line, that I may know what to depend upon: and I shall see you have not forgotten the pretty hand you were taught, in happy days, by

Your true friend,
Clarissa Harlowe.

HANNAH BURTON.

Monday, July 3.

HONORED MADDAM,—I have not forgot to write, and never will forget anything you, my dear young lady, was so good as to larn me. I am very sorrowfull for your misfortens, my dearest young lady; so sorrowfull, I do not know what to do. Gladd at harte would I be to be able to come to you. But indeed I have not been able to stir out of my rome here at my mother's, ever since I was forsed to leave my plase with a roomatise, which has made me quite and clene helpless. I will pray for you night and day, my dearest, my kindest, my goodest young lady, who have been so badly used; and I am very sorry I cannot come to do you love and sarvice; which will ever be in the harte of mee to do, if it was in my power: who am,

Your most dewtifull sarvant to command,
Hannah Burton.

MISS CLARISSA HARLOWE TO MRS. JUDITH NORTON

Thursday, June 29.

MY DEAR MRS. NORTON,—I address myself to you after a very long silence, principally to desire you to satisfy me in two or three points, which it behoves me to know.

My father, and all the family, I am informed, are to be at my Uncle Harlowe's this day, as usual. Pray acquaint me, if they *have* been there? And if they were cheerful on the anniversary occasion? And also, if you have heard of any journey, or intended journey, of my brother, in company with Captain Singleton and Mr. Solmes.

Strange things have happened to me, my dear worthy and maternal friend—very strange things! Mr. Lovelace has proved a very barbarous and ungrateful man to me. But, God be praised, I have escaped from him.

Say nothing to any of my friends that you have heard from me.

Pray, do you think my father would be prevailed upon, if I were to supplicate him by letter, to take off the heavy curse he laid upon me at my going from Harlowe Place? I can expect no other favour from him: but that being literally fulfilled as to my prospects in this life, I hope it will be thought to have operated far enough: and my heart is *so* weak!—it is *very* weak! But for my father's *own* sake—what *should* I say? Indeed, I hardly know how I *ought* to express myself on this sad subject! But it will give ease to my mind to be released from it.

Your unfortunate
Clarissa Harlowe.

MRS. NORTON. [*In answer.*]

Saturday, July 1.

YOUR LETTER, my dearest young lady, cuts me to the heart! Why will you not let me know all your distresses!

My son is very good to me. A few hours ago he was taken with a feverish disorder. But I hope it will go off happily, if his ardour for business will give him the recess from it which his good master is willing to allow him.

You have been misinformed as to your family's being at your Uncle Harlowe's. They did not intend to be there. Nor was the day kept at all. Indeed, they have not stirred out, but to church (and that but three times), ever since the day you went away.

I have not heard a syllable of such a journey as you mention, of your brother, Captain Singleton, and Mr. Solmes. There has been some talk indeed of your brother's setting out for his northern estates: but I have not heard of it lately.

I am afraid no letter will be received from you. No evil can have happened to you, which they do not *expect* to hear of; so great is their antipathy to the wicked man, and so bad is his character.

I cannot but think hardly of their unforgivingness: but there is no judging for others by one's self.

You are escaped, my dearest miss—happily, I hope—that is to say, with your honour—else how great must be your distress! Yet from your letter I dread the worst.

I am very seldom at Harlowe Place. The house is not the house it used to be, since you went from it. Then they are *so* relentless!

Your Hannah left her place ill some time ago; and, as she is still at her mother's at St. Albans, I am afraid she continues ill. If so, as you are among strangers, and I cannot encourage you at present to come into *these* parts, I shall think it my duty to attend you (let it be taken as it will) as soon as my Tommy's indisposition will permit; which I hope will be soon.

I have a little money by me. Will you be so good to command it, my beloved young lady? It is most of it your own bounty to me.

Let your sufferings be what they will, I am sure you have been innocent in your intention. So do not despond. None are made to suffer above what they *can,* and therefore *ought* to bear.

You see, my dearest Miss Clary, that I make no scruple to call the step you took a false one. In *you* it was less excusable than it would have been in any other young lady; not only because of your superior talents, but because of the opposition between *your* character and *his:* so that if you had been provoked to quit your father's house, it needed not to have been with him.

Your ever affectionate and faithful servant,

Judith Norton.

Miss Cl. Harlowe to Lady Betty Lawrance

Thursday, June 29.

Madam,—I hope you'll excuse the freedom of this address, from one who has not the honour to be personally known to you, although you must have heard much of Clarissa Harlowe. It is only to beg the favour of a line from your ladyship's hand in answer to the following questions:

1. Whether you wrote a letter, dated, as I have a memorandum, Wednesday, June 7, congratulating your Nephew Lovelace on his supposed nuptials, as reported to you by Mr. Spurrier, your ladyship's steward, as from one Captain Tomlinson: and in it reproaching Mr. Lovelace as

guilty of slight, etc., in not having acquainted your ladyship and the family with his marriage?

2. Whether your ladyship wrote to Miss Montague to meet you at Reading, in order to attend you to your Cousin Leeson's in Albemarle Street; on your being obliged to be in town on your *old Chancery affair,* I remember are the words? And whether you bespoke your nephew's attendance there on Sunday night the 11th?
3. Whether your ladyship and Miss Montague *did* come to town at that time? And whether you went to Hampstead on Monday, in a hired coach and four, your own being repairing; and took from thence to town the young creature whom you visited there?

Your ladyship will probably guess that these questions are not asked for reasons favourable to your Nephew Lovelace. But be the answer what it will, it can do *him* no hurt, nor *me* any good; only that I think I owe it to my former hopes (however deceived in them), and even to charity, that a person, of whom I was once willing to think better, should not prove so egregiously abandoned, as to be wanting, in *every* instance, to that veracity which is indispensable in the character of a gentleman.

Be pleased, madam, to direct to me (keeping the direction a secret for the present) to be left at the Belle Savage on Ludgate Hill, till called for. I am

Your ladyship's most humble servant,
Clarissa Harlowe.

Lady Betty Lawrance to Miss Cl. Harlowe

Saturday, July 1.

Dear Madam,—I find that all is not as it should be between you and my Nephew Lovelace. It will very much afflict me, and all his friends, if he has been guilty of any designed baseness to a lady of your character and merit.

We have been long in expectation of an opportunity to congratulate you and ourselves upon an event most earnestly wished for by us all; since all our hopes of *him* are built upon the power *you* have over him: for, if ever man adored a woman, he is that man, and you, madam, are that woman.

Miss Montague, in her last letter to me, in answer to one of mine, inquiring if she knew from him whether he could call you his, or was likely soon to have that honour, has these words: "I know not what to make of my Cousin Lovelace, as to the point your ladyship is so earnest about. He sometimes says he is actually married to Miss Cl. Harlowe: at other times, that it is her own fault if he be not: he speaks of her not only with love, but with reverence: yet owns that there is a misunderstanding between them; but confesses that she is wholly faultless."

This is what my Niece Montague writes.

God grant, my dearest young lady, that he may not have so heinously offended you that you *cannot* forgive him! If you are not already married, and refuse to be his, I shall lose all hopes that he ever will marry, or be the man I wish him to be. So will Lord M. So will Lady Sarah Sadleir.

I will now answer your questions: but, indeed, I hardly know what to write, for fear of widening still more the unhappy difference between you. But yet such a young lady must command everything from me. This then is my answer:

I wrote not any letter to him on or about the 7th of June.

Neither I nor my steward know such a man as Captain Tomlinson.

I wrote not to my niece to meet me at Reading, nor to accompany me to my Cousin Leeson's in town.

My Chancery affair, though, like most Chancery affairs, it be of long standing, is nevertheless now in so good a way that it cannot give me occasion to go to town.

Nor have I been in town these six months: nor at Hampstead for several years.

Neither shall I have any temptation to go to town, except to pay my congratulatory compliments to Mrs. Lovelace. On which occasion I should go with the greatest pleasure; and should hope for the favour of your accompanying me to Glenham Hall, for a month at least.

Be what will the reason of your inquiry, let me entreat you, my dear young lady, for Lord M.'s sake; for my sake; for this giddy man's sake, soul as well as body; and for all our family's sakes; not to suffer this answer to widen differences so far as to make you refuse him, if he already has not the honour of calling you his; as I am apprehensive he has not, by your signing by your family name.

And here let me offer to you my mediation to compose the difference between you, be it what it will. Your cause, my dear young lady, cannot be put into the hands of anybody living more devoted to your service, than into those of

Your sincere admirer, and humble servant,

Eliz. Lawrance.

MISS CLARISSA HARLOWE TO MRS. HODGES

Enfield, June 29.

MRS. HODGES,—I am under a kind of necessity to write to you, having no one among my relations to whom I dare write, or hope a line from, if I did. It is but to answer a question. It is this:

Whether you know such a man as Captain Tomlinson? And, if you do, whether he be very intimate with my Uncle Harlowe?

I must desire you, Mrs. Hodges, that you will not let my uncle, nor any of my relations, know that I write to you.

You used to say that you would be glad to have it in your power to serve me. That, indeed, was in my prosperity. But I dare say you will not refuse me in a particular that will oblige me without hurting yourself.

Direct, for a particular reason, to Mrs. Dorothy Salcomb, to be left till called for, at the Four Swans Inn, Bishopsgate Street.

You know my handwriting well enough, were not the contents of the letter sufficient to excuse my name, or any other subscription, than that of

Your Friend.

MRS. HODGES.

Sat., July 1.

MADDAM,—I return you an anser, as you wish me to doe. Master is acquented with no sitch man. I am shure no sitch ever came to our house. And master sturs very little out. He has no harte to stur out.

I axed master, if soe bee he knoed sitch a man as one Captain Tomlinson? But sayed not whirfor I axed. He sed, No, not he.

Your humble sarvant, to wish you well,

Sarah Hodges.

MISS CL. HARLOWE TO LADY BETTY LAWRANCE

Monday, July 3.

MADAM,—I cannot excuse myself from giving your ladyship this one trouble more; to thank you, as I most heartily do, for you kind letter.

I must own to you, madam, that the honour of being related to ladies as eminent for their virtue as for their descent, was at first no small inducement with me to lend an ear to Mr. Lovelace's address.

I had another motive, which I knew would of itself give me merit with your whole family; a presumptuous one, in the hope that I might be an humble means in the hand of Providence to reclaim a man who had, as I thought, good sense enough at bottom to be reclaimed; or at least gratitude enough to acknowledge the intended obligation, whether the generous hope were to succeed or not.

But I have been most egregiously mistaken in Mr. Lovelace; the only man, I persuade myself, pretending to be a gentleman, in whom I could have been so *much* mistaken: for while I was endeavouring to save a drowning wretch, I have been, not accidentally, but premeditatedly, and of set purpose, drawn in after him. And he has had the glory to add to the list of those he has ruined, a name that, I will be bold to say, would not have disparaged his own. And this, madam, by means that would shock humanity to be made acquainted with.

My whole end is served by your ladyship's answer to the questions I took the liberty to put to you in writing. Nor have I a wish to make the unhappy man more odious to you than is necessary to excuse myself for absolutely declining your offered mediation.

When your ladyship shall be informed of the following particulars:

That after he had compulsatorily, as I may say, tricked me into the act of going off with him, he could carry me to one of the vilest houses, as it proved, in London:

That he could be guilty of a wicked attempt, in resentment of which I found means to escape from him to Hampstead:

That, after he had found me out there (I know not how), he could procure two women, dressed out richly, to personate your ladyship and Miss Montague; who, under pretence of engaging me to make a visit in town to your Cousin Leeson (promising to return with me that evening to Hampstead), betrayed me back again to the vile house: where, again made a prisoner, I was first robbed of my senses; and then of my honour. Why should I seek to conceal that disgrace from others which I cannot hide from myself?

When your ladyship shall know that, in the shocking progress to this ruin, wilful falsehoods, repeated forgeries (particularly of one letter from your ladyship, another from Miss Montague, and a third from Lord M.), and numberless perjuries, were not the least of his crimes:

You will judge that I can have no principles that will make me worthy of an alliance with ladies of yours and your noble sister's character, if I could not from my soul declare that such an alliance can never *now* take place.

Your ladyship's grateful and obliged servant,

Clarissa Harlowe.

MISS CLARISSA HARLOWE TO MRS. NORTON

Sunday Evening, July 2.

HOW KINDLY, my beloved Mrs. Norton, do you soothe the anguish of a bleeding heart! Surely you are mine own mother; and, by some unaccountable mistake, I must have been laid to a family that, having newly found out, or at least suspected, the imposture, cast me from their hearts, with the indignation that such a discovery will warrant.

But that I may not make you think me more guilty than I am, give me leave briefly to assure you, that when my story is known I shall be entitled to more compassion than blame, even on the score of going away with Mr. Lovelace.

Although your son should recover, I charge you, my dear Mrs. Norton, that you do not think of coming to me. I don't know still, but your mediation with my mother (although at present your interposition would be so little attended to) may be of use to procure me the revocation of that most dreadful part of my father's curse, which only remains to be fulfilled.

Let me briefly say that it is necessary to my present and future hopes that you keep well with my family. And moreover, should you come, I may be traced out by that means by the most abandoned of men.

Then the people I am now with seem to be both honest and humane: and there is in the same house a widow lodger, of low fortunes, but of great merit—almost such another serious and good woman as the dear one to whom I am now writing; who has, as she says, given over all other thoughts of the world but such as shall assist her to leave it happily.

You are very obliging in your offer of money. But although I was forced to leave my clothes behind me, yet I took several things of value with me, which will keep me from present want.

But what shall I do if my father cannot be prevailed upon to recall his malediction? O my dear Mrs. Norton, what a weight must a father's curse have upon a heart so apprehensive as mine!

I *can* little account *to myself* for my silence to you, my kind, my dear maternal friend! I was very desirous, for your sake, as well as for my own, that you should have it to say that we did not correspond: had they thought we did, every word you could have dropped in my favour would have been rejected; and my mother would have been forbid to see you, or to pay any regard to what you should say.

But I might have written to you for advice, in my precarious situation, perhaps you will think. But, indeed, my dear Mrs. Norton, I was not lost for want of advice. And this will appear clear to you from what I have already hinted, were I to explain myself no further: for what need had the cruel spoiler to have had recourse to unprecedented arts—I will speak out plainer still (but you must not at present report it), to stupefying potions, and to the most brutal and outrageous force, had I been wanting in my duty?

I am sorry, for your sake, to leave off so heavily.

Let me desire you to be secret in what I have communicated to you; at least till you have my consent to divulge it.

Your ever dutiful

Cl. Harlowe.

Mrs. Norton to Miss Clarissa Harlowe

Monday Night, July 3.

Oh, the barbarous villainy of this detestable man!

And is there a man in the world who could offer violence to so sweet a creature!

And are you sure you are now out of his reach?

You command me to keep secret the particulars of the vile treatment you have met with; or else, upon an unexpected visit which Miss Harlowe favoured me with, soon after I had received your melancholy letter, I should have been tempted to own I had heard from you, and to have communicated to her such parts of your two letters as would have demonstrated your penitence, and your earnestness to obtain the revocation of your father's malediction, as well as his protection from outrages that may still be offered to you. But then your sister would probably have expected a sight of the letters, and even to have been permitted to take them with her to the family.

Yet they *must* one day be acquainted with the sad story: and it is impossible but they must pity you, and forgive you, when they know your early penitence, and your unprecedented sufferings; and that you have fallen by the brutal force of a barbarous ravisher, and not by the vile arts of a seducing lover.

The wicked man gives it out at Lord M.'s, as Miss Harlowe tells me, that he is actually married to you: yet she believes it not; nor had I the heart to let her know the truth.

She put it close to me, whether I had not corresponded with you from the time of your going away? I could safely tell her (as I did) that I had not: but I said, that I was well informed that you took extremely to heart your father's imprecation; and that, if she would excuse me, I would say it would be a kind and sisterly part, if she would use her interest to get you discharged from it.

I need not, I am sure, exhort you to despise such a man as this; since not to be able to do so, would be a reflection upon a sex to which you have always been an honour.

My heart labours under a *double* affliction: for my poor boy is very, *very* bad—a violent fever—nor can it be brought to intermit—pray for *him,* my dearest miss—for his recovery, if God see fit. I hope God *will* see fit. If not (how can I bear to suppose that!), pray for *me,* that He will give me that patience and resignation which I have been wishing to you.

Your ever affectionate
Judith Norton.

Miss Cl. Harlowe to Mrs. Judith Norton

Thursday, July 6.

You need not, you say, exhort me to despise such a man as him by whom I have suffered—indeed you need not: for I would choose the cruellest death rather than to be his. And yet, my dear Mrs. Norton, I will own to you, *that once I could have loved him—ungrateful man! had he permitted me to love him, I* once *could have loved him.*

O my beloved Mrs. Norton, you cannot imagine what I have suffered! But indeed my heart is broken! I am sure I shall not live to take possession of that independence, which you think would enable me to atone in some measure for my past conduct.

While this is my opinion, you may believe I shall not be easy till I can obtain a last forgiveness.

I will write. But to *whom* is my doubt.

Yet were I able to engage my mother's pity, would it not be a means to make *her* still more unhappy than I have already made her, by the opposition she would meet with, were she to try to give force to that pity?

To my sister then, I think, I will apply—yet how hard-hearted has my sister been! But I will not ask for protection; and yet I am in hourly dread that I shall want protection. All I will ask for at present (preparative to the last forgiveness I will implore) shall be only to be freed from the heavy curse that seems to have operated as far as it *can* operate as to *this* life.

But why do I thus add to your distresses? It is not, my dear Mrs. Norton, that I have so *much* feeling for my *own* calamity that I have *none* for *yours:* since yours is indeed an addition to my own. But you have one consolation (a very great one) which I have not: that *your* afflictions, whether respecting your *more* or your *less* deserving child, rise not from any fault of your own.

Your truly sympathizing and dutiful

Clarissa Harlowe.

MISS HOWE TO CLARISSA HARLOWE

Wednesday, July 5.

MY DEAR CLARISSA,—I have at last heard from you from a quarter I little expected.

From my mother.

She had for some time seen me uneasy and grieving; and justly supposed it was about you. And this morning dropped a hint, which made me conjecture that she must have heard something of you more than I knew. And when she found that this added to my uneasiness, she owned she had a letter in her hands of yours, dated the 29th of June, directed for me.

You may guess that this occasioned a little warmth that could not be wished for by either.

In short, *she* resented that I should disobey her: *I* was as much concerned that she should open and withhold from me *my* letters: and at last she was pleased to compromise the matter with me by giving up the letter, and permitting me to write to you *once* or *twice;* she to see the contents of what I wrote. For, besides the value she has for you, she could not but have a great curiosity to know the occasion of so sad a situation as your melancholy letter shows you to be in.

(But I shall get her to be satisfied with hearing me read what I write; putting in between hooks, thus ( ), what I intend not to read to her.)

Need I to remind you, Miss Clarissa Harlowe, of *three* letters I wrote to you, to none of which I had any answer; except to the *first,* and that a few lines only, promising a letter at large; though you were well enough, the day after you received my *second,* to go joyfully back again with him to the vile house? But more of these by and by. I must hasten to take notice of your letter of Wednesday last week; which you could *contrive* should fall into my mother's hands.

Let me tell you that that letter has almost broken my heart. Good God! what have you brought yourself to, Miss Clarissa Harlowe? Could I have believed, that after you had escaped from the miscreant (with such mighty pains and earnestness escaped), and after such an attempt as he had made, you would have been prevailed upon not only to forgive him, but (without being married too) to return with him to that horrid house!—A house I had given you such an account of!—Surprising! What an intoxicating thing is *this love?* I *always* feared that you, even you, were not proof against its *inconsistent* effects.

Your intellect is touched! I am sure my heart bleeds for you: but, excuse me, my dear, I doubt your intellect was touched before you left Hampstead; or you would never have let him find you out there; or, when he did, suffer him to prevail upon you to return to the horrid brothel.

I tell you, I sent you *three letters:* the *first* of which, dated the 7th and 8th of June (for it was written at twice), came safe to your hands, as you sent me word by a few lines dated the 9th: had it not, I should have doubted my own safety; since in it I gave you such an account of the abominable house, and threw such cautions in your way in relation to that Tomlinson, as the more surprised me that you could think of going back to it again, after you had escaped from it, and from Lovelace—O my dear!

The *second,* dated June 10, was given into your own hand at Hampstead, on Sunday the 11th, as you was lying upon a couch, in a strange way, according to my messenger's account of you, bloated, and flush-coloured; I don't know how.

The *third* was dated the 20th of June. Having not heard one word from you since the promising billet of the 9th, I own I did not spare you in it. I ventured it by the usual conveyance, by that Wilson's, having no other: so cannot be sure you received it.

You have heard that I have been ill, you say. I had a cold,

indeed; but it was so slight a one that it confined me not an hour. But I doubt not that strange things you have *heard,* and *been told,* to induce you to take the step you took.

My mother tells me she sent you an answer, desiring you not to write to me, because it would grieve me. To be sure I *am* grieved; *exceedingly* grieved; and, *disappointed* too, you must permit me to say.

My love for you, and my concern for your honour, may possibly have made me a little of the severest: if you think so, place it to its proper account; to *that* love, and to *that* concern: which will but do justice to

Your afflicted and faithful

A. H.

P.S. My mother has so much real concern for your misfortunes, that, thinking it will be a consolation to *you,* and that it will oblige *me,* she consents that you shall write to me the *particulars at large of your sad story:* but it is on condition that I show her all that has passed between us, relating to yourself and the vilest of men.

God grant that you may be able to clear your conduct *after* you had escaped from Hampstead; as all *before* that time was noble, generous, and prudent: the man a devil, and you a saint!

MISS CLARISSA HARLOWE TO MISS HOWE

Thursday, July 6.

WHAT WOULD I have given for weeks past for the favour of a letter from my dear Miss Howe, in whose friendship I placed all my remaining comfort? Little did I think that the next letter she would honour me with, should be in such a style as should make me look more than once at the subscription, that I might be sure (the name not being written at length) that it was not signed by another A. H. For surely, thought I, this is my sister Arabella's style.

But what have *I,* sunk in my fortunes; my character forfeited; my honour lost (while *I* know it, I care not *who* knows it); destitute of friends, and even of hope; what have *I* to do to show a spirit of repining and expostulation to a dear friend, because she is not *more* kind than a sister?

I find, by the rising bitterness which will mingle with the gall in my ink, that I am not yet subdued enough to my condition: and so, begging your pardon, that I should rather have formed my expectations of favour from the indulgence you *used* to show me, than from what I *now deserve* to have shown me, I will endeavour to give a particular answer to your letter; although it will take me up too much time to think of sending it by your messenger to-morrow: he can put off his journey, he says, till Saturday.

You tell me that in your first letter you gave me such an account of the vile house I was in, and such cautions about that Tomlinson, as make you wonder how I could think of going back.

Alas, my dear! I was tricked, most vilely tricked back, as you shall hear in its place.

Without *knowing* the house was so very *vile* a house from your *intended* information, I disliked the people too much, ever *voluntarily* to have returned to it. But had you really written such cautions about Tomlinson, and the house, as you seem to have *purposed* to do, they must, had they come in time, have been of infinite service to me. But not one word of either, whatever was your *intention,* did you mention to me, in that *first* of the *three* letters you so warmly TELL ME you *did* send me. *I will enclose it to convince you.*[1]

But your account of your messenger's delivering to me your second letter, and the description he gives of me, as *lying upon a couch, in a strange way, bloated and flush-coloured, you don't know how,* absolutely puzzles and confounds me.

Lord have mercy upon the poor Clarissa Harlowe! What can this mean! *Who* was the messenger you sent? Was *he* one of Lovelace's creatures too!

But indeed, I know nothing of ANY messenger from you.

Believing myself secure at Hampstead, I stayed longer there than I would have done, in hopes of the letter promised me in your short one of the 9th, brought me by my own messenger,

[1] The letter she encloses was Mr. Lovelace's forged one.

in which you undertake to send for and engage Mrs. Townsend in my favour.

I wondered I heard not from you: and was told you were sick; and, at another time, that your mother and you had had words on my account, and that you had refused to admit Mr. Hickman's visits upon it: so that I supposed, at one time, that you was not *able* to write; at another, that your mother's prohibition had its *due* force with you. But now I have no doubt that the wicked man must have intercepted your letter; and I wish he found not means to *corrupt your messenger* to tell you so strange a story.

It was on Sunday, June 11, you say, that the man gave it me. I was at church twice that day with Mrs. Moore.

Allow me a little pause, my dear, at this place.

[Clarissa continues her narrative to Miss Howe as from the moment she found herself tricked back to the vile Mrs. Sinclair's house. Ed.]

And thus was led the poor sacrifice into the old wretch's too well-known parlour.

The called-for tea was ready presently.

I was made to drink two dishes, with milk, complaisantly urged by the pretended ladies helping me each to one. I was stupid to their hands; and, when I took the tea, almost choked with vapours; and could hardly swallow.

I thought, *transiently* thought, that the tea, the last dish particularly, had an odd taste. They, on my palating it, observed that the milk was *London milk;* far short in goodness of what they were accustomed to from their own dairies.

I have no doubt that my two dishes were prepared for me; in which case it was more proper for their purpose, that *they* should help me, than that I should help *myself*. Ill before, I found myself still more and more disordered in my head; a heavy torpid pain increasing fast upon me. But I imputed it to my terror.

Nevertheless, at the pretended lady's motion, I went upstairs, attended by Dorcas; who affected to weep for joy that once more she saw my *blessed* face, that was the vile creature's word;

and immediately I set about taking out some of my clothes, ordering what should be put up, and what sent after me.

While I was thus employed, up came the pretended Lady Betty, in a hurrying way. My dear, you won't be long before you are ready. My nephew is very busy in writing answers to his letters: so, I'll just whip away, and change my dress, and call upon you in an instant.

O madam! I *am* ready! I am *now* ready! You must not leave me here: and down I sunk, affrighted, into a chair.

This instant, this instant, I will return—before you can be ready—before you can have packed up your things—we would not be late—don't let us be late.

And away she hurried before I could say another word. Her pretended niece went with her, without taking notice to me of her going.

I had no suspicion yet that these women were not indeed the ladies they personated; and I blamed myself for my weak fears.

So, recovering my stupefied spirits, as well as they could be recovered (for I was heavier and heavier; and wondered to Dorcas what ailed me; rubbing my eyes, and taking some of her snuff, pinch after pinch, to very little purpose), I pursued my employment: but when that was over, all packed up that I designed to be packed up; and I had nothing to do but to *think;* and found them tarry so long; I thought I should have gone distracted. I shut myself into the chamber that had been mine; I kneeled, I prayed; yet knew not what I prayed for: then ran out again: It was almost dark night, I said: where, where was Mr. Lovelace?

He came to me, taking no notice at first of my consternation and wildness (what they had given me made me incoherent and wild): All goes well, said he, my dear! A line from Captain Tomlinson!

All indeed did go well for the villainous project of the most cruel and most villainous of men!

I *demanded* his aunt! I *demanded* his cousin! The evening, I said, was closing! My head was very, *very* bad, I remember I said—and it grew worse and worse.

Terror, however, as yet kept up my spirits; and I insisted upon his going himself to hasten them.

He called his servant.

He ordered him to fly to his Cousin Leeson's, and to let Lady Betty and his cousin know how uneasy we both were at their delay: adding, of his own accord, Desire them, if they don't come instantly, to send their coach, and we will go without them.

I thought this was considerably and fairly put. But now, indifferent as my head was, I had a little time to consider the man and his behaviour. He terrified me with his looks, and with his violent emotions, as he gazed upon me. His sentences short, and pronounced as if his breath were touched. Never saw I his abominable eyes look as then they looked—triumph in them!—fierce and wild; and more disagreeable than the women's at the vile house appeared to me when I first saw them: and at times, such a leering, mischief-boding cast! Yet his behaviour was decent—a decency, however, that I might have seen to be struggled for—for he snatched my hand two or three times, with a vehemence in his grasp that hurt me; speaking words of tenderness through his shut teeth, as it seemed; and let it go with a beggar-voiced humble accent, like the vile woman's just before; half-inward; yet his words and manner carrying the appearance of strong and almost convulsed passion!

I complained once or twice of thirst. My mouth seemed parched. At the time, I supposed that it was my terror (gasping often as I did for breath) that parched up the roof of my mouth. I called for water: some table-beer was brought me: beer, I suppose, was a better vehicle (if I were not dosed enough before) for their potions. I told the maid that she knew I seldom tasted malt-liquor: yet, suspecting nothing of this nature, being extremely thirsty, I drank it, as what came next: and instantly, as it were, found myself much worse than before; as if inebriated, I should fancy: I know not how.

His servant was gone twice as long as he needed: and just before his return, came one of the pretended Lady Betty's with a letter for Mr. Lovelace.

He sent it up to me. I read it: and then it was that I thought myself a lost creature; it being to put off her going to Hampstead that night, on account of violent fits which Miss Montague was pretended to be seized with; for then immediately came into my head his vile attempt upon me in this house; the revenge that my flight might too probably inspire him with on that occasion, and because of the difficulty I made to forgive him, and to be reconciled to him; his very looks wild and dreadful to me; and the women of the house such as I had more reason than ever, even from the pretended Lady Betty's hint, to be afraid of: all these crowding together in my apprehensive mind, I fell into a kind of frenzy.

I have not remembrance how I was for the time it lasted: but I know that, in my first agitations, I pulled off my head-dress, and tore my ruffles in twenty tatters, and ran to find him out.

When a little recovered, I insisted upon the hint he had given of their coach. But the messenger, he said, had told him that it was sent to fetch a physician, lest his chariot should be put up, or not ready.

I then insisted upon going directly to Lady Betty's lodgings.

Mrs. Leeson's was now a crowded house, he said: and as my earnestness could be owing to nothing but groundless apprehension (and O what vows, what protestations of his honour did he then make!), he hoped I would not add to their present concern. Charlotte, indeed, was used to fits, he said, upon any great surprises, whether of joy or grief; and they would hold her for a week together, if not got off in a few hours.

All impatient with grief and apprehension, I still declared myself resolved not to stay in that house till morning. All I had in the world, my rings, my watch, my little money, for a coach; or, if one were not to be got, I would go on foot to Hampstead that night, though I walked it by myself.

A coach was hereupon sent for, or pretended to be sent for. Any price, he said, he would give to oblige me, late as it was; and he would attend me with all his soul. But no coach was to be got.

Let me cut short the rest. I grew worse and worse in my head; now stupid, now raving, now senseless. The vilest of vile women was brought to frighten me.

I remember I pleaded for mercy. I remember that I said *I would be his—indeed I would be his*—to obtain his mercy. But no mercy found I! My strength, my intellects, failed me—and then such scenes followed—O my dear, such dreadful scenes!—

fits upon fits (faintly indeed and imperfectly remembered) procuring me no compassion—but death was withheld from me. That would have been too great a mercy!

. . . . . .

Thus was I tricked and deluded back by blacker hearts of my own sex than I thought there were in the world; who appeared to me to be persons of honour: and, when in his power, thus barbarously was I treated by this villainous man!

The very hour that I found myself in a place of safety, I took pen to write to you. The apprehensions I had lain under, that I should not be able to get away; the fatigue I had in effecting my escape; the difficulty of procuring a lodging for myself;—these, together with the recollection of what I had suffered from him, and my farther apprehensions of my insecurity, and my desolate circumstances, had so disordered me, that I remember I rambled strangely in that letter.

The letter I received from your mother was a dreadful blow to me. But nevertheless it had the good effect upon me (labouring, as I did just then, under a violent fit of vapourish despondency, and almost yielding to it) which profuse bleeding and blisterings have in paralytical or apoplectical strokes; reviving my attention, and restoring me to spirits to combat the evils I was surrounded by—sluicing off, and diverting into a new channel the overcharging woes which threatened once more to overwhelm my intellects.

She then gives the substance of the letters she wrote to Mrs. Norton, to Lady Betty Lawrance, and to Mrs. Hodges; as also of their answers; whereby she detected all Mr. Lovelace's impostures. She proceeds as follows:

And now, honoured madam, and my dearest Miss Howe, who are to sit in judgment upon my case, permit me to lay down my pen with one request, which, with the greatest earnestness, I make to you both: and that is, That you will neither of you open your lips in relation to the potions and the violences I have hinted at. Not that I am solicitous that my disgrace should be hidden from the world, or that it should not be generally known that the man has proved a villain to me: for this, it seems, everybody but myself expected from his character. But suppose as his actions by me are really of a *capital nature,* it were insisted upon that I should appear to prosecute him and his accomplices in a court of justice, how do you think I could bear that?

But since my character, *before* the capital enormity, was lost in the eye of the world; and that from the very hour I left my father's house; and since all my own hopes of worldly happiness are entirely over; let me slide quietly into my grave; and let it not be remembered, except by one friendly tear, and no more, dropped from your gentle eye, mine own dear Anna Howe, on the happy day that shall shut up all my sorrows, that there was such a creature as

Clarissa Harlowe.

Saturday, July 8.

MISS HOWE TO MISS CLARISSA HARLOWE

Sunday, July 9.

MAY HEAVEN signalize its vengeance, in the face of all the world, upon the most abandoned and profligate of men!

The letter you sent me enclosed as mine, of the 7th of June, is a villainous forgery. The hand, indeed, is astonishingly like mine; and the cover, I see, is actually my cover: but yet the letter is not so exactly imitated, but that (had you had any suspicions about his vileness at the time) you, who so well know my hand, might have detected it.

Apprehensive for *both* our safeties from the villainy of such a daring and profligate contriver, I must call upon you, my dear, to resolve upon taking legal vengeance of the infernal wretch.

She then gives the particulars of the report made by the young fellow whom she sent to Hampstead with her letter; and who supposed he had delivered it into her own hand.

I enclose not only the rough draft of my long letter mentioned above; but the heads of that which the young fellow thought he delivered into your own hands at Hampstead. And when you have perused them, I will leave you to judge how much reason I had to be surprised that you wrote me not an answer to either of those letters; one of which you owned you had received (though it proved to be his forged one); the other delivered into your own hands, as I was assured; and both of them of so much concern to your honour; and still how much more surprised I must be, when I received a letter from Mrs. Townsend, dated June 15, from Hampstead, importing, "That Mr. Lovelace, who had been with you several days, had, on the Monday before, brought Lady Betty and his cousin, richly dressed, and in a coach and four, to visit you: who, with your own consent, had carried you to town with them—to your former lodgings; where you still were: that the Hampstead women believed you to be married; and reflected upon me as a fomenter of differences between man and wife: that he himself was at Hampstead the day before; viz. Wednesday the 14th; and boasted of his happiness with you.

What a fatality, my dear, has appeared in your case, from the very beginning till this hour! Had my mother permitted——

But can I blame *her;* when you have a *father* and *mother* living, who have so much to answer for? So much! as no father and mother, considering the child they have driven, persecuted, exposed, renounced, ever had to answer for!

Monday, July 10.

I now, my dearest friend, resume my pen, to obey my mother, in giving you her opinion upon your unhappy story.

She still harps upon the old string, and will have it that all your calamities are owing to your first fatal step; for she believes (what I cannot) that your relations had intended, after one general trial more, to comply with your aversion, if they had found it as riveted a one, as, let me say, it was a folly to suppose it would not be found to be, after so many *ridiculously* repeated experiments.

As to your latter sufferings from that vilest of miscreants, she is unalterably of opinion, that if all be as you have related (which she doubts not) with regard to the potions, and to the violences you have sustained, you ought, by all means, to set on foot a prosecution against him, and against his devilish accomplices.

If, inferred she, such complicated villainy as this (where perjury, potions, forgery, subornation, are all combined to effect the ruin of an innocent creature, and to dishonour a family of eminence, and where those very crimes, as may be supposed, are proofs of her innocence) is to go off with impunity, what case will deserve to be brought into judgment; or what malefactor ought to be hanged?

For her own part, she declares that were *she* your mother she would forgive you upon no other terms: and, upon your compliance with these, she herself will undertake to reconcile all your family to you.

. . . . . .

My mother will have me add that she must *insist* upon your prosecuting the villain. She repeats that she makes that a condition on which she permits our future correspondence. I asked her if she would be willing that I should appear to support you in court if you complied? By all means, she said, if that would induce you to begin with him, and with the horrid women.

I am, and ever will be,

Your affectionate and faithful

Anna Howe.

Monday, July 10.

I cannot, my dearest friend, suffer the enclosed to go unaccompanied by a few lines, to signify to you that they are both less tender in some places than I would have written, had they not been to pass my mother's inspection. The principal reason, however, of my writing thus separately is, to beg of you to permit me to send you money and necessaries; which you must needs want: and that you will let me know if either I, or *anybody I can influence,* can be of service to you.

Your ever devoted

Anna Howe.

Once more forgive me, my dearest creature, for my barbarous tauntings in mine of the 5th!

Miss Clarissa Harlowe to Miss Howe

Tuesday, July 11.

Forgive you, my dear! Most cordially do I forgive you. I most heartily thank you, my best and only love, for the opportunity you gave me of clearing it up; and for being generously ready to acquit me of intentional blame, the moment you had read my melancholy narrative.

As you are so earnest to have all the particulars of my sad story before you, I will, if life and spirits be lent me, give you an ample account of all that has befallen me. But this, it is very probable, you will not see, till after the close of my last scene.

And indeed, my *dear* friend, I do so earnestly wish for the last closing scene, and with so much comfort find myself in a declining way, that I even sometimes ungratefully regret that naturally healthy constitution, which used to double upon me all my enjoyments.

As to the earnestly recommended prosecution, I may possibly touch upon it more largely hereafter, if ever I shall have better spirits; for they are at present extremely sunk and low. But, just now, I will only say that I would sooner suffer every evil (the repetition of the capital one excepted) than appear publicly in a court to do myself justice. And I am heartily grieved that your mother prescribes such a measure as the condition of our future correspondence: for the continuance of your friendship, my dear, and the desire I had to correspond with you to my life's end, were all my remaining hopes and consolation.

O my dear! what would I give to obtain a revocation of my father's malediction! A reconciliation is not to be hoped for. You, who never loved my father, may think my solicitude on this head a weakness: but the *motive* for it, sunk as my spirits *at times* are, is not *always* weak.

. . . .

I have written a letter to Miss Rawlins of Hampstead; the answer to which, just now received, has helped me to the knowledge of the vile contrivance by which this wicked man got your letter of June the 10th.

And, for fear of being traced by Mr. Lovelace, I directed her to superscribe her answer, To Mrs. Mary Atkins; to be left till called for, at the Belle Savage Inn, on Ludgate Hill.

In her answer she tells me "that the vile wretch prevailed upon Mrs. Bevis to personate me, and persuaded her to lie along on a couch: a handkerchief over her neck and face; pretending to be ill; the credulous woman drawn in by false notions of your ill offices to keep up a variance between a man and his wife—and so taking the letter from your messenger as me.

I thank you, my dear, for the drafts of your two letters which were intercepted by this horrid man. I see the great advantage they were of to him, in the prosecution of his villainous designs against the poor wretch whom he has so long made the sport of his abhorred inventions.

Adieu, my dearest friend! May *you* be happy! And then your Clarissa cannot be wholly miserable!

Miss Howe to Miss Clarissa Harlowe

Wedn. Night, July 12.

I write, my dearest creature, I cannot *but* write, to express my concern on your dejection. Let me beseech you, my charming excellence, let me beseech you, not to give way to it.

Comfort yourself, on the contrary, in the triumphs of a virtue unsullied; a will wholly faultless. Who could have withstood the trials that you have surmounted? Your Cousin Morden will soon come. He will see justice done you, I make no doubt, as well with regard to what concerns your person as your estate. And many happy days may you yet see; and much good may you still do, if you will not heighten unavoidable accidents into guilty despondency.

But why, my dear, this pining solicitude continued after a reconciliation with relations as unworthy as implacable; whose wills are governed by an all-grasping brother, who finds his account in keeping the breach open? On this over-solicitude it is now plain to me that the vilest of men built all his schemes. He saw that you thirsted after it beyond all reason for hope. The view, the hope, I own, extremely desirable, had your family been Christians; or even had they been pagans who had bowels.

I shall send this short letter by *young* Rogers, as we call him; the fellow I sent to you to Hampstead; an innocent, though pragmatical rustic. Admit him, I pray you, into your presence, that he may report to me how you look, and how you are.

Mr. Hickman should attend you; but I apprehend that all his motions, and mine own too, are watched by the execrable wretch: as indeed his are by an agent of mine; for I own that I am so apprehensive of his plots and revenge, now I know that he has intercepted my vehement letters against him, that he is the subject of my dreams, as well as of my waking fears.

. . . . . .

My mother, at my earnest importunity, has just given me leave to write, and to receive your letters—but fastened this condition upon the concession, that yours must be under cover to Mr. Hickman (this with a view, I suppose, to give him consideration with me); and upon this further condition, that she is to see all we write.

Pray let me know what the people are with whom you lodge? Shall I send Mrs. Townsend to direct you to lodgings either more safe or more convenient for you?

Adieu, my dearest creature. Comfort *yourself*, as you would in the like unhappy circumstances comfort

Your own
Anna Howe.

Miss Clarissa Harlowe to Miss Howe

Thursday, July 13.

I am extremely concerned, my dear Miss Howe, for being primarily the occasion of the apprehensions you have of this wicked man's vindictive attempts. What a wide-spreading error is mine!

If I find that he sets on foot any machination against you, or against Mr. Hickman, I do assure you I will consent to prosecute him, although I were sure I should not survive my first appearance at the bar he should be arraigned at.

I own the justice of your mother's arguments on that subject; but must say that I think there are circumstances in my particular case which will excuse me, although on a slighter occasion than that you are apprehensive of I should decline to appear against him.

Your messenger has now *indeed* seen me. I talked with him on the cheat put upon him at Hampstead: and am sorry to have reason to say, that had not the poor young man been very *simple*, and very *self-sufficient*, he had not been so grossly deluded.

I think I cannot be more private than where I am. I hope I am safe. All the risk I run, is in going out and returning from morning prayers; which I have two or three times ventured to do; once at Lincoln's Inn Chapel, at eleven; once at St. Dunstan's, Fleet Street, at seven in the morning, in a chair both times; and twice, at six in the morning, at the neighbouring church in Covent Garden. The wicked wretches I have escaped from will not, I hope, come to church to look for me; especially at so early prayers; and I have fixed upon the privatest pew in the latter *church* to hide myself in; and perhaps I may lay out a little matter in an ordinary gown, by way of disguise; my face half hid by my mob. I am very careless, my dear, of my appearance now. Neat and clean takes up the whole of my attention.

The man's name at whose house I lodge is Smith—a glove-*maker,* as well as *seller*. His wife is the shopkeeper. A dealer also in stockings, ribbands, snuff, and perfumes. A matron-like woman, plain-hearted, and prudent. The husband an honest, industrious man.

Two neat rooms, with plain, but clean furniture, on the first floor, are mine; one they call the dining-room.

There is, up another pair of stairs, a very worthy widow lodger, Mrs. Lovick by name; who, although of low fortunes, is much respected, as Mrs. Smith assures me, by people of condition of her acquaintance, for her piety, prudence, and understanding. With her I propose to be well acquainted.

I thank you, my dear, for your kind, your seasonable advice and consolation. I hope I shall have more grace given me than to despond, in the *religious* sense of the word: especially as I can apply to myself the comfort you give me, that neither my will, nor my inconsiderateness, has contributed to my calamity. But, nevertheless, the irreconcilableness of my relations, whom I love with an unabated reverence; my apprehensions of fresh violences (this wicked man, I doubt, will not yet let me rest); my being destitute of protection; my youth, my sex, my unacquaintedness with the world, subjecting me to insults; my reflections on the scandal I have given, added to the sense of the indignities I have received from a man of whom I deserved not ill; all together will undoubtedly bring on the effect that cannot be undesirable to me.

At present my head is much disordered. I have not indeed enjoyed it with any degree of clearness since the violence done to that, and to my heart too, by the wicked arts of the abandoned creatures I was cast among.

All I will at present add, are my thanks to your mother for her indulgence to us; due compliments to Mr. Hickman; and my request that you will believe me to be, to my last hour, and beyond it, if possible, my beloved friend, and my *dearer* self (for what is now my self?)

Your obliged and affectionate
Clarissa Harlowe.

MR. LOVELACE TO JOHN BELFORD, ESQ.

Friday, July 7.

I HAVE three of thy letters at once before me to answer; in each of which thou complainest of my silence; and in one of them tellest me that thou canst not live without I scribble to thee every day, or every other day at least.

Why, then, die, Jack, if thou wilt. What heart, thinkest thou, can I have to write, when I have lost the only subject worth writing upon?

Help me again to my angel, to my CLARISSA; and thou shalt have a letter from me, or writing at least, part of a letter, every hour. All that the charmer of my heart shall say, that will I put down: every motion, every air of her beloved person, every look, will I try to describe; and when she is silent I will endeavour to tell thee her thoughts, either what they are, or what I would have them to be—so that, having *her,* I shall never want a subject. Having lost her, my whole soul is a blank: the whole creation round me, the elements above, beneath, and everything I *behold* (for nothing can *I enjoy*), are a blank without her!

Oh, return, return, thou only charmer of my soul! Return to thy adoring Lovelace! What is the light, what the air, what the town, what the country, what's anything, without thee? Light, air, joy, harmony, in my notion, are but parts of thee; and could they be all expressed in one word, that word would be CLARISSA.

O my beloved CLARISSA, return thou then; once more return to bless thy LOVELACE, who now, by the loss of thee, knows the value of the jewel he has slighted; and rises every morning but to curse the sun that shines upon everybody but him!

. . . . . .

Well, but, Jack, 'tis a surprising thing to me that the dear fugitive cannot be met with; cannot be heard of. She is so poor a plotter (for plotting is not her talent) that I am confident, had I been at liberty, I should have found her out before now; although the different emissaries I have employed about town, round the adjacent villages, and in Miss Howe's vicinage, have hitherto failed of success. But my lord continues so weak and low-spirited, that there is no getting from him. I would not disoblige a man whom I think in danger still: for would his gout, now it has got him down, but give him, like a fair boxer, the rising blow, all would be over with him. And here he makes me sit hours together entertaining him with my rogueries (a pretty amusement for a sick man!): and yet, whenever he has the gout, he prays night and morning with his chaplain. But what must *his* notions of religion be, who, after he has nosed and mumbled over his responses, can give a sigh or groan of satisfaction, as if he thought he had made up with Heaven; and return with a new appetite to my stories?—encouraging them, by shaking his sides with laughing at them, and calling me a sad fellow, in such an accent as shows he takes no small delight in his kinsman.

To see such an old Trojan as this, just dropping into the grave, which I hoped ere this would have been dug, and filled up with him; crying out with pain, and grunting with weakness; yet in the same moment crack his leathern face into an horrible laugh, and call a young sinner charming varlet, encoring him, as formerly he used to do the Italian eunuchs; what a preposterous, what an unnatural adherence to old habits!

My two cousins are generally present when I *entertain,* as the old peer calls it.

These are smart girls; they have life and wit; and yesterday, upon Charlotte's raving against me upon a related enterprise, I told her that I had had it in debate several times, whether she were or were not too near of kin to me: and that it was once a moot point with me, whether I could not love her dearly for a month or so: and perhaps it was well for her that another pretty little puss started up and diverted me just as I was entering the course.

MR. LOVELACE TO JOHN BELFORD, ESQ.

Sunday Night, July 9.

NOW, JACK, have I a subject with a vengeance. I am in the very height of my trial for all my sins to my beloved fugitive. For here, to-day, at about five o'clock, arrived Lady Sarah Sadleir and Lady Betty Lawrance, each in her chariot and six.

And now I enter upon my TRIAL

With horrible grave faces was I received. The two antiques only bowed their tabby heads; making longer faces than ordinary; and all the old lines appearing strong in their furrowed foreheads and fallen cheeks. How do you, cousin? and, How do you, Mr. Lovelace? looking all round at one another, as who should say, Do you speak first; and, Do you: for they seemed resolved to lose no time.

I took my seat. Lord M. looked horribly glum; his fingers clasped, and turning round and round, under and over, his but just disgouted thumbs; his sallow face, and goggling eyes, cast upon the floor, on the fireplace, on his two sisters, on his two kinswomen, by turns; but not once deigning to look upon me.

At last, Mr. Lovelace!—Cousin Lovelace!

What's the matter *now,* madam?

The matter now!—Why, Lady Betty has two letters from Miss Harlowe which have told us what's the matter.

Then they all chorused upon me. Such a character as Miss Harlowe's! cried one—A lady of so much generosity and good sense! Another: How charmingly she writes! the two maiden monkeys, looking at her fine handwriting: her perfections my crimes. What can you expect will be the end of these things? cried Lady Sarah. Damned, damned doings! vociferated the peer, shaking his loose-fleshed wabbling chaps, which hung on his shoulders like an old cow's dew-lap.

For my part I hardly knew whether to sing or say what I had to reply to these all-at-once attacks upon me! Fair and softly, ladies. One at a time, I beseech you. I am not to be hunted down without being heard, I hope. Pray let me see these letters.

There they are: that's the first. Read it out, if you can.

I opened a letter from my charmer, dated *Thursday, June 29*, our wedding-day, that was to be, and written to Lady Betty Lawrance.

Well, madam, said I, with as much philosophy as I could assume; and may I ask—Pray, what was your ladyship's answer?

There's a copy of it, tossing it to me, very disrespectfully.

This answer was dated *July 1*.

Well, madam; and, pray, may I be favoured with the lady's other letter? I presume it is in reply to yours.

It is, said the peer: but, sir, let me ask you a few questions before you read it. Give *me* the letter, Lady Betty.

There it is, my lord.

Then on went the spectacles, and his head moved to the lines: A charming pretty hand! I have often heard that this lady is a *genius*.

And so, Jack, repeating my lord's wise comments and questions will let thee into the contents of this merciless letter.

"*Monday, July 3*" (reads my lord).—Let me see! That was last *Monday;* no longer ago! "*Monday, July the third.* Madam—I cannot excuse myself"—um, um, um, um, um, um (humming inarticulately, and skipping),—"I must own to you, madam, that the honour of being related——"

Off went the spectacles. Now, tell me, sir-r, has not this lady lost all the friends she had in the world for your sake?

She has very implacable friends, my lord: we all know that.

But has she not lost them all for your sake? Tell me that.

I believe so, my lord.

Well then! I am glad thou art not so graceless as to deny that.

On went the spectacles again. "I must own to you, madam, that the honour of being related to ladies as eminent for their virtue as for their descent"—*Very pretty, truly!* said my lord, repeating, "*as eminent for their virtue as for their descent*, was, at first, no small inducement with me to lend an ear to Mr. Lovelace's address."

There is dignity, born dignity, in this lady, cried my lord.

Lady Sarah. She would have been a grace to our family.

Lady Betty. Indeed she would.

Lovel. To a *royal* family, I will venture to say.

Lord M. Then what a devil——

Lovel. Please to read on, my lord. It cannot be *her* letter, if it does not make you admire her more and more as you read. Cousin Charlotte, Cousin Patty, pray attend. Read on, my lord.

Miss Charlotte. Amazing fortitude!

Miss Patty only lifted up her dove's eyes.

Lord M. (reading). "And the rather, as I was determined, had it come to effect, to do everything in my power to deserve your favourable opinion."

Then again they chorused upon me!

A blessed time of it, poor I! I had nothing for it but impudence!

Lovel. Pray read on, my lord—I told you how you would all admire her—or, shall I read?

Lord M. Damned assurance! (Then reading.) "I had another motive, which I knew would of itself give me merit with your whole family (*they were all ear*); a presumptuous one; a punishably presumptuous one, as it has proved: in the hope that I might be an humble means in the hands of Providence to reclaim a man who had, as I thought, good sense enough at bottom to be reclaimed; or at least gratitude enough to acknowledge the intended obligation, whether the generous hope were to succeed or not."—Excellent young creature!

Excellent young creature! echoed the ladies, with their handkerchiefs at their eyes, attended with nose-music.

His lordship had pulled off his spectacles to wipe them. His eyes were misty; and he thought the fault in his spectacles.

Lord M. (Again saddling and reading.) "But I have been most egregiously mistaken in Mr. Lovelace!

"The only man, I persuade myself, pretending to be a gentleman, in whom I could have been so much mistaken. For while I was endeavouring to save a drowning wretch, I have been, not accidentally, but premeditatedly, and of set purpose, drawn in after him." What say you to this, sir-r?

Lady S. and Lady B. Ay, sir, what say you to this?

Lovel. Say! Why I say it is a very pretty metaphor, if it would but hold. But if you please, my lord, read on.

Lord M. I will. "And he has had the glory to add to the list of those he has ruined, a name that, I will be bold to say, would not have disparaged his own. And this, madam, by means that would shock humanity to be made acquainted with."

Then again, in a hurry, off went the spectacles.

This was a plaguy stroke upon me. I thought myself an oak in impudence; but, by my troth, this had almost felled me.

Lord M. What say you to this, SIR-R!

Remember, Jack, to read all their *sirs* in this dialogue with a double *rr, sir-r!* denoting indignation rather than respect.

They all looked at me as if to see if I could blush.

The lady, it is plain, thought that the reclaiming of a man from bad habits was a much *easier task* than, in the *nature of things,* it *can* be.

She writes, as your lordship has read, "That in endeavouring to save a drowning wretch, she had been, not accidentally, but premeditatedly, and of set purpose, drawn in after him." But how is this, ladies? You see by her own words that I am still far from being out of danger myself. Had she found me, in a quagmire suppose, and I had got out of it by her means, and left her to perish in it; that would have been a crime indeed. But is not the fact quite otherwise? Has she not, if her allegory prove what she would have it prove, got out herself, and left me floundering still deeper and deeper in? What she should have done, had she been in earnest to save me, was to join her hand with mine, that so we might by our united strength help one another out. I held out my hand to her, and besought her to give me hers: but no, truly! she was determined to get out herself as fast as she could, let me *sink* or *swim:* refusing her assistance (against her own principles) because she saw I wanted it. You see, ladies, you see, my lord, how pretty tinkling words run away with ears inclined to be musical.

But what right, proceeded I, has this lady to complain of me, when she as good as says—Here, Lovelace, you have acted the part of a villain by me. You would *repair your fault:* but I won't let you, that I may have the satisfaction of exposing you; and the pride of refusing you.

But was that the case? Was that the case? Would I pretend to say I would *now* marry the lady, if she would have me?

Lovel. You find she renounces Lady Betty's mediation.

Lord M. (interrupting me). *Words are wind; but deeds are mind:* what signifies your cursed quibbling, Bob? Say plainly, if she will have you, will you have her? Answer me, yes or no; and lead us not *a wild-goose chase* after your meaning.

Lovel. She knows I would. But here, my lord, if she thus goes on to expose herself and me, she will make it a dishonour to us both to marry.

The next article of my indictment was for forgery; and for personating of Lady Betty and my Cousin Charlotte. Two shocking charges, thou'lt say: and so they were! The peer was outrageous upon the *forgery* charge. The ladies vowed never to forgive the *personating* part. Not a peacemaker among them. So we all turned women, and scolded.

My lord told me that he believed in his conscience there was not a viler fellow upon *God's earth* than me. What signifies mincing the matter? said he.

Indeed, Cousin Lovelace, said Lady Betty, with great gravity, we do not any of us, as Lady Sarah says, deserve at your hands the treatment you give us: and let me tell you that I don't think my character, and your Cousin Charlotte's, ought to be prostituted, in order to ruin an innocent lady. She must have known early the good opinion we all have of her, and how much we wished her to be your wife. This good opinion of ours has been an inducement to her (you see she says so) to listen to your address. And this, with her friends' folly, has helped to throw her into your power. How you have requited her is too apparent. It becomes the character we all bear, to disclaim your actions by her.

Lovel. Why this is talking somewhat like. I would have you all disclaim my actions. I own I have done very vilely by this lady. One step led to another. I am cursed with an enterprising spirit. I hate to be foiled——

Foiled! interrupted Lady Sarah. What a shame to talk at this rate! Did the lady set up a contention with you? All nobly sincere and plain-hearted, have I heard Miss Clarissa Harlowe is: above art, above disguise; neither the coquette, nor the prude! Poor lady! She deserved a better fate from the man for whom she took the step which she so freely blames!

This above half affected me. Had this dispute been so handled by every one, I had been ashamed to look up. I began to be bashful.

Charlotte asked if I did not still seem inclinable to do the lady justice, if she would accept of *me?* It would be, she dared to say, the greatest felicity the family could know (she would answer for one) that this fine lady were of it.

They all declared to the same effect; and Lady Sarah put the matter home to me.

They then fell into warm admirations and praises of the lady; all of them preparatory, as I knew, to the grand question: and thus it was introduced by Lady Sarah.

We have said as much as I think we can say upon these letters of the poor lady. To dwell upon the mischiefs that may ensue from the abuse of a person of her rank, if all the reparation be not made that now can be made, would perhaps be to little purpose. But you seem, sir, still to have a just opinion of her, as well as affection for her. Her virtue is not in the least questionable. She could not resent as she does, had she anything to reproach herself with. She is, by everybody's account, a fine woman; has a good estate in her own right; is of no contemptible family; though I think, with regard to her, they have acted as imprudently as unworthily. I, who have not been abroad twice this twelvemonth, came hither purposely, so did Lady Betty, to see if justice may not be done her; and also whether we, and my Lord M. (your nearest relations, sir) have, or have not, any influence over you. And, for my own part, as your determination shall be in this article, such shall be mine, with regard to the disposition of all that is within my power.

Lady Betty. And mine.

And mine, said my lord: and valiantly he swore to it.

Lovel. Far be it from me to think slightly of favours you may any of you be glad I would deserve! But as far be it from me to enter into conditions against my own liking, with sordid views! As to future mischiefs, let them come. I have not done with the Harlowes yet. They were the aggressors; and I should be glad they would let me hear from them, in the way they should hear from me, in the like case. Perhaps I should not be sorry to be *found,* rather than be obliged to *seek,* on this occasion.

Miss Charlotte (reddening). Spoke like a man of violence, rather than a man of reason! I hope you'll allow that, cousin.

Lady Sarah. Well, but since what is done, *is* done, and cannot be undone, let us think of the next best. Have you any objection against marrying Miss Harlowe, if she will have you?

Lovel. There can possibly be but one: that she is to everybody, no doubt, as well as to Lady Betty, pursuing that maxim peculiar to herself (*and let me tell you, so it ought to be*); that what she cannot conceal from herself, she will publish to all the world.

Miss Patty. The lady, to be sure, writes this in the bitterness of her grief, and in despair.

Lovel. And so, when her grief is allayed; when her despairing fit is over—and this from *you,* Cousin Patty! *Sweet girl!* And would *you,* my dear, in the like case (whispering her), have yielded to entreaty—would you have meant no more by the like exclamations?

I had a rap with her fan, and a blush; and from Lord M. a reflection, that I turned into jest everything they said.

I asked if they thought the Harlowes deserved any consideration from me; and whether that family would not exult over me, were I to marry their daughter, as if I *dared* not to do otherwise?

Lady Sarah. Once I was angry with that family, as we all were. But now I pity them; and think that you have but too well justified the worst treatment they gave you.

Lord M. Their family is of standing. All gentlemen of it, and rich, and reputable.

Lovel. The Harlowes are a narrow-souled and implacable family. I hate them: and though I revere the lady, scorn all relation to them.

Lord M. How would my sister Lovelace have reproached herself for all her indulgent folly to this favourite boy of hers, had she lived till now, and been present on this occasion!

Lady Sarah. Well, but, begging your lordship's pardon, let us see if anything can be done for this poor lady.

Miss Ch. If Mr. Lovelace has nothing to object against the lady's character (and I presume to think he is not *ashamed* to do her justice, though it may make against himself), I cannot see but honour and generosity will compel from him all that we expect.

Lady Betty. My Niece Charlotte has called upon you so justly, and has put the question to you so properly, that I cannot but wish you would speak to it directly, and without evasion.

All in a breath then bespoke my seriousness, and my justice: and in this manner I delivered myself, assuming an air sincerely solemn.

"I am very sensible that the performance of the task you have put me upon, will leave me without excuse: but I will not have recourse either to evasion or palliation.

"As my Cousin Charlotte has severely observed, I am not *ashamed* to do justice to Miss Harlowe's merit.

"I own to you all, and, what is more, with high regret (if not with *shame,* Cousin Charlotte), that I have a great deal to answer for in my usage of this lady. The sex has not a nobler mind, nor a lovelier person of it. And, for *virtue,* I could not have believed (excuse me, ladies) that there ever was a woman who *gave,* or *could* have given, such illustrious, such uniform proofs of it: for, in her whole conduct, she has shown herself to be equally above temptation and art; and, I had almost said, human frailty.

"The step she so freely blames herself for taking, was truly what she calls *compulsatory:* for though she was provoked to *think* of going off with me, she intended it not, nor was provided to do so: neither would she ever have had the *thought* of it, had her relations left her free, upon her offered composition to renounce the man she did *not* hate, in order to avoid the man she *did.*

"It piqued my pride, I own, that I could so little depend upon the force of those impressions which I had the vanity to hope I had made in a heart so delicate; and in my worst devices against her, I encouraged myself that I abused no confidence; for none had she in my honour.

"I know, proceeded I, how much I condemn myself in the

justice I am doing to this excellent creature. But yet I *will* do her justice, and cannot help it if I would. And I hope this shows that I am not so totally abandoned as I have been thought to be.

"Indeed, with me, she has done more honour to the sex in her fall, if it be to be called a fall (in truth it ought not), than ever any other could do in her standing.

"In short, ladies, in a word, my lord, Miss Clarissa Harlowe is an angel; if ever there was or could be one in human nature: and is, and ever was, as pure as an angel in her will: and this justice I must do her."

Lady Betty. Well, sir, this is a noble character. If you think as you speak, surely you cannot refuse to do the lady all the justice now in your power to do her.

They all joined in this demand.

I pleaded that I was sure she would not have me: that, when she had taken a resolution, she was not to be moved: unpersuadableness was a Harlowe sin: that, and her name, I told them, were all she had of theirs.

All were of opinion that she might, in her present desolate circumstances, be brought to forgive me. Lady Sarah said that Lady Betty and she would endeavour to find out the *noble sufferer,* as they justly called her; and would take her into their protection, and be guarantees of the justice that I would do her; as well after marriage as before.

Miss Charlotte. Permit me to make a proposal. Since we are all of one mind in relation to the justice due to Miss Harlowe, if Mr. Lovelace will oblige himself to marry her, I will make Miss Howe a visit, little as I am acquainted with her; and endeavour to engage her interest to forward the desired reconciliation. And if this can be done, I make no question but all may be happily accommodated; for everybody knows the love there is between Miss Harlowe and Miss Howe.

This motion was highly approved of; and I gave my honour, as desired, in the fullest manner they could wish.

Lady Sarah. Well then, Cousin Charlotte, begin your treaty with Miss Howe, out of hand.

Lady Betty. Pray do. And let Miss Harlowe be told, that I am ready to receive her as the most welcome of guests: and I will not have her out of my sight till the knot is tied.

Lady Sarah. Tell her from me, that she shall be my daughter, instead of my poor Betsey! And shed a tear in remembrance of her lost daughter.

Lord M. What say you, sir, to this?

Lovel. CONTENT, my lord. I speak in the language of your house.

Lord M. Give me thy hand, Bob! Thou talkest like a man of honour at last. I hope we may depend upon what thou sayest?

The ladies' eyes put the same question to me.

Lovel. You may, my lord. You may, ladies. Absolutely you may.

The two venerables (no longer tabbies with me now) hinted at rich presents on their own parts; and my lord declared that he would make such overtures in my behalf, as should render my marriage with Miss Harlowe the best day's work I ever made; and what, he doubted not, would be as agreeable to that family as to myself.

Thus, at present, by a single hair, hangs over my head the matrimonial sword. And thus ended my trial. And thus are we all friends; and cousin and cousin, and nephew and nephew, at every word.

Did ever comedy end more happily than this long trial?

MR. LOVELACE TO JOHN BELFORD, ESQ.

Wedn. July 12.

THUS, JACK, have I at once reconciled myself to all my relations—and, if the lady refuses me, thrown the fault upon her. This, I knew, would be in my power to do at any time: and I was the more arrogant to them, in order to heighten the merit of my compliance.

But, after all, it would be very whimsical, would it not, if all my plots and contrivances should end in wedlock? What a punishment would this come out to be, upon myself too, that all this while I have been plundering my own treasury?

And then, can there be so much harm done, if it can be so easily repaired by a few magical words; as *I, Robert,* take thee, Clarissa; and I, Clarissa, take thee, Robert, with the rest of the for-better and for-worse legerdemain, which will hocus-pocus all the wrongs, the crying wrongs, that I have done to Miss Harlowe, into acts of kindness and benevolence to Mrs. Lovelace?

MISS HOWE TO MISS CLARISSA HARLOWE

Thursday Night, July 13.

I AM to acquaint you, that I have been favoured with a visit from Miss Montague and her sister, in Lord M.'s chariot and six.

They came in the name of Lord M. and Lady Sarah and Lady Betty, his two sisters, to desire my interest to engage you to put yourself into the protection of Lady Betty; who will not part with you till she sees all the justice done you that now can be done.

And their joint strength, united with Lord M.'s, has so far succeeded, that the wretch has bound himself to them, and to these young ladies, in the solemnest manner, to wed you in their presence, if they can prevail upon you to give him your hand.

I made a great many objections for you—all, I believe, that you could have made yourself had you been present. But I have no doubt to advise you, my dear (and so does my mother), instantly to put yourself into Lady Betty's protection, with a resolution to take the wretch for your husband. All his future grandeur (he wants not pride) depends upon his sincerity to you; and the young ladies vouch for the depth of his concern for the wrongs he has done you.

Your melancholy letter brought by Rogers, with his account of your indifferent health, confirmed to him by the woman of the house, as well as by your looks, and by your faintness while you talked with him, would have given me inexpressible affliction, had I not been cheered by this agreeable visit from the young ladies. I hope you will be equally so on my imparting the subject of it to you.

Indeed, my dear, you must not hesitate. You *must* oblige them. The alliance is splendid and honourable. Very few will know anything of his brutal baseness to you. All must end, in a little while, in a general reconciliation; and you will be able to resume your course of doing the good to every deserving object, which procured you blessings wherever you set your foot.

I am concerned to find that your father's inhuman curse affects you so much as it does. Yet you are a noble creature to put it as you put it—I hope you are indeed more solicitous to get it revoked for their sakes than for your own. It is for *them* to be penitent, who hurried you into evils you could not well avoid. You are apt to judge by the unhappy event rather than upon the true merits of your case. Upon my honour, I think you faultless in almost every step you have taken. What has not that vilely insolent and ambitious, yet stupid, brother of yours to answer for?—that spiteful thing your sister too!

Mr. Hickman shall attend you at Slough; and Lady Betty herself, and one of the Miss Montagues, with proper equipages, will be at Reading to receive you; and carry you directly to the seat of the former: for I have expressly stipulated that the wretch himself shall not come into your presence till your nuptials are to be solemnized, unless you give leave.

Your ever affectionate

Anna Howe.

MISS HOWE TO MISS CHARLOTTE MONTAGUE

Tuesday Morning, July 18.

MADAM,—I take the liberty to write to you by this special messenger. In the frenzy of my soul I write to you, to demand of you, and of any of your family who can tell, news of my beloved friend; who, I doubt, has been spirited away by the base arts of one of the blackest—oh, help me to a name bad enough to call him by! Her piety is proof against self-attempts. It must, it must be he, the only wretch who could injure such an innocent; and now—who knows what he has done with her!

I wrote to her the very moment you and your sister left me. I urged her, with earnestness, to comply with the desires of all your family. Having no answer I wrote again on Sunday night; and sent it by a particular hand, who travelled all night; chiding her for keeping a heart so impatient as mine in such cruel suspense, upon a matter of so much importance to her; and therefore to me. And very angry I was with her in my mind.

But, judge my astonishment, my distraction, when last night the messenger, returning post-haste, brought me word that she had not been heard of since Friday morning! And that a letter lay for her at her lodgings which came by the post; and must be mine!

She went out about six that morning; only intending, as they believe, to go to morning prayers at Covent Garden Church, just by her lodgings, as she had done divers times before. Went on foot! Left word she should be back in an hour. Very poorly in health!

Lord, have mercy upon me! What shall I do! I was a distracted creature all last night!

O madam! you know not how I love her! My own soul is not dearer to me than my Clarissa Harlowe! Nay, she *is* my soul—for I now have none—only a miserable one, however—for she was the joy, the stay, the prop of my life. Never woman loved woman as we love one another. It is impossible to tell you half her excellences. But now—who knows, whether the dear injured has not all her woes, her undeserved woes, completed in death; or is not reserved for a worse fate! This I leave to your inquiry—for—your—(shall I call the man—your?) relation I understand is still with you.

I make no apology for giving you this trouble, nor for desiring you to favour with a line by this messenger,

Your almost distracted

Anna Howe.

MR. LOVELACE TO JOHN BELFORD, ESQ.

M. Hall, Sat. Night, July 15.

ALL UNDONE, undone, by Jupiter! A curse upon all my plots and contrivances!

The moment thou receivest this, I bespeak thy assistance. This messenger rides for life and death—and I hope he'll find you at your town lodgings; if he meet not with you at Edgware; where, being Sunday, he will call first.

This cursed, cursed woman, on Friday dispatched man and horse with the joyful news (as she thought it would be to me) in an exulting letter from Sally Martin, that she had found out my angel as on Wednesday last; and on Friday morning, after she had been at prayers at Covent Garden Church—praying for my reformation perhaps—got her arrested by two sheriff's officers, as she was returning to her lodgings, who (villains!) put her into a chair they had in readiness, and carried her to one of the cursed fellow's houses.

She has arrested her for £150, pretendedly due for board and lodgings: a sum (besides the low villainy of the proceeding) which the dear soul could not possibly raise; all her clothes and effects, except what she had on and with her when she went away, being at the old devil's.

And here, for an aggravation, has the dear creature lain already two days; for I must be gallanting my two aunts and my two cousins, and giving Lord M. an airing after his lying-in—pox upon the whole family of us!—and returned not till within this hour: and now returned to my distraction, on receiving the cursed tidings and the exulting letter.

Hasten, hasten, dear Jack; for the love of God, hasten to the injured charmer! She deserved not this! I dare not stir. It will be thought done by my contrivance—and if I am absent from this place, that will confirm the suspicion.

Hasten to her! Clear me of this cursed job. Most sincerely, by all that's sacred, I swear you may! Yet have I been such a villainous plotter, that the charming sufferer will hardly believe it; although the proceeding be so dirtily low.

Set her free the moment you see her: without conditioning, free! On your knees, for me, beg her pardon: and assure her that, wherever she goes, I will not molest her: no, nor come near her, without her leave: and be sure allow not any of the damned crew to go near her. Only let her permit *you* to receive her commands from time to time. You have always been her friend and advocate. What would I now give had I permitted you to have been a successful one!

Let her have all her clothes and effects sent her instantly, as a small proof of my sincerity. And force upon the dear creature, who must be moneyless, what sums you can get her to take. Let me know how she has been treated. If roughly, woe be to the guilty!

A line! a line! a kingdom for a line! with tolerable news, the first moment thou canst write!

Miss Charlotte Montague to Miss Howe

M. Hall, Tuesday Afternoon.

Dear Miss Howe,—Your letter has infinitely disturbed us all.

This wretched man has been half distracted ever since Saturday night.

We knew not what ailed him till your letter was brought.

Vile wretch as he is, he is, however, innocent of this new evil.

A horrid mistake of his general orders has subjected her to the terror and disgrace of an arrest.

But she must be now quite at liberty.

My Lord M., my Lady Sarah Sadleir, and my Lady Betty Lawrance, will all write to you this very afternoon.

And so will the wretch himself.

But you shall have all the particulars, just, and true, and fair, from,

Dear madam,
Your most faithful and obedient servant,
Ch. Montague.

Miss Montague to Miss Howe

M. Hall, July 18.

Dear Madam,—In pursuance of my promise, I will minutely inform you of everything we know relating to this shocking transaction.

When we returned from you on Thursday night, and made our report of the kind reception both we and our message met with, in that you had been so good as to promise to use your interest with your dear friend; it put us all into such good humour with one another, and with my Cousin Lovelace, that we resolved upon a little tour of two days, the Friday and Saturday, in order to give an airing to my lord and Lady Sarah; both having been long confined, one by illness, the other by melancholy. My lord, Lady Sarah, Lady Betty, and myself, were in the coach; and all our talk was of dear Miss Harlowe, and of our future happiness with her. Mr. Lovelace and my sister (who is his favourite, as he is hers) were in his phaeton: and whenever we joined company that was still the subject.

As to him, never man praised woman as he did her: never man gave greater hopes, and make better resolutions. He is none of those that are governed by interest. He is too proud for that. But most sincerely delighted was he in talking of her; and of his hopes of her returning favour. He said, however, more than once, that he feared she would not forgive him; for, from his heart, he must say he deserved not her forgiveness: and often and often, that there was not such a woman in the world.

We returned not till Saturday night, all in as good humour with one another as we went out. But never was there a greater alteration in man when he came home, and received a letter from a messenger, who, it seems, had been flattering himself in hopes of a reward, and had been waiting for his return from the night before. In *such* a fury! The man fared but badly. He instantly shut himself up to write.

He would not see us all that night; neither breakfast nor dine with us next day. He ought, he said, never to see the light; and bid my sister, whom he called an *innocent* (and who was very desirous to know the occasion of all this), shun him; saying, he was a wretch, and made so by his own inventions and the consequences of them.

None of us could get out of him what so disturbed him. We should too soon hear, he said, to the utter dissipation of all *his* hopes, and of all *ours*.

Late on Monday night he received a letter from Mr. Belford, his most favoured friend, by his own messenger; who came back in a foam, man and horse. Whatever were the contents, he was not easier, but like a madman rather: but still would not let us know the occasion. But to my sister he said, Nobody, my dear Patsey, who can think but of half the plagues that pursue an intriguing spirit, would ever quit the right path.

He was out when your messenger came: but soon came in; and bad enough was his reception from us all. And he said that his own torments were greater than ours, than Miss Harlowe's, or yours, madam, all put together. He would see your letter. He always carries everything before him: and said, when he had read it, that he thanked God he was not such a villain as you, with too great an appearance of reason, thought him.

Thus then he owned the matter to be:

He had left general directions to the people of the lodgings the dear lady went from, to find out where she was gone to, if possible, that he might have an opportunity to importune her to be his, before their difference was public. The wicked people (*officious* at least, if not wicked) discovered where she was on Wednesday; and, for fear she should remove before they could have his orders, they put her under a *gentle restraint,* as they call it; and dispatched away a messenger to acquaint him with it; and to take his orders.

This messenger arrived on Friday afternoon; and stayed here till we returned on Saturday night: and when he read the letter he brought—I have told you, madam, what a fury he was in.

The letter he retired to write, and which he dispatched away so early on Sunday morning, was to conjure his friend Mr. Belford, on receipt of it, to fly to the lady, and set her free; and to order all her things to be sent her; and to clear him of so *black* and *villainous* a fact, as he justly called it.

And by this time he doubts not that all is happily over; and the beloved of his soul (as he calls her at every word) in an easier and happier way than she was before the horrid fact. And now he owns that the reason why Mr. Belford's letter set him into stronger ravings was, because of his keeping him wilfully (and on purpose to torment him) in suspense; and reflecting very heavily upon him (for Mr. Belford, he says, was ever the lady's friend and advocate); and only mentioning that he had waited upon her; referring to his next for further particulars; which Mr. Belford could have told him at the time.

He forbore going up himself, that it might not be imagined he was guilty of so black a contrivance; and that he went up to complete any base views in consequence of it.

My sister joins her thanks with mine to your good mother and self for the favours you heaped upon us last Thursday. We beseech your continued interest as to the subject of our visit. It shall be all our studies to oblige and recompense the dear lady to the utmost of our power, for what she has suffered from the unhappy man.

We are, dear madam,

Your obliged and faithful servants,

Charlotte }
Martha } *Montague.*

DEAR MISS HOWE,—We join in the above request of Miss Charlotte and Miss Patty Montague, for your favour and interest; being convinced that the accident was an accident; and no plot or contrivance of a wretch too full of them. We are, madam,

Your most obedient humble servants,

M.
Sarah Sadleir.
Eliz. Lawrance.

DEAR MISS HOWE,—After what is written above, by names and characters of such unquestionable honour, I might have been excused signing a name almost as hateful to myself, as I KNOW it is to you. But the *above* will have it so. Since, therefore, I *must* write, it shall be the truth; which is, that if I may be once more admitted to pay my duty to the most deserving and most injured of her sex, I will be content to do it with a halter about my neck; and attended by a parson on my right hand, and the hangman on my left, be doomed, at her will, either to the church or the gallows.

Your most humble servant,

Robert Lovelace.

Tuesday, July 18.

MR. BELFORD TO ROBERT LOVELACE, ESQ.

Sunday Night, July 16.

WHAT a cursed piece of work hast thou made of it, with the most excellent of women!

I will give thee an account of a scene that wants but her affecting pen to represent it justly; and it would wring all the black blood out of thy callous heart.

Thou only, who art the author of her calamities, shouldst have attended her in her prison.

This last act, however unintended by thee, yet a consequence of thy general orders, and too likely to be thought agreeable to thee, by those who know thy other villainies by her, has finished thy barbarous work. And I advise thee to trumpet forth everywhere, how much in earnest thou art to marry her, whether true or not.

Thou mayest *safely* do it. She will not live to put thee to the trial; and it will a little palliate for thy enormous usage of her, and be a means to make mankind, who know not what I know of the matter, herd a little longer with thee, and forbear to hunt thee to thy fellow-savages in the Libyan wilds and deserts.

Your messenger found me at Edgware, expecting to dinner with me several friends, whom I had invited three days before. I sent apologies to them, as in a case of life and death; and speeded to town to the wicked woman's: for how knew I but shocking attempts might be made upon her by the cursed wretches; perhaps by your connivance, in order to mortify her into your measures?

Finding the lady not there, I posted away to the officer's, although Sally told me that she had been just come from thence; and that she had refused to see her, or (as she sent down word) anybody else; being resolved to have the remainder of that Sunday to herself, as it might, perhaps, be the last she should ever see.

I had the same thing told me, when I got thither.

I sent up to let her know that I came with a commission to set her at liberty. I was afraid of sending up the name of a man known to be your friend. She absolutely refused to see *any man,* however, for that day, or to answer further to anything said from me.

Having, therefore, informed myself of all that the officer, and his wife, and servant, could acquaint me with, as well in relation to the horrid arrest, as to her behaviour, and the women's to her; and her ill state of health; I went back to Sinclair's, as I will still call her, and heard the three women's story: from all which I am enabled to give you the following shocking particulars; which may serve till I can see the unhappy lady herself to-morrow, if then I can gain admittance to her.

Your villain it was that *set* the poor lady, and had the impudence to appear, and abet the sheriff's officers in the cursed transaction. He thought, no doubt, that he was doing the most acceptable service to his blessed master. They had got a chair; the head ready up, as soon as service was over. And as she came out of the church, at the door fronting Bedford Street, the officers, stepping to her, whispering that they had an action against her.

She was terrified, trembled, and turned pale.

Action! said she. What is that? I have committed *no bad action!* Lord bless me! Men, what mean you?

That you are our prisoner, madam.

Prisoner, sirs! What—How—Why—What have I done?

You must go with us. Be pleased, madam, to step into this chair.

With *you!* With *men!* Must go with *men!* I am not used to go with *strange men!* Indeed you must excuse me!

We can't excuse you: we are sheriff's officers. We have a writ against you. You *must* go with us, and you shall know at whose suit.

Suit! said the charming innocent; I don't know what you mean. Pray, men, don't lay hands upon me; they offering to put her into the chair. I am not used to be thus treated—I have done nothing to deserve it.

She then spied thy villain. O thou wretch, said she, where is thy vile master? Am I again to be *his prisoner?* Help, good people!

A crowd had before begun to gather.

My master is in the country, madam, many miles off. If you please to go with these men, they will treat you civilly.

The people were most of them struck with compassion. A fine young creature! A thousand pities! cried some. While some few threw out vile and shocking reflections! But a gentleman interposed, and demanded to see the fellows' authority.

They showed it. Is your name Clarissa Harlowe, madam? said he.

Yes, yes, indeed, ready to sink, my name *was* Clarissa Harlowe: but it is now *Wretchedness!* Lord, be merciful to me! what is to come next?

You *must* go with these men, madam, said the gentleman: they have authority for what they do.

Well, if I must go, I must—I cannot resist—but I will not be carried to the woman's! I will rather die at your feet than be carried to the woman's!

You won't be carried there, madam, cried thy fellow.

Only to *my* house, madam, said one of the officers.

Where is that?

In High Holborn, madam.

I know not where High Holborn is: but anywhere, except to the woman's.

And stepping into the chair, threw herself on the seat, in the utmost distress and confusion. Carry me, carry me out of sight—cover me—cover me up—for ever! were her words.

. . . . . .

The unhappy lady fainted away when she was taken out of the chair at the officer's house.

Several people followed the chair to the very house, which is in a wretched court. Sally was there; and satisfied some of the inquirers that the young gentlewoman would be exceedingly well used: and they soon dispersed.

Dorcas was also there; but came not in her sight. Sally, as a favour, offered to carry her to her former lodgings: but she declared they should carry her thither a corpse, if they did.

Very gentle usage the women boast of: so would a vulture, could it speak, with the entrails of its prey upon its rapacious talons. Of this you'll judge from what I have to recite.

And who do you think, *Miss Harlowe,* for I understand, said the cursed creature, you are not married; who do you think is to pay for your board and your lodgings; such handsome lodgings! for so long a time as you were at Mrs. Sinclair's?

Lord have mercy upon me! Miss Martin (I think you are Miss Martin!)—and is this the cause of such a disgraceful insult upon me in the open streets?

And cause enough, *Miss Harlowe*—one hundred and fifty

guineas, or pounds, is no small sum to lose—and by a young creature who would have bilked her lodgings.

You amaze me, Miss Martin! What language do you talk in? —*Bilk my lodgings!* What is that?

She stood astonished and silent for a few moments.

But recovering herself, and turning from her to the window, she wrung her hands (the cursed Sally showed me how!); and lifting them up—*Now,* Lovelace! Now indeed do I think I *ought* to forgive thee! But who shall forgive Clarissa Harlowe! —O my sister! O my brother! Tender mercies were your cruelties to *this!*

Rowland, for that is the officer's name, told her she had friends enough to pay the debt, if she would write.

She would trouble nobody; she had no friends; was all they could get from her, while Sally stayed: but yet spoken with a patience of spirit, as if she enjoyed her griefs.

About six in the evening, Rowland's wife pressed her to drink tea. She said she had rather have a glass of water; for her tongue was ready to cleave to the roof of her mouth.

The woman brought her a glass, and some bread and butter. She tried to taste the latter; but could not swallow it: but eagerly drank the water; lifting up her eyes in thankfulness for that!!!

The divine Clarissa, Lovelace—reduced to rejoice for a cup of cold water! By whom *reduced.*

. . . . . .

Again they asked her if they should send any word to her lodgings?

These are my lodgings now, are they not? was all her answer.

She sat up in a chair all night, the back against the door; having, it seems, thrust a broken piece of a poker through the staples where a bolt had been on the inside.

. . . . . .

Next morning, Sally and Polly both went to visit her.

Sally told her that she had written in a very favourable manner in her behalf to you; and that she every hour expected an answer; and made no doubt that you would come up with the messenger, and generously pay the whole debt, and ask her pardon for neglecting it.

This disturbed her so much that they feared she would have fallen into fits. She could not bear your name, she said. She hoped she should never see you more: and were you to intrude yourself, dreadful consequences might follow.

Surely, they said, she would be glad to be released from her confinement.

Indeed she *should,* now they had begun to alarm her with *his* name, who was the author of all her woes: and who, she now saw plainly, gave way to this new outrage in order to bring her to his own infamous terms.

Why then, they asked, would she not write to her friends to pay Mrs. Sinclair's demand?

Because she hoped she should not long trouble anybody; and because she knew that the payment of the money, if she were able to pay it, was not what was aimed at.

She besought them to leave her. She wanted not these instances, she said, to convince her of the company she was in: and told them that, to get rid of such visitors, and of the still worse she was apprehensive of, she would write to one friend to raise the money for her; though it would be death for her to do so; because that friend could not do it without her mother, in whose eye it would give a selfish appearance to a friendship that was above all sordid alloys.

They advised her to write out of hand.

But how much must I write for? What is the sum? Should I not have had a bill delivered me? God knows, I took not your lodgings. But he that could treat me as he has done could do this!

Don't speak against Mr. Lovelace, *Miss Harlowe.* He is a man I greatly esteem (cursed toad!). And, 'bating that he will take his advantage where he can, of us silly credulous women, he is a man of honour.

She lifted up her hands and eyes instead of speaking: and well she might! For any words she could have used could not have expressed the anguish she must feel on being comprehended in the US.

She must write for one hundred and fifty guineas, at least: two hundred, if she were short of money, might as well be written for.

Mrs. Sinclair, she said, had all her clothes. Let them be sold, *fairly* sold, and the money go as far as it would go. She had also a few other valuables; but no money (none at all) but the poor half-guinea, and the little silver they had seen. She would give bond to pay all that her apparel, and the other matters she had, would fall short of. She had great effects belonging to her of right. Her bond would, and must, be paid, were it for a thousand pounds. But her clothes she should never want. She believed, if not too much undervalued, those, and her few valuables, would answer everything. She wished for no surplus but to discharge the last expenses; and forty shillings would do as well for those as forty pounds. "Let my ruin, said she, lifting up her eyes, be LARGE! Let it be COMPLETE, *in this life!* For a *composition,* let it be COMPLETE." And there she stopped. No doubt alluding to her father's extensive curse!

Will not Mrs. Sinclair, proceeded she, think my clothes a security till they can be sold? They are very good clothes. A suit or two but just put on, as it were; never worn. They cost much more than is demanded of me. *My father loved to see me fine.* All shall go. But let me have the particulars of her demand. I suppose I must pay for my *destroyer* (that was her well-adapted word!) and his servants, as well as for myself. I am content to do so. Indeed, I am content to do so—I am above wishing that anybody who could *thus* act should be so much as expostulated with, as to the justice and equity of this payment. If I have but enough to pay the demand, I shall be satisfied; and will leave the baseness of such an action as this, as an aggravation of a guilt which I thought could *not* be aggravated.

I own, Lovelace, I have malice in this particularity, in order to sting thee to the heart. And, let me ask thee, what now thou canst think of thy barbarity, thy unprecedented barbarity, in having reduced a person of her rank, fortune, talents, and virtue, so low?

The wretched women, it must be owned, act but in their profession; a profession thou hast been the principal means of reducing these two to act in.

Till I came, they thought thou wouldst not be displeased at anything she suffered, that could help to mortify her into a state of shame and disgrace; and bring her to comply with thy views, when thou shouldst come to release her from these wretches, as from a greater evil than cohabiting with thee.

When thou considerest these things, thou wilt make no difficulty of believing that this their own account of their behaviour to this admirable woman has been far short of their insults: and the less, when I tell thee, that, all together, their usage had such effects upon her, that they left her in violent hysterics; ordering an apothecary to be sent for, if she should continue in them, and be worse; and particularly (as they had done from the first) that they kept out of her way any edged or pointed instrument; especially a penknife; which, pretending to mend a pen, they said, she might ask for.

At twelve, Saturday night, Rowland sent to tell them that she was so ill that he knew not what might be the issue; and wished her out of his house.

And this made them as heartily wish to hear from you. For their messenger, to their great surprise, was not then returned from M. Hall.

Early on Sunday morning both devils went to see how she did. But their apprehension of what might be the issue was, no doubt, their principal consideration: nothing else could have softened such flinty bosoms.

They sent for the apothecary Rowland had had to her, and gave him, and Rowland, and his wife, and maid, strict orders, many times repeated, for the utmost care to be taken of her—no doubt, with an Old Bailey forecast.

When I first came, and told them of thy execrations for what they had done, and joined my own to them, they were astonished. The mother said she had thought she had known Mr. Lovelace better; and expected thanks, and not curses.

Under what shocking disadvantages, and with this addition to them, that I am thy friend and intimate, am I to make a visit to this unhappy lady to-morrow morning!

J. Belford.

MR. BELFORD TO ROBERT LOVELACE, ESQ.

Monday, July 17.

ABOUT SIX this morning I went to Rowland's. Mrs. Sinclair was to follow me, in order to dismiss the action; but not to come in sight.

Rowland, upon inquiry, told me that the lady was extremely ill; and that she had desired that no one but his wife or maid should come near her.

I said I *must* see her. I had told him my business overnight; and I *must* see her.

His wife went up: but returned presently, saying she could not get her to speak to her; yet that her eyelids moved; though she either would not, or could not, open them to look up at her.

Oons, woman, said I, the lady may be in a fit: the lady may be dying. Let me go up. Show me the way.

A horrid hole of a house, in an alley they call a court; stairs wretchedly narrow, even to the first-floor rooms: and into a den they led me, with broken walls, which had been papered, as I saw by a multitude of tacks, and some torn bits held on by the rusty heads.

A bed at one corner, with coarse curtains tacked up at the feet to the ceiling.

The windows dark and double-barred, the tops boarded up to save mending; and only a little four-paned eyelet-hole of a casement to let in air; more, however, coming in at broken panes than could come in at that.

To finish the shocking description, in a dark nook stood an old broken-bottomed cane couch, without a squab, or coverlid, sunk at one corner, and unmortised by the failing of one of its worm-eaten legs, which lay in two pieces under the wretched piece of furniture it could no longer support.

And this, thou horrid Lovelace, was the bedchamber of the divine Clarissa!!!

I had leisure to cast my eye on these things: for, going up softly, the poor lady turned not about at our entrance; nor, till I spoke, moved her head.

She was kneeling in a corner of the room, near the dismal window, against the table, on an old bolster (as it seemed to be) of the cane couch, half-covered with her handkerchief; her back to the door; which was only shut to (no need of fastenings!); her arms crossed upon the table, the forefinger of her right hand in her Bible. She had perhaps been reading in it, and could read no longer. Paper, pens, ink, lay by her book on the table. Her dress was white damask, exceeding neat; but her stays seemed not tight-laced. I was told afterwards that her laces had been cut when she fainted away at her entrance into this cursed place; and she had not been solicitous enough about her dress to send for others. Her head-dress was a little discomposed; her charming hair, in natural ringlets, as you have heretofore described it, but a little tangled, as if not lately combed, irregularly shading one side of the loveliest neck in the world; as her disordered, rumpled handkerchief did the other. Her face (oh, how altered from what I had seen it! Yet lovely in spite of all her griefs and sufferings!) was reclined, when we entered, upon her crossed arms; but so as not more than one side of it to be hid.

Something rose in my throat, I know not what, which made me, for a moment, guggle, as it were, for speech: which, at last, forcing its way, Con—con—confound you both, said I to the man and woman, is this an apartment for such a lady?

Sir, we would have had the lady to accept of our own bed-chamber; but she refused it. We are poor people—and we expect nobody will stay with us longer than they can help it.

You are people chosen purposely, I doubt not, by the damned woman who has employed you: and if your usage of this lady has been but half as bad as your house, you had better never to have seen the light.

Up then raised the charming sufferer her lovely face; but with such a significance of woe overspreading it that I could not, for the soul of me, help being visibly affected.

She waved her hand two or three times towards the door, as if commanding me to withdraw; and displeased at my intrusion; but did not speak.

Permit me, madam—I will not approach one step farther without your leave—permit me. for one moment, the favour of your ear!

No—no—go, go, MAN! with an emphasis—and would have

said more; but, as if struggling in vain for words, she seemed to give up speech for lost, and dropped her head down once more, with a deep sigh, upon her left arm; her right, as if she had not the use of it (numbed, I suppose), self-moved, dropping down on her side.

I dare not approach you, dearest lady, without your leave: but on my knees I beseech you to permit me to release you from this damned house, and out of the power of the accursed woman who was the occasion of your being here!

She lifted up her sweet face once more, and beheld me on my knees. Never knew I before what it was to pray so heartily.

Are you not—are you not Mr. Belford, sir? I think your name is Belford?

It is, madam, and I ever was a worshipper of your virtues and an advocate for you; and I come to release you from the hands you are in.

And in whose to place me? Oh, leave me, leave me! Let me never rise from this spot! Let me never, never more believe in man!

This moment, dearest lady, this very moment, if you please, you may depart whithersoever you think fit. You are absolutely free, and your own mistress.

I had now as lief die here in this place as anywhere. I will owe no obligation to any friend of *him* in whose company you have seen me. So, pray, sir, withdraw.

Then turning to the officer, Mr. Rowland I think your name is? I am better reconciled to your house than I was at first. If you can but engage that I shall have nobody come near me but your wife (no *man!*), and neither of those women who have sported with my calamities, I will die with you, and in this very corner. And you shall be well satisfied for the trouble you have had with me. I have value enough for that—for, see, I have a diamond ring; taking it out of her bosom; and I have friends will redeem it at a high price, when I am gone.

But for *you,* sir, looking at me, I beg you to withdraw. If you mean me well, God, I hope, will reward you for your good meaning; but to the friend of my *destroyer* will I not owe an obligation.

You will owe no obligation to me, nor to anybody. You

have been detained for a debt you do not owe. The action is dismissed; and you will only be so good as to give me your hand into the coach, which stands as near to this house as it could draw up. And I will either leave you at the coach door, or attend you whithersoever you please, till I see you safe where you would wish to be.

Will you then, sir, *compel* me to be beholden to you?

You will inexpressibly oblige me, madam, to command me to do you either service or pleasure.

Why then, sir (looking at me)—but why do you mock me in that humble posture! Rise, sir! I cannot speak to you else.

I arose.

Only, sir, take this ring. I have a sister, who will be glad to have it at the price it shall be valued at, for the *former* owner's sake! Out of the money she gives, let this man be paid; handsomely paid: and I have a few valuables more at my lodgings (Dorcas, or the MAN William, can tell where that is); let them, and my clothes at the wicked woman's, where you have seen me, be sold, for the payment of my lodging first, and next of your *friend's* debts, that I have been arrested for, as far as they will go; only reserving enough to put me into the ground, anywhere, or anyhow, no matter.—Tell your friend I wish it may be enough to satisfy the whole demand; but if it be not, he must make it up himself; or, if he think fit to draw for it on Miss Howe, she will repay it, *and with interest,* if he insist upon it.—And this, sir, if you promise to perform, you will do me, as you offer, both pleasure and service: and say you *will,* and take the ring and withdraw. If I want to say anything more to you (you seem to be a humane man), I will let you know—and so, sir, God bless you.

I approached her, and was going to speak——

Don't speak, sir: here's the ring.

I stood off.

And won't you take it? Won't you do this last office for me? I have no other person to ask it of; else, believe me, I would not request it of *you.* But take it or not, laying it upon the table—you must withdraw, sir: I am very ill. I would fain get a little rest, if I could. I find I am going to be bad again.

And offering to rise, she sunk down through excess of weakness and grief, in a fainting fit.

The maid coming in just then, the woman and she lifted her up on the decrepit couch; and I withdrew with this Rowland; who wept like a child, and said he never in his life was so moved.

They recovered her by hartshorn and water. I went down meanwhile; for the detestable woman had been below some time. Oh, how did I curse her!

You will observe that I did not mention one word to the lady about *you*. I was afraid to do it. For 'twas plain that she could not bear your name: and yet I wanted to clear your intention of this brutal, this sordid-looking villainy.

I sent up again, by Rowland's wife, when I heard that the lady was recovered, beseeching her to quit that devilish place; and the woman assured her that she was at full liberty to do so; for that the action was dismissed.

But she cared not to answer her: and was so weak and low that it was almost as much out of her power as inclination, the woman told me, to speak.

Being told that she desired not to be disturbed, and seemed inclined to doze, I took this opportunity to go to her lodgings in Covent Garden; to which Dorcas (who first discovered her there, as Will was the setter from church) had before given me a direction.

The man's name is Smith, a dealer in gloves, snuff, and such petty merchandise: his wife the shopkeeper: he a maker of the gloves they sell. Honest people, it seems.

I thought to have got the woman with me to the lady; but she was not within.

I talked with the man, and told him what had befallen the lady; owing, as I said, to a mistake of orders; and gave her the character she deserved; and desired him to send his wife, the moment she came in, to the lady; directing him whither; not doubting that her attendance would be very welcome to her: which he promised.

He told me that a letter was left for her there on Saturday.

I thought it right to take the letter back with me; and,

dismissing my coach, took a chair, as a more proper vehicle for the lady, if I could prevail upon her to leave Rowland's.

Monday Night, July 17.

On my return to Rowland's, I found that the apothecary was just gone up. Mrs. Rowland being above with him, I made the less scruple to go up too, as it was probable that to ask for leave would be to ask to be denied; hoping also that the letter I had with me would be a good excuse.

She was sitting on the side of the broken couch, extremely weak and low; and, I observed, cared not to speak to the man; and no wonder; for I never saw a more shocking fellow, of a profession tolerably genteel, nor heard a more illiterate one prate—physician in ordinary to this house, and others like it, I suppose!

I besought her excuse; and, winking for the apothecary to withdraw, told her that I had been at her new lodgings, to order everything to be got ready for her reception, presuming she would choose to go thither: that I had a chair at the door: that Mr. Smith and his wife had been full of apprehensions for her safety: that I had brought a letter, which was left there for her.

This took her attention. She held out her charming hand—From the only friend I have in the world! said she, looking at the seals.

I besought her to think of quitting that wretched hole.

Whither could she go, she asked, to be safe and uninterrupted for the short remainder of her life; and to avoid being again visited by the creatures who had insulted her before?

I gave her the solemnest assurances that she should not be invaded in her new lodgings by anybody; and said that I would particularly engage my honour, that *the person who had most offended her should not come near her without her own consent.*

Your honour, sir! Are you not that man's friend!

I am not a friend, madam, to his vile actions to the *most excellent of women.*

Do you flatter me, sir? Then are you a MAN. But oh, sir, your friend, holding her face forward with great earnestness, your *barbarous* friend, what has he not to answer for!

There she stopped: her heart full; and putting her hand over her eyes and forehead, the tears trickled through her fingers: resenting thy barbarity, it seemed, as Cæsar did the stab from his distinguished Brutus!

Though she was so very much disordered, I thought I would not lose this opportunity to assert your innocence of this villainous arrest.

There is no defending the unhappy man in any of his vile actions by you, madam; but of this last outrage, by all that's good and sacred, he is innocent.

O wretches! what a sex is yours! Have you all one dialect? *Good and sacred!* If, sir, you can find an oath, or a vow, or an adjuration, that my ears have not been twenty times a day wounded with, then speak it, and I may again believe a MAN.

I was excessively touched at these words, knowing thy baseness, and the reason she had for them.

But say you, sir; for I would not, methinks, have the wretch capable of this sordid baseness!—Say you that he is innocent of this *last* wickedness? Can you *truly* say that he is?

By the great God of Heaven!——

Nay, sir, if you swear, I must doubt you! If you yourself think your WORD insufficient, what reliance can I have on your OATH!

Madam, said I, I have a regard, a regard a gentleman *ought* to have, to my word; and whenever I forfeit it to you——

Nay, sir, don't be angry with me. It is grievous to me to question a gentleman's veracity. But your friend calls himself a *gentleman*.

I would give you, madam, demonstration, if your grief and your weakness would permit it, that he has no hand in this barbarous baseness: and that he resents it as it ought to be resented.

Well, well, sir (with quickness), he will have his account to make up somewhere else; not to me. I should not be sorry to find him able to acquit his intention on this occasion. Let him know, sir, only one thing, that when you heard me, in the bitterness of my spirit, most vehemently exclaim against the undeserved usage I have met with from him, that even *then*, in *that* passionate moment, I was able to say, "Give him, good God! repentance and amendment; that I may be the last poor creature who shall be ruined by him!"

I represented to her that she would be less free where she was from visits she liked not, than at her own lodgings. I told her that it would probably bring her, in particular, *one visitor* who, otherwise, I would engage should not come near her, without her consent.

I assured her, in the strongest terms, that you were resolved not to molest her: and, as a proof of the sincerity of my professions, besought her to give me directions (in pursuance of my friend's express desire) about sending all her apparel, and whatever belonged to her, to her new lodgings.

She seemed pleased; and gave me instantly out of her pocket her keys; asking me if Mrs. Smith might not attend me; and she would give *her* further directions? To which I cheerfully assented; and then she told me that she would accept of the chair I had offered her.

She gave the maid something; probably the only half-guinea she had: and then with difficulty, her limbs trembling under her, and supported by Mrs. Rowland, got downstairs.

I offered my arm: she was pleased to lean upon it. I doubt, sir, said she, as she moved, I have behaved rudely to you: but, if you knew all, you would forgive me.

I know enough, madam, to convince me that there is not such purity and honour in any woman upon earth; nor any one that has been so barbarously treated.

She looked at me very earnestly. What she thought, I cannot say; but, in general, I never saw so much soul in a woman's eyes as in hers.

I ordered my servant to keep the chair in view; and to bring me word how she did when set down. O Mrs. Smith, said she, as soon as she saw her, did you not think I was run away? You don't know what I have suffered since I saw you. I have been in a prison!—Arrested for debts I owe not! But, thank God, I am here!

I was resolved to lose no time in having everything which belonged to the lady at the cursed woman's sent her. Accordingly I took coach to Smith's, and procured the lady (to whom

I sent up my compliments, and inquiries how she bore her removal), ill as she sent me down word she was, to give proper directions to Mrs. Smith: whom I took with me to Sinclair's; and who saw everything looked out, and put into the trunks and boxes they were first brought in, and carried away in two coaches.

The conversation which Mrs. Smith and I had (in which I not only expatiated on the merits of the lady, but expressed my concern for her sufferings; though I left her room to suppose her married, yet without averring it), gave me high credit with the good woman: so that we are perfectly well acquainted already: by which means I shall be enabled to give you accounts from time to time of all that passes; and which I will be very industrious to do, provided I may depend upon the solemn promises I have given the lady, in your name, as well as in my own, that she shall be free from all personal molestation from you.

I ordered the abandoned women to make out your account. They answered, *that* they would do with a *vengeance*. Indeed they breathe nothing but revenge. For now, they say, you will assuredly marry; and your example will be followed by all your friends and companions—as the old one says, to the utter ruin of her poor house.

Tuesday, July 18. Afternoon.

She has two handsome apartments, a bedchamber and dining-room, with light closets in each. She has already a nurse (the people of the house having but one maid); a woman whose care, diligence, and honesty, Mrs. Smith highly commends. She has likewise the benefit of the voluntary attendance, and *love*, as it seems, of a widow gentlewoman, Mrs. Lovick her name, who lodges over her apartment, and of whom she seems very fond, having found something in her, she thinks, resembling the qualities of her worthy Mrs. Norton.

About seven o'clock this morning, it seems, the lady was so ill that she yielded to their desires to have an apothecary sent for, one Mr. Goddard, a man of skill and eminence; and of conscience too; demonstrated as well by general character, as by his prescriptions to this lady: for, pronouncing her case to be grief, he ordered, for the present, only innocent juleps, by way of cordial; and, as soon as her stomach should be able to bear it, light kitchen diet; telling Mrs. Lovick that that, with air, moderate exercise, and cheerful company, would do her more good than all the medicines in his shop.

This has given me, as it seems it has the lady (who also praises his modest behaviour, paternal looks, and genteel address), a very good opinion of the man; and I design to make myself acquainted with him; and, if he advises to call in a doctor, to wish him, for the fair patient's sake, more than the physician's (who wants not practice), my worthy friend Dr. H., whose character is above all exception, as his humanity I am sure will distinguish him to the lady.

Mrs. Lovick gratified me with an account of a letter she had written from the lady's mouth to Miss Howe; she being unable to write herself with steadiness.

It was to this effect;

"That she had been involved in a dreadful calamity, which she was sure, when known, would exempt her from the effects of her friendly displeasure, for not answering her first; having been put under an arrest.—Could she have believed it?—That she was released but the day before: and was now so weak, and so low, that she was obliged to get a widow gentlewoman in the same house to account thus for her silence: that she would, as soon as able, answer—begged of her, meantime, not to be uneasy for her; since (only that this was a calamity which came upon her when she was far from being well; a load laid upon the shoulders of a poor wretch, ready before to sink under too heavy a burden) *it was nothing to the evil she had before suffered:* and one felicity seemed likely to issue from it; which was, that she should be at rest, in an honest house, with considerate and kind-hearted people; having assurance given her that she should not be molested by the wretch, whom it would be death for her to see.

Your sincere well-wisher,

J. Belford.

MR. BELFORD TO ROBERT LOVELACE, ESQ.

Tuesday Night, July 18.

I AM JUST COME from the lady. I was admitted into the dining-room, where she was sitting in an elbow-chair, in a very weak and low way. She made an effort to stand up when I entered; but was forced to keep her seat. You'll excuse me, Mr. Belford: I ought to rise, to thank you for all your kindness to me. I was to blame to be so loath to leave that sad place; for I am in Heaven here, to what I was there: and good people about me too! I have not had good people about me for a long, long time before; so that (with a half smile) I had begun to wonder whither they were all gone.

Her nurse and Mrs. Smith, who were present, took occasion to retire: and, when we were alone, You seem to be a person of humanity, sir, said she: you hinted, as I was leaving *my prison*, that you were not a stranger to my sad story.

I told her I knew enough to be convinced that she had the merit of a saint, and the purity of an angel: and was proceeding, when she said, No flighty compliments! No undue attributes, sir!

I then mentioned your grief, your penitence, your resolutions of making her all the amends that were possible now to be made her: and, in the most earnest manner, I asserted your innocence as to the last villainous outrage.

Her answer was to this effect: It is painful to me to think of him. The amends you talk of cannot be made. This last violence you speak of *is nothing to what preceded it*. That *cannot* be atoned for; nor palliated: this *may:* and I shall not be sorry to be convinced that he cannot be guilty of so very low a wickedness.—Yet, after his vile forgeries of hands—after his baseness in imposing upon me the most infamous persons as ladies of honour of his own family—what are the iniquities he is not capable of?

I would then have given her an account of the trial you stood with your friends: your own previous resolutions of marriage, had she honoured you with the requested *four words:* all your family's earnestness to have the honour of her alliance: and the application of your two cousins to Miss Howe, by general consent, for that young lady's interest with her: but, having just touched upon these topics, she cut me short, saying, that was a cause before another tribunal: Miss Howe's letters to her were upon that subject; and she would write her thoughts to *her* as soon as she was able.

I then attempted more particularly to clear you of having any hand in the vile Sinclair's officious arrest; a point she had the generosity to *wish* you cleared of: and, having mentioned the outrageous letter you had written to me on this occasion, she asked if I had that letter about me?

I owned I had.

She wished to see it.

This puzzled me horribly: for you must needs think that most of the free things which, among us rakes, pass for wit and spirit, must be shocking stuff to the ears or eyes of persons of delicacy of that sex: and then such an air of levity runs through thy most serious letters; such a false bravery, endeavouring to carry off ludicrously the subjects that most affect thee; that those letters are generally the least fit to be seen, which ought to be most to thy credit.

Something like this I observed to her; and would fain have excused myself from showing it: but she was so earnest, that I undertook to read some parts of it, resolving to omit the most exceptionable.

I know thou'lt curse me for that; but I thought it better to oblige her than to be suspected myself; and so not have it in my power to serve thee with her, when so good a foundation was laid for it; and when she knows as bad of thee as I can tell her.

Thou rememberest the contents, I suppose, of thy furious letter. Her remarks upon the different parts of it which I read to her, were to the following effect:

"The plots and contrivances which he curses, and the exultings of the wicked wretches on finding me out, show me that all his guilt was premeditated: nor doubt I that his dreadful perjuries, and inhuman arts, as he went along, were to pass for fine stratagems; for witty sport; and to demonstrate a superiority of inventive talents! O my cruel, cruel brother! had it not been for thee, I had not been thrown upon so pernicious and so despicable a plotter!"

On that passage where thou sayest, *Let me know how she has been treated: if roughly, woe be to the guilty!* this was her remark, with an air of indignation: "What a man is your friend, sir! Is such a one as *he* to set himself up to punish the guilty? All the *rough* usage I could receive from them was infinitely *less*—" And there she stopped a moment or two: then proceeding—"And who shall punish *him?* What an assuming wretch! Nobody but *himself* is entitled to injure the innocent! He is, I suppose, on earth, to act the part which the malignant fiend is supposed to act below—dealing out punishments, at his pleasure, to every inferior instrument of mischief!"

What, thought I, have I been doing! I shall have this savage fellow think I have been playing him booty, in reading part of his letter to this sagacious lady! Yet if thou art angry, it can only, in reason, be at thyself; for who would think I might not communicate to her some of the least exceptionable parts of a letter (as a proof of thy sincerity in exculpating thyself from a criminal charge) which thou wrotest to thy friend, to convince *him* of thy innocence?

You have read enough, said she. He is a wicked, wicked man! What has he not vowed! What has he not invented! And all for what?—Only to ruin a poor young creature, whom he ought to have protected; and whom he had first deprived of all other protection!

She arose, and turned from me, her handkerchief at her eyes: and, after a pause, came towards me again. "I hope, said she, I talk to a man who has a better heart: and I thank you, sir, for all your kind, though ineffectual, pleas in my favour formerly, whether the motives for them were compassion, or principle, or both."

Enough, and too much, of this subject, sir! If he will never more let me behold his face, that is all I have now to ask of him. Indeed, indeed, clasping her hands, *I never will,* if I can, by any means not criminally desperate, avoid it.

What could I say for thee? There was no room, however, *at*

that time, to touch this string again, for fear of bringing upon myself a prohibition, not only of the subject, but of ever attending her again.

I gave some distant intimations of money matters. I should have told thee, that when I read to her that passage where thou biddest me force what sums upon her I can get her to take—she repeated, No, no, no, no! several times with great quickness; and I durst no more than just intimate it again—and that so darkly, as left her room to seem not to understand me.

Methinks I have a kind of holy love for this angel of a woman; and it is matter of astonishment to me that thou couldst converse with her a quarter of an hour together, and hold thy devilish purposes.

It is my opinion (if thou holdest thy purposes to marry) that thou canst not do better than to procure thy *real* aunts, and thy *real* cousins, to pay her a visit, and to be thy advocates: but, if they decline personal visits, letters from them, and from my Lord M., supported by Miss Howe's interest, may, perhaps, effect something in thy favour.

But these are only my hopes, founded on what I *wish* for thy sake. The lady, I really think, would choose death rather than thee: and the two women are of opinion, though they know not half of what she has suffered, that her heart is actually broken.

Mr. Belford to Robert Lovelace, Esq.

Wednesday, July 19.

This morning I took chair to Smith's; and, being told that the lady had a very bad night, but was up, I sent for her worthy apothecary; who, on his coming to me, approving of my proposal of calling in Dr. H.; I bid the women acquaint her with the designed visit.

It seems she was at first displeased; yet withdrew her objection: but, after a pause, asked them what she should do? She had effects of value, some of which she intended, as soon as she *could,* to turn into money; but, till then, had not a single guinea to give the doctor for his fee.

Mrs. Lovick said she had five guineas by her: they were at her service.

She would accept of three, she said, if she would take *that* (pulling a diamond ring from her finger) till she repaid her; but on no other terms.

Having been told I was below with Mr. Goddard, she desired to speak one word with me, before she saw the doctor.

She was sitting in an elbow-chair, leaning her head on a pillow; Mrs. Smith and the widow on each side her chair; her nurse, with a phial of hartshorn, behind her; in her own hand her salts.

Raising her head at my entrance, she inquired if the doctor knew Mr. Lovelace?

I told her no; and that I believed you never saw him in your life.

Was the doctor my friend?

He was; and a very worthy and skilful man. I named him for his eminence in his profession: and Mr. Goddard said he knew not a better physician.

I have but one condition to make before I see the gentleman; that he refuse not his fees from me. If I am poor, sir, I am proud. I will not be under obligation. You may *believe,* sir, I will not. I suffer this visit, because I would not appear ungrateful to the few friends I have left, nor obstinate to such of my relations as may some time hence, for their private satisfaction, inquire after my behaviour in my sick hours. So, sir, you know the condition. And don't let me be vexed: I am very ill; and cannot debate the matter.

Seeing her so determined, I told her, if it must be so, it should.

The doctor paid his respects to her with the gentlemanly address for which he is noted: and she cast up her sweet eyes to him with that benignity which accompanies her every graceful look.

I would have retired; but she forbid it.

He took her hand, the lily not of so beautiful a white; Indeed, madam, you are very low, said he: but, give me leave to say, that you can do more for yourself than all the faculty can do for you.

He then withdrew to the window. And, after a short conference with the women, he turned to me, and to Mr. Goddard, at the other window: We can do nothing here, speaking low, but by cordials and nourishment. What friends has the lady? She seems to be a person of condition; and, ill as she is, a very fine woman.—A single lady, I presume?

I whisperingly told him she was. That there were extraordinary circumstances in her case; as I would have apprised him, had I met with him yesterday. That her friends were very cruel to her; but that she could not hear them named without reproaching herself; though they were much more to blame than she.

I knew I was right, said the doctor. A love case, Mr. Goddard! A love case, Mr. Belford! There is one person in the world who can do her more service, than all the faculty.

Mr. Goddard said he had apprehended her disorder was in her mind; and had treated her accordingly: and then told the doctor what he had done: which he approving of, again taking her charming hand, said, My good young lady, you will require very little of our assistance. You must, in a great measure, be your own doctress. Come, *dear* madam (forgive me the familiar tenderness; your aspect commands love, as well as reverence; and a father of children, some of them older than yourself, may be excused for this familiar address), cheer up your spirits. Resolve to do all in your power to be well; and you'll soon grow better.

You are very kind, sir, said she. I will take whatever you direct. My spirits have been hurried. I shall be better, I believe, before I am worse. The care of my good friends here, looking at the women, shall not meet with an ungrateful return.

The doctor wrote. He would fain have declined his fee. As her malady, he said, was rather to be relieved by the soothings of a friend, than by the prescriptions of a physician, he should think himself greatly honoured to be admitted rather to *advise* her in the *one* character, than to *prescribe* to her in the *other*.

She answered that she should be always glad to see so humane a man: that his visits would *keep her in charity with his sex:* but that, were she to *forget* that he was her *physician*, she might be apt to abate of the confidence in his skill, which might be necessary to effect the amendment that was the end of his visits.

We all withdrew together; and the doctor and Mr. Goddard having a great curiosity to know something more of her story, at the motion of the latter we went into a neighbouring coffee-house, and I gave them, in confidence, a brief relation of it.

Three o'clock, Afternoon.

I just now called again at Smith's; and am told she is somewhat better; which she attributed to the soothings of her doctor. She expressed herself highly pleased with both gentlemen; and said that their behaviour to her was perfectly *paternal.*

Mrs. Smith told me that after we were gone, she gave the keys of her trunks and drawers to her and the widow Lovick, and desired them to take an inventory of them; which they did in her presence.

They also informed me that she had requested them to find her a purchaser for two rich dressed suits; one never worn, the other not above once or twice.

This shocked me exceedingly—*perhaps it may thee a little! ! !* Her reason for so doing, she told them, was that she should never live to wear them: that her sister, and other relations, were above wearing them: that her mother would not endure in her sight anything that was hers: that she wanted the money: that she would not be obliged to anybody, when she had effects by her for which she had no occasion: and yet, said she, I expect not that they will fetch a price answerable to their value.

As to disposing of the two suits of apparel, I told Mrs. Smith, that she should pretend that, upon inquiry, she had found a friend who would purchase the richest of them; but (*that she might not mistrust*) would stand upon a good bargain. And having twenty guineas about me, I left them with her, in part of payment; and bid her *pretend* to get her to part with it for as little more as she could induce her to take.

Adieu.

MR. LOVELACE TO JOHN BELFORD, ESQ.

M. Hall, Wedn. Night, July 19.

YOU MIGHT well apprehend that I should think you were playing me booty in communicating my letter to the lady.

You ask, who would think you might not read to her the least exceptionable parts of a letter written in my own defence? *I'll tell you who*—the man who, in the same letter that he asks this question, tells the friend whom he exposes to her resentment, "That there is such an air of levity runs through his most serious letters, that those of his are *least fit to be seen,* which ought to be *most to his credit.*" And now what thinkest thou of they self-condemned folly?

But as to thy opinion, and the two women's at Smith's, that her heart is broken; that is the true women's language: I wonder how *thou* camest into it: thou who hast seen and heard of so many *female deaths* and *revivals.*

I'll tell thee what makes *against* this notion of theirs.

Her time of life and charming constitution: the good she ever delighted to do, and fancied she was born to do; and which she may still continue to do, to as high a degree as ever; nay, higher; since I am no sordid varlet, thou knowest: her religious turn; a turn that will always teach her to bear *inevitable* evils with patience; the contemplation upon her last noble triumph over me, and over the whole crew; and upon her succeeding escape from us all: her will unviolated: and the inward pride of having *not deserved* the treatment she has met with.

How is it possible to imagine that a woman who has all these *consolations* to reflect upon, will die of a broken heart?

But now to current topics, and the present state of matters here. It is true, as my servant told thee, that Miss Howe had engaged, before this cursed woman's officiousness, to use her interest with her friend in my behalf: and yet she told my cousins, in the visit they made her, that it was her opinion that she would never forgive me. I send to thee enclosed copies of all that passed on this occasion between my Cousins Montague, Miss Howe, myself, Lady Betty, Lady Sarah, and Lord M. I long to know what Miss Howe wrote to her friend, in order to induce her to marry the *despicable plotter;* the *man whose friendship is no credit to anybody;* the *wicked, wicked man.*

Lady Sarah and Lady Betty, finding the treaty upon the success of which they have set their foolish hearts likely to run into length, are about departing to their own seats; having taken from me the best security the nature of the case will admit of, that is to say, *my word,* to marry the lady, if she will have me.

And, after all (methinks thou askest), art thou still resolved to repair, if reparation be put into thy power?

Why, Jack, I must needs own that my heart has now and then some retrograde motions, upon thinking seriously of the irrevocable ceremony.

'Tis ungentlemanly, Jack, *man* to *man,* to lie.—But matrimony I do not *heartily* love—although with a CLARISSA—yet I am in earnest to marry her.

Of this I am absolutely convinced, that if a man ever intends to marry, and to enjoy in peace his own reflections; and not be afraid of retribution, or of the consequences of his own example; he should never be a rake.

This looks like conscience; don't it, Belford?

But, being in earnest still, as I have said, all I have to do, in my present uncertainty, is to brighten up my faculties, by filing off the rust they have contracted by the town smoke, a long imprisonment in my close attendance to so little purpose on my fair perverse; and to brace up, if I can, the relaxed fibres of my mind, which have been twitched and convulsed like the nerves of some tottering paralytic, by means of the tumults she has excited in it; that so I may be able to present to her a husband as worthy as I can be of her acceptance; or, if she reject me, be in a capacity to resume my usual gaiety of heart, and show others of the misleading sex, that I am not discouraged, by the difficulties I have met with from this sweet individual of it, from endeavouring to make myself as acceptable to them as before.

Miss Howe to Miss Clarissa Harlowe

Thursday Morn. July 20.

What, my dearest creature, have been your sufferings! What must have been your anguish on so disgraceful an insult, committed in the open streets, and in the broad day!

How was I shocked at the receiving of your letter written by another hand, and only dictated by you! You must be very ill. Nor is it to be wondered at. But I hope it is rather from hurry, and surprise, and lowness, which *may* be overcome, than from a grief given way to, which may be attended with effects I cannot bear to think of.

But whatever you do, my dear, you must not despond! Hitherto you have been in no fault: but despair would be all your own; and the worst fault you can be guilty of.

My dear creature, send me a few lines, though *ever so few,* in your hand, if possible. For they will revive my heart; especially if they can acquaint me of your amended health.

His relations are persons of *so much* honour—they are so *very* earnest to rank you among them—the wretch is so *very* penitent: *every one* of *his* family says he is—*your own* are so implacable—your last distress, though the consequence of his former villainy, yet neither brought on by his direction, nor with his knowledge; and so much resented by him—that my mother is absolutely of opinion that *you should be his*—especially if, yielding to my wishes, as expressed in my letter, and those of all his friends, you *would* have complied, had it not been for this horrid arrest.

I will enclose the copy of the letter I wrote to Miss Montague last Tuesday, on hearing that nobody knew what was become of you; and the answer to it, underwritten and signed by Lord M., Lady Sarah Sadleir, and Lady Betty Lawrance, as well as by the young ladies; and also by the wretch himself.

I am obliged to accompany my mother soon to the Isle of Wight. My Aunt Harman is in a declining way, and insists upon seeing us both—and Mr. Hickman too, I think.

It would be death to me to set out for the little island, and not see you first: and yet my mother (fond of exerting an authority that she herself, by that exertion, often brings into question) insists that my next visit to you *must* be a congratulatory one as Mrs. Lovelace.

Your ever affectionate
Anna Howe.

Miss Clarissa Harlowe to Miss Howe

Thursday Afternoon.

You pain me, my dearest Miss Howe, by the ardour of your noble friendship. I will be very brief, because I am not well; yet a good deal better than I was; and because I am preparing an answer to yours of the 13th. But, beforehand, I must tell you, my dear, I will *not* have that man. Don't be angry with me. But indeed I won't. So let him be asked no questions about me, I beseech you.

I do *not* despond, my dear. I hope I may say, *I will not* despond. Is not my condition greatly mended? I thank Heaven it is!

I am no prisoner now in a vile house. I am not now in the power of that man's devices. I am not now obliged to hide myself in corners for fear of him. One of his intimate companions is become my warm friend, and engages to keep him from me, and that by his own consent. I am among honest people. I have all my clothes and effects restored to me. The wretch himself bears testimony to my honour.

Indeed, I am very weak and ill: but I have an excellent physician, Dr. H., and as worthy an apothecary, Mr. Goddard. Their treatment of me, my dear, is perfectly *paternal!* My mind, too, I can find, begins to strengthen: and methinks, at times, I find myself superior to my calamities.

I shall have sinkings sometimes. I must expect such. And my father's maledict——But you will chide me for introducing that, now I am enumerating my comforts.

Love me still, however. But let it be with a weaning love. I am not what I was when we were *inseparable* lovers, as I may say. Our *views* must now be different. Resolve, my dear, to make a worthy man happy, because a worthy man must make *you* so. And so, my dearest love, for the present adieu! Adieu, my dearest love! But I shall soon write again, I hope!

MR. LOVELACE TO JOHN BELFORD, ESQ.

M. Hall, Friday, July 21.

JUST RETURNED from an interview with this Hickman: a precise fop of a fellow, as starched as his ruffles.

He stroked his chin, and hardly knew what to say. At last, after parenthesis within parenthesis, apologizing for apologies, in imitation, I suppose, of Swift's digression in praise of digressions—I presume—I presume, sir, you were privy to the visit made to Miss Howe by the young ladies your cousins, in the name of Lord M., and Lady Sarah Sadleir, and Lady Betty Lawrance?

I *was*, sir: and Miss Howe had a letter afterwards, signed by his lordship and by those ladies, and underwritten by myself. Have you seen it, sir?

I can't say but I have. It is the principal cause of this visit: for Miss Howe thinks your part of it is written with such an air of levity—pardon me, sir—that she knows not whether you are in earnest or not in your address to *her* for her interest in her *friend*.

You see, Mr. Hickman, something of me. Do *you* think I am in jest, or in earnest?

I see, sir, you are a gay gentleman, of fine spirits, and all that. All I beg in Miss Howe's name is, to know if you really, and *bona fide*, join with your friends in desiring her to use her interest to reconcile you to Miss Harlowe?

I should be extremely glad to be reconciled to Miss Harlowe; and should owe great obligations to Miss Howe, if she could bring about so happy an event.

Well, sir, and you have no objections to marriage, I presume, as the condition of that reconciliation?

I never liked matrimony in my life. I must be plain with you, Mr. Hickman.

I am sorry for it: I think it a very happy state.

I hope you will find it so, Mr. Hickman.

I doubt not but I shall, sir. And I dare say, so would you, if you were to have Miss Harlowe.

If I could be happy in it with anybody, it would be with Miss Harlowe.

I am surprised, sir!—Then, after all, you don't think of marrying Miss Harlowe! After the hard usage——

What hard usage, Mr. Hickman? I don't doubt but a lady of her niceness has represented what would appear trifles to any other, in a very strong light.

If what I have had hinted to me, sir—excuse me—has been offered to the lady, she has more than trifles to complain of.

What would Miss Howe think if her friend is the *more* determined against me, because she thinks (in revenge to me, I verily believe that!) of encouraging another lover?

How, sir! Sure this cannot be the case! I can tell you, sir, if Miss Howe thought this, she would not approve of it at all: for, little as you think Miss Howe likes you, sir, and little as she approves of your actions by her friend, I know she is of opinion that she ought to have nobody living but you: and should continue single all her life if she be not yours.

But, I fancy, all this time you are in jest, sir. If not, we must surely have heard of him.

Heard of him! Ay, sir, we have all heard of him—but none of us care to be intimate with him—except this lady—and that, as I told you, in spite to me. His name, in short, is DEATH! DEATH! sir, stamping, and speaking loud, and full in his ear; which made him jump half a yard high.

You may gather, from what I have *said,* that I prefer Miss Harlowe, and that upon the justest grounds, to all the women in the world: and I wonder that there should be any difficulty to believe, from what I have signed, and from what I have promised to my relations, and enabled them to promise for me, that I should be glad to marry that excellent creature upon her own terms. I acknowledge to you, Mr. Hickman, that I have basely injured her. If she will honour me with her hand, I declare that it is my intention to make her the best of husbands. But, nevertheless, I must say that if she goes on appealing her case, and exposing us both, as she does, it is impossible to think the knot can be knit with reputation to either. And although,

Mr. Hickman, I have delivered my apprehensions under so ludicrous a figure, I am afraid that she will ruin her constitution; and, by seeking Death when she may shun him, will not be able to avoid him when she would be glad to do so.

This cool and honest speech let down his stiffened muscles into complacency. He was my very obedient and faithful humble servant several times over, as I waited on him to his chariot: and I was his almost as often.

And so *exit* Hickman.

Mr. Belford to Robert Lovelace, Esq.

Friday Noon, July 21.

This morning I was admitted, as soon as I sent up my name, into the presence of the divine lady.

She had had a tolerable night, and was much better in spirits; though weak in person; and visibly declining in looks.

Mrs. Lovick and Mrs. Smith were with her.

She had been writing, she said, a letter to her sister: but had not pleased herself in it; though she had made two or three essays: but that the last must go.

By hints I had dropped from time to time, she had reason, she said, to think that I knew everything that concerned her and her family; and, if so, must be acquainted with the heavy curse her father had laid upon her; which had been dreadfully fulfilled in one part, as to her prospects in this life, and that in a very short time; which gave her great apprehensions of the other part. She had been applying herself to her sister, to obtain a revocation of it.

I said something reflecting upon her friends; as to what they would deserve to be thought of, if the unmerited imprecation were not withdrawn. Upon which she took me up, and talked in such a dutiful manner of her parents, as must doubly condemn them (if they remain implacable) for their inhuman treatment of such a daughter.

I then besought her, while she was capable of such glorious instances of generosity and forgiveness, to extend her goodness to a man whose heart bled in every vein of it for the injuries he had done her; and who would make it the study of his whole life to repair them.

The women would have withdrawn when the subject became so particular. But she would not permit them to go. She told me, that if after this time I was for entering with so much earnestness into a subject so very disagreeable to *her,* my visits must not be repeated.

Meantime, you may let him know, said she, that I reject him with my whole heart—yet that, although I say this with such a determination as shall leave no room for doubt, I say it not however with passion. On the contrary, tell him that I am trying to bring my mind into such a frame, as to be able to *pity* him (poor perjured wretch! what has he not to answer for!); and that I shall not think myself qualified for the state I am aspiring to, if, after a few struggles more, I cannot *forgive* him too: and I hope, clasping her hands together, uplifted, as were her eyes, my dear *earthly* father will set me the example my *heavenly* one has already set us all; and, by forgiving his fallen daughter, teach her to forgive the man, who then, I hope, will not have destroyed my eternal prospects, as he has my temporal!

What magnanimity! No wonder a virtue so solidly founded could baffle all thy arts: and that it forced thee (in order to carry thy accursed point) to have recourse to those unnatural ones, which robbed her of her charming senses.

I repeated my offers to write to any of her friends; and told her that, having taken the liberty to acquaint Dr. H. with the cruel displeasure of her relations, as what I presumed lay nearest her heart, he had proposed to write himself, to acquaint her friends how ill she was, if she would not take it amiss.

It was kind in the *doctor,* she said: but begged that no step of that sort might be taken without her knowledge and consent. She would wait to see what effects her letter to her sister would have. All she had to hope for was, that her father would revoke his malediction, previous to the last blessing she should then implore: for the rest, her friends would think she could not suffer too much; and she was content to suffer: for now nothing could happen that could make her wish to live.

[Here Clarissa rehearses for Mr. and Mrs. Smith, Mrs. Lovick and Mr. Belford the chief events in her affecting story. Ed.]

She retired to her chamber soon after, and was forced, it seems, to lie down. We all went down together; and, for an hour and half, dwelt upon her praises; Mrs. Smith and Mrs. Lovick repeatedly expressing their astonishment, that there could be a man in the world capable of offending, much more of wilfully injuring, such a lady; and repeating that they had an angel in their house. I thought they had; and that as assuredly as there is a devil under the roof of good Lord M.

I hate thee heartily! By my faith I do! Every hour I hate thee more than the former!

J. Belford.

Mr. Lovelace to John Belford, Esq.

Sat. July 22.

What dost hate me for, Belford? And why more and more? Have I been guilty of any offence thou knewest not before? If *pathos* can move such a heart as thine, can it alter facts? What nonsense thy hatred, thy *augmented* hatred, when I still persist to marry her, pursuant to word given to thee, and to faith plighted to all my relations?

I rejoice that she is already so much better, as to hold with strangers such a long and interesting conversation.

Strange, confoundedly strange, and as perverse (that is to say, as *womanly*) as strange, that she should refuse, and sooner choose to die (O the obscene word! and yet how free does thy pen make with it to me!) than be mine, who offended her by acting *in* character, while her parents acted shamefully *out of theirs,* and when I am now willing to act *out of my own* to oblige her: yet *I* not to be forgiven! *They* to be faultless with her! And marriage the only medium to repair all breaches, and to salve her own honour! Surely thou must see the inconsistence of her *forgiving* unforgivingness, as I may call it!

I am very desirous to see what she has written to her sister; what she is about to write to Miss Howe; and what return she will have from the Harlowe-Arabella. Canst thou not form some scheme to come at the copies of these letters, or at the substance of them at least, and of that of her other correspondences?

I tell thee, that I am every day, every hour, more and more in love with her: and, at this instant, have a more vehement passion for her than ever I had in my life!—and that with views absolutely honourable, in *her own sense* of the word: nor have I varied, so much as in *wish,* for this week past; firmly fixed, and wrought into my very nature as the *life of honour,* or of generous confidence in me, was, in preference to the life of *doubt* and *distrust.*

I shall go on Monday morning to a kind of ball, to which Colonel Ambrose has invited me. It is given on a family account. I care not on what: for all that delights me in the thing is, that Mrs. and Miss Howe are to be there; Hickman, of course; for the old lady will not stir abroad without him. The colonel is in hopes that Miss Arabella Harlowe will be there likewise; for all the men and women of fashion round him are invited.

As I shall go in my lord's chariot, I would have had one of my Cousins Montague to go with me: but they both refused: and I shall not choose to take either of thy brethren. It would look as if I thought I wanted a bodyguard: besides, one of them is too rough, the other too smooth, and too great a fop for some of the staid company that will be there; and for *me* in particular. Men are known by their companions; and a fop (as Tourville, for example) takes great pains to hang out a sign by his dress of what he has in his shop. Thou, indeed, art an exception; dressing like a coxcomb, yet a very clever fellow. Nevertheless so clumsy a beau, that thou seemest to me to owe thyself a double spite, making thy ungracefulness appear the *more* ungraceful, by thy remarkable tawdriness, when thou art out of mourning.

But, although I put on these lively airs, I am sick at my soul! My whole heart is with my charmer! With what indifference shall I look upon all the assembly at the colonel's, my beloved in my ideal eye, and engrossing my whole heart?

MISS HOWE TO MISS ARABELLA HARLOWE

Thursday, July 20.

MISS HARLOWE,—I cannot help acquainting you (however it may be received, coming from *me*) that your poor sister is dangerously ill, at the house of one Smith, who keeps a glover's and perfume shop in King Street, Covent Garden. She knows not that I write. Some violent words, in the nature of an imprecation, from her father, afflict her greatly in her weak state. I presume not to direct you what to do in this case. You are her sister. I therefore could not help writing to you, not only for her sake, but for your own. I am, madam,

Your humble servant,

Anna Howe.

Miss Arabella Harlowe.

Thursday, July 20.

Miss Howe,—I have yours of this morning. All that has happened to the unhappy body you mention is what we foretold and expected. Let *him,* for whose sake she abandoned us, be her comfort. We are told he has remorse, and would marry her. We don't believe it, indeed. She *may be* very ill. Her disappointment may make her so, or ought. Yet is she the only one I know who is disappointed.

I cannot say, miss, that the notification from you is the *more* welcome for the liberties you have been pleased to take with our whole family, for resenting a conduct that it is a shame any young lady should justify. Excuse this freedom, occasioned by greater. I am, miss,

Your humble servant,

Arabella Harlowe.

Miss Howe.

Friday, July 21.

Miss Arabella Harlowe,—If you had half as much sense as you have ill-nature, you would (notwithstanding the exuberance of the latter) have been able to distinguish between a kind intention to you all (that you might have the less to reproach yourselves with, if a deplorable case should happen), and an officiousness I owed you not, by reason of freedoms at least reciprocal. I will not, for the *unhappy body's* sake, as you call a sister you have helped to make so, say all that I *could say*. If what I fear happen, you shall hear (whether desired or not) all the mind of

Anna Howe.

Miss Arabella Harlowe to Miss Howe

Friday, July 21.

Miss Ann Howe,—Your pert letter I have received. You, that spare nobody, I cannot expect should spare me. You are very happy in a prudent and watchful mother—but else mine cannot be exceeded in prudence: but we had all too good an opinion of somebody, to think watchfulness needful. There may possibly be some reason why *you* are so much attached to her in an error of this flagrant nature.

I help to make a sister unhappy! It is false, miss! It is all her doings!—except, indeed, what she may owe to somebody's advice—you know who can best answer for that.

Let us *know your mind* as soon as you please: as we shall know it to be *your* mind, we shall judge what attention to give it. That's all, from, etc.

Ar. H.

Miss Howe to Miss Arabella Harlowe

Sat. July 22.

It may be the *misfortune* of some people to engage *every*body's notice: others may be the *happier,* though they may be the more *envious,* for nobody's thinking them worthy of any. But one would be glad people had the sense to be thankful for that want of consequence which subjected them not to hazards they would hardly have been able to manage under.

I own to you, that had it not been for the prudent advice of that admirable somebody (whose principal fault is the superiority of her talents, and whose misfortune to be brothered and sistered by a couple of creatures who are not able to comprehend her excellences), I might at one time have been plunged into difficulties. But, pert as the superlatively pert may think me, I thought not myself *wiser,* because I was *older;* nor for that *poor* reason qualified to prescribe to, much less to maltreat, a genius so superior.

I repeat it with gratitude, that the dear creature's advice was of very great service to me—and this before my mother's *watchfulness* became necessary. But how it would have fared with me, I cannot say, had I had a brother or sister who had deemed it their *interest,* as well as a gratification of their *sordid envy,* to misrepresent me.

Your admirable sister, in effect, saved *you,* miss, as well as *me*—with this difference: you, *against* your will—me, *with* mine: and but for *your* own brother, and *his* own sister, would not have been lost herself.

Would to Heaven both sisters had been obliged with their own wills! The most admirable of her sex would never then have been out of her father's house! *You,* miss—I don't know what had become of *you.* But, let what would have happened, you would have met with the humanity you have not shown, whether you had deserved it or not: nor, at worst, lost either a kind sister, or a pitying friend, in the most excellent of sisters.

But why run I into length to such a poor thing? Why push I so weak an adversary? whose first letter is all low malice, and whose next is made up of falsehood and inconsistence, as well as spite and ill-manners! Yet I was willing to give you a *part* of my mind. Call for more of it; it shall be at your service: from one who, though she thanks God she is not your sister, is not your *enemy:* but that she is *not* the latter, is withheld but by two considerations; one, that you bear, though unworthily, a relation to a sister so excellent; the other, that you are not of consequence enough to engage anything but the pity and contempt of

A. H.

MRS. HARLOWE TO MRS. HOWE

Sat. July 22.

DEAR MADAM,—I send you, enclosed, copies of five letters that have passed between Miss Howe and my Arabella. You are a person of so much prudence and good sense, and (being a mother yourself) can so well enter into the distresses of all our family, upon the rashness and ingratitude of a child we once doted upon, that I dare say you will not countenance the strange freedoms your daughter has taken with us all. These are not the only ones we have to complain of; but we were silent on the others, as they did not, as these have done, spread themselves out upon paper. We only beg that we may not be reflected upon by a young lady who knows not what we have suffered, and do suffer, by the rashness of a naughty creature who has brought ruin upon herself, and disgrace upon a family which she has robbed of all comfort. I offer not to prescribe to your known wisdom in this case; but leave it to you to do as you think most proper. I am, madam,

Your most humble servant,

Charl. Harlowe.

Mrs. Howe

Sat. July 22.

Dear Madam,—I am highly offended with my daughter's letters to Miss Harlowe. I knew nothing at all of her having taken such a liberty. These young creatures have such romantic notions, some of *love*, some of *friendship*, that there is no governing them in either. Nothing but time, and dear experience, will convince them of their absurdities in both. I have chidden Miss Howe very severely. I had before so just a notion of what your whole family's distress must be, that, as I told your brother, Mr. Antony Harlowe, I had often forbid her corresponding with the poor fallen angel—for surely never did young lady more resemble what we imagine of angels, both in person and mind. But, tired out with her headstrong ways (I am sorry to say this of my own child), I was forced to give way to it again. And, indeed, so sturdy was she in her will that I was afraid it would end in a fit of sickness, as too often it did in fits of sullens.

I believe, however, you will have no more such letters from my Nancy. I have been forced to use compulsion with her upon Miss Clary's illness (and it seems she is very bad), or she would have run away to London, to attend upon her: and this she calls doing the duty of a friend; forgetting that she sacrifices to her romantic friendship her duty to her fond indulgent mother.

There are a thousand excellences in the poor sufferer, notwithstanding her fault: and, if the hints she has given to my daughter be true, she has been most grievously abused. But I think your forgiveness and her father's forgiveness of her ought to be all at your own choice; and nobody should intermeddle in that, for the sake of due authority in parents: and besides, as Miss Harlowe writes, it was what everybody expected, though Miss Clary would not believe it till she smarted for her credulity. And, for these reasons, I offer not to plead anything in alleviation of her fault, which is aggravated by her admirable sense, and a judgment above her years.

I am, madam, with compliments to good Mr. Harlowe, and all your afflicted family,

Your most humble servant,
Annabella Howe.

MISS HOWE TO MISS CLARISSA HARLOWE

Sat. July 22.

MY DEAREST FRIEND,—We are busy in preparing for our little journey and voyage: but I will be ill, I will be very ill, if I cannot hear you are better before I go.

I dispatch this by an extraordinary way, that it may reach you time enough to move you to *consider well* before you absolutely decide upon the contents of mine of the 13th, on the subject of the two Misses Montague's visit to me; since, according to what you write, must I answer them.

In your last you conclude very positively that you will not be his. To be sure, he rather deserves an infamous death than such a wife. But, as I really believe him innocent of the arrest, and as all his family are such earnest pleaders, and will be guarantees for him, I think the compliance with *their* entreaties, and *his own*, will be now the best step you can take; your own family remaining implacable, as I *can assure you they do*. He is a man of sense; and it is not impossible but he may make you a good husband, and in time may become no bad man.

My mother is entirely of my opinion: and on Friday, pursuant to a hint I gave you in my last, Mr. Hickman had a conference with the strange wretch: and though he liked not, by any means, his behaviour to himself; nor, indeed, had reason to do so; yet he is of opinion that he is sincerely determined to marry you if you will condescend to have him.

Perhaps Mr. Hickman may make you a private visit before we set out. If I may not attend you myself, I shall not be easy except he does. And he will then give you an account of the admirable character the surprising wretch gave of you, and of the justice he does to your virtue.

He was as acknowledging to his relations, though to his own condemnation, as his two cousins told me. All that he apprehends, as he said to Mr. Hickman, is that if you go on exposing *him*, wedlock itself will not wipe off the dishonour to both: and moreover, "that you would ruin your constitution by your immoderate sorrow; and, by seeking death when you might avoid it, would not be able to escape it when you would wish to do so."

So, my dearest friend, I charge you, if you *can*, to get over your aversion to this vile man. You may yet live to see many happy days, and be once more the delight of all your friends neighbours, and acquaintance, as well as a stay, a comfort, and a blessing, to your Anna Howe.

Miss Clarissa Harlowe to Miss Howe

Sunday, July 23

You set before me your reasons, enforced by the opinion of your honoured mother, why I should think of Mr. Lovelace for a husband.

And I have as well weighed the whole matter, and your arguments in support of your advice, as at present my head and my heart will let me weigh them.

I am, moreover, willing to believe, not only from your own opinion, but from the assurances of one of Mr. Lovelace's friends, Mr. Belford, a good-natured and humane man, who spares not to censure the author of my calamities (*I think*, with undissembled and undesigning sincerity), that that man is innocent of the disgraceful arrest:

And even, if you please, in sincere compliment to your opinion, and to that of Mr. Hickman, that (over-persuaded by his friends, and ashamed of his unmerited baseness to me) he would in earnest marry *me*, if I would have *him*.

"Well, and now, what is the result of all? It is this: that I must abide by what I have already declared—and that is (don't be angry at me, my best friend), that I have much more pleasure in thinking of death than of such a husband. In short, as I declared in my last, that I cannot (forgive me, if I say, I *will* not) ever be his.

"But you will expect my reasons: I know you will: and if I give them not, will conclude me either obstinate, or implacable, or both: and those would be sad imputations, if just, to be laid to the charge of a person who thinks and talks of *dying*. And yet, to say that resentment and disappointment have no part in my determination, would be saying a thing hardly to be credited. For I own I *have* resentments, strong resentments, but not unreasonable ones, as you will be convinced, if already you are not so, when you know all my story.

"I have one reason to give in support of my resolution, that, I believe, yourself will allow of: but having owned that I have resentments, I will begin with those considerations in which anger and disappointment have too great a share; in hopes that, having once disburdened my mind upon paper, and to my Anna Howe, of those corroding, uneasy passions, I shall prevent them for ever from returning to my heart, and to have their place supplied by better, milder, and more agreeable ones.

"My pride, then, my dearest friend, although a great deal mortified, is not *sufficiently* mortified, if it be necessary for me to submit to make that man my choice, whose actions are, and ought to be, my abhorrence! What! shall I, who have been treated with such premeditated and perfidious barbarity, as is painful to be thought of, and cannot with modesty be described, think of taking the violator to my heart? Can I vow duty to one so wicked, and hazard my salvation by joining myself to so great a profligate, now I *know* him to be so? Do you think your Clarissa Harlowe so lost, so *sunk*, at least, as that she could, for the sake of patching up, in the world's eye, a broken reputation, meanly appear indebted to the generosity, or perhaps *compassion*, of a man who has, by means so inhuman, robbed her of it? Indeed, my dear, I should not think my penitence for the rash step I took, anything better than a specious delusion, if I had not got above the least wish to have Mr. Lovelace for my husband.

"I once indeed hoped, little thinking him so *premediatedly* vile a man, that I might have the happiness to reclaim him: I vainly believed that he loved me well enough to suffer my advice for his good, and the example I humbly presumed I should be enabled to set him, to have weight with him; and the rather, as he had no mean opinion of my morals and understanding: but now, what hope is there left for this my *prime* hope? *Were* I to marry him, what a figure should I make, preaching virtue and morality to a man whom I had trusted with opportunities to seduce me from all my own duties? And then, supposing I were to have children by such a husband, must it not, think you, cut a thoughtful person to the heart, to look round upon her little family, and think she had given them a father destined, without a miracle, to perdition; and whose immoralities, propagated among them by his vile example, might, too probably, bring down a curse upon them?

"Let me then repeat, that I truly despise this man! If I know my own heart, indeed I do! I pity him! *Beneath* my very pity as he is, I nevertheless pity him! But this I could not do, if I still loved him: for, my dear, one must be greatly sensible of the baseness and ingratitude of those we love. I love him not, therefore! My soul disdains communion with him.

"The single life, at such times, has offered to me, as the life, the *only* life, to be chosen. But in *that,* must I not *now* sit brooding over my past afflictions, and mourning my faults till the hour of my release? And would not every one be able to assign the reason why Clarissa Harlowe chose solitude, and to sequester herself from the world?

"What then, my dear and only friend, can I wish for but death? And what, after all, *is* death? 'Tis but a cessation from mortal life: 'tis but the finishing of an appointed course: the refreshing inn after a fatiguing journey: the end of a life of cares and troubles; and, if happy, the beginning of a life of immortal happiness.

"But now, my dear, for *your* satisfaction let me say that, although I wish not for life, yet would I not, like a poor coward, desert my post when I *can* maintain it, and when it is my *duty* to maintain it.

"More than once, indeed, was I urged by thoughts so sinful: but then it was in the height of my distress: and once, particularly, I have reason to believe, I saved myself by my *desperation* from the most shocking personal insults; from a repetition, as far as I know, of his vileness; the base women (with so much reason dreaded by me) present, to intimidate *me,* if not to assist him!"

As I am of opinion, that it would have manifested more of revenge and despair than of principle, had I committed a violence upon myself, when the villainy was *perpetrated;* so I should think it equally criminal, were I now *wilfully* to neglect myself; were I *purposely* to run into the arms of death (*as that man supposes I shall do*), when I might avoid it.

Nor, my dear, whatever are the suppositions of such a short-sighted, such a low-souled man, must you impute to gloom, to melancholy, to despondency, nor yet to a spirit of faulty pride, or still *more* faulty revenge, the resolution I have taken never to marry *this;* and if not *this,* any man. So far from deserving this imputation, I do assure you (my dear and *only* love) that I will do everything I can to prolong my life, till God, in mercy to me, shall be pleased to call for it.

"But here, my dear, is another reason; a reason that will convince you yourself that I ought not to think of wedlock; but of a preparation for a quite different event. I am persuaded, as much as that I am now alive, that I shall not long live. The strong sense I have ever had of my fault, the loss of my reputation, my disappointments, the determined resentment of my friends, *aiding* the barbarous usage I have met with where I least deserved it, have seized upon my heart: seized upon it, before it was so well fortified by *religious considerations* as I hope it now is. Don't be concerned, my dear. But I am sure, if I may say it with as little presumption as grief, That God will soon *dissolve my substance;* and *bring me to death, and to the house appointed for all living.*"

And now, my dearest friend, you know all my mind. And you will be pleased to write to the ladies of Mr. Lovelace's family that I think myself infinitely obliged to them for their good opinion of me; and that it has given me greater pleasure than I thought I had to come in this life, that, upon the little knowledge they have of me, and that not personal, I was thought worthy (after the ill-usage I have received) of an alliance with their honourable family: but that I can by no means think of their kinsman for a husband: and do you, my dear, extract from the above such reasons as you think have any weight in them.

Clarissa Harlowe.

MRS. NORTON TO MISS CLARISSA HARLOWE

Monday, July 24.

EXCUSE, my dearest young lady, my long silence. I have been extremely ill. My poor boy has also been at death's door; and, when I hoped that he was better, he has relapsed.

Very angry letters have passed between your sister and Miss Howe. Every one of your family is incensed against that young lady. I wish you would remonstrate against her warmth; since it can do no good; for they will not believe but that her interposition has your connivance; nor that you are so ill as Miss Howe assures them you are.

Before she wrote, they were going to send up young Mr. Brand, the clergyman, to make private inquiries of your health, and way of life. But now they are so exasperated that they have laid aside their intention.

We have flying reports here, and at Harlowe Place, of some fresh insults which you have undergone: and that you are about to put yourself into Lady Betty Lawrance's protection. I believe they would now be glad (as I should be) that you would do so; and this, perhaps, will make them suspend for the present any determination in your favour.

How unhappy am I, that the dangerous way my son is in prevents my attendance on you! Let me beg of you to write me word how you are, both as to person and mind.

Your ever affectionate
Judith Norton.

MISS CLARISSA HARLOWE TO MRS. NORTON

Monday Night, July 24.

MY DEAR MRS. NORTON,—Had I not fallen into fresh troubles, which disabled me for several days from holding a pen, I should not have forborne inquiring after your health, and that of your son. I pray to Heaven, my dear good friend, to give you comfort in the way most desirable to yourself.

I am exceedingly concerned at Miss Howe's writing about me

to my friends. Least of all can I expect that either your mediation or hers will avail me.

She then gives a brief account of the arrest: of her dejection under it: of her apprehensions of being carried to her former lodgings: of Mr. Lovelace's avowed innocence as to that insult: of her release by Mr. Belford: of Mr. Lovelace's promise not to molest her: of her clothes being sent her: of the earnest desire of all his friends, and of himself, to marry her: of Miss Howe's advice to comply with their requests: and of her declared resolution rather to die than be his, sent to Miss Howe, to be given to his relations, but as the day before. After which she thus proceeds:

Now, my dear Mrs. Norton, you will be surprised, perhaps, that I should have returned such an answer: but, when you have everything before you, you, who know me so well, will not think me wrong. And, besides, I am upon a *better preparation* than for an earthly husband.

I have written to my sister. Last Friday I wrote. So the die is thrown. I hope for a gentle answer. But perhaps they will not vouchsafe me *any*. It is my *first* direct application, you know.

It will be a great satisfaction to me to hear of your perfect recovery; and that my foster-brother is out of danger. But why said I, *out of danger?*

Don't be uneasy you cannot answer your wishes to be with me. The people of the house where I am are courteous and honest. There is a widow who lodges in it (have I not said so formerly?), a good woman; who is the better for having been a proficient in the school of affliction.

I have as humane a physician (whose fees are his least regard), and as worthy an apothecary, as ever patient was visited by. My nurse is diligent, obliging, silent, and sober. So I am not unhappy *without:* and *within*—I hope, my dear Mrs. Norton, that I shall be every day more and more happy *within.*

Then, as I have told you, I have all my clothes in my own possession.

So you see, my venerable and dear friend, that I am not always turning the dark side of my prospects, in order to move compassion; a trick imputed to me, too often, by my hard-hearted sister; when, if I know my own heart, it is above all trick or artifice.

As to the day[1]—I have passed it, as I ought to pass it. It has been a very heavy day to me! More for my friends' sake, too, than for my own! How did *they* use to pass it! What a festivity! How have they now passed it! To *imagine* it, how grievous! Adieu, my dearest Mrs. Norton!

Adieu!

MISS CLARISSA HARLOWE TO MISS ARABELLA HARLOWE

Friday, July 21.

IF, MY DEAREST SISTER, I did not think the state of my health very precarious, and that it was my duty to take this step, I should hardly have dared to approach you after having found your censures so dreadfully justifed as they have been.

I have not the courage to write to my father himself; nor yet to my mother. And it is with trembling that I address myself to you, to beg of you to intercede for me, that my father will have the goodness to revoke that heaviest part of the very heavy curse he laid upon me, which relates to HEREAFTER: for, as to the HERE, *I have* indeed *met with my punishment from the very wretch in whom I was supposed to place my confidence.*

As I hope not for restoration to favour, I may be allowed to be very earnest on this head: yet will I not use any arguments in support of my request, because I am sure my father, were it in his power, would not have his poor child miserable for ever.

I have the most grateful sense of my mother's goodness in sending me up my clothes. I would have acknowledged the favour the moment I received them, with the most thankful duty, but that I feared any line from me would be unacceptable.

I would not give fresh offence: so will decline all other commendations of duty and love; appealing to my heart for both, where *both* are flaming with an ardour that nothing but death can extinguish: therefore only subscribe myself, without so much as a name,

My dear and happy sister,
Your afflicted servant.

[1] Clarissa's birthday.

A letter directed for me, at Mr. Smith's, a glover, in King Street, Covent Garden, will come to hand.

MR. BELFORD TO ROBERT LOVELACE, ESQ.

Edgware, Monday, July 24.

HER IMPLACABLE FRIENDS have refused her the current cash she left behind her; and wished, as her sister wrote to her, to see her reduced to want: probably, therefore, they will not be sorry that she is reduced to such straits; and will take it for a justification from Heaven of their wicked hard-heartedness. Thou canst not suppose she would take supplies from thee: to take them from me would, in her opinion, be taking them from thee. Miss Howe's mother is an avaricious woman; and, perhaps, the daughter can do nothing of that sort unknown to her; and, if she *could,* is too noble a girl to deny it, if charged. And then Miss Harlowe is firmly of opinion that she shall never want nor wear the things she disposes of.

The lady shut herself up at six o'clock yesterday afternoon; and intends not to see company till seven or eight this; not even her nurse—imposing upon herself a severe fast. And why? *It is her* BIRTHDAY! Blooming—yet declining in her very blossom! What must be her reflections! What ought to be thine!

MR. BELFORD TO ROBERT LOVELACE, ESQ.

Wednesday, July 26.

I CAME NOT to town till this morning early.

I hastened to Smith's; and had but a very indifferent account of the lady's health. I sent up my compliments; and she desired to see me in the afternoon.

Mrs. Lovick told me, that after I went away on Saturday, she actually parted with one of her best suits of clothes to a gentlewoman who is her (Mrs. Lovick's) benefactress, and who bought them for a niece who is very speedily to be married, and whom she fits out and portions as her intended heiress.

About three o'clock I went again to Smith's. I saw a visible alteration in her countenance for the worse; and Mrs. Lovick respectfully accusing her of too great assiduity to her pen, and of her abstinence the day before, I took notice of the alteration; and told her that her physician had greater hopes of her than she had of herself; and I would take the liberty to say that despair of recovery allowed not room for cure.

She said she neither despaired nor hoped.

Writing is all my diversion, continued she; and I have subjects that cannot be dispensed with.

She then stepped to her closet, and brought to me a parcel sealed up with three seals: Be so kind, said she, as to give this to your friend. A very grateful present it ought to be to him: for, sir, this packet contains all his letters to me. Such letters they are, as, compared with his actions, would reflect dishonour upon all his sex, were they to fall into other hands.

As to my letters to him, they are not many. He may either keep or destroy them, as he pleases.

I thought, Lovelace, I ought not to forego this opportunity to plead for you: I therefore, with the packet in my hand, urged all the arguments I could think of in your favour.

I would not interrupt you, Mr. Belford, said she, though I am far from being pleased with the subject of your discourse. The motives for your pleas in his favour are generous. But I have written my full mind on this subject to Miss Howe, who will communicate it to the ladies of his family.

Her apothecary came in. He advised her to the air, and blamed her for so great an application, as he was told she made, to her pen; and he gave it as the doctor's opinion, as well as his own, that she would recover, if she herself desired to recover, and would use the means.

But, noble-minded as they see this lady is, they know not half her nobleness of mind, nor how deeply she is wounded; and depend too much upon her *youth,* which I doubt will not do in this case, and upon *time,* which will not alleviate the woes of such a mind: for, having been bent upon doing good, and upon reclaiming a libertine whom she loved, she is disappointed in all her darling views, and will never be able, I fear, to look up with satisfaction enough in herself to make life desirable to her. Her grief seems to me to be of such a nature, that *time,* which alleviates most other persons' afflictions, will *give increase to hers.*

Thou, Lovelace, mightest have seen all this superior excellence, as thou wentest along. In every word, in every sentiment, in every action, is it visible. But thy cursed inventions and intriguing spirit ran away with thee.

Mr. Goddard took his leave; and I was going to do so too, when the maid came up, and told her a gentleman was below, who very earnestly inquired after her health, and desired to see her: his name Hickman.

She was overjoyed.

I would have withdrawn; but I suppose she thought it was likely I should have met him upon the stairs; and so she forbid it.

She shot to the stairs-head to receive him, and, taking his hand, asked half a dozen questions (without waiting for any answer) in relation to Miss Howe's health; acknowledging, in high terms, her goodness in sending him to see her, before she set out upon her little journey.

He gave her a letter from that young lady, which she put into her bosom, saying she would read it by and by.

He was visibly shocked to see how ill she looked.

You look at me with concern, Mr. Hickman, said she. O sir! times are strangely altered with me since I saw you last at my dear Miss Howe's! What a cheerful creature was I then!—my heart at rest!—but I will not pain you!

Indeed, madam, said he, I am grieved for you at my soul.

He turned away his face with visible grief in it.

Her own eyes glistened: but she turned to each of us, presenting one to the other—him to me, as a gentleman *truly* deserving to be *called so*—me to him, as *your* friend, indeed (how was I, at that instant, ashamed of myself!); but, nevertheless, as a man of humanity; detesting my friend's baseness; and desirous of doing her all manner of good offices.

Mr. Hickman received my civilities with a coldness, which, however, was rather to be expected on your account, than that it deserved exception on mine. And the lady invited us both to breakfast with her in the morning; he being obliged to return the next day.

MR. BELFORD TO ROBERT LOVELACE, ESQ.

Thursday, July 27.

I WENT this morning, according to the lady's invitation, to breakfast, and found Mr. Hickman with her.

Mr. Hickman and I went afterwards to a neighbouring coffee-house; and he gave me some account of your behaviour at the ball on Monday night, and of your treatment of him in the conference he had with you before that; which he represented in a more favourable light than you had done yourself: and yet he gave his sentiments of you with great freedom, but with the politeness of a gentleman.

He told me how very determined the lady was against marrying you; that she had, early this morning, set herself to write a letter to Miss Howe, in answer to one he brought her, which he was to call for at twelve, it being almost finished before he saw her at breakfast; and that at three he proposed to set out on his return.

This gentleman is a little finical and formal. But I think Mr. Hickman is an agreeable, sensible man, and not at all deserving of the treatment or the character you give him.

But you are really a strange mortal: because you have advantages in your person, in your air, and intellect, above all the men I know, and face that would deceive the devil, you can't think any man else tolerable.

Mr. Hickman tells me he should have been happy with Miss Howe some weeks ago (for all the settlements have been some time engrossed); but that she will not marry, she declares, while her dear friend is so unhappy.

. . . . . .

I threw myself in Mr. Hickman's way, on his return from the lady.

He was excessively moved at taking leave of her; being afraid, as he said to me (though he would not tell her so), that he should never see her again. She charged him to represent everything to Miss Howe in the most favourable light that the truth would bear.

He told me of a tender passage at parting; which was, that having saluted her at her closet door, he could not help once more taking the same liberty, in a more fervent manner, at the stairs-head, whither she accompanied him; and this in the thought, that it was the last time he should ever have that honour; and offering to apologize for his freedom (for he had pressed her to his heart with a vehemence that he could neither account for nor resist). "Excuse you, Mr. Hickman! that I will: you are my brother, and my friend: and to show you that the good man, who is to be happy with my beloved Miss Howe, is very dear to me, you shall carry to her this token of my love" (offering her sweet face to his salute, and pressing his hand between hers).

Thy true friend,
J. Belford.

MISS HOWE TO MISS CLARISSA HARLOWE

Tuesday, July 25.

YOUR two affecting letters were brought to me (as I had directed any letter from you should be) to the colonel's, about an hour before we broke up. I could not forbear dipping into them there; and shedding more tears over them than I will tell you of; although I dried my eyes as well as I could, that the company I was obliged to return to, and my mother, should see as little of my concern as possible.

How can I bear the thoughts of losing so dear a friend!

You may excuse your relations. It was ever your way to do so. But, my dear, other people must be allowed to judge as they please. I am not *their* daughter, nor the sister of your brother and sister—I thank Heaven I am not.

But if you are displeased with me for the freedoms I took so long ago as you mention, I am afraid, if you knew what passed upon an application I made to your sister very lately (in hopes to procure you the absolution your heart is so much set upon), that you would be still *more* concerned.

Once more, forgive me. I owned I was too warm. But I have no example to the contrary but from you: and the treatment you meet with is very little encouragement to me to endeavour to imitate you in your dutiful meekness.

You leave it to me to give a negative to the hopes of the noble family, whose only disgrace is that so very vile a man is so nearly related to them. But yet—alas! my dear, I am so fearful of consequences, so *selfishly* fearful, if this negative must be given —I don't know what I should say—but give me leave to suspend, however, this negative, till I hear from you again.

This earnest courtship of you into their splendid family is so *very* honourable to you—they *so justly* admire you—you must have had such a *noble triumph* over the base man—he is so *much* in earnest—the world knows so *much* of the unhappy affair—you may do *still* so *much* good—your will is *so* inviolate —your relations are *so* implacable—think, my dear, and *re*-think.

. . . . . .

Know then, my dear, that I accompanied my mother to Colonel Ambrose's. A splendid company, and all pleased with one another, till Colonel Ambrose introduced one who, the moment he was brought into the great hall, set the whole assembly into a kind of agitation.

It was your villain.

I thought I should have sunk as soon as I set my eyes upon him. My mother was also affected; and, coming to me, Nancy, whispered she, can you bear the sight of that wretch without too much emotion? If not, withdraw into the next apartment.

I could not remove. Everybody's eyes were glanced from him to me. I sat down, and fanned myself, and was forced to order a glass of water. Oh, that I had the eye the basilisk is reported to have, thought I, and that his life were within the power of it! —directly would I kill him.

He entered with an air so hateful to me, but so agreeable to every other eye, that I could have looked him dead for that too.

Miss D'Oily, upon his complimenting her, among a knot of ladies, asked him, in their hearing, how Miss Clarissa Harlowe did?

He heard, he said, you were not so well as he wished you to be, and as you deserved to be.

O Mr. Lovelace, said she, what have you to answer for on that young lady's account, if all be true that I have heard?

I have a great deal to answer for, said the unblushing villain: but that dear lady has so many excellences, and so much delicacy, that little sins are great ones in her eye.

Little sins! replied Miss D'Oily: Mr. Lovelace's character is so well known that nobody believes he can commit *little* sins.

You are very good to me, Miss D'Oily.

Indeed I am not.

Then I am the only person to whom you are *not* very good: and so I am the less obliged to you.

I still kept my seat, and he either saw me not or would not yet see me; and addressing himself to my mother, taking her unwilling hand, with an air of high assurance, I am glad to see you here, madam. I hope Miss Howe is well. I have reason to complain greatly of her: but hope to owe to her the highest obligation that can be laid on man.

She would have flung from him. But, detaining her hand—Less severe, dear madam, said he, be less severe in *this* place, I beseech you. May I not ask if Miss Howe be here?

She would not have been here, replied my mother, had she known whom she had been to see.

And is she here, then? Thank Heaven! He disengaged her hand, and stepped forward into company.

Dear Miss Lloyd, said he, with an air (taking her hand as he quitted my mother's), tell me, tell me, is Miss Arabella Harlowe here? Or will she be here? I was informed she would—and this, and the opportunity of paying my compliments to your friend Miss Howe, were great inducements with me to attend the colonel.

Miss Arabella Harlowe, excuse me, sir, said Miss Lloyd, would be very little inclined to meet you here, or anywhere else.

Perhaps so, my dear Miss Lloyd: but, perhaps, for that very reason, I am more desirous to see *her*.

Miss Harlowe, sir, said Miss Biddulph, with a threatening air, will hardly be here without her *brother*. I imagine, if one come, both will come.

Heaven grant they both may! said the wretch. Nothing, Miss Biddulph, shall *begin* from me to disturb this assembly, I assure you, if they do. One calm half-hour's conversation with that brother and sister would be a most fortunate opportunity to me, in presence of the colonel and his lady, or whom else they should choose.

Then turning round, as if desirous to find out the one or the other, or both, he 'spied me, and, with very low bow, approached me.

I was all in a flutter, you may suppose. He would have taken my hand. I refused it, all glowing with indignation: everybody's eyes upon us.

I went from him to the other end of the room, and sat down, as I thought, out of his hated sight: but presently I heard his odious voice, whispering, behind my chair (he leaning upon the back of it, with impudent unconcern), *Charming Miss Howe!* looking over my shoulder: *one request*—(I started up from my seat; but could hardly stand neither, for very indignation)—Oh, this sweet, but becoming disdain! whispered on the insufferable creature. I am sorry to give you all this emotion: but either here, or at your own house, let me entreat from you one quarter of an hour's audience. I beseech you, madam, but one quarter of an hour, in any of the adjoining apartments.

Not for a *kingdom*, fluttering my fan. I knew not what I did. But I could have killed him.

We are so much observed—else on my knees, my dear Miss Howe, would I beg your interest with your charming friend.

She'll have nothing to say to you.

I had not then your letters, my dear.

Killing words! But indeed I have deserved them, and a dagger in my heart besides. I am so conscious of my demerits, that I have no hope but in *your* interposition. Could I owe that favour to Miss Howe's mediation which I cannot hope for on any other account——

My mediation, vilest of men!—*my* mediation!—I abhor you! —from my *soul*, I abhor you, vilest of men! Three or four times I repeated these words, stammering too.

You can call me nothing, madam, so bad as I will call myself. I *have* been, indeed, the vilest of men: but now I am not so. Permit me—everybody's eyes are upon us!—but one moment's audience—to exchange but ten words with you, dearest Miss

Howe—in whose presence you please—for your dear friend's sake—but ten words with you in the next apartment.

It is an insult upon me, to presume that I would exchange *one* with you, if I could help it! Out of my way! Out of my sight—fellow!

And away I would have flung: but he took my hand. I was excessively disordered—everybody's eyes more and more intent upon us.

Mr. Hickman, whom my mother had drawn on one side, to enjoin him a patience which perhaps needed not to have been enforced, came up just then with my mother, who had him by his leading-strings—by his sleeve, I should say.

Mr. Hickman, said the bold wretch, be my advocate but for ten words in the next apartment with Miss Howe, in your presence, and in yours, madam, to my mother.

Hear, Nancy, what he has to say to you. To get rid of him, hear his *ten words*.

Excuse me, madam! his very breath—Unhand me, sir!

He sighed, and looked—Oh, how the practised villain sighed and looked! He then let go my hand, with such a reverence in his manner, as brought blame upon me from some, that I would not hear him. And this incensed me the more.

I was going out of the assembly in great disorder. He was at the door as soon as I.

How kind this is! said the wretch; and, ready to follow me, opened the door for me.

I turned back upon this, and, not knowing what I did, snapped my fan just in his face, as he turned short upon me; and the powder flew from his wig.

He then turned to my mother, resolved to be even with *her too:* Where, good madam, could miss get all this spirit?

The company round smiled; for I need not tell you that my mother's high-spiritedness is pretty well known.

The gentlemen were as ready as I to wish he had broken his neck, rather than been present, I believe: for nobody was regarded but he. So little of the fop; yet so elegant and rich in his dress: his person so specious: his air so intrepid: so much meaning and penetration in his face: so much gaiety, yet so little of the monkey: though a travelled gentleman, yet no affectation; no mere toupet-man; but all manly; and his courage and wit, the one so known, the other so dreaded.

When the wretch saw how industriously I avoided him (shifting from one part of the hall to another), he at last boldly stepped up to me, as my mother and Mr. Hickman were talking to me; and thus before them accosted me:

I beg your pardon, madam; but, by your mother's leave, I must have a few moments' conversation with you, either here, or at your own house; and I beg you will give me the opportunity.

Nancy, said my mother, hear what he has to say to you. In my presence you may: and better in the adjoining apartment, if it must be, than to come to you at our own house.

I retired to one corner of the hall, my mother following me, and he, taking Mr. Hickman under the arm, following her— Well, sir, said I, what have you to say? Tell me *here*.

I have been telling Mr. Hickman, said he, how much I am concerned for the injuries I have done to the most excellent woman in the world: and yet, that she obtained such a glorious triumph over me the last time I had the honour to see her, as, with my penitence, ought to have qualified her former resentments: but that I will, with all my soul, enter into any measures to obtain her forgiveness of me. My Cousins Montague have told you this. Lady Betty, and Lady Sarah, and my Lord M. are engaged for my honour. I know your power with the dear creature. My cousins told me you gave them hopes you would use it in my behalf. My Lord M. and his two sisters are impatiently expecting the fruits of it. You must have heard from her before now: I hope you have. And will you be so good as to tell me, if I may have any hopes?

If I must speak on this subject, let me tell you that you have broken her heart. You know not the value of the lady you have injured. You deserve her not. And she despises you as she ought.

Dear Miss Howe, mingle not passion with denunciations so severe. I must know my fate. I will go abroad once more, if I find her absolutely irreconcilable. But I hope she will give me leave to attend upon her, to know my doom from her own mouth.

It would be death immediate for her to see you. And what must *you* be, to be able to look her in the face?

I then reproached him (with vehemence enough you may believe) on his baseness, and the evils he had made you suffer: the distress he had reduced you to: all your friends made your enemies: the vile house he had carried you to: hinted at his villainous arts; the dreadful arrest: and told him of your present deplorable illness, and resolution to die rather than to have him.

He vindicated not any part of his conduct, but that of the arrest; and so solemnly protested his sorrow for his usage of you, accusing himself in the freest manner, and by *deserved* appellations, that I promised to lay before you this part of our conversation.

Now, my dear, you have before you the reason why I suspend the decisive negative to the ladies of his family: my mother, Miss Lloyd, and Miss Biddulph, who were inquisitive after the subject of our retired conversation, and whose curiosity I thought it was right, in some degree, to gratify (especially as those young ladies are of our select acquaintance), are all of opinion that you should be his.

You will let Mr. Hickman know your whole mind; and when he acquaints me with it, I will tell you all my own.

Meantime, may the news he will bring me of the state of your health be favourable! prays, with the utmost fervency,

Your ever faithful and affectionate

Anna Howe.

MISS CLARISSA HARLOWE TO MISS HOWE

Thursday, July 27.

MY DEAREST MISS HOWE,—After I have thankfully acknowledged your favour in sending Mr. Hickman to visit me before you set out upon your intended journey, I must chide you for suspending the decisive negative, which, upon such full deliberation, I had entreated you to give to Mr. Lovelace's relations.

I am sorry that I am obliged to *repeat* to you, my dear, who know me so well, that, were I sure I should live *many years*, I would not have Mr. Lovelace: much less can I think of him, as it is probable I may not live *one*.

Having in my former said so much on the freedoms you have

taken with my friends, I shall say the less now: but *your hint*, that something else has newly passed between some of them and you, gives me great concern, and that as well for *my own* sake as for *theirs;* since it must necessarily incense them against me. But since what is done cannot be helped, I must abide the consequences: yet I dread, *more than before,* what may be my sister's answer, if an answer be at all vouchsafed.

But if my letter should be answered, and that in such terms as will make me loath to communicate it to so warm a friend—you must not, my dear, take upon you to censure my relations; but allow for them, as they know not what I have suffered; as being filled with *just* resentments against me (*just* to them, if they *think* them just); and as not being able to judge of the reality of my penitence.

And after all, what can they do for me? They can only pity me: and what will that do, but augment their own *grief;* to which at present their *resentment* is an alleviation? For can they by their pity restore to me my lost reputation?

Your account of the gay unconcerned behaviour of Mr. Lovelace at the colonel's, does not surprise me at all, after I am told that he had the intrepidity to go thither, knowing who were *invited* and *expected.* Only this, my dear, I really wonder at, that Miss Howe could imagine that I could have a thought of such a man for a husband.

Since you are so loath, my dear, to send the desired negative to the ladies of his family, I will only trouble you to transmit the letter I shall enclose for that purpose; directed indeed to yourself, because it was to you that those ladies applied themselves on this occasion; but to be sent by you to any one of the ladies at your own choice.

Your ever affectionate and obliged
Clarissa Harlowe.

MISS CLARISSA HARLOWE TO MISS HOWE

Thursday, July 27.

MY DEAREST MISS HOWE,—Since you seem loath to acquiesce in my determined resolution, signified to you as soon as I was able to hold a pen, I beg the favour of you, by this, or by any other way you think most proper, to acquaint the worthy ladies who have applied to you in behalf of their relation, that, although I am infinitely obliged to their generous opinion of me, yet I cannot consent to *sanctify*, as I may say, Mr. Lovelace's repeated breaches of all moral sanctions, and hazard my *future* happiness by an union with a man, through whose premeditated injuries, in a long train of the basest contrivances, I have forfeited my *temporal* hopes.

Be pleased to acquaint them that I deceive myself, if my resolution on this head (however ungratefully, and even inhumanly, he has treated me) be not owing more to *principle* than *passion*. Nor can I give a stronger proof of the truth of this assurance, than by declaring that I *can* and *will* forgive him, on this one easy condition, *that he will never molest me more.*

In whatever way you choose to make this declaration, be pleased to let my most respectful compliments to the ladies of the noble family, and to my Lord M., accompany it. And do you, my dear, believe that I shall be, to the last moment of my life,

Your ever obliged and affectionate
Clarissa Harlowe.

Mr. Lovelace to John Belford, Esq.

Friday, July 28.

I am encouraged to hope, what it will be very surprising to me if it do not happen; that is, in plain English, that the dear creature is in the way to be a mamma.

This cursed arrest, because of the ill effects the terror might have had upon her, in that hoped-for circumstance, has concerned me more than on any other account. It would be the pride of my life to prove, in this charming frost-piece, the triumph of nature over principle, and to have a young Lovelace by such an angel; and then, for its sake, I am confident she will live and will legitimate it. And what a meritorious little cherub would it be, that should lay an obligation upon both parents before it was born, which neither of them would be able to repay! Could I be sure it is so, I should be out of all pain for her recovery; *pain*, I say, since were she to *die* (*die!* abominable word! how I hate it!) I verily think I should be the most miserable man in the world.

But the silly dear's harping so continually upon one string, dying, dying, dying, is what I have no patience with. I hope all this melancholy jargon is owing entirely to the way I would have her to be in. And it being new to her, no wonder she knows not what to make of herself; and so fancies she is breeding death, when the event will turn out quite the contrary.

Miss Howe to Miss Clarissa Harlowe

Friday Night, July 28.

I WILL NOW, my dearest friend, write to you all my mind, without reserve, on your resolution not to have this vilest of men. You gave me reasons so worthy of the pure mind of my Clarissa, in support of this your resolution, that nothing but self-love, lest I should lose my ever-amiable friend, could have prevailed upon me to wish you to alter it.

I have only one thing that saddens my heart on this occasion; and that is, the bad state of health Mr. Hickman (unwillingly) owns you are in.

For Heaven's sake, then, for the world's sake, for the honour of our sex, and for *my* sake, once more I beseech you, try to overcome this shock; and if you *can* overcome it, I shall then be as happy as I wish to be; for I cannot, indeed I cannot, think of parting with you for many, many years to come.

You wish I had not mediated for you to your friends. I wish so too; because my mediation was ineffectual; because it may give new ground for the malice of some of them to work upon; and because you are angry with me for doing so.

For this reason, I forbear saying anything on so nice a subject as your letter to your sister.

You intimate that were I actually married, and Mr. Hickman to *desire* it, you would think of obliging me with a visit on the occasion; and that perhaps, when with me, it would be difficult for you to remove far from me.

Lord, my dear, what a stress do you seeem to lay upon Mr. Hickman's *desiring* it! Policy, as well as veneration for *you*, would undoubtedly make the man, if not a fool, *desire* this.

I send this day to the Misses Montague, your letter of just reprobation of the greatest profligate in the kingdom; and hope I shall not have done amiss that I transcribe some of the paragraphs of your letter of the 23rd, and send them with it, as you at first intended should be done.

Your
Anna Howe.

Miss Howe to the two Misses Montague

Sat., July 29.

Dear Ladies,—I have not been wanting to use all my interest with my beloved friend, to induce her to forgive and be reconciled to your kinsman (though he has so ill deserved it); and have even *repeated* my earnest advice to her on this head.

You will see, by the enclosed, her immovable resolution, grounded on noble and high-souled motives, which I cannot but *regret* and *applaud* at the same time: *applaud,* for the justice of her determination, which will confirm all your worthy house in the opinion you had conceived of her unequalled merit; and *regret,* because I have but too much reason to apprehend, as well by that, as by the report of a gentleman just come from her, that she is in such a declining way as to her health, that her thoughts are very differently employed than on a continuance here.

The enclosed letter she thought fit to send to me unsealed, that, after I had perused it, I might forward it to you: and this is the reason it is superscribed by myself and sealed with my seal.

Believe me to be, with a high sense of your merits,

Dear ladies,
Your most obedient humble servant,
Anna Howe.

Mrs. Norton to Miss Clarissa Harlowe

Friday, July 28.

My dearest Young Lady,—I have the consolation to tell you that my son is once again in an hopeful way, as to his health. He desires his duty to you. He is very low and weak.

And so am I. But this is the first time that I have been able, for several days past, to sit up to write, or I would not have been so long silent.

Your letter to your sister is received and answered. You have the answer by this time, I suppose. I wish it may be to your satisfaction: but am afraid it will not: for, by Betty Barnes, I find they were in a great ferment on receiving yours, and much divided whether it should be answered or not. They will not yet believe that you are so ill as (to my infinite concern) I find you are. What passed between Miss Harlowe and Miss Howe has been, as I feared it would be, an aggravation.

Methinks I am sorry you refuse the wicked man: but doubt not, nevertheless, that your motives for doing so are more commendable than my wishes that you would not. But as you would be resolved, as I may say, on life, if you gave way to such a thought; and as I have so much interest in your recovery, I cannot forbear showing this regard to myself; and to ask you if you cannot get over your just resentments?—But I dare say no more on this subject.

What a dreadful thing indeed was it for my dearest tender young lady to be arrested in the streets of London! Yet this, to such a mind as yours, must be light, compared to what you had suffered before.

O my dearest Miss Clary, how shall we know what to pray for, when we pray, but that *God's will may be done,* and that we may be *resigned to it!*

I am glad you are with such honest people; and that you have all your effects restored.

Your talent at moving the passions is always hinted at; and this Betty of your sister never comes near me that she is not full of it. But as you say, whom has it moved that you *wished* to move? Yet were it not for this unhappy notion, I am sure your mother would relent. Forgive me, my dear Miss Clary; for I must try one way to be convinced if my opinion be not just. But I will not tell you what that is, unless it succeeds. I will try, in pure duty and love to *them,* as well as to *you.*

Your ever affectionate friend and servant,

Judith Norton.

MRS. NORTON TO MRS. HARLOWE

Friday, July 28.

HONOURED MADAM,—Being forbidden (without leave) to send you anything I might happen to receive from my beloved Miss Clary, and so ill, that I cannot attend to *ask* your leave, I give you this trouble, to let you know that I have received a letter from her; which, I think, I should hereafter be held inexcusable, as things may happen, if I did not desire permission to communicate to you, and that as soon as possible.

Applications have been made to the dear young lady from Lord M., from the two ladies his sisters, and from both his nieces, and from the wicked man himself, to forgive and marry him. This, in noble indignation for the usage she has received from him, she has absolutely refused.

The letter I have received will show how truly penitent the dear creature is; and if I have your permission, I will send it sealed up, with a copy of mine, to which it is an answer. But as I resolve upon this step without her knowledge (and indeed I do), I will not acquaint her with it unless it, be attended with desirable effects: because, otherwise, besides making me incur her displeasure, it might quite break her already half-broken heart. I am,

Honoured madam,
Your dutiful and ever obliged servant,
Judith Norton.

MRS. HARLOWE TO MRS. JUDITH NORTON

Sunday, July 30.

WE ALL KNOW your virtuous prudence, worthy woman: we all do. But your partiality to this your rash favourite is likewise known. And we are no less acquainted with the unhappy body's power of painting her distresses so as to pierce a stone.

Every one is of opinion that the dear naughty creature is working about to be forgiven and received; and for this reason it is that Betty has been forbidden (not by *me*, you may be sure!) to mention any more of her letters; for she did speak to my Bella of some moving passages you read to her.

This will convince you that nothing will be heard in her favour. To what purpose, then, should I mention anything about her? But you may be sure that I *will,* if I can have but one second. However, that is not at all likely, until we see what the *consequences* of her crime will be: and who can tell that?—She may—How can I speak it, and my once darling daughter unmarried!—She may be with child! This would perpetuate her stain. Her brother may come to some harm; which God forbid! One child's ruin, I hope, will not be followed by another's murder!

As to her grief and her present misery, whatever it be, she must bear with it; and it must be short of what I hourly bear for her! Indeed I am afraid nothing but her being at the last extremity of all will make her father, and her uncles, and her other friends, forgive her.

Her father indeed has, at her earnest request, withdrawn the curse, which, in a passion, he laid upon her, at her first wicked flight from us. But Miss Howe (*it is a sad thing, Mrs. Norton, to suffer so many ways at once!*) had made matters so difficult by her undue liberties with us all, as well by speech in all companies, as by letters written to my Bella, that we could hardly prevail upon him to hear her letter read.

These liberties of Miss Howe with us; the general cry against us abroad wherever we are spoken of; and the *visible,* and not seldom *audible,* disrespectfulness which high and low treat us with to our faces, as we go to and from church, and even *at* church (for nowhere else have we the heart to go), as if none of us had been regarded but upon her account; and as if she were innocent, we all in fault; are constant aggravations, you must needs think, to the whole family.

And is she *really* ill?—so *very* ill?—But she *ought* to sorrow. She has given a double measure of it.

But does she *really* believe she shall not *long* trouble us?—But O my Norton!—she must, she *will* long trouble us—for can she think her death, if we should be deprived of her, will put an end to our afflictions?

Perhaps I may find an opportunity to pay you a visit, as in your illness, and then may weep over the letter you mention, with you. But, for the future, write nothing to me about the poor girl that you think may not be communicated to us all.

Your unhappy friend,
Charlotte Harlowe.

MISS CLARISSA HARLOWE TO MRS. JUDITH NORTON

Sat., July 29.

I CONGRATULATE you, my dear Mrs. Norton, with all my heart, on your son's recovery; which I pray to God, with your own health, to perfect.

I write in some hurry, being apprehensive of the consequence of the hints you give of some method you propose to try in my favour (with my relations, I presume you mean): but you will not tell me what, you say, if it prove unsuccessful.

Now I must beg of you that you will not take any step in my favour with which you do not first acquaint me.

You suppose I should have my sister's answer to my letter by the time yours reached my hand. I have it; and a severe one, a very severe one, it is.

I have reason to be very thankful that my father has withdrawn that heavy malediction which affected me so much—a parent's curse, my dear Mrs. Norton!

But I can write nothing but what must give you trouble. I will therefore, after repeating my desire that you will not intercede for me but with my previous consent, conclude with the assurance, that I am, and ever will be,

Your most affectionate and dutiful
Clarissa Harlowe.

MISS ARAB. HARLOWE TO MISS CL. HARLOWE

Thursday, July 27.

O MY UNHAPPY LOST SISTER!--What a miserable hand have you made of your romantic and giddy expedition!—I pity you at my heart.

You may *well* grieve and repent! Lovelace has left you!—In what way or circumstances you know best.

I wish your conduct had made your case more pitiable. But 'tis your own seeking!

God help you!—for you have not a friend will look upon you! Poor, wicked, undone creature!—fallen, as you are, against warning, against expostulation, against duty!

But it signifies nothing to reproach you. I weep over you.

My poor mother!—your rashness and folly have made *her* more miserable than *you* can be. Yet she has besought my father to grant your request.

My uncles joined with her; for they thought there was a little more modesty in your letter than in the letters of your pert advocate: and my father is pleased to give me leave to write; but only these words for *him,* and no more: "That he withdraws the curse he laid upon you, at the first hearing of your wicked flight, so far as it is in his power to do it; and hopes that your present punishment may be all that you will meet with. For the rest, he will never own you, nor forgive you; and grieves he has such a daughter in the world."

All this, and more, you have deserved from him and from all of *us:* but what have you done to this abandoned libertine, to deserve what you have met with at *his* hands?—I fear, I fear, sister!—But no more! A blessed four months' work have you made of it.

My brother is now at Edinburgh, sent thither by my father (though he knows not this to be the motive), that he may not meet your triumphant deluder.

We are told he would be glad to marry you: but why then did he abandon you? He had kept you till he was tired of you, no question; and it is not likely he would wish to have you but upon the terms you have already without all doubt been *his.*

You ought to advise your friend Miss Howe to concern herself less in your matters than she does, except she could do it with more decency. She has written three letters to me: very insolent ones.

Monday last was your birthday. Think, poor ungrateful wretch, as you are! how we all used to keep it; and you will not wonder to be told that we ran away from one another that day. But God give you true penitence, if you have it not already! And it *will* be true, if it be equal to the shame and the sorrow you have given us all.

Your afflicted sister,
Arabella Harlowe.

Your Cousin Morden is every day expected in England. He, as well as others of the family, when he comes to hear what a blessed piece of work you have made of it, will wish you never had had a being.

MISS CLARISSA HARLOWE TO MISS HOWE

Sunday, July 30.

YOU HAVE given me great pleasure, my dearest friend, by your approbation of my reasonings, and of my resolution founded upon them, never to have Mr. Lovelace. This approbation is so *right* a thing, give me leave to say, from the nature of the case, and from the strict honour and true dignity of mind, which I always admired in my Anna Howe, that I could hardly tell to what, but to my evil destiny, which of late would not let me please anybody, to attribute the advice you gave me to the contrary.

But let not the ill state of my health, and what that may naturally tend to, sadden you. I have told you that I will not run away from life, nor avoid the means that may continue it, if God see fit: and if He do *not,* who shall repine at His will?

The shock which you so earnestly advise me to try to get above, was a shock the greatest that I could receive. But, my dear, as it was not occasioned by my *fault*, I hope I am already got above it. I hope I am.

I am more grieved (at times, however) for *others,* than for *myself*. And so I *ought*. For as to *myself,* I cannot but reflect that I have had an escape, rather than a loss, in missing Mr. Lovelace for a husband—even had he *not* committed the vilest of all outrages.

You are very obliging to me, *intentionally,* I know, when you tell me it is in my power to hasten the day of Mr. Hickman's happiness.

In the first place, you know it is *not* in my power to say *when*

I can dismiss my physician; and you should not put the celebration of a marriage *intended* by *yourself,* and so *desirable* to your *mother,* upon so precarious an issue.

I am glad you have sent my letter to Miss Montague. I hope I shall hear no more of this unhappy man.

Then, to this hour, I know not by what means several of his machinations to ruin me were brought about; so that some material parts of my sad story must be defective, if I were to sit down to write it. But I have been thinking of a way that will answer the end wished for by your mother and you full as well; perhaps better.

Mr. Lovelace, it seems, has communicated to his friend Mr. Belford all that has passed between himself and me, as he went on. Mr. Belford has not been able to deny it. So that (as we may observe by the way) a poor young creature, whose indiscretion has given a libertine power over her, has a reason *she little thinks of,* to regret her folly; since these wretches, who have no more honour in one point than in another, scruple not to make her weakness a part of their triumph to their brother-libertines.

I have nothing to apprehend of this sort, if I have the justice done me in his letters which Mr. Belford assures me I have: and therefore the particulars of my story, and the base arts of this vile man, will, I think, be best collected from those very letters of his (if Mr. Belford can be prevailed upon to communicate them); to which I dare appeal with the same truth and fervour as he did, who says: *O that one would hear me! and that mine adversary had written a book! Surely I would take it upon my shoulders, and bind it to me as a crown! For I covered not my transgressions as Adam, by hiding mine iniquity in my bosom.*

There is one way which may be fallen upon to induce Mr. Belford to communicate these letters; since he seems to have (and declares he always had) a sincere abhorrence of his friend's baseness to me: but that, you'll say when you hear it, is a strange one.

I think to make Mr. Belford the executor of my last will (don't be surprised): and with this view I permit his visits with the less scruple: and every time I see him, from his concern for me, am more and more inclined to do so. If I hold in the same mind, and if he accept the trust, and will communicate the materials in his power, those, joined with what you can furnish, will answer the whole end.

Your mother, I am sure, would not consent that *you* should take this office upon you. It might subject *Mr. Hickman* to the insults of that violent man. *Mrs. Norton* cannot, for several reasons respecting herself. My *brother* looks upon what I ought to have as his right: my *Uncle Harlowe* is already one of my trustees (as my Cousin Morden is the other) for the estate my grandfather left me: but you see I could not get from my own family the few guineas I left behind me at Harlowe Place; and my *Uncle Antony* once threatened to have my grandfather's will controverted. My *father!*—To be sure, my dear, I could not expect that my *father* would do all I wish should be done: and a *will* to be executed by a father for a daughter (parts of it, perhaps, absolutely against his own judgment), carries somewhat daring and prescriptive in the very *word.*

If indeed my *Cousin Morden* were to come in time, and would undertake this trust—but even *him* it might subject to hazards; and the more, as he is a man of great spirit; and as the other man (of *as* great) looks upon me (unprotected as I have long been) as his property.

Now Mr. Belford, as I have already mentioned, knows everything that has passed. You don't know, my dear, what instances of sincere humanity this Mr. Belford has shown, not only on occasion of the cruel arrest, but on several occasions since. And Mrs. Lovick has taken pains to inquire after his general character; and hears a very good one of him, for justice and generosity in all his concerns of *meum* and *tuum,* as they are called: he has a knowledge of law matters; and has two executorships upon him at this time, in the discharge of which his honour is unquestioned.

This is certain: my brother will be more acquiescent a great deal in such a case with the articles of my will, as he will see that it will be to no purpose to controvert some of them, which else, I dare say, he would controvert, or persuade my other friends to do so.

My father has been so good as to take off the heavy malediction he laid me under. I must be now solicitous for a last blessing; and that is all I shall presume to petition for. My sister's letter, communicating this grace, is a severe one: but as she writes to me as *from everybody,* how could I expect it to be otherwise?

If your relations in the little island join their solicitations with your mother's commands, to have your nuptials celebrated before you leave them, let me beg of you, my dear, to oblige them. How grateful will the notification that you have done so, be to

Your ever faithful and affectionate

Cl. Harlowe!

Miss Clarissa Harlowe to Miss Harlowe

Saturday, July 29.

I REPINE NOT, my dear sister, at the severity you have been pleased to express in the letter you favoured me with; because that severity was accompanied with the grace I had petitioned for; and because the reproaches of mine own heart are stronger then any other person's reproaches can be: and yet I am not half so culpable as I am imagined to be: as would be allowed, if all the circumstances of my unhappy story were known; and which I shall be ready to communicate to Mrs. Norton, if she be commissioned to inquire into them; or to you, my sister, if you can have patience to hear them.

I remembered with a bleeding heart what day the 24th of July was. I began with the eve of it; and I passed the day itself—*as it was fit I should pass it.* Nor have I any comfort to give to my dear and ever honoured father and mother, and to you, my Bella, but this—that, as it was the first *unhappy* anniversary of my birth, in all probability it will be the *last.*

Believe me, my dear sister, I say not this merely to move compassion; but from the *best* grounds. And as, on that account, I think it of the highest importance to my peace of mind to obtain one further favour, I would choose to owe to your intercession, *as my sister,* the leave I beg, to address half a dozen lines (with the hope of having them answered as I wish) to either or to both my honoured parents, to beg their *last blessing.*

This blessing is all the favour I have now to ask: it is all I *dare* to ask: yet am I afraid to rush at once, though by *letter,* into the presence of either. And if I did not ask it, it might seem to be owing to stubbornness and want of duty, when my heart is all humility and penitence. Only, be so good as to embolden me to attempt this task—write but this one line, "Clary Harlowe, you are at liberty to write as you desire." This will be enough—and shall to my last hour be acknowledged as the greatest favour by

Your truly penitent sister,
Clarissa Harlowe.

MRS. NORTON TO MISS CLARISSA HARLOWE

Monday, July 31.

MY DEAREST YOUNG LADY,—I must indeed own that I took the liberty to write to your mother, offering to enclose to her, if she gave me leave, yours of the 24th.

They would choose, no doubt, that you should owe to *themselves,* and not to my humble mediation, the favour for which you so earnestly sue, and of which I would not have you despair: for I will venture to assure you that your mother is ready to take the first opportunity to show her maternal tenderness: and this I gather from several hints I am not at liberty to explain myself upon.

I long to be with you, now I am better, and now my son is in a fine way of recovery. But is it not hard to have it signified to me, that at present it will not be taken well if I go? But if you would have me come, I will rely on my good intentions, and risk every one's displeasure.

Mr. Brand has business in town; to solicit for a benefice which it is expected the incumbent will be obliged to quit for a better preferment: and when there, he is to inquire privately after your way of life, and of your health.

He is one of those puzzling, over-doing gentlemen who think they see farther into matters than anybody else, and are fond of discovering mysteries where there are none, in order to be thought shrewd men.

I am just now told that you have written a second letter to your sister: but am afraid they will wait for Mr. Brand's report before further favour will be obtained from them; for they will not yet believe you are so ill as I fear you are.

But you would soon find that you have an indulgent mother, were she at liberty to act according to her own inclination. And this gives me great hopes that all will end well at last: for I verily think you are in the right way to a reconciliation.

Your ever affectionate
Judith Norton.

Your good mother has privately sent me five guineas: she is pleased to say, to help us in the illness we have been afflicted with; but, more likely, that I might send them to you as from myself. I hope, therefore, I may send them up, with ten more I have still left.

Miss Clarissa Harlowe to Mrs. Norton

Wednesday, Aug. 2.

You give me, my dear Mrs. Norton, great pleasure in hearing of yours and your son's recovery.

You tell me that you did actually write to my mother, *offering* to enclose to her mine of the 24th past: and you say it was not *required* of you. That is to say, although you cover it over as gently as you could, that your offer was rejected; which makes it evident that no plea will be heard for me. Yet you bid me hope that the grace I sued for would, *in time,* be granted.

The grace I then sued for was indeed granted: but you are afraid, you say, that they will wait for Mr. Brand's report before favour will be obtained in return to the second letter which I wrote to my sister: and you add that I have an indulgent mother, were she at liberty to act according to her own inclination; and that all will end well at last.

But what, my dear Mrs. Norton, what is the grace I sue for in my second letter? It is not that they will receive me into favour––if they think it is, they are mistaken. I do not, I cannot expect that: nor, as I have often said, should I, if they *would* receive me, bear to live in the eye of those dear friends whom I have so grievously offended. 'Tis only, simply, a blessing I ask: a blessing to *die* with; not to *live* with. Do they know that? And do they know that their unkindness will perhaps shorten my date? So that their favour, if ever they intend to grant it, may come too late?

Once more, I desire you not to think of coming to me. I have no uneasiness now, but what proceeds from the apprehension of seeing a man I would not see for the world, if I could help it; and from the severity of my nearest and dearest relations: a severity *entirely their own,* I doubt; for you tell me that my *brother is at Edinburgh!* You would therefore heighten their severity, and make yourself enemies besides, if you were to come to me—don't you see that you would?

Don't afflict yourself about money matters on my account. I have no occasion for money. I am glad my mother was so considerate to you.

Adieu, my ever indulgent friend. You say all will be at last happy—and I *know* it will—I confide that it will, with as much security, as you may, that I will be to my last hour

Your ever grateful and affectionate

Cl. Harlowe.

MR. LOVELACE TO JOHN BELFORD, ESQ.

Tuesday, Aug. 1.

I AM most confoundedly chagrined and disappointed: for here, on Saturday, arrived a messenger from Miss Howe with a letter to my cousins; which I knew nothing of till yesterday; when Lady Sarah and Lady Betty were procured to be here, to sit in judgment upon it with the old peer and my two kinswomen. And never was bear so miserably baited as thy poor friend!—And for what?—Why, for the cruelty of Miss Harlowe: for have I committed any *new* offence? And would I not have succeeded in her favour upon her own terms, if I could? And is it fair to punish me for what is my misfortune, and not my fault? Such *event-judging* fools as I have for my relations! I am ashamed of them all.

In that of Miss Howe was enclosed one to *her* from Miss Harlowe, to be transmitted to my cousins, containing a final rejection of me; and that in very vehement and positive terms; yet she pretends that in this rejection she is governed more by *principle* than *passion* (damned lie, as ever was told!). And, as a proof that she is, says that she *can* forgive me, and *does,* on this one condition, That I will never molest her more—the whole letter so written as to make *herself* more admired, *me* more detested.

"What the devil, cried I, is all this for? Is it not enough to be despised and rejected? Can I help her implacable spirit? Would I not repair the evils I have made her suffer?" Then was I ready to curse them all, herself and Miss Howe for company: and heartily I swore that she should yet be mine.

I now swear it over again to thee. "Were her death to follow in a week after the knot is tied, by the Lord of Heaven, it *shall* be tied, and she shall die a Lovelace." Tell her so, if thou wilt: but at the same time, tell her that I have no *view of her fortune;* and that I will solemnly resign that, and all pretensions to it, in whose favour she pleases, if she resign life issueless. I am not so low-minded a wretch as to be *guilty* of any sordid views to her fortune. Let her judge for herself, then, whether it be not for her honour rather to leave this world a Lovelace than a Harlowe.

But do not think I will entirely rest a cause so near my heart, upon an advocate who so much more admires his client's adversary than his client. I will go to town in a few days, in order to throw myself at her feet: and I will carry with me, or have at hand, a *resolute, well-prepared* parson; and the ceremony shall be performed, let what will be the consequence.

But if she will permit me to attend her for this purpose at either of the churches mentioned in the licence (which she has by her, and, thank Heaven! has not returned me with my letters), then will I not disturb her; but meet her at the altar in either church, and will engage to bring my two cousins to attend her, and even Lady Sarah and Lady Betty; and my Lord M. in person shall give her to me.

Or, if it will be still more agreeable to her, I will undertake that either Lady Sarah or Lady Betty, or both, shall go to town, and attend her down; and the marriage shall be celebrated in their presence, and in that of Lord M., either here or elsewhere, at her own choice.

Do not play me booty, Belford; but sincerely and warmly use all the eloquence thou art master of, to prevail upon her to choose one of these three methods. One of them she *must* choose—by my soul, she must.

. . . .

My Cousin Charlotte, finding me writing on with too much earnestness to have any regard for politeness to her, and guessing at my subject, besought me to let her see what I had written.

I obliged her. And she was so highly pleased on seeing me so much in earnest, that *she* offered, and I accepted her offer, to write a letter to Miss Harlowe; with permission to treat me in it as she thought fit.

Putting, therefore, my whole confidence in this letter, I postpone all my other alternatives, as also my going to town, till my empress send an answer to my Cousin Montague.

Miss Montague to Miss Clarissa Harlowe

Tuesday, Aug. 1.

Dearest Madam,—All our family is deeply sensible of the injuries you have received at the hands of one of it, whom you only can render in any manner worthy of the relation he stands in to us all: and if, as an act of mercy and charity, the greatest your pious heart can show, you will be pleased to look over his past wickedness and ingratitude, and suffer yourself to be our kinswoman, you will make us the happiest family in the world: and I can engage that Lord M., and Lady Sarah Sadleir, and Lady Betty Lawrance, and my sister, who are all admirers of your virtues and of your nobleness of mind, will for ever love and reverence you, and do everything in all their powers to make you amends for what you have suffered from Mr. Lovelace. This, madam, we should not, however, dare to petition for, were we not assured that Mr. Lovelace is most sincerely sorry for his past vileness to you; and that he will, on his knees, beg your pardon, and vow eternal love and honour to you.

Let me, *our dearest cousin,* entreat you to give me your permission for my journey to London; and put it in the power of Lord M., and of the ladies of the family, to make you what reparation they *can* make you, for the injuries which a person of the greatest merit in the world has received from one of the most audacious men in it; and you will infinitely oblige us all; and particularly her who repeatedly presumes to style herself

Your affectionate cousin and obliged servant,

Charlotte Montague.

Mr. Belford to Robert Lovelace, Esq.

Thursday Morning, Aug. 3, Six o'clock.

I was admitted to her presence last night; and found her visibly altered for the worse. When I went home, I had your letter of Tuesday last put into my hands. Let me tell thee, Lovelace, that I insist upon the performance of thy engagement to me that thou wilt not personally molest her.

Mr. Belford dates again on Thursday morning ten o'clock; and gives an account of a conversation which he had just held with the lady upon the subject of Miss Montague's letter to her, preceding, and upon Mr. Lovelace's alternatives, which Mr. Belford supported with the utmost earnestness. But, as the result of this conversation will be found in the subsequent letters, Mr. Belford's pleas and arguments in favour of his friend, and the lady's answers, are omitted.

Miss Clarissa Harlowe to Miss Montague

Thursday, Aug. 3.

Dear Madam,—I am infinitely obliged to you for your kind and condescending letter. A letter, however, which heightens my regrets, as it gives me a new instance of what a happy creature I might have been in an alliance so much approved of by such worthy ladies; and which, on their accounts, and on that of Lord M., would have been so reputable to myself, and was once so desirable.

But indeed, indeed, madam, my heart sincerely repulses the man, who, descended from such a family, could be guilty, *first*, of such premeditated violence as he has been guilty of; and, as *he* knows, *further* intended me, on the night previous to the day he set out for Berkshire; and *next*, pretending to spirit, could be so mean as to wish to lift into that family a person he was capable of abasing into a companionship with the most abandoned of her sex.

Allow me then, dear madam, to declare with fervour that I think I never could deserve to be ranked with the ladies of a family so splendid and so noble, if, by vowing love and honour at the altar to such a violator, I could *sanctify*, as I may say, his unprecedented and elaborate wickedness.

Permit me, however, to make one request to my good Lord M., and to Lady Betty and Lady Sarah, and to your kind self and your sister. It is, that you will all be pleased to join your authority and interests to prevail upon Mr. Lovelace not to molest me further.

Every worldly good attend you, dear madam, and every branch of the honourable family, is the wish of one whose misfortune it is, that she is obliged to disclaim any other title than that of, dear madam,

Your and their obliged and faithful servant,

Clarissa Harlowe.

MR. BELFORD TO ROBERT LOVELACE, ESQ.

Thursday Afternoon, Aug. 3.

I AM just now agreeably surprised by the following letter, delivered into my hands by a messenger from the lady. The letter she mentions, as enclosed, I have returned, without taking a copy of it. The contents of it will soon be communicated to you, I presume, by other hands. They are an absolute rejection of thee—*Poor Lovelace!*

TO JOHN BELFORD, ESQ.

Aug. 3.

SIR,—You have frequently offered to oblige me in anything that shall be within your power: and I have such an opinion of you, as to be willing to hope that at the times you made these offers you meant more than mere compliment.

I have, therefore, two requests to make to you: the first I will now mention; the other, if this shall be complied with, otherwise not.

It behoves me to leave behind me such an account as may clear up my conduct to several of my friends who will not at present concern themselves about me: and Miss Howe, and her mother, are very solicitous that I will do so.

It is very evident to me that your wicked friend has given you, from time to time, a circumstantial account of all his behaviour *to* me, and devices *against* me; and you have more than once assured me that he has done my character all the justice I could wish for, both by writing and speech.

Now, sir, if I may have a fair, a faithful specimen from his letters or accounts to you, written upon some of the most interesting occasions, I shall be able to judge whether there will or will not be a necessity for me, for my honour's sake, to enter upon the solicited task.

If, sir, you think fit to comply with my request, the passages I would wish to be transcribed are those which he has written to you on or about the 7th and 8th of June, when I was alarmed by the wicked pretence of a fire; and what he has written from Sunday, June 11, to the 19th. And in doing this you will much oblige

Your humble servant,
Cl. Harlowe.

Now, Lovelace, I see not why I may not oblige her, upon her honour, and under the restrictions, and for the reasons she has given; and this without breach of the confidence due to friendly communications.

I long to know what the second request is: but this I know, that if it be anything less than cutting *thy* throat, or endangering *my* own neck, I will certainly comply; and be proud of having it in my power to oblige her.

MR. BELFORD TO MISS CLARISSA HARLOWE

Aug. 3, 4.

MADAM,—You have engaged me to communicate to you, upon honour, what Mr. Lovelace has written to me in relation to yourself, in the period preceding your going to Hampstead, and in that between the 11th and 19th of June: and you assure me you have no view in this request but to see if it be necessary for you, from the account he gives, to touch the painful subjects yourself, for the sake of your own character.

Your commands, madam, are of a very delicate nature, as they may seem to affect the *secrets of private friendship*: but as I know you are not capable of a view, the motives to which you will not own; and as I think the communication may do some credit to my unhappy friend's character, as an *ingenuous* man; though his actions by the most excellent woman in the world have lost him all title to that of an *honourable* one; I obey you with the greater cheerfulness.

He then proceeds with his extracts, and concludes them with an address to her in his friend's behalf, in the following words:

"And now, madam, I have fulfilled your commands; and, I hope, have not disserved my friend with you; since you will hereby see the justice he does to your virtue in every line he writes.

I am, madam, with the most profound veneration,

Your most faithful humble servant,

J. Belford.

Miss Clarissa Harlowe to John Belford, Esq.

Friday, Aug. 4.

Sir,—I hold myself extremely obliged to you for your communications. I will make no use of them that you shall have reason to reproach either yourself or me with.

. . . . . .

And now, sir, acknowledging gratefully your favour in the extracts, I come to the second request I had to make you; which requires a great deal of courage to mention: and which courage nothing but a great deal of distress, and a very destitute condition, can give. But, if improper, I can but be denied; and dare to say I shall be at least excused.

"If then I request the *only* person possessed of materials that will enable him to do my character justice;

"And who has courage, independence, and ability to oblige me;

"To be the protector of my memory, as I may say;

"And to be my *executor;* and to see some of my dying requests performed;

"And if I leave it to him to do the whole in his own way, manner, and time; consulting, however, in requisite cases, my dear Miss Howe;

"I presume to hope that this my second request may be granted."

Clarissa Harlowe.

MR. BELFORD TO MISS CLARISSA HARLOWE

Friday, Aug. 4.

MADAM,—I am so sensible of the honour done me in yours of this day, that I would not delay for one moment the answering of it. I hope you will live to see many happy years; and to be your own executrix in those points which your heart is most set upon. But, in case of survivorship, I most cheerfully accept of the sacred office you are pleased to offer me; and you may absolutely rely upon my fidelity, and, if possible, upon the literal performance of every article you shall enjoin me.

All I beg is that you will not suffer any future candidate or event to displace me; unless some new instances of unworthiness appear either in the morals or behaviour of,

Madam,

Your most obliged and faithful servant,

J. Belford.

MR. BELFORD TO ROBERT LOVELACE, ESQ.

Friday Night, Aug 4.

I HAVE actually delivered to the lady the extracts she requested me to give her from your letters.

The lady is extremely uneasy at the thoughts of your attempting to visit her. For Heaven's sake (your word being given), and for pity's sake (for she is really in a very weak and languishing way), let me beg of you not to think of it.

But what thinkest thou is the second request she had to make to me? No other than that I would be her *executor!* Her motives will appear before thee in proper time; and then, I dare to answer, will be satisfactory.

You cannot imagine how proud I am of this trust. I am afraid I shall too soon come into the execution of it.

Saturday Morning, Aug. 5.

I am just returned from visiting the lady, and thanking her in person for the honour she has done me; and assuring her, if called to the sacred trust, of the utmost fidelity and exactness.

I found her very ill. She said she had received a second hard-hearted letter from her sister; and she had been writing a letter (and that on her knees) directly to her mother; which, *before,* she had not had the courage to do. It was for a last blessing and forgiveness.

MISS ARAB. HARLOWE TO MISS CL. HARLOWE

Thursday Morn., Aug. 3.

SISTER CLARY,—I wish you would not trouble me with any more of your letters. You had always a knack at writing; and depended upon making every one do what you would when you wrote. But your wit and your folly have undone you. And now, as all naughty creatures do, when they can't help themselves, you come begging and praying, and make others as uneasy as yourself.

When I wrote last to you, I *expected* that I should not be at rest.

And so you'd creep on, by little and little, till you'll want to be received again.

But you only hope for *forgiveness* and a *blessing,* you say. A blessing for what, Sister Clary? Think for what! However, I read your letter to my father and mother.

I won't tell you what my father said—one who has the true sense you boast to have of your misdeeds may guess, without my telling you, what a justly incensed father would say on such an occasion.

My poor mother—O wretch! what has not your ungrateful folly cost my poor mother! Had you been less a darling, you would not, perhaps, have been so graceless: but I never in my life saw a cockered favourite come to good.

My heart is full, and I can't help writing my mind; for your crimes have disgraced us all; and I am afraid and ashamed to go to any public or private assembly or diversion: and why?—I *need* not say why, when your actions are the subjects either of the open talk or of the affronting whispers of both sexes at all such places.

Your grieved sister,
Arabella Harlowe.

MISS CLARISSA HARLOWE TO HER MOTHER

Sat., Aug. 5.

HONOURED MADAM,—No self-convicted criminal ever approached her angry and just judge with greater awe, nor with a truer contrition, than I do you by these lines.

Indeed I must say, that if the matter of my humble prayer had not respected my future welfare, I had not dared to take this liberty. But my heart is set upon it, as upon a thing next to God Almighty's forgiveness necessary for me.

Had my happy sister known my distresses, she would not have wrung my heart, as she has done, by a severity which I must needs think unkind and unsisterly.

But complaint of any unkindness from her belongs not to me: yet, as she is pleased to write that it must be seen that my penitence is less owing to disappointment than to true conviction, permit me, madam, to insist upon it, that, if such a plea can be allowed me, I am actually *entitled* to the blessing I sue for; since my humble prayer is founded upon a true and unfeigned repentance: and this you will the readier believe, if the creature who never, to the best of her remembrance, told her mamma a wilful falsehood, may be credited, when she declares, as she does, in the most solemn manner, that she met the seducer with a determination not to go off with him: that the rash step was owing more to compulsion than to infatuation: and that her heart was so little in it, that she repented and grieved from the moment she found herself in his power; and for every moment after, for several weeks *before* she had any cause from him to apprehend the usage she met with.

Wherefore, on my knees, my ever-honoured mamma, I do most humbly beg your blessing; say but, in so many words (I ask you not, madam, to call me your daughter): *Lost, unhappy wretch, I forgive you! and may God bless you!* This is all! Let me, on a blessed scrap of paper, but see one sentence to this effect under your dear hand, that I may hold it to my heart in my most trying struggles, and I shall think it a passport to Heaven. And, if I do not too much presume, and it were WE instead of I, and both your honoured names subjoined to it, I should then have nothing more to wish.

I can conjure you, madam, by no subject of motherly tenderness, that will not, in the opinion of my severe censurers (before whom this humble address must appear), add to my reproach: let me therefore, for God's sake, prevail upon you to pronounce me blessed and forgiven, since you will thereby sprinkle comfort through the last hours of

Your
Clarissa Harlowe.

MISS MONTAGUE TO MISS CLARISSA HARLOWE

Monday, Aug. 7.

DEAR MADAM,—We were all of opinion *before* your letter came, that Mr. Lovelace was utterly unworthy of you, and deserved condign punishment, rather than to be blessed with such a wife: and hoped far *more* from your kind consideration for *us* than any we supposed you could have for so base an *injurer.*

I am, however, commanded to write in all the subscribing names, to let you know how greatly your sufferings have affected us: to tell you that my Lord M. has forbid him ever more to enter the doors of the apartments where he shall be: and as you labour under the unhappy effects of your friends' displeasure, which may subject you to inconveniences, his lordship, and Lady Sarah, and Lady Betty, beg of you to accept, for your life, or, at least, till you are admitted to enjoy your own estate, of one hundred guineas per quarter, which will be regularly brought you by an especial hand, and of the enclosed bank bill for a beginning. And do not, dearest madam, we all beseech you, do not think you are beholden (for this token of Lord M.'s and Lady Sarah's and Lady Betty's love to you) to the *friends of this vile man;* for he has not one friend left among us.

We each of us desire to be favoured with a place in your esteem; and to be considered upon the same foot of relationship, as if what once was so much our pleasure to hope *would* be, *had* been. And it shall be our united prayer that you may recover health and spirits, and live to see many happy years: and, since this wretch can no more be pleaded for, that, when he is gone abroad, as he now is preparing to do, we may be permitted the honour of a personal acquaintance with a lady who has no equal. These are the earnest requests, dearest young lady, of

Your affectionate friends,
and most faithful servants,
M.
Sarah Sadleir.
Eliz. Lawrance.
Charl. Montague.
Marth. Montague.

MR. LOVELACE TO JOHN BELFORD, ESQ.

Sat. Aug. 5.

I AM so excessively disturbed at the contents of Miss Harlowe's answer to my Cousin Charlotte's letter of Tuesday last, that I have hardly patience or consideration enough to weigh what you write.

She had need indeed to cry out for mercy herself from *her* friends, who knows not how to show any! She is a true daughter of the Harlowes—by my soul, Jack, she is a true daughter of the Harlowes! Yet has she so many excellences that I must love her; and, fool that I am, love her the more for her despising me.

But no more of thy cursed knell; thy changes upon death's candlestick turned bottom upwards: she'll live to bury me; I see that: for, by my soul, I can neither eat, drink, nor sleep; nor, what is still worse, love any woman in the world but her.

Were she sure she should live but a day, she ought to die a wife. If her *Christian revenge* will not let her wish to do so for her *own* sake, ought she not for the sake of her family, and of her sex, which she pretends sometimes to have so much concern for?

I have one half of the house to myself; and that the best; for the great enjoy that least which costs them most: *grandeur* and *use* are two things: the common part is theirs; the state part is mine: and here I lord it, and *will* lord it as long as I please; while the two pursy sisters, the old gouty brother, and the two musty nieces, are stived up in the other half, and dare not stir for fear of meeting me: whom (that's the jest of it) they have forbidden coming into their apartments, as I have them into mine. And so I have them all prisoners, while I range about as I please.

But what a whirlwind does she raise in my soul by her proud contempts of me! Never, never was mortal man's pride so mortified! How does she sink me, even in my own eyes! "*Her heart* sincerely repulses me, she says, for my MEANNESS." Yet she intends to reap the benefit of what she calls so! Curse upon her *haughtiness,* and her *meanness,* at the same time!

I will venture one more letter to her, however; and if that don't do, or procure me an answer, then will I endeavour to see her, let what *will* be the consequence. If she get out of my way, I will do some noble mischief to the vixen girl whom she most loves and then quit the kingdom for ever.

And now, Jack, since thy hand is in at communicating the contents of private letters, tell her this, if thou wilt. And add to it, that if SHE abandon me, GOD will: and what then will be the fate of

Her

Lovelace!

MR. LOVELACE TO JOHN BELFORD, ESQ.

Monday, Aug. 7.

AND so you have actually delivered to the fair implacable extracts of letters written in the confidence of friendship! Take care—take care, Belford—I do indeed love you better than I love any man in the world: but this is a very delicate point. My heart is bent upon having her. And have her I will, though I marry her in the agonies of death.

She is very earnest, you say, that I will not offer to molest her. *That,* let me tell her, will absolutely depend upon herself, and the answer she returns, whether by pen and ink, or the contemptuous one of silence, which she bestowed upon my last four to her: and I will write it in such humble, and in such reasonable terms, that, if she be not a true Harlowe, she *shall* forgive me. But as to the *executorship* which she is for conferring upon thee—thou shalt not be her *executor:* let me perish if thou shalt. Nor shall she die. Nobody shall be anything, nobody shall *dare* to be anything to her but I—thy happiness is already too great, to be admitted daily to her presence; to look upon her, to talk to her, to hear her talk, while I am forbid to come within view of her window. What a reprobation is this of the man who was once more dear to her than all the men in the world! And now to be able to look down upon me, while her exalted head is hid from me among the stars, sometimes with scorn, at other times with pity, I cannot bear it.

This I tell thee, that if I have not success in my effort by letter, I will overcome the creeping folly that has found its way to my heart, or I will tear it out in her presence, and throw it at hers, that she may see how much more tender than her own that organ is, which she, and you, and every one else, have taken the liberty to call callous.

MR. LOVELACE TO MISS CLARISSA HARLOWE

Monday, Aug. 7.

LITTLE as I have reason to expect either your patient ear, or forgiving heart, yet cannot I forbear to write to you once more (as a more pardonable intrusion, perhaps, than a visit would be), to beg of you to put it in my power to atone, as far as it is possible to atone, for the injuries I have done you.

Your angelic purity, and my awakened conscience, are standing records of your exalted merit and of my detestable baseness: but your forgiveness will lay me under an eternal obligation to you—forgive me, then, my dearest life, my earthly good, the visible anchor of my future hope! As you (who believe you have something to be forgiven for) hope for pardon yourself, forgive me, and consent to meet me, upon your own conditions, and in whose company you please, at the holy altar, and to give yourself a title to the most repentant and affectionate heart that ever beat in a human bosom.

But perhaps a time of probation may be required. It may be impossible for you, as well from *indisposition* as *doubt,* so soon to receive me to absolute favour as my heart wishes to be received. In this case I will submit to your pleasure; and there shall be no penance which you can impose that I will not cheerfully undergo, if you will be pleased to give me hope that, after an expiation, suppose of months, wherein the regularity of my future life and actions shall convince you of my reformation, you will at last be mine.

Let me beg the favour then of a few lines, encouraging me in this *conditional* hope, if it must not be a still *nearer* hope, and a more generous encouragement.

I do most solemnly assure you that no temporal or worldly views induce me to this earnest address. I deserve not forgiveness from *you.* Nor do my Lord M. and his sisters from *me.* I despise them from my heart for presuming to imagine that I will be controlled by the prospect of any benefits in their power to confer. There is not a person breathing but yourself who shall prescribe to me. Your whole conduct, madam, has been so nobly principled, and your resentments are so admirably just, that you appear to me even in a divine light; and in an infinitely more amiable one at the same time, than you could have appeared in, had you not suffered the barbarous wrongs that now fill my mind with anguish and horror at my own recollected villainy to the most excellent of women.

Eternally yours,

R. Lovelace.

MISS CLARISSA HARLOWE TO LORD M. AND TO THE LADIES OF HIS HOUSE

Tuesday, Aug. 8.

EXCUSE ME, my good lord, and my ever-honoured ladies, from accepting of your noble quarterly bounty; and allow me to return, with all grateful acknowledgment and true humility, the enclosed earnest of your goodness to me.

But give me leave to express my concern that you have banished your kinsman from your presence and favour: since now, perhaps, he will be under less restraint than ever; and since I in particular, who had hoped by your influences to remain unmolested for the remainder of my days, may be again subjected to his persecutions.

Your ever grateful and obliged

Clarissa Harlowe.

Mr. Belford to Robert Lovelace, Esq.

Thursday Night, Aug. 10.

The lady was gone to chapel: but I had the satisfaction to hear she was not worse; and left my compliments, and an intimation that I should be out of town for three or four days.

On Sunday, in compliance with her doctor's advice, she took a little airing. Mrs. Lovick, and Mr. Smith and his wife, were with her. After being at Highgate Chapel at divine service, she treated them with a little repast; and in the afternoon was at Islington Church, in her way home; returning tolerably cheerful.

On Wednesday she received a letter from her Uncle Harlowe, in answer to one she had written to her mother on Saturday on her knees. It must be a very cruel one, Mrs. Lovick says, by the effects it had upon her: for, when she received it, she was intending to take an afternoon airing in a coach; but was thrown into so violent a fit of hysterics upon it, that she was forced to lie down; and (being not recovered by it) to go to bed about eight o'clock.

Miss Clarissa Harlowe to Robert Lovelace, Esq.

Friday, Aug. 11.

It is a cruel alternative to be either forced to see you or to write to you.

Were I capable of diguising or concealing my real sentiments, I might safely, I dare say, give you the remote hope you request, and yet keep all my resolutions. But I must tell you, sir, that, were I to live more years than perhaps I may weeks, and there were not another man in the world, I could not, I would not, be yours.

Religion enjoins me not only to forgive injuries, but to return good for evil. And accordingly I tell you that, wherever you go, I wish you happy.

And now having, with great reluctance I own, complied with one of your compulsatory alternatives, I expect the fruits of it.

Clarissa Harlowe.

Mr. John Harlowe to Miss Clarissa Harlowe

In answer to hers to her mother.

Monday, Aug. 7.

Poor ungrateful, naughty Kinswoman,—Your mother neither caring, nor being *permitted* to write, I am desired to set pen to paper, though I had resolved against it.

And so I am to tell you that your letters, joined to the occasion of them, almost break the hearts of us all.

Were we sure you had seen your folly, and were *truly* penitent, and, at the same time, that you were so very ill as you pretend, I know not what might be done for you.

Your mother *can't* ask, and your sister knows not in modesty *how* to ask; and so *I* ask you, If you have any reason to think yourself with child by this villain? You *must* answer this, and answer it truly, before anything can be resolved upon about you.

And this is all from

Your afflicted uncle,
John Harlowe.

Miss Clarissa Harlowe to John Harlowe, Esq.

Thursday, Aug. 10.

Honoured Sir,—It was an act of charity I begged: only for a last blessing, that I might die in peace. I ask not to be received again, as my severe sister is pleased to say is my view.

I could not look forward to my last scene with comfort, without seeking at least to obtain the blessing I petitioned for; and that with a contrition so deep, that I deserved not, were it known, to be turned over from the tender nature of a mother to the upbraiding pen of an uncle; and to be wounded by a cruel question, put by him in a shocking manner; and which a little, a very little time, will better answer than I can: for I am not either a hardened or shameless creature: if I were, I should not have been so solicitous to obtain the favour I sued for.

And permit me to say that I asked it as well for my father and mother's sake as for my own; for I am sure *they* at least will be uneasy, after I am gone, that they refused it to me.

I should still be glad to have theirs, and yours, sir, and all your blessings and your prayers; but, denied in such a manner, I will not presume again to ask it: relying entirely on the Almighty's; which is never denied when supplicated for with such true penitence as I hope mine is.

Your unhappy
Clarissa Harlowe.

Mr. Antony Harlowe to Miss Cl. Harlowe

Aug. 12.

Unhappy Girl!—Brother John has hurt your niceness, it seems, by asking you a plain question, which your mother's heart is too full of grief to let her ask; and modesty will not let your sister ask, though but the consequence of your actions. And yet it *must* be answered before you'll obtain from your father and mother, and us, the notice you hope for, I can tell you that.

You lived several guilty weeks with one of the vilest fellows that ever drew breath, at bed as well as board, no doubt (for is not his character known?); and pray don't be ashamed to be asked after what may naturally come of such free living. This modesty indeed would have become you for eighteen years of your life—you'll be pleased to mark that—but makes no good figure compared with your behaviour since the beginning of April last. So pray don't take it up, and wipe your mouth upon it, as if nothing had happened.

Would to the Lord you had acted up but to one half of what you know. Then had we not been disappointed and grieved, as we all have been: and nobody more than him who was

Your loving uncle,
Antony Harlowe.

Miss Clarissa Harlowe to Antony Harlowe, Esq.

Sunday, Aug. 13.

Honoured Sir,—As to the question required of me to answer, and which is allowed to be too shocking either for a mother to put to a daughter, or a sister to a sister; and which, however, *you* say I *must* answer:—O sir!—And *must* I answer? This then be my answer: "A *little* time, a much *less* time than is imagined, will afford a more satisfactory answer to my whole family, and even to my *brother* and *sister,* than I can give in words."

Nevertheless, be pleased to let it be remembered that I did not petition for a restoration to favour. I could not hope for that. Nor yet to be put in possession of any part of my own estate. Nor even for means of necessary subsistence from the produce of that estate—but only for a blessing; for a *last* blessing!

And may you, my dear uncle, and your no less now than ever dear brother, my second papa, as he used to bid me call him, be blessed and happy in them, and in each other! And, in order to this, may you all speedily banish from your remembrance for ever

The unhappy
Clarissa Harlowe.

Mr. Lovelace to John Belford, Esq.

Sunday, Aug. 13.

I don't know what a devil ails me; but I never was so much indisposed in my life.

. . . . . .

Lord M. paid me just now a cursed gloomy visit, to ask me how I do after bleeding. His sisters both drove away yesterday, God be thanked. But they asked not my leave; and hardly bid me good-bye. My lord was more tender, and more dutiful, than I expected. Men are less unforgiving than women. I have reason to say so, I am sure. For besides implacable Miss Harlowe and the old ladies, the two Montague apes haven't been near me yet.

. . . . . .

Neither eat, drink, nor sleep! A piteous case, Jack! If I should die like a fool now, people would say Miss Harlowe had broken my heart That she *vexes* me to the heart is certain.

. . . . . .

I was forced to leave off, I was so ill, at this place. And what dost think? Why, Lord M. brought the parson of the parish to pray by me; for his chaplain is at Oxford. I was lain down in my night-gown over my waistcoat, and in a doze: and, when I opened my eyes, who should I see but the parson kneeling on one side the bed; Lord M. on the other; Mrs. Greme, who had been sent for to *tend me,* as they call it, at the feet: God be thanked, my lord! said I, in an ecstasy. Where's Miss? For I supposed they were going to marry me.

But I grow better and better every hour, *I* say: the *doctor* says not: but I am sure I know best: and I will soon be in London, depend on't. But say nothing of this to my dear, cruel, and implacable Miss Harlowe.

Thy Lovelace.

Mr. Belford to Miss Clarissa Harlowe

Sat. Morn. Aug. 19.

Madam,—I think myself obliged in honour to acquaint you that I am afraid Mr. Lovelace will try his fate by an interview with you.

I wish to Heaven you could prevail upon yourself to receive his visit. All that is respectful, even to veneration, and all that is penitent, will you see in his behaviour, if you can admit of it. But as I am obliged to set out directly for Epsom, and as I think it more likely that Mr. Lovelace will *not* be prevailed upon than that he *will,* I thought fit to give you this intimation, lest, if he should come, you should be too much surprised

It is impossible he can be in town till Monday at soonest And if he resolve to come, I hope to be at Mr. Smith's before him.

I am, madam, with the profoundest veneration,

Your most faithful and most obedient servant,

J. Belford.

Mr. Lovelace to John Belford, Esq.

London, Aug. 21, Monday.

That thou mightest have as little notice as possible of the time I was resolved to be in town, I set out in my lord's chariot and six yesterday, as soon as I had dispatched my letter to thee, and arrived in town last night: for I knew I could have no dependence on thy friendship where Miss Harlowe's humour was concerned.

I had no other place so ready, and so was forced to go to my old lodgings, where also my wardrobe is; and there I poured out millions of curses upon the whole crew, and refused to see either Sally or Polly; and this not only for suffering the lady to escape, but for the villainous arrest, and for their detestable insolence to her at the officer's house.

I took a chair to Smith's, my heart bounding in almost audible thumps to my throat, with the assured expectation of seeing my beloved.

Your servant, madam.—Will, let the fellows move to some distance, and wait.

You have a young lady lodges here; Miss Harlowe, madam: is she above?

Sir, sir, and please your honour (the woman is struck with my figure, thought I): Miss Harlowe, sir! There is, indeed, such a young lady lodges here—but, but——

But what, madam? I must see her. One pair of stairs, is it not? Don't trouble yourself—I shall find her apartment. And was making towards the stairs.

Sir, sir, the lady—the lady is not at home. She is abroad—she is in the country——

In the country! Not at home! Impossible! You will not pass this story upon me, good woman. I *must* see her. I have business of life and death with her.

Indeed, sir, the lady is not at home! Indeed, sir, she is abroad!——

She then rung a bell: John, cried she, pray step down!—Indeed, sir, the lady is not at home.

Down came John, the good man of the house, when I expected one of his journeymen, by her saucy familiarity.

My dear, said she, the gentleman will not believe Miss Harlowe is abroad.

John bowed to my fine clothes: Your servant, sir. Indeed the lady is abroad. She went out of town this morning by six o'clock—into the country—by the doctor's advice.

Still I would not believe either John or his wife. I am sure, said I, she cannot be abroad. I heard she was very ill—she is not able to go out in a coach. Do you know Mr. Belford, friend?

Yes, sir; I have the honour to know 'Squire Belford. He is gone into the country to visit a sick friend. He went on Saturday, sir.

Well, and Mr. Belford wrote me word that she was exceeding ill. How then can she be gone out?

O sir, she is very ill, very ill, indeed—she could hardly walk to the coach.

Where is her servant?

Her servant, sir, is her nurse: she has no other. And *she* is gone with her.

Well, friend, I must not believe you. You'll excuse me; but I must go upstairs myself. And was stepping up.

John hereupon put on a serious and a less respectful face: Sir, this house is mine; and——

And what, friend? not doubting then but she was above. I must and will see her. I have authority for it. I am a justice of peace. I have a search-warrant.

And up I went; they following me, muttering, and in a plaguy flutter.

The first door I came to was locked. I tapped at it.

The lady, sir, has the key of her own apartment.

On the inside, I question not, my honest friend; tapping again. And being assured, if she heard my voice, that her timorous and soft temper would make her betray herself, by some flutters, to my listening ear, I said aloud, I am confident Miss Harlowe is here. Dearest madam, open the door: admit me but for one moment to your presence.

But neither answer nor fluttering saluted my ear; and, the people being very quiet, I led on to the next apartment; and, the key being on the outside, I opened it, and looked all round it and into the closet.

The man said he never saw so uncivil a gentleman in his life.

Hark thee, friend, said I; let me advise thee to be a little decent; or I shall teach thee a lesson thou never learnedst in all thy life.

Sir, said he, 'tis not like a gentleman to affront a man in his own house.

Then prithee, man, replied I, don't crow upon thine own dunghill.

I stepped back to the locked door: My dear Miss Harlowe, I beg of you to open the door, or I'll break it open; pushing hard against it, that it cracked again.

The man looked pale; and, trembling with his fright, made a plaguy long face; and called to one of his bodice-makers above: *Joseph, come down quickly.*

Joseph came down: a lion's-face, grinning fellow; thick, and short, and bushy-headed, like an old oak pollard. Then did Master John put on a sturdier look. But I only hummed a tune, traversed all the other apartments, sounded the passages with my knuckles, to find whether there were private doors, and walked up the next pair of stairs, singing all the way; John, and Joseph, and Mrs. Smith, following me trembling.

I looked round me there, and went into two open-door bedchambers; searched the closets, the passages, and peeped through the keyhole of another: No Miss Harlowe, by Jupiter! What shall I do! What shall I do! as the girls say. Now will she be grieved that she is out of the way.

I said this on purpose to find out whether these people knew the lady's story; and had the answer I expected from Mrs. Smith: I believe not, sir.

Why so, Mrs. Smith? Do you know who I am?

I can guess, sir.

Whom do you guess me to be?

Your name is Mr. Lovelace, sir, I make no doubt.

Well, but my good, dear Mrs. Smith, whither is the lady gone? And when will she return?

I can't tell, sir.

Don't tell fibs, Dame Smith; don't tell fibs; chucking her under the chin: which made John's upper lip, with chin shortened, rise to his nose. I am sure you know! But here's another pair of stairs: let us see; who lives up there? But hold, here's another room locked up, tapping at the door: Who's at home? cried I.

That's Mrs. Lovick's apartment. She is gone out, and has the key with her.

Widow Lovick! rapping again, I believe you are at home: pray open the door.

John and Joseph muttered and whispered together.

No whispering, honest friends: 'tis not manners to whisper.

Where shall I find my dear Miss Harlowe?

My beloved Miss Harlowe! (calling at the foot of the third pair of stairs) if you are above, for Heaven's sake answer me. I am coming up.

Sir, said the good man, I wish you'd walk down. The servants' rooms, and the working-rooms, are up those stairs, and another pair; and nobody's there that you want.

Shall I go up, and see if Miss Harlowe be there, Mrs. Smith?

You may, sir, if you please.

Then I won't; for if she was, you would not be so obliging.

Down I went, they paying diligent attendance on my steps.

Well, Mrs. Smith, with a grave air, I am heartily sorry Miss Harlowe is abroad. You don't tell me where she is?

Indeed, sir, I cannot.

You *will* not, you mean. She could have no notion of my coming. I came to town but last night. I have been very ill. She has almost broken my heart by her cruelty. You know my story, I doubt not. Tell her I must go out of town to-morrow morning. But I will send my servant to know if she will favour me with one half-hour's conversation; for, as soon as I get down, I shall set out for Dover in my way to France, if I have not a countermand from *her* who has the sole disposal of my fate.

MR. LOVELACE TO JOHN BELFORD, ESQ.

Tuesday, Aug. 22.

I MUST write on to divert myself: for I can get no rest; no refreshing rest. I awaked just now in a cursed fright. How a man may be affected by dreams!

"Methought I had an interview with my beloved. I found

her all goodness, condescension, and forgiveness. She suffered herself to be overcome in my favour by the joint intercessions of Lord M., Lady Sarah, Lady Betty, and my two Cousins Montague, who waited upon her in deep mourning; the ladies in long trains sweeping after them; Lord M. in a long black mantle trailing after *him*. They told her they came in these robes to express their sorrow for my sins against her, and to implore her to forgive me.

"I myself, I thought, was upon my knees, with a sword in my hand, offering either to put it up in the scabbard, or to thrust it into my heart, as she should command the one or the other.

"At that moment her Cousin Morden, I thought, all of a sudden, flashed in through a window with his drawn sword. Die, Lovelace! said he, this instant die, and be damned, if in earnest thou repairest not by marriage my cousin's wrongs!

"I was rising to resent this insult, I thought, when Lord M. ran between us with his great black mantle, and threw it over my face: and instantly my charmer, with that sweet voice which has so often played upon my ravished ears, wrapped her arms round me, muffled as I was in my lord's mantle: O spare, spare my Lovelace! and spare, O Lovelace, my beloved Cousin Morden! Let me not have my distresses augmented by the fall of either or both of those who are so dear to me!

"At this, charmed with her sweet mediation, I thought I would have clasped her in my arms: when immediately the most angelic form I had ever beheld, all clad in transparent white, descended in a cloud, which, opening, discovered a firmament above it, crowded with golden cherubs and glittering seraphs, all addressing her with: Welcome, welcome, welcome! and, encircling my charmer, ascended with her to the region of seraphims; and instantly, the opened cloud closing, I lost sight of *her*, and of the *bright form* together, and found wrapped in my arms her azure robe (all stuck thick with stars of embossed silver), which I had caught hold of in hopes of detaining her; but was all that was left me of my beloved Clarissa. And then (horrid to relate!) the floor sinking under *me*, as the firmament had opened for *her*, I dropped into a hole more frightful than that of Elden; and, tumbling over and over down it, without view of a bottom, I awaked in a panic; and was as effectually disordered for half an hour, as if my dream had been a reality."

Wilt thou forgive me troubling thee with such visionary stuff? Thou wilt see by it only that, sleeping or waking, my Clarissa is always present with me.

But here this moment is Will, come running hither to tell me that his lady actually returned to her lodgings last night between eleven and twelve; and is now there, though very ill.

The chair is come. I fly to my beloved.

Mr. Lovelace to John Belford, Esq.

Curse upon my stars! Disappointed again! It was about eight when I arrived at Smith's. The woman was in the shop.

So, old acquaintance, how do you now? I know my love is above. Let her be acquainted that I am here, waiting for admission to her presence, and can take no denial.

Indeed, sir, you are mistaken. The lady is not in this house, nor near it.

I'll see that.

Up went I without further ceremony; attended now only by the good woman.

I went into each apartment, except that which was locked before, and was now also locked: and I called to my Clarissa in the voice of love: but by the still silence was convinced she was not there.

I then went up two pair of stairs, and looked round the first room: but no Miss Harlowe.

And who, pray, is in this room?

A widow gentlewoman, sir—Mrs. Lovick.

Oh, my dear Mrs. Lovick! said I. I am intimately acquainted with Mrs. Lovick's character from my cousin John Belford. I must see Mrs. Lovick by all means. Good Mrs. Lovick, open the door.

She did.

Your servant, madam. Be so good as to excuse me. You have

heard my story. You are an admirer of the most excellent woman in the world. Dear Mrs. Lovick, tell me what is become of her?

The poor lady, sir, went out yesterday on purpose to avoid you.

How so? She knew not that I would be here.

She was afraid you would come, when she heard you were recovered from your illness.

Tell me of a truth, good Mrs. Lovick, where I may see this dear lady. Upon my soul, I will neither frighten nor offend her. I will only beg of her to hear me speak for one half-quarter of an hour; and, if she will have it so, I will never trouble her more.

Sir, said the widow, it would be death for her to see you. She was at home last night; I'll tell you truth: but fitter to be in bed all day. She came home, she said, to die; and, if she could not avoid your visit, she was unable to fly from you; and believed she should die in your presence.

And yet go out again this morning early? How can that be, widow?

Why, sir, she rested not two hours, for fear of you. Her fear gave her strength, which she'll suffer for when that fear is over. And finding herself, the more she thought of your visit, the less able to stay to receive it, she took chair, and is gone nobody knows whither.

She said: Whither *can* I go, Mrs. Lovick? Whither *can* I go, Mrs. Smith? Cruel, cruel man! Tell him I called him so, if he come again! God give him that peace which he denies me!

Sweet creature! cried I, and looked down, and took out my handkerchief.

The widow wept. I wish, said she, I had never known so excellent a lady, and so great a sufferer! I love her as my own child!

Mrs. Smith wept.

I then gave over the hope of seeing her for this time. I was extremely chagrined at my disappointment, and at the account they gave of her ill-health.

Would to Heaven, said I, she would put it in my power to repair her wrongs! I have been an ungrateful wretch to her.

I need not tell you, Mrs. Lovick, how much I have injured her, nor how much she suffers by her relations' implacableness.

Why will you not, sir, why will you not let her die in peace? 'Tis all she wishes for. You don't look like a hard-hearted gentleman! How can you thus hunt and persecute a poor lady, whom none of her relations will look upon?

And then she wept again. Mrs. Smith wept also. My seat grew uneasy to me.

I besought Mrs. Smith to let me have one of her rooms but till I could see her; and were it but for one, two, or three days I would pay a year's rent for it; and quit it the moment the interview was over. But they desired to be excused; and were sure the lady would not come to the house till I was gone, were it for a *month.*

While I was there, a letter was brought by a particular hand They seemed very solicitous to hide it from me; which made me suspect it was for her. I desired to be suffered to cast an eye upon the seal and the superscription; promising to give it back to them unopened.

Looking upon it, I told them I knew the hand and seal. It was from her sister. And I hoped it would bring her news that she would be pleased with.

They joined most heartily in the same hope: and giving the letter to them again, I civilly took my leave, and went away.

MR. BELFORD TO ROBERT LOVELACE, ESQ.

Tuesday, Aug. 22.

I AM EXTREMELY concerned for the poor, unprotected lady; she was so excessively low and weak on Saturday that I could not be admitted to her speech: and to be driven out of her lodgings, when it was fitter for her to be in bed, is such a piece of cruelty as he only could be guilty of, who could act as thou hast done by such an angel.

Canst thou thyself say, on reflection, that it has not the look of a wicked and hardened sportiveness in thee, for the sake of a wanton humour only (since it can answer no end that thou proposest to thyself, but the direct contrary), to hunt from place to place a poor lady, who, like a harmless deer that has already a barbed shaft in her breast, seeks only a refuge from thee, in the shades of death?

MR. LOVELACE TO JOHN BELFORD, ESQ.

Wednesday Morn. Aug. 23.

ALL ALIVE, dear Jack, and in ecstasy! Likely to be once more a happy man! For I have received a letter from my beloved Miss HARLOWE; in consequence, I suppose, of that which I mentioned in my last to be left for her from her sister. And I am setting out for Berks directly, to show the contents to my Lord M., and to receive the congratulations of all my kindred upon it.

TO ROBERT LOVELACE, ESQ.

Tuesday Night, 11 o'clock (Aug. 22).

SIR,—I have good news to tell you. I am setting out with all diligence for my father's house. I am bid to hope that he will receive his poor penitent with a goodness peculiar to himself; for I am overjoyed with the assurance of a thorough reconciliation, through the interposition of a dear, blessed friend whom I always loved and honoured. I am so taken up with my preparation for this joyful and long-wished-for journey that I cannot spare one moment for any other business, having several matters of the last importance to settle first. So pray, sir, don't disturb or interrupt me—I beseech you, don't. You may possibly in time see me at my father's; at least, if it be not your own fault.

I will write a letter, which shall be sent you when I am got thither and received: till when, I am, etc.

Clarissa Harlowe.

I dispatched instantly a letter to the dear creature, assuring her, with the most thankful joy, "that I would directly set out for Berks, and wait the issue of the happy reconciliation and the charming hopes she had filled me with. I poured out upon her a thousand blessings. I declared that it should be the study of my whole life to merit such transcendent goodness: and that there was nothing which her father or friends should require at my hands that I would not for *her* sake comply with, in order to promote and complete so desirable a reconciliation."

MR. LOVELACE TO JOHN BELFORD, ESQ.

ALTHOUGH I have the highest opinion that man can have of the generosity of my dear Miss Harlowe, yet I cannot for the heart of me account for this agreeable change in her temper, but one way. Faith and troth, Belford, I verily believe, laying all circumstances together, that the dear creature unexpectedly finds herself in the way I have so ardently wished her to be in; and that this makes her, at last, incline to favour me, that she may set the better face upon her gestation when at her father's.

If this be the case, all her falling away, and her fainting fits, are charmingly accounted for. Nor is it surprising that such a sweet novice in these matters should not, for some time, have known to what to attribute her frequent indispositions. If this should be the case, how shall I laugh at *thee!* and (when I am sure of her) at the dear novice *herself*, that all her grievous distresses shall end in a man-child: which I shall love better than all the cherubims and seraphims that may come after; though there were to be as many of them as I beheld in my dream; in which a vast expanse of firmament was stuck as full of them as it could hold.

MR. BELFORD TO ROBERT LOVELACE, ESQ.

Sat. Aug. 26.

IT IS IMPOSSIBLE to account for the contents of her letter to you; or to reconcile those contents to the facts I have to communicate.

Mrs. Smith told me she was so ill on Wednesday night, that she had desired to receive the Sacrament; and accordingly it was administered to her by the parson of the parish: whom she besought to take all opportunities of assisting her in her solemn preparation.

This the gentleman promised: and called in the morning to inquire after her health; and was admitted at the first word.

He stayed with her about half an hour; and when he came down, with his face turned aside, and a faltering accent: "Mrs. Smith, said he, you have an angel in your house. I will attend her again in the evening, as she desires, and as often as I think it will be agreeable to her."

Her increased weakness she attributed to the fatigues she had undergone by your means; and to a letter she had received from her sister, which she answered the same day.

Mrs. Smith told me that two different persons had called there, one on Thursday morning, one in the evening, to inquire after her state of health; and seemed as if commissioned from her relations for that purpose; but asked not to see her, only were very inquisitive after her visitors (particularly, it seems, after *me:* what could they mean by that?), after her way of life, and expenses; and one of them inquired after her manner of supporting them; to the latter of which Mrs. Smith said she had answered, as the truth was, that she had been obliged to sell some of her clothes, and was actually about parting with more; at which the inquirist (a grave old farmer-looking man) held up his hands, and said: Good God! this will be sad, sad news to somebody! I believe I must not mention it. But Mrs. Smith says she desired he *would,* let him come from whom he would. He shook his head, and said, if she died, the flower of the world would be gone, and the family she belonged to would be no more than a common family.[1]

"Mrs. Lovick gave her her sister's letter; and she was so much affected with the contents of it that she was twice very nigh fainting away; and wept bitterly, as Mrs. Lovick told Mrs. Smith; dropping some warmer expressions than ever they had heard proceed from her lips, in relation to her friends; calling them cruel, and complaining of ill offices done her, and of vile reports raised against her."

On Wednesday morning, when she received your letter in answer to hers, she said: Necessity may well be called the mother of invention—but calamity is the test of integrity. I hope I have not taken an inexcusable step——And there she stopped a minute or two; and then said: I shall now, perhaps, be allowed to die in peace.

[1] This man came from her Cousin Morden.

I stayed till she came in. She was glad to see me; but, being very weak, said she must sit down before she could go upstairs; and so went into the back shop; leaning upon Mrs. Lovick: and when she had sat down, "I am glad to see you, Mr. Belford, said she; I *must* say so—let misreporters say what they will."

I wondered at this expression; but would not interrupt her.

Oh! sir, said she, I have been grievously harassed. Your friend, who would not let me live with reputation, will not pemit me to die in peace. You see how I am. Is there not a great alteration in me within this week? But 'tis all for the better. Yet were I to wish for life, I must say that your friend, your barbarous friend, has *hurt* me greatly.

She was so very weak, so short-breathed, and her words and action so very moving, that I was forced to walk from her; the two women and her nurse turning away their faces also, weeping.

A letter and packet were brought her by a man on horseback from Miss Howe, while we were talking. She retired upstairs to read it; and while I was in discourse with Mrs. Smith and Mrs. Lovick, the doctor and apothecary both came in together. They confirmed to me my fears as to the dangerous way she is in. They had both been apprised of the new instances of implacableness in her friends, and of your persecutions: and the doctor said he would not for the world be either the unforgiving father of that lady, or the man who had brought her to this distress. Her heart's broken: she'll die, said he: there is no saving her.

When she was told we were all three together, she desired us to walk up. She arose to receive us, and after answering two or three general questions relating to her health, she addressed herself to us to the following effect.

As I may not, said she, see you three gentlemen together again, let me take this opportunity to acknowledge my obligations to you all. I am inexpressibly obliged to you, sir, and to you, sir (curtsying to the doctor and to Mr. Goddard), for your *more* than friendly, your *paternal* care and concern for me. Humanity in your profession, I dare say, is far from being a rare qualification, because you are gentlemen *by* your profession: but so much kindness, so much humanity, did never desolate creature meet with, as I have met with from you both.

This gentleman (bowing to me), who, some people think, should have been one of the last I should have thought of for my executor, is nevertheless (such is the strange turn that things have taken!) the only one I can choose; and therefore I have chosen him for that charitable office, and he has been so good as to accept of it: for, rich as I may boast myself to be, I am rather so in *right* than in *fact*, at this present. I repeat therefore my humble thanks to you all three, and beg of God to return to you and yours (looking to each) a hundred fold the kindness and favour you have shown me; and that it may be in the power of you and of yours, to the end of time, to *confer* benefits, rather than to be obliged to *receive* them. Once more, then, I thank ye all three for your kindness to me: and God Almighty make you that amends which at present I cannot!

She retired from us to her closet with her eyes full; and left us looking upon one another.

We had hardly recovered ourselves when she, quite easy, cheerful, and smiling, returned to us. Doctor, said she (seeing we had been moved), you will excuse me for the concern I give you; and so will you, Mr. Goddard, and you, Mr. Belford; for 'tis a concern that only generous natures can show; and to such natures *sweet* is the pain, if I may so say, that attends such a concern. But as I have some few preparations still to make, and would not (though in ease of Mr. Belford's future cares, which is, and ought to be, part of my study) undertake more than it is likely I shall have time lent me to perform, I would beg of you to give me your opinions (you see my way of living; and you may be assured that I will do nothing wilfully to shorten my life) how long it may possibly be before I may hope to be released from all my troubles.

They both hesitated, and looked upon each other. Don't be afraid to answer me, said she, each sweet hand pressing upon the arm of each gentleman, with that mingled freedom and reserve which virgin modesty, mixed with conscious dignity, can only express, and with a look serenely earnest: Tell me how long you think I may hold it? And believe me, gentlemen, the shorter you tell me my time is likely to be, the more comfort you will give me.

What you have undergone within a few days past has much

hurt you: and should you have fresh troubles of those kinds, I could not be answerable for your holding it——And there he paused.

How long, doctor? I believe I *shall* have a little more ruffling —I am afraid I shall—but there can happen only one thing that I shall not be tolerably easy under——How long then, sir?

He was silent.

A fortnight, sir?

He was still silent.

Ten days? A week? How long, sir? with smiling earnestness.

If I *must* speak, madam: if you have not better treatment than you have lately met with, I am afraid——There again he stopped.

Afraid of what, doctor? Don't be afraid. How long, sir?

That a fortnight or three weeks may deprive the world of the finest flower in it.

A fortnight or three weeks yet, doctor? But God's will be done! I shall, however, by this means, have full time, if I have but strength and intellect, to do all that is now upon my mind to do. And so, sirs, I can but once more thank you (turning to each of us) for all your goodness to me; and, having letters to write, will take up no more of your time.

She then retired, with a cheerful and serene air. The two gentlemen went away together. I went down to the women, and, inquiring, found that Mrs. Lovick was this day to bring her twenty guineas more, for some other of her apparel.

The widow told me that she had taken the liberty to expostulate with her upon the *occasion* she had for raising this money to such great disadvantage; and it produced the following short and affecting conversation between them.

None of my friends will wear anything of mine, said she. I shall leave a great many good things behind me. And as to what I want the money for—don't be surprised: but suppose I want it to purchase a house?

You are all mystery, madam.

Why then, Mrs. Lovick, I will explain myself. I have a man, not a woman, for my executor: and think you that I will leave to his care anything that concerns my own person? Now, Mrs. Lovick, smiling, do you comprehend me?

Mrs. Lovick wept.

O fie! proceeded the lady, drying up her tears with her own handkerchief, and giving her a kiss. Why this kind weakness for one with whom you have been so little a while acquainted? Dear, good Mrs. Lovick, don't be concerned for me on a prospect with which I have occasion to be pleased; but go to-morrow to your friends, and bring me the money they have agreed to give you.

Thus, Lovelace, it is plain that she means to bespeak her *last* house!

Mrs. Lovick tells me that the lady spoke of a letter she had received from her favourite divine, Dr. Lewen, in the time of my absence; and of an answer she had returned to it.

The Rev. Dr. Lewen to Miss Clarissa Harlowe

Friday, Aug. 18.

Presuming, dearest and ever-respectable young lady, upon your former favour, and upon your opinion of my judgment and sincerity, I cannot help addressing you by a few lines, on your present unhappy situation.

What I principally write for now is, to put you upon doing a piece of justice to yourself, and to your sex, in the prosecuting for his life (I am assured his life is in your power) the most profligate and abandoned of men, as *he* must be who could act so basely as I understand Mr. Lovelace has acted by you.

And let me add another consideration: the prevention, by this means, of the mischiefs that may otherwise happen between your brother and Mr. Lovelace, or between the latter and your Cousin Morden, who is now, I hear, arrived, and resolves to have justice done you.

In a word, the reparation of your family dishonour now rests in your own bosom: and which only one of these two alternatives *can* repair; to wit, either to marry the offender, or to prosecute him at law.

He, and all his friends, I understand, solicit you to the first: and it is certainly, now, all the amends within his power to make. But I am assured that you have rejected *their* solicitations, and *his*, with the indignation and contempt that his foul actions have deserved: but yet that you refuse not to extend to him the Christian forgiveness he has so little reason to expect, provided he will not disturb you further.

It is a terrible circumstance, I once more own, for a young lady of your delicacy to be under the obligation of telling so shocking a story in public court: but it is still a worse imputation that she should pass over so mortal an injury unresented.

Conscience, honour, justice, and the cares of Heaven are on your side: and modesty would, by some, be thought but an empty name, should *you* refuse to obey their dictates.

Wounded as I think all these are by the injuries you have received, you will believe that the knowledge of your distresses must have afflicted beyond what I am able to express,

Your sincere admirer and humble servant,

Arthur Lewen.

MISS CLARISSA HARLOWE TO THE REV. DR. LEWEN

Sat. Aug. 19.

REVEREND AND DEAR SIR,—I thought, till I received your affectionate and welcome letter, that I had neither father, uncle, brother left; nor hardly a friend among my former favourers of your sex.

It is certain that creatures who cannot stand the shock of *public shame* should be doubly careful how they expose themselves to the danger of incurring *private guilt,* which may possibly bring them to it. But as to *myself,* suppose there were no objections from the declining way I am in as to my health; and supposing I could have prevailed upon myself to appear against this man; were there not room to apprehend that the end so much wished for by my friends (to wit, his condign punishment) would not have been obtained, when it came to be seen that I had consented to give him a clandestine meeting; and, in consequence of that, had been weakly tricked out of myself; and further still, had not been able to avoid living under one roof with him for several weeks; which I did (not only without complaint, but) without *cause* of complaint?

And had he been *pardoned,* would he not then have been at liberty to do as much mischief as ever? And then would my brother, or my Cousin Morden, have been more secure than now?

The injury I have received from him is indeed of the highest nature, and it was attended with circumstances of unmanly baseness and premeditation; yet, I bless God, it has not tainted my mind; it has not hurt my morals. I have, through grace, triumphed over the deepest machinations. I have escaped from him. I have renounced him. The man whom once I could have loved, I have been enabled to despise: and shall not *charity* complete my triumph? And shall I not *enjoy* it? And where would be my triumph if he *deserved* my forgiveness? Poor man! He has had a loss in losing me! I have the pride to think so, because I think I know my own heart. I have had none in losing him!

May the Almighty bless you, dear and reverend sir, for all your goodness to me of long time past, as well as for that which engages my present gratitude!

Clarissa Harlowe.

MISS ARAB. HARLOWE TO MISS CL. HARLOWE

Monday, Aug. 21.

SISTER CLARY,—I find by your letters to my uncles, that they, as well as I, are in great disgrace with you for writing our minds to you.

We can't help it, Sister Clary.

You don't think it worth your while, I find, a second time to press for the blessing you pretend to be so earnest about. You think, no doubt, that you have done your duty in asking for it: so you'll sit down satisfied with that, I suppose, and leave it to your wounded parents to repent hereafter that they have not done *theirs,* in giving it to you, at the *first* word; and in making such inquiries about you as you think ought to have been made. Fine encouragement to inquire after a runaway daughter! living with her fellow as long as he would live with her! You repent also (with your *full mind,* as you modestly call it) that you wrote to me.

So we are not likely to be applied to any more, I find, in this way.

Well then, since this is the case, Sister Clary, let me, *with all humility,* address myself with a proposal or two to you; to which you will be *graciously* pleased to give an answer.

Now you must know that we have had hints given us from several quarters, that you have been used in such a manner by the villain you ran away with, that his life would be answerable for his crime if it were fairly to be proved.

If, Clary, there be anything but jingle and affected period in what proceeds from your *full mind,* and your *dutiful consciousness;* and if there be truth in what Mrs. Norton and Mrs. Howe have acquainted us with; you may yet justify your character to us, and to the world, in everything but your scandalous elopement; and the law may reach the villain: and, could we but bring him to the gallows, what a meritorious revenge would that be to our whole injured family, and to the innocents he has deluded, as well as the saving from ruin many others!

Let me, therefore, know (*if you please*) whether you are willing to appear to do *yourself,* and *us,* and your *sex,* this justice? If *not,* Sister Clary, we shall know what to think of you; for neither *you* nor *we* can suffer more than we have done from the scandal of your fall: and, if *you will,* Mr. Ackland and Counsellor Derham will both attend you to make *proper inquiries,* and to take minutes of your story, to found a process upon, if it will bear one with as great a probability of success as we are told it may be prosecuted with.

But if you will not agree to this, I have another proposal to make to you, and that in the name of every one in the family; which is, that you will think of going to Pennsylvania to reside there for some few years till all is blown over; and, if it please God to spare you, and your unhappy parents, till they can be satisfied that you behave like a true and uniform penitent; at least till you are one-and-twenty: you may then come back to your own estate, or have the produce of it sent you thither, as you shall choose. A period which my father fixes, because it is the *custom;* and because he thinks your *grandfather* should have fixed it; and because, let *me* add, you have fully proved by your fine conduct, that you were not at years of discretion at *eighteen.* Poor, doting, though good old man!—your grandfather, he thought——But I would not be too severe.

Mr. Hartley has a widow sister at Pennsylvania, with whom he will undertake you may board, and who is a sober, sensible, and well-read woman. And if you were once well there, it would rid your father and mother of a world of cares, and fears, and scandal; and I think is what you should wish for of all things.

Mr. Hartley will engage for all accommodations in your passage suitable to your rank and fortune; and he has a concern in a ship, which will sail in a month; and you may take your secret-keeping Hannah with you, or whom you will of your *newer* acquaintance. 'Tis presumed that your companions will be of your own sex.

These are what I had to communicate to you; and if you'll oblige me with an answer (which the hand that conveys this will call for on Wednesday morning), it will be very condescending.

Arabella Harlowe.

Miss Cl. Harlowe to Miss Arab. Harlowe

Tuesday, Aug. 22.

Write to me, my hard-hearted sister, in what manner you please, I shall always be thankful to you for your notice. But (think what you will of me) I cannot see Mr. Ackland and the counsellor on such a business as you mention.

I *know* that this is Dr. Lewen's opinion. He has been so good as to enforce it in a kind letter to me. I have answered his letter; and given such reasons as I hope will satisfy *him.*

To your other proposal, of going to Pennsylvania, this is my answer: If nothing happen within a month which may full as effectually rid my parents and friends of that world of cares, and fears, and scandals, which you mention, and if I am *then* able to be carried on board of ship, I will cheerfully obey my father and mother, although I were sure to die in the passage.

I will only pray that Heaven will give you, for *your own* sake, a kinder heart than at present you seem to have; since a kind heart, I am convinced, is a greater blessing to its possessor than it can be to any other person.

Your ever affectionate sister,

Cl. Harlowe.

Mrs. Norton to Miss Clarissa Harlowe

Tuesday, Aug. 22.

My dearest young Lady,—The letters you sent me I now return by the hand that brings you this.

It is impossible for me to express how much I have been affected by them, and by your last of the 17th. Indeed, my dear Miss Clary, you are very harshly used; indeed you are! And if you should be taken from us, what grief and what punishment are they not treasuring up against themselves in the heavy reflections which their rash censures and unforgivingness will occasion them!

But I find to what your Uncle Antony's cruel letter is owing, as well as one you will be still more afflicted by [God help you, my poor dear child!], when it comes to your hand, written by your sister, with proposals to you.

It was finished to send you yesterday, I know; and I apprise you of it, that you should fortify your heart against the contents of it.

The motives are owing to the information of that officious Mr. Brand, who has acquainted them (from some enemy of yours in the neighbourhood about you) that visits are made you, highly censurable, by a man of a free character, and an intimate of Mr. Lovelace; who is often in private with you; sometimes twice or thrice a day.

Your Cousin Morden has been among them. He is exceedingly concerned for your misfortunes; and as they will not believe Mr. Lovelace would marry you, he is determined to go to Lord M.'s, in order to inform himself from Mr. Lovelace's own mouth whether he intends to do you that justice or not.

Your most affectionate and faithful

Judith Norton.

Mr. Lovelace to John Belford, Esq.

Monday Noon, Aug. 28.

But what is the meaning I hear nothing from thee? And why dost thou not let me into the grounds of the sudden reconciliation between my beloved and her friends, and the cause of the generous invitation which she gives me of attending her at her father's some time hence?

I begin to be afraid, after all, that this letter was a stratagem to get me out of town, and for nothing else: for, in the first place, Tourville, in a letter I received this morning, tells me that the lady is actually very ill (I am sorry for it with all my soul!). This, thou'lt say, I may think a reason why she cannot *set out as yet*: but then, I have heard on the other hand but last night, that the family is as implacable as ever; and my lord and I expect this very afternoon a visit from Colonel Morden; who undertakes, it seems, to question me as to my intention with regard to his cousin.

This convinces me that if she *has* apprised her friends of my offers to her, they will not believe me to be in earnest till they are assured that I am so from my own mouth. But then I understand that the intended visit is an officiousness of Morden's own, without the desire of any of her friends.

Now, Jack, what can a man make of all this? My intelligence as to the continuance of her family's implacableness is not to be doubted; and yet when I read her letter, what can one say? Surely the dear little rogue will not lie!

What I mean by all this, is to let thee see what a stupid figure I shall make to all my own family, if my Clarissa has been capable of saying the *thing that is not*. By my soul, Jack, if it were only that I should be *outwitted* by such a novice at plotting, and that it would make me look silly to my kinswomen here, who know I value myself upon my contrivances, it would vex me to the heart; and I would instantly clap a feather bed into a coach and six, and fetch her away, sick or well, and marry her at my leisure.

But Colonel Morden is come, and I must break off.

MR. BELFORD TO ROBERT LOVELACE, ESQ.

Monday Noon, Aug. 22.

I GOT to town in the evening, and went directly to Smith's. I found Mrs. Lovick and Mrs. Smith in the back shop, and I saw they had been both in tears. They told me that the doctor and Mr. Goddard were but just gone; as was also the worthy clergyman who often comes to pray by her; and all three were of opinion that she would hardly live to see the entrance of another week.

I sent up my compliments; and she returned that she would take it for a favour if I would call upon her in the morning, by eight o'clock.

She had a pretty good night, it seems; and this morning went in a chair to St. Dunstan's Church.

The chairmen told Mrs. Smith that after prayers they carried her to a house in Fleet Street, whither they never waited on her before. And where dost think this was? Why, to an undertaker's! She went into the back shop, and talked with the master of it about half an hour, and came from him with great serenity; he waiting upon her to her chair with a respectful countenance, but full of curiosity and seriousness.

'Tis evident that she then went to bespeak her *house* that she talked of. *As soon as you can, sir,* were her words to him as she got into the chair. Mrs. Smith told me this with the same surprise and grief that I heard it.

Tuesday, Aug. 29.

I was at Smith's at half an hour after seven. They told me that the lady was gone in a chair to St. Dunstan's; but was better than she had been in either of the two preceding days; and that she said to Mrs. Lovick and Mrs. Smith, as she went into the chair: I have a good deal to answer for to you, my good friends, for my vapourish conversation of last night.

If, Mrs. Lovick, said she, smiling, I have no new matters to discompose me, I believe my spirits will hold out purely.

She returned immediately after prayers.

Mr. Belford, said she, as she entered the back shop where I was, and upon my approaching her, I am very glad to see you. I hope, sir, you'll breakfast with me. I was quite vapourish yesterday. I had a very bad spirit upon me. But I hope I shall be no more so. And to-day I am perfectly serene. This day rises upon me as if it would be a bright one.

She desired me to walk up, and invited Mr. Smith and his wife, and Mrs. Lovick also, to breakfast with her. I was better pleased with her liveliness than with her looks.

The good people retiring after breakfast, the following conversation passed between us.

Pray, sir, let me ask you, said she, if you think I may promise myself that I shall be no more molested by your friend?

I hesitated: for how could I answer for such a man?

What shall I do if he comes again? You see how I am. I cannot fly from him now. If he has any pity left for the poor creature whom he has thus reduced, let him not come. But have you heard from him lately? And will he come?

I hope not, madam; I have not heard from him since Thursday last, that he went out of town, rejoicing in the hopes your letter gave him of a reconciliation between your friends and you, and that he might in good time see you at your father's; and he is gone down to give all his friends joy of the news, and is in high spirits upon it.

Alas for me! I shall then surely have him come up to persecute me again! As soon as he discovers that that was only a stratagem to keep him away, he will come up; and who knows but even *now* he is upon the road? I thought I was so bad that I should have been out of his and everybody's way before now; for I expected not that this contrivance would serve me above two or three days; and by this time he must have found out that I am not so happy as to have any hope of a reconciliation with my family; and then he will come, if it be only in revenge for what he will think a deceit; but is not, I hope, a wicked one.

I believe I looked surprised to hear her confess that her letter was a stratagem only; for she said: You wonder, Mr. Belford, I observe, that I could be *guilty of such an artifice. I doubt it is not right:* it was done in a hurry of spirits. Yet, 'tis strange too, that neither you nor he found out my meaning on perusal of my letter.

And then I began to account for it as an *innocent* artifice.

She then explained all to me, and that, as I may say, in six words. A *religious* meaning is couched under it, and that's the reason that neither you nor I could find it out.

"Read but for my *father's house, heaven,* said she, and for the interposition of my dear blessed friend, suppose the *mediation* of my *Saviour* (which I humbly rely upon); and all the rest of the letter will be accounted for." I hope (repeated she) that it is a pardonable artifice.

My surprise being a little over, she proceeded: As to the letter that came from my sister while your friend was here, you will *soon* see, sir, that it is the cruellest letter she ever wrote me.

And then she expressed a deep concern for what might be the consequence of Colonel Morden's intended visit to you; and besought me, that if now, or at any time hereafter, I had opportunity to prevent any further mischief, without detriment or danger to myself, I would do it.

This conversation, I found, as well from the length as the nature of it, had fatigued her; and seeing her change colour once or twice, I made my excuse, and took leave of her: desiring her permission, however, to attend her in the evening.

I long for the particulars of the conversation between you and Mr. Morden: the lady, as I have hinted, is full of apprehensions about it. And I beseech you enable me to make good my engagements to the poor lady that you will not invade her again.

Mr. Lovelace to John Belford, Esq.

Tuesday Morn. Aug. 29.

Now, Jack, will I give thee an account of what passed on occasion of the visit made us by Colonel Morden.

After some general talk of the times, and of the weather, and such nonsense as Englishmen generally make their introductory topics to conversation, the colonel addressed himself to Lord M. and to me, as follows:

I need not, my lord, and Mr. Lovelace, as you know the relation I bear to the Harlowe family, make any apology for entering upon a subject which, on account of that relation, you must think is the principal reason of the honour I have done myself in this visit.

Miss Harlowe, Miss Clarissa Harlowe's affair, said Lord M., with his usual forward bluntness. That, sir, is what you mean. She is, by all accounts, the most excellent woman in the world.

I am glad to hear that is your lordship's opinion of her. It is every one's.

It is not only my opinion, Colonel Morden, but it is the opinion of all my family. Of my sisters, of my nieces, and of Mr. Lovelace himself.

Col. Would to Heaven it had been always Mr. Lovelace's opinion of her!

Lovel. You have been out of England, colonel, a good many years. Perhaps you are not yet fully apprised of all the particulars of this case.

Col. I have been out of England, sir, about seven years. My Cousin Clary was then about *twelve* years of age: but never was there at *twenty* so discreet, so prudent, and so excellent a creature. All that knew her, or saw her, admired her. Mind and person, never did I see such promises of perfection in any young lady: and I am told, nor is it to be wondered at, that as she advanced to maturity, she more than justified and made good those promises. Then, as to fortune—what her father, what her uncles, and what I myself intended to do for her, besides what her grandfather had done—there is not a finer fortune in the county.

Lovel. All this, colonel, and more than this, is Miss Clarissa Harlowe; and had it not been for the implacableness and violence of her family (all resolved to push her upon a match as unworthy *of* her as hateful *to* her), she had still been happy.

Col. I own, Mr. Lovelace, the truth of what you observed just now, that I am not thoroughly acquainted with all that has passed between you and my cousin. But permit me to say that when I first heard that you made your addresses to her, I knew but of one objection against you. That, indeed, a very great one: and upon a letter sent me, I gave her my free opinion upon the subject. But had it not been for that, I own that, in my private mind, there could not have been a more suitable match: for you are a gallant gentleman, graceful in your person, easy and genteel in your deportment, and in your family, fortunes, and expectations, happy as a man can wish to be. Your education has given you great advantages; your manners are engaging, and you have travelled; and I know, if you'll excuse me, you make better observations than you are governed by. All these qualifications make it not at all surprising that a young lady should love you: and that this love, joined to that indiscreet warmth wherewith my cousin's friends would have forced her inclinations in favour of men who are far your inferiors in the qualities I have named, should throw her upon your protection: but then, if there were these two strong motives, the one to *induce,* the other to *impel* her, let me ask you, sir, if she were not doubly entitled to generous usage from a man whom she chose for her protector; and whom, let me take the liberty to say, she could so amply reward for the protection he was to afford her?

Lovel. Miss Clarissa Harlowe was entitled, sir, to the best usage that man could give her. I know what will be your inference; and have only to say that time past cannot be recalled. Perhaps I wish it could.

The colonel then in a very manly strain set forth the wickedness of attempting a woman of virtue and character.

He was going on, when, interrupting him, I said: But you yourself are a man of gallantry; and, possibly, were you to be put to the question, might not be able to vindicate every action of your life any more than I.

Col. You are welcome, sir, to put what questions you please to me. And, I thank God, I can both *own* and be *ashamed* of my errors.

Lord M. looked at *me;* but as the colonel did not by his manner seem to intend a reflection, I had no occasion to take it for one; especially as I can as readily *own* my errors, as he or any man can his, whether *ashamed* of them or not.

He proceeded: As you seem to call upon me, Mr. Lovelace, I will tell you (without boasting of it) what has been my general practice, till lately, that I hope I have reformed it a good deal.

I have taken liberties which the laws of morality will by no means justify; and once I should have thought myself warranted to cut the throat of any young fellow who should make as free with a sister of mine as I have made with the sisters and daughters of others. But then I took care never to promise anything I intended not to perform. A modest ear should as soon have heard downright obscenity from my lips as matrimony, if I had not intended it. But when once a man makes a promise,

I think it ought to be performed; and a woman is well warranted to appeal to every one against the perfidy of a deceiver; and is always sure to have the world of her side.

Now, sir, continued he, I believe you have so much honour as to own that you could not have made way to so eminent a virtue without promising marriage; and that very explicitly and solemnly——

I know very well, colonel, interrupted I, all you would say. You will excuse me, I am sure, that I break in upon you, when you find it is to answer the end you drive at.

I own to you, then, that I have acted very unworthily by Miss Clarissa Harlowe; and I'll tell you further, that I heartily repent of my ingratitude and baseness to her Nay, I will say *still* further, that I am so grossly culpable *as to her,* that even to plead that the abuses and affronts I daily received from her implacable relations were in any manner a provocation to me to act vilely by her, would be a mean and low attempt to excuse myself—so low and so mean that it would doubly condemn me.

He looked upon Lord M., and then upon me, two or three times. And my lord said: My kinsman speaks what he thinks, I'll answer for him.

Lovel. I do, sir; and what can I say more? And what further, in your opinion, can be done?

Col. Done! sir? Why, sir (in a haughty tone he spoke), I need not tell you that reparation follows repentance.

I hesitated (for I relished not the manner of his speech and his haughty accent), as undetermined whether to take proper notice of it or not.

Col. Let me put this question to you, Mr. Lovelace: Is it true, as I have heard it is, that you would marry my cousin if she would have you?

This wound me up a peg higher.

Lovel. Some questions, as they may be put, imply *commands,* colonel. I would be glad to know how I am to take yours? And what is to be the end of your interrogatories?

Col. My questions are not meant by me as commands, Mr. Lovelace. The *end* is, to prevail upon a gentleman to act *like* a gentleman, and a man of honour.

Lovel. (*briskly*) And by what arguments, sir, do you propose to prevail upon me?

Col. By what arguments, sir, prevail upon a gentleman to act like a gentleman! I am surprised at that question from Mr. Lovelace.

Lovel. Why so, sir?

Col. WHY so, sir (*angrily*)—Let me——

Lovel. (*interrupting*) I don't choose, colonel, to be repeated upon in that accent.

Lord M. Come, come, gentlemen, I beg of you to be willing to understand one another. You young gentlemen are so warm——

Col. Not I, my Lord—I am neither very young nor unduly warm. Your nephew, my lord, can make me be everything he would have me to be.

Lovel. And that shall be whatever you please to be, colonel.

Col. (*fiercely*) The choice be yours, Mr. Lovelace. Friend or foe! as you do or are willing to do justice to one of the finest women in the world.

Lord M. I guessed from both your characters what would be the case when you met. Let me interpose, gentlemen, and beg you but to understand one another. You *both shoot at one mark;* and if you are patient, will both *hit it.* Let me beg of you, colonel, to give no challenges——

Col. Challenges, my lord! They are things I ever was readier to accept than to offer. But does your lordship think that a man so nearly related as I have the honour to be to the most accomplished woman on earth——

Lord M. (*interrupting*) We all allow the excellences of the lady—and we shall all take it as the greatest honour to be allied to her that can be conferred upon us.

Col. So you ought, my lord!

Lord M. So we *ought,* colonel! And so we *do!* And pray let *every one* do as he ought!—and no *more* than he *ought;* and you, colonel, let me tell you, will not be so hasty.

Lovel. (*coolly*) Come, come, Colonel Morden, don't let this dispute, whatever you intend to make of it, go farther than with you and me. You deliver yourself in very high terms. But here, beneath this roof, 'twould be inexcusable for me to take that notice of it which perhaps it would become me to take elsewhere.

Col. This is spoken as I wish the man to speak whom I should be pleased to call my friend, if all his actions were of a piece; and as I would have the man speak whom I would think it worth my while to call my foe. But, Mr. Lovelace, as my lord thinks we aim at *one mark,* let me say that, were we permitted to be alone for six minutes, I dare say we should soon understand one another perfectly well. And he moved to the door.

Lovel. I am entirely of your opinion, sir, and will attend you.

My lord rang, and stepped between us: Colonel, return, I beseech you, return, said he; for he had stepped out of the room, while my lord held me. Nephew, you shall not go out.

The bell and my lord's raised voice brought in Mowbray, and Clements, my lord's gentleman; the former in his careless way, with his hands behind him: What's the matter, Bobby? What's the matter, my lord?

Only—only—only, stammered the agitated peer, these young gentlemen are—are—are—*are* young gentlemen, that's all. Pray, Colonel Morden (who again entered the room with a sedater aspect), let this cause have a fair trial, I beseech you.

Col. With all my heart, my lord.

Mowbray whispered me: What is the cause, Bobby? Shall I take the gentleman to task for thee, my boy?

Not for the world, whispered I. The colonel is a gentleman, and I desire you'll not say one word.

Well, well, well, Bobby, I have done. I can turn thee loose to the best man upon God's earth; that's all, Bobby; strutting off to the other end of the room.

Col. I am sorry, my lord, I should give your lordship the least uneasiness. I came not with such a design.

Lord M. Indeed, colonel, I thought you did, by your taking fire so quickly. I am glad to hear you say you did not. How soon a little *spark kindles into a flame;* especially when it meets with such combustible spirits!

Col. If I had had the least thought of proceeding to extremities, I am sure Mr. Lovelace would have given me the honour of a meeting where I should have been less an intruder: but I came with an amicable intention—to reconcile differences rather than to widen them.

Lovel. Well, then, Colonel Morden, let us enter upon the subject in your own way. I don't know the man I should sooner choose to be upon terms with than one whom Miss Clarissa Harlowe so much respects. But I cannot bear to be treated, either in word or accent, in a menacing way.

Lord M. Well, well, well, well, gentlemen, this is somewhat like. *Angry men make to themselves beds of nettles,* and when they lie down in them are uneasy with everybody. But I hope you are friends. Let me hear you say you are. I am persuaded, colonel, that you don't know all this unhappy story. You don't know how desirous my kinsman is, as well as all of us, to have this matter end happily. You don't know, do you, colonel, that Mr. Lovelace, at all our requests, is disposed to marry the lady?

Col. At all your requests, my lord? I should have hoped that Mr. Lovelace was disposed to do justice for the *sake* of justice; and when at the same time the doing of justice was doing himself the highest honour.

Lovel. This is in very high language, colonel.

Col. High language, Mr. Lovelace? Is it not *just* language?

Lovel. It is, colonel. And I think the man that does honour to Miss Clarissa Harlowe does me honour. But, nevertheless, there is a manner in speaking that may be liable to exception, where the words, without that manner, can bear none.

Col. Your observation in the general is undoubtedly just: but *if* you have the value for my cousin that you say you have, you must needs think——

Lovel. You must allow me, sir, to interrupt you—IF I have the value *I say* I have. I hope, sir, when *I say* I *have* that value, there is no room for that *if,* pronounced as you pronounced it with an emphasis.

Col. You have broken in upon me twice, Mr. Lovelace. I am as little accustomed to be broken in upon as you are to be *repeated* upon.

Lord M. Two barrels of gunpowder, by my conscience! What a devil will it signify talking, if thus you are to blow one another up at every wry word?

Lovel. No man of honour, my lord, will be easy to have his veracity called in question, though but by implication.

Col. Had you heard me out, Mr. Lovelace, you would have found that my *if* was rather an *if* of *inference* than of *doubt*. But 'tis really a strange liberty gentlemen of free principles take; who at the same time that they would resent unto death the imputation of being capable of telling an untruth to a man, will not scruple to break through the most solemn oaths and promises to a woman. I must assure you, Mr. Lovelace, that I always made a conscience of my vows and promises.

Lovel. You did right, colonel. But let me tell you, sir, that you know not the man you talk to, if you imagine he is not able to rise to a proper resentment, when he sees his generous confessions taken for a mark of base-spiritedness.

Col. (*warmly, and with a sneer*) Far be it from me, Mr. Lovelace, to impute to you the baseness of spirit you speak of; for what would that be, but to imagine that a man who has done a very flagrant injury, is not ready to show his *bravery* in defending it——

Mowbr. This is damned severe, colonel. It is, by Jove! I could not take so much at the hands of any man breathing as Mr. Lovelace before this took at yours.

Col. Who are you, sir? What pretence have you to interpose in a cause where there is an acknowledged guilt on one side, and the honour of a considerable family wounded in the tenderest part by that guilt on the other?

Mowbr. (*whispering to the colonel*) My dear child, you will oblige me highly if you will give me the opportunity of answering your question. And was going out.

The colonel was held in by my lord. And I brought in Mowbray.

Col. Pray, my good lord, let me attend this officious gentleman, I beseech you do. I will wait upon your lordship in three minutes, depend upon it.

Lovel. Mowbray, is this acting like a friend by me, to suppose me incapable of answering for myself? And shall a man of honour and bravery, as I know Colonel Morden to be (rash as perhaps in this visit he has shown himself), have it to say that he comes to my Lord M.'s house, in a manner naked as to attendants and friends, and shall not for that reason be rather borne with than insulted? This moment, my dear Mowbray, leave us. You have really no concern in this business; and if you are my friend, I desire you'll ask the colonel pardon for interfering in it in the manner you have done.

Mowbr. Well, well, Bob; thou shalt be arbiter in this matter. I know I have no business in it. And, colonel (*holding out his hand*), I leave you to one who knows how to defend his own cause as well as any man in England.

Col. (*taking Mowbray's hand, at Lord M.'s request*) You need not tell me *that,* Mr. Mowbray. I have no doubt of Mr. Lovelace's ability to defend his own cause, were it a cause to be defended. And let me tell you, Mr. Lovelace, that I am astonished to think that a brave man, and a generous man, as you have appeared to be in two or three instances that you have given in the little knowledge I have of you, should be capable of acting as you have done by the most excellent of her sex.

Lord M. Well, but, gentlemen, now Mr. Mowbray is gone, and you have both shown instances of courage and generosity to boot, let me desire you to lay your heads together amicably, and think whether there be anything to be done to make all end happily for the lady?

Lovel. But hold, my lord, let me say one thing, now Mowbray *is* gone; and that is, that I think a gentleman ought not to put up tamely one or two severe things that the colonel has said.

Lord M. What the devil canst thou mean? I thought all had been over. Why, thou hast nothing to do but to confirm to the colonel that thou art willing to marry Miss Harlowe, if she will have thee.

Col. Mr. Lovelace will not scruple to say *that,* I suppose, notwithstanding all that has passed: but if you think, Mr. Lovelace, I have said anything I should *not* have said, I suppose it is this: that the man who has shown so little of the *thing* honour to a defenceless unprotected woman, ought not to stand so nicely upon the *empty name* of it with a man who is expostulating with him upon it. I am sorry to have cause to say this, Mr. Lovelace; but I would on the same occasion repeat it to a king upon his throne, and surrounded by all his guards.

Lord M. But what is all this, but more *sacks upon the mill? more coals upon the fire?* You have a mind to quarrel both of you, I see that. Are you not willing, nephew, are you not *most* willing, to marry this lady, if she can be prevailed upon to have you?

Lovel. Damn me, my Lord, if I'd marry an empress upon such treatment as this.

Lord M. Why now, Bob, thou art more choleric than the colonel. It was *his* turn just now. And now you see he is cool, you are all gunpowder.

Lovel. I own the colonel has many advantages over me; but, perhaps, there is one advantage he has not, if it were put to the trial.

Col. I came not hither, as I said before, to seek the occasion: but if it be offered me, I won't refuse it. And since we find we disturb my good Lord M., I'll take my leave, and will go home by the way of St. Albans.

Lovel. I'll see you part of the way, with all my heart, colonel.

Col. I accept your civility very cheerfully, Mr. Lovelace.

Lord M. (*interposing again, as we were both for going out*) And what will this do, gentlemen? Suppose you kill one another, will the matter be bettered or worsted by that? Will the lady be made happier or unhappier, do you think, by either or both of your deaths? Your characters are too well known to make fresh instances of the courage of either needful. And I think, if the honour of the lady is your view, colonel, it can be no other way so effectually promoted as by marriage. And, sir, if *you* would use your interest with her, it is very probable that *you* may succeed, though nobody else can.

Lovel. I think, my lord, I have said all that a man can say (since what is passed cannot be recalled); and you see Colonel Morden rises in proportion to my coolness, till it is necessary for me to assert myself, or even *he* would despise me.

Lord M. Let me ask you, colonel: Have you any way, any method, that you think reasonable and honourable to propose, to bring about a reconciliation with the lady? That is what we all wish for. And I can tell you, sir, it is not a little owing to her family, and to their implacable usage of her, that her resentments are heightened against my kinsman; who, however, has used her vilely; but is willing to repair her wrongs.

Lovel. Not, my lord, for the sake of her family; nor for this gentleman's haughty behaviour; but for *her own sake,* and in full sense of the wrongs I have done her.

Col. As to my haughty behaviour, as you call it, sir, I am mistaken if you would not have gone beyond it in the like case of a relation so meritorious, and so unworthily injured. And, sir, let me tell you, that if your motives are not love, honour, and justice, and if they have the least tincture of mean compassion for *her,* or of an uncheerful assent on *your part,* I am sure it will neither be desired nor accepted by a person of my cousin's merit and sense; nor shall I wish that it should.

Lovel. Don't think, colonel, that I am meanly compounding off a debate, that I should as willingly go through with you as to eat or drink, if I have the occasion given me for it: but thus much I will tell you, that my lord, that Lady Sarah Sadleir, Lady Betty Lawrance, my two Cousins Montague, and myself, have written to her in the most solemn and sincere manner, to offer her such terms as no one but herself would refuse, and this long enough before Colonel Morden's arrival was dreamt of.

Col. What reason, sir, may I ask, does she give against listening to so powerful a mediation, and to such offers?

Lovel. It looks like capitulating, or else——

Col. It looks not like any such thing to *me,* Mr. Lovelace, who have as good an opinion of your spirit as man can have. And what, pray, is the part I act, and my motives for it? Are they not, in desiring that justice may be done to my Cousin Clarissa Harlowe, that I seek to establish the honour of *Mrs. Lovelace,* if matters can once be brought to bear?

Lovel. Were she to honour me with her acceptance of that name, Mr. Morden, I should not want you or any man to assert the honour of Mrs. Lovelace.

Col. I believe it. But till she *has* honoured you with that acceptance, she is nearer to me than to you, Mr. Lovelace. And I speak this only to show you that in the part I take I mean rather to deserve your thanks than your displeasure, though against *yourself,* were there occasion. Nor ought you to take it amiss, if you rightly weigh the matter: for, sir, whom does a lady want protection against but her injurers? And who has been her *greatest* injurer? Till, therefore, she becomes entitled to your protection, as *your wife,* you yourself cannot refuse me some merit in wishing to have justice done *my cousin.* But, sir, you was going to say, that if it were not to look like capitulating, you would hint the reasons my cousin gives against accepting such an honourable mediation?

I then told him of my sincere offers of marriage; "I made no difficulty, I said, to own my apprehensions that my unhappy behaviour to her had greatly affected her: but that it was the implacableness of her friends that had thrown her into despair, and given her a contempt for life." I told him "that she had been so good as to send me a letter to divert me from a visit my heart was set upon making her: a letter on which I built great hopes, because she assured me in it that she was *going to her father's;* and that *I might see her there, when she was received, if it were not my own fault.*"

Col. Is it possible? And were you, sir, thus earnest? And did she send you such a letter?

Lord M. confirmed both; and also that, in obedience to her desires, and that intimation, I had come down without the satisfaction I had proposed to myself in seeing her.

It is very true, colonel, said I: and I should have told you this before: but your heat made me decline it; for, as I said, it had an appearance of meanly capitulating with you. An abjectness of heart, of which had I been capable, I should have despised *myself* as much as I might have expected *you* would despise me.

Lord M. proposed to enter into the proof of all this: he said, in his phraseological way, *That one story was good till another was heard:* that the Harlowe family and I, 'twas true, had behaved like so many *Orsons* to one another; and that they had been very free with all our family besides: that nevertheless, for the lady's sake more than for theirs, or even for *mine* (he could tell me), he would do greater things for me than they could ask, if she could be brought to have me: and that this he *wanted* to declare, and would *sooner* have declared, if he could have brought us sooner to patience and a good understanding.

The colonel made excuses for his warmth on the score of his affection to his cousin.

My regard for her made me readily admit them: and so a fresh bottle of burgundy, and another of champagne, being put upon the table, we sat down in good humour, after all this blustering, in order to enter closer into the particulars of the case: which I undertook, at both their desires, to do.

[Mr. Lovelace shows Col. Morden copies of his repentant letter to Clarissa, and her letter to Lovelace about meeting him at her father's house. Col. Morden, impressed, feels that Clarissa has carried her resentments too far, and promises to discuss the whole matter with the Harlowe family as soon as the brother returns from Edinburgh. He inquires the name of Lovelace's friend who has been attending Clarissa—John Belford. Ed.]

MR. BELFORD TO ROBERT LOVELACE, ESQ.

Thursday, 11 o'clock, Aug. 31.

I AM just from the lady, whom I left cheerful and serene.

She was far from rejoicing, as I had done, at the disappointment her letter gave you when explained.

She said she meant only an innocent allegory. And then she again expressed a good deal of apprehension lest you should still take it into your head to molest her, when her time, she said, was so short that she wanted every moment of it.

But she was much pleased that the conference between you and Colonel Morden, after two or three such violent sallies, as I acquainted her you had had between you, ended so amicably; and said she must absolutely depend upon the promise I had given her to use my utmost endeavors to prevent further mischief on her account.

Thursday, Three o'clock, Aug. 31.

On my revisit to the lady I found her almost as much a sufferer from joy as she had sometimes been from grief: for she had just received a very kind letter from her Cousin Morden; which she was so good as to communicate to me.

COLONEL MORDEN TO MISS CLARISSA HARLOWE

Tuesday, Aug. 29.

I SHOULD NOT, my dearest cousin, have been a fortnight in England, without either doing myself the honour of waiting upon you in person, or of writing to you, if I had not been busying myself almost all the time in your service.

I was yesterday with Mr. Lovelace and Lord M. I need not tell *you,* it seems, how very desirous the whole family and all the relations of that nobleman are of the honour of an alliance with you; nor how exceedingly earnest the ungrateful man is to make you all the reparation in his power.

I think, my dear cousin, that you cannot now do better than to give him the honour of your hand. He says such just and great things of your virtue, and so heartily condemns himself, that I think there is honourable room for you to forgive him: and the more room, as it seems you are determined against a legal prosecution.

But, my dear cousin, there may possibly be something in this affair to which I may be a stranger. If there be, and you will acquaint me with it, all that a *naturally* warm heart can do in your behalf shall be done.

I hope I shall be able, in my next visits to my several cousins, to set all right with them.

But if I find them inflexible, I will set out, and attend you without delay; for I long to see you, after so many years' absence.

Meanwhile I beg the favour of a few lines, to know if you have reason to doubt Mr. Lovelace's sincerity. For my part, I can have none, if I am to judge from the conversation that passed between us yesterday, in presence of Lord M.

Your affectionate kinsman, and humble servant,

Wm. Morden.

MISS CL. HARLOWE TO WM. MORDEN, ESQ.

Thursday, Aug. 31.

I MOST heartily congratulate you, dear sir, on your return to your native country.

I heard with much pleasure that you were come; but I was both afraid and ashamed, till you encouraged me by a first notice, to address myself to you.

How consoling is it to my wounded heart to find that you have not been carried away by that tide of resentment and displeasure with which I have been so unhappily overwhelmed; but that, while my still nearer relations have not thought fit to examine into the truth of vile reports raised against me, you have informed yourself of my innocence, and generously *credited* the information!

I have not the least reason to doubt Mr. Lovelace's sincerity in his offers of marriage: nor that all his relations are heartily desirous of ranking me among them.

Nor think me, my dear cousin, blamable for refusing him. I had given Mr. Lovelace no reason to think me a weak creature.

I can indeed forgive him. But that is because I think his crimes have set me above him. Can I be above the man, sir, to whom I shall give my hand and my vows, and with them a sanction to the most premeditated baseness?

Nor is it so much from pride, as from principle, that I say this. What, sir! when virtue, when chasity, is the crown of a woman, and particularly of a wife, shall your cousin stoop to marry the man who could not form an attempt upon *hers* but upon a presumption that she was capable of receiving his offered hand, when he had found himself mistaken in the vile opinion he had conceived of her? Hitherto he has not had reason to think me weak. Nor will I give him an instance so flagrant, that weak I am in a point in which it would be criminal to be *found* weak.

One day, sir, you will perhaps know all my story. But, whenever it is known, I beg that the author of my calamities may not be vindictively sought after. As the law will not be able to reach him when I am gone, the apprehension of any other sort of vengeance terrifies me.

God long preserve you, my dearest cousin, and bless you in letting me know that you still love me; and that I have one near and dear relation who can pity and forgive me is the prayer of

Your ever grateful and affectionate
Clarissa Harlowe.

MR. LOVELACE TO JOHN BELFORD, ESQ.

Thursday, Aug. 31.

I CANNOT but own that I am cut to the heart by *this* Miss Harlowe's interpretation of her letter. She ought never to be forgiven. *She,* a meek person, and a penitent, and innocent, and pious, and I know not what, who can deceive with a foot in the grave!

Lord M. himself, who is not one of those (to speak in his own phrase) *who can penetrate a millstone,* sees the deceit, and thinks it unworthy of her; though my Cousins Montague vindicate her.

She is to send me a letter after she is in heaven, is she? The devil take such *allegories;* and the devil take thee for calling this absurdity an *innocent* artifice!

I insist upon it, that if a woman of her character, at such a critical time, is to be justified in such a deception, a man in full health and vigor of body and mind, as I am, may be excused for all his stratagems and attempts against her. And, thank my stars, I can now sit me down with a quiet conscience on that score.

But, notwithstanding all, you may let her know from me that I will *not* molest her, since my visits would be so shocking to her: and I hope she will take this into her consideration as a piece of generosity which she could hardly expect after the deception she has put upon me. And let her further know, that if there be anything in my power, that will contribute either to her ease or honour, I will obey her, at the very first intimation, however disgraceful or detrimental to myself.

If her cursed relations could be brought as cheerfully to perform *their* parts, I'd answer life for life for her recovery.

I am now so impatient to hear oftener of her, that I take the hint accidentally given me by our two fellows meeting at Slough, and resolve to go to our friend Doleman's at Uxbridge; whose wife and sister, as well as he, have so frequently pressed me to give them my company for a week or two. There shall I be within two hours' ride, if anything should happen to induce her to see me: for it will well become her piety, and avowed charity, should the worst happen (the Lord of Heaven and Earth, however, avert that worst!), to give me that pardon from her *lips,* which she has not denied me by *pen and ink*. And as she wishes my reformation, she knows not what good effects such an interview may have upon me.

But, if the worst happen!—as, by your continual knelling, I know not what to think of it!—(Yet, once more, Heaven avert that worst! How natural is it to pray, when one cannot help oneself!)—THEN say not, in so many dreadful words, what the event is—only, that you advise me to take a trip to Paris—and that will stab me to the heart.

MR. BELFORD TO ROBERT LOVELACE, ESQ.

Thursday Night, Aug. 31.

WHEN I attended her about seven in the evening, she told me that she found herself in a very petulant way after I had left her. Strange, said she, that the pleasure I received from my cousin's letter should have such an effect upon me! But I could not help giving way to a *comparative* humour, as I may call it, and to think it very hard that my nearer relations did not take the methods which my Cousin Morden kindly took, by inquiring into my merit or demerit, and giving my cause a fair audit before they proceeded to condemnation.

She had hardly said this, when she started, and a blush overspread her sweet face, on hearing, as I also did, a sort of lumbering noise upon the stairs, as if a large trunk were bringing up between two people: and, looking upon me with an eye of concern, Blunderers! said she, they have brought in *something* two hours before the time. Don't be surprised, sir—it is all to save *you* trouble.

Before I could speak, in came Mrs. Smith: O madam, said

she, what have you done? Mrs. Lovick, entering, made the same exclamation. Lord have mercy upon me, madam, cried I, what have you done! For, she stepping at the instant to the door, the women told me it was a coffin. O Lovelace! that thou hadst been there at the moment!

With an intrepidity of a piece with the preparation, having directed them to carry it into her bedchamber, she returned to us: They were not to have brought it in till after dark, said she. Pray excuse me, Mr. Belford: and don't you, Mrs. Lovick, be concerned: nor you, Mrs. Smith. Why should you? There is nothing more in it than the unusualness of the thing.

We were all silent still, the women in grief, I in a manner stunned.

I took my leave; telling her she had done wrong, very wrong; and ought not, by any means, to have such an object before her.

Down I posted; got a chair; and was carried home, extremely shocked and discomposed: yet, weighing the lady's arguments, I know not why I was so affected—except, as she said, at the unusualness of the thing.

MR. BELFORD TO ROBERT LOVELACE, ESQ.

Friday Morn. Sept. 1.

I REALLY was ill and restless all night. Thou wert the subject of my execration, as she of my admiration, all the time I was quite awake: and, when I dozed, I dreamt of nothing but of flying hour-glasses, death's-heads, spades, mattocks, and eternity.

However, not being able to keep away from Smith's, I went thither about seven. The lady was just gone out: she had slept better, I found, than I, though her solemn repository was under her window not far from her bedside.

I was prevailed upon by Mrs. Smith and her nurse Shelburne to go up and look at the devices. Mrs. Lovick has since shown me a copy of the draft by which all was ordered.

The principle device, neatly etched on a plate of white metal, is a crowned serpent, with its tail in its mouth, forming a ring, the emblem of eternity; and in the circle made by it is this inscription:

CLARISSA HARLOWE
April x
[Then the year]
ÆTAT. XIX.

For ornaments: at top, an hour-glass winged. At bottom, an urn.

Under the hour-glass, on another plate, this inscription:

> HERE the wicked cease from troubling: and HERE the weary be at rest. Job iii, 17.

Over the urn, near the bottom:

> Turn again unto thy rest, O my soul! for the Lord hath rewarded thee. And why? Thou hast delivered my soul from death; mine eyes from tears; and my feet from falling. Ps. cxvi, 7, 8.

Over this text is the head of a white lily snapped short off, and just falling from the stalk; and this inscription over that, between the principal plate and the lily:

> The days of man are but as grass. For he flourisheth as a flower of the field: for, as soon as the wind goeth over it, it is gone; and the place thereof shall know it no more. Ps. ciii, 15, 16.

The date, April 10, she accounted for, as not being able to tell what her *closing-day* would be; and as that was the fatal day of her leaving her father's house.

She discharged the undertaker's bill after I went away, with as much cheerfulness as she could ever have paid for the clothes she sold to purchase this her *palace:* for such she called it; reflecting upon herself for the expensiveness of it, saying that they might observe in *her* that pride left not poor mortals to the last: but indeed she did not know but her father would permit it, *when furnished,* to be carried down to be deposited with her ancestors; and, in that case, she ought not to discredit those ancestors in her *appearance amongst them.*

Friday, Sept. 1, Two o'clock, at Smith's.

I will just mention then (your servant waiting here till I have written) that the lady has had two very severe fits: in the last of which, whilst she lay, they sent to the doctor and Mr. Goddard, who both advised that a messenger should be dispatched for me, as her executor; being doubtful whether, if she had a third, it would not carry her off.

She was tolerably recovered by the time I came; and the doctor made her promise before me, that, while she was so weak, she would not attempt any more to go abroad; for, by Mrs. Lovick's description, who attended her, the shortness of her breath, her extreme weakness, and the fervour of her devotions when at church, were contraries which, pulling different ways (the soul aspiring, the body sinking), tore her tender frame in pieces.

MR. LOVELACE TO JOHN BELFORD, ESQ.

Uxbridge, Sept. 1 Twelve o'clock at Night.

WHATEVER thou dost, don't let the wonderful creature leave us! Set before her the sin of her preparation, as if she thought she could depart when she pleased. She'll persuade herself, at this rate, that she has nothing to do, when all is ready, but to lie down and go to sleep: and such a lively fancy as hers will make a reality of a jest at any time.

A *jest,* I call all that has passed between her and me; a mere jest to die for—for has not her triumph over me, from first to last, been infinitely greater than her sufferings from me?

Tell the dear creature that she must not be wicked in her piety. There is a *too much,* as well as a *too little,* even in righteousness.

I know thou wilt think I am going to claim some merit to myself for having given her such opportunities of signalizing her virtues. But I am not; for, if I did, I must share that merit with her implacable relations, who would justly be entitled to *two-thirds* of it, at least: and my soul disdains a partnership in anything with such a family.

I admire her more than ever; and my love for her is less *personal,* as I may say, more *intellectual,* than ever I thought it could be to woman.

I am confident (would it please the Fates to spare her, and make her mine) I could love her with a purity that would draw on *my own* FUTURE, as well as ensure *her* TEMPORAL, happiness. And hence, by necessary consequence, shall I be the most miserable of all men, if I am deprived of her.

Indeed it is to this *deep concern* that my *levity* is owing: for I struggle and struggle, and try to buffet down my cruel reflections as they rise: and when I cannot, I am forced, as I have often said, to try to make myself laugh, that I may not cry; for one or other I must do.

. . . . . .

After all, as I am so little distant from the dear creature, and as she is so very ill, I think I cannot excuse myself from making her *one* visit. Nevertheless, if I thought her so near—(what word shall I use that my soul is not shocked at!), and that she would be *too much discomposed* by a visit, I would not think of it.

O Jack! how my conscience, that gives edge even to thy blunt reflections, tears me! Even this moment would I give the world to push the cruel reproacher from me by one ray of my usual gaiety! Sick of myself! Sick of the remembrance of my vile plots; and of my *light,* my momentary ecstasy (villainous burglar, felon, thief, that I was!), which has brought upon me such *durable* and such *heavy* remorse! what would I give that I had not been guilty of such barbarous and ungrateful perfidy to the most excellent of God's creatures!

I would end, methinks, with one sprightlier line! But it will not be. Let me tell thee then, and rejoice at it if thou wilt, that I am

Inexpressibly miserable!

MR. BELFORD TO ROBERT LOVELACE, ESQ.

Sat. Morning, Sept. 2.

I HAVE some little pleasure given me by thine, just now brought me. I see now that thou hast a little humanity left.

The lady is alive, and serene, and calm, and has all her noble intellects clear and strong: but *nineteen* will not, however, save her. She says she will now content herself with her closet duties and the visits of the parish minister; and will not attempt to go out. Nor, indeed, will she, I am afraid, ever walk up or down a pair of stairs again.

As to thy seeing her, I believe the least hint of that sort, now, would cut off some hours of her life.

What has contributed to her serenity, it seems, is that, taking the alarm her fits gave her, she has entirely finished, and signed and sealed, her last will: which she had deferred doing till this time, in hopes, as she said, of some good news from Harlowe Place; which would have induced her to alter some passages in it.

Saturday, Six in the Afternoon.

I called just now, and found the lady writing to Miss Howe. She made me a melancholy compliment, that she showed me not Miss Howe's letter, because I should soon have that and all her papers before me. But she told me that Miss Howe had very considerately obviated to Colonel Morden several things which might have occasioned misapprehensions between him and me; and had likewise put a lighter construction, for the sake of peace, on some of your actions than they deserved.

She added that her Cousin Morden was warmly engaged in her favour with her friends: and one good piece of news Miss Howe's letter contained; that her father would give up some matters, which (appertaining to her of right) would make my executorship the easier in some particulars that had given her a little pain.

Miss Howe to Miss Clarissa Harlowe

Tuesday, Aug 29.

My dearest Friend,—We are at length returned to our own home. I had intended to wait on you in London: but my mother is very ill. And you are likewise very ill—I see *that* by yours of the 25th. What shall I do if I lose two such near, and dear, and tender friends?

I see, I see, my dear, you are very bad—and I cannot bear it. Do, my beloved Miss Harlowe, if you *can* be better, do, for *my* sake, *be* better; and send me word of it. Let the bearer bring me a line. Be sure you send me a line. If I lose you, my more than sister, and lose my mother, I shall distrust my own conduct, and will not marry. And why should I? Creeping, cringing in courtship! O my dear, these men are a vile race of *reptiles* in *our day,* and mere *bears* in *their own.* See in Lovelace all that is desirable in figure, in birth, and in fortune: but in his heart a devil! See in Hickman—indeed, my dear, I cannot tell what any body can see in Hickman, to be always preaching in his favour. And is it to be expected that I, who could hardly bear control from a mother, should take it from a husband?

Wednesday, Aug. 30.

My mother, Heaven be praised! has had a fine night, and is much better. Her fever has yielded to medicine! And now I can write once more with freedom and ease to you, in hopes that *you* also are better. If this be granted to my prayers, I shall again be happy. I write with still the more alacrity, as I have an opportunity given me to touch upon a subject in which you are nearly concerned.

You must know then, my dear, that your Cousin Morden has been here with me. He told me of an interview he had on Monday at Lord M.'s with Lovelace; and asked me abundance of questions about you, and about that villainous man.

I could have raised a fine flame between them if I would: but, observing that he is a man of very lively passions, and believing you would be miserable if anything should happen to him from a quarrel with a man who is known to have so many advantages at his sword, I made not the worst of the subjects we talked of. But, as I could not tell untruths in his favour, you must think I said enough to make him curse the wretch.

I told him how ill you were, and communicated to him some of the contents of your letter. He admired *you,* cursed *Lovelace,* and raved against all your *family.*

He says that none of your friends think you so ill as you are; nor will believe it. He is sure they all love you, and that dearly too.

If they do, their present hardness of heart will be the subject of everlasting remorse to them should you be taken from us. But now it seems (barbarous wretches!) you are to *suffer within an inch of your life.*

He asked me questions about Mr. Belford: and when he had heard what I had to say of that gentleman, and his disinterested services to you, he raved at some villainous surmises thrown out against you by that officious pedant, Brand: who, but for his gown, I find, would come off poorly enough between your cousin and Lovelace.

He was so uneasy about you himself, that on Thursday the 24th he sent up an honest serious man, one Alston, a gentleman farmer, to inquire of your condition, your visitors, and the like; who brought him word that you was very ill, and was put to great straits to support yourself: but as this was told him by the gentlewoman of the house where you lodge, who it seems mingled with it some tart, though deserved, reflections upon your relations' cruelty, it was not credited by them: and I myself hope it cannot be true; for surely you could not be so *unjust,* I will say, to my friendship, as to suffer any inconveniences for want of money. I think I could not forgive you if it were so.

The colonel (as one of your trustees) is resolved to see you put into possession of your estate: and, in the meantime, he has actually engaged them to remit to him for you the produce of it accrued since your grandfather's death (a very considerable sum).

Your cousin imagines that, before a reconciliation takes

place, they will insist that you shall make such a will as to that estate as they shall approve of: but he declares he will not go out of England till he has seen justice done you by *everybody;* and that you shall not be imposed on either by friend or foe——

Your cousin says that the whole family is *too rich* to be either *humble, considerate,* or *contented.* And as for himself, he has an ample fortune, he says, and thinks of leaving it wholly to you.

I need not say how much I am, and will ever be,

Your affectionate, etc.

Anna Howe.

Miss Howe to Miss Clarissa Harlowe

Thursday, Aug. 31.

THE COLONEL thought fit once, in praise of Lovelace's *generosity,* to say, that (*as a man of honour ought*) he took to himself all the blame, and acquitted you of the consequences of the precipitate step you had taken; since, he said, as you loved him, and was in his power, he *must* have had advantages, which he would *not* have had, if you had continued at your father's, or at any friend's.

But in this case, I averred that there was no need of anything but the strictest truth to demonstrate Lovelace to be the blackest of villains, you the brightest of innocents.

This he caught at; and swore that if anything uncommon or barbarous in the seduction were to come out, as indeed one of the letters you had written to your friends, and which had been shown him, very strongly implied; that is to say, my dear, if anything *worse* than perjury, breach of faith, and abuse of a generous confidence were to appear! he would avenge his cousin to the utmost.

I will dispatch these by Rogers; and if my mother gets well soon (as I hope she will), I am resolved to see you in town, and tell you everything that now is upon my mind; and particularly, mingling my soul with yours, how much I am, and will ever be, my dearest, dear friend,

Your affectionate
Anna Howe.

I cannot express how much your staggering lines, and your conclusion, affect me!

MR. BELFORD TO ROBERT LOVELACE, ESQ.

Sunday Evening, Sept. 3.

THEY HAD SENT for Mr. Goddard when she was so ill last night; and not being able to see him out of her own chamber, he, for the first time, saw her *house,* as she calls it. He was extremely shocked and concerned at it; and chid Mrs. Smith and Mrs. Lovick for not persuading her to have such an object removed from her bedchamber: and when they excused themselves on the *little authority* it was reasonable to suppose they must have with a lady so much their superior, he reflected warmly on those who had *more* authority, and who left her to proceed with such a shocking and solemn whimsy, as he called it.

It is placed near the window, like a harpsichord, though covered over to the ground: and when she is so ill that she cannot well go to her closet, she writes and reads upon it, as others would upon a desk or table.

The doctor told Mrs. Smith that he believed she would hold out long enough for any of her friends to have notice of her state, and to see her, and hardly longer; and since he could not find that she had any certainty of seeing her Cousin Morden (which made it plain that her relations continued inflexible), he would go home and write a letter to her father, take it as she would.

MISS CLARISSA HARLOWE TO MISS HOWE

Saturday, Sept. 2.

I WRITE, my beloved Miss Howe, though very ill still: but I could not by the return of your messenger; for I was then unable to hold a pen.

Your mother's illness gave me great distress for you, till I read farther. You bewailed it as became a daughter so sensible. May you be blessed in each other for many, very many, happy years to come!

What, I wonder, has again happened between you and Mr. Hickman? Although I know it not, I dare say it is owing to some pretty petulance, to some half-ungenerous advantage taken of his obligingness and assiduity.

My dear friends know not that I *have* actually suffered within *less* than *an inch of my life.*

Poor Mr. Brand! He meant well, I believe. I am afraid all will turn heavily upon him, when he probably imagined that he was taking the best method to oblige.

I must lay down my pen. I am very ill. I believe I shall be better by and by. The bad writing would betray me, although I had a mind to keep from you what the event must soon——

Sunday Morning (Sept. 3), Six o'clock.

Hither I had written, and was forced to quit my pen. And so much weaker and worse I grew, that had I resumed it, to have closed here, it must have been with such trembling unsteadiness that it would have given you more concern for me, than the delay of sending it away by last night's post can do.

Mr. Lovelace, you tell me, thought fit to entrust my cousin with the copy of his letter of penitence to me, and with my answer to it, rejecting him and his suit: and Mr. Belford moreover acquaints me how much concerned Mr. Lovelace is for his baseness, and how freely he accused himself to my cousin.

All my apprehension is what may happen when I am gone; lest then my cousin, or any other of my family, should endeavour to avenge me, and risk their own more precious lives on that account.

When I began this letter, I did not think I could have run to such a length. But 'tis to YOU, my dearest friend, and *you* have a title to the spirits you raise and support; for they are no longer mine, and will subside the moment I cease writing to you.

But what do you bid me hope for, when you tell me that, if your mother's health will permit, you will see me in town? I *hope* your mother's health will be perfected as you wish; but I dare not promise myself so great a favour; so great a *blessing*, I will call it—and indeed I know not if I should be able to bear it now!

God for ever bless you, and all you love and honour, and reward you here and hereafter for your kindness to

Your ever obliged and affectionate

Clarissa Harlowe.

MRS. NORTON TO MISS CLARISSA HARLOWE

Thursday, Aug. 31.

I HAD written sooner, my dearest young lady, but that I have been endeavouring ever since the receipt of your last letter to obtain private audience of your mother, in hopes of leave to communicate it to her. But last night I was surprised by an invitation to breakfast at Harlowe Place this morning.

When I came, I found there was to be a meeting of all your family with Colonel Morden at Harlowe Place.

The colonel, when he came, began the discourse by *renewing*, as he called it, his solicitations in your favour. He set before them your penitence; your ill-health; your virtue, though once betrayed and basely used: he then read to them Mr. Lovelace's letter, a most contrite one indeed; and your *high-souled* answer; for that was what he justly called it; and he treated as it deserved Mr. Brand's officious information.

He then told them that he had the day before waited upon Miss Howe, and had been shown a letter from you to her, and permitted to take some memorandums from it, in which you appeared, both by handwriting and the contents, to be so very ill that it seemed doubtful to him if it were possible for you to get over it. And when he read to them that passage where you ask Miss Howe, "What can be done for you now, were your friends to be ever so favourable? and wish, for *their* sakes more than for your *own*, that they would still relent"; and then say, "You are very ill—you must drop your pen—and ask excuse for your crooked writing; and take, as it were, a last farewell of Miss Howe: *Adieu, my dear, adieu,*" are your words—

O my child! my child! said your mamma, weeping, and clasping her hands.

Dear madam, said your brother, be so good as to think you have more children than this ungrateful one.

Yet your sister seemed affected.

Your Uncle Harlowe, wiping his eyes, O cousin, said he, if one thought the poor girl was really so ill——

She *must*, said your Uncle Antony. This is written to her private friend.

Your Uncle Harlowe wished they did not carry their resentments too far.

I begged for God's sake, wringing my hands, and with a bended knee, that they would permit me to go up to you; engaging to give them a faithful account of the way you were in. But I was chidden by your brother; and this occasioned some angry words between him and Mr. Morden.

I believe, sir, I believe, madam, said your sister to her father and mother, we need not trouble my cousin to read any more. It does but grieve and disturb you. My sister Clary seems to be ill: I think, if Mrs. Norton were permitted to go up to her, it would be right. Wickedly as she has acted, if she be truly penitent——

Here she stopped; and every one being silent, I stood up once more, and besought them to let me go: and then I offered to read a passage or two in your letter to me of the 24th. But I was taken up again by your brother; and this occasioned still higher words between the colonel and him.

Your mother, hoping to gain upon your inflexible brother, and to divert the anger of the two gentlemen from each other, proposed that the colonel should proceed in reading the minutes he had taken from your letter.

He accordingly read "of your resuming your pen: that you thought you had taken your last farewell; and the rest of that very affecting passage in which you are obliged to break off more than once, and afterwards to take an airing in a chair." Your brother and sister were affected at this; and he had recourse to his snuff-box.

Your sister called you sweet soul; but with a low voice:

then grew hard-hearted again; yet said nobody could help being affected by your pathetic grief—but that it was your talent.

Your mother could not stand this, but retired to a corner of the room, and sobbed and wept. Your father for a few minutes could not speak, though he seemed inclined to say something.

Your uncles were also both affected: but your brother went round to each; and again reminded your mother that she had other children: What was there, he said, in what was read, but the result of the talent you had of moving the passions?

This set Mr. Morden up again: Fie upon you, Cousin Harlowe! said he. I see plainly to whom it is owing that all relationship and ties of blood with regard to this sweet sufferer are laid aside.

Your brother pretended the honour of the family; and declared that no child ought to be forgiven who abandoned the most indulgent of parents against warning, against the light of knowledge, as you had done.

But, sir, and ladies, said I, rising from my seat in the window, and humbly turning round to each, if I may be permitted to speak, my dear miss asks only for a blessing. She does not beg to be received to favour: she is very ill, and asks only for a last blessing.

Come, come, goody Norton (I need not tell you who said this), you are up again with your lamentables! A good woman, as you are, to forgive so readily a crime that has been as disgraceful to your part in her education as to her family, is a weakness that would induce one to suspect your virtue if you were to be encountered by a temptation *properly adapted*.

By some such charitable logic, said Mr. Morden, as this is my cousin Arabella captivated, I doubt not. If to be uncharitable and unforgiving is to give a proof of virtue, you, Mr. James Harlowe, are the most virtuous young man in the world.

I knew how it would be, replied your brother in a passion, if I met Mr. Morden upon this business. I would have declined it: but you, sir, to his father, would not permit me so to do.

Are we, said your father, to be made still more unhappy among ourselves, when the villain lives that ought to be the object of every one's resentment who has either a value for the family or for this ungrateful girl?

That's the man, said your cousin, whom last Monday, as you know, I went purposely to make the object of mine. But what could I say when I found him so willing to repair his crime? And I give it as my opinion, and have written accordingly to my poor cousin, that it is best for all round that his offer should be accepted: and let me tell you——

Tell me nothing, said your father, quite enraged, of that very vile fellow! I would rather see the rebel die a hundred deaths, were it possible, than that she should give such a villain as him a relation to my family.

Well, but there is no room to think, said your mother, that she *will* give us such a relation, my dear. The poor girl will lessen, I fear, the number of our relations; not increase it. If she be so ill as we are told she is, let us send Mrs. Norton up to her. That's the *least* we can do. Let us take her, however, out of the hands of that Belford.

Both your uncles supported this motion; the latter part of it especially.

Your brother observed, in his ill-natured way, what a fine piece of consistency it was in you, to refuse the vile injurer and the amends he offered; yet to throw yourself upon the protection of his fast friend.

Miss Harlowe was apprehensive, she said, that you would leave all you *could* leave to that pert creature Miss Howe (so she called her) if you should die.

Oh, do not, do not suppose *that,* my Bella, said your poor mother. I cannot think of parting with my Clary. With all her faults, she is my child. Her reasons for her conduct are not heard. It would break my heart to lose her. I think, my dear, to your father, none so fit as I to go up, if you will give me leave: and Mrs. Norton shall accompany me.

This was a sweet motion; and your father paused upon it. Mr. Morden offered his service to escort her. Your uncles seemed to approve of it. But your brother dashed all. I hope, sir, said he to his father; I hope, madam, to his mother, that you will not endeavour to recover a faulty daughter by losing an inculpable son. I do declare, that if ever my Sister Clary darkens these doors again, I never will.

Good God! said the colonel, what a declaration is this! And

suppose, sir, and suppose, madam (turning to your father and mother), this *should* be the case, whether is it better, think you, that you should lose for ever such a daughter as my Cousin Clary, or that your son should go to Edinburgh, and reside there upon an estate which will be the better for his residence upon it?

Your brother's passionate behaviour hereupon is hardly to be described. He resented it, as promoting an alienation of the affection of the family to him. And to such a height were resentiments carried, every one siding with him, that the colonel, with hands and eyes lifted up, cried out: What hearts of flint am I related to! O Cousin Harlowe, to your father, are you resolved to have had but one daughter? Are you, madam, to be taught, by a son who has no bowels, to forget that you are a mother?

But then turning to them (with the more indignation, as it seemed, as he had been obliged to show a humanity which, however, no brave heart should be ashamed of), I leave ye all, said he, fit company for one another. I will never open my lips to any of you more upon this subject. I will instantly make my will, and in me shall the dear creature have the father, uncle, brother she has lost. I will prevail upon her to take the tour of France and Italy with me; nor shall she return till ye know the value of *such* a daughter.

And saying this he hurried out of the room, went into the courtyard, and ordered his horse.

Mr. Antony Harlowe went to him there, just as he was mounting; and said he hoped he should find him cooler in the evening (for he till then had lodged at his house), and that then they would converse calmly; and every one, meantime, would weigh all matters well. But the angry gentleman said: Cousin Harlowe, I shall endeavour to discharge the obligations I owe to your civility since I have been in England: but I have been so treated by that hot-headed young man (who, as far as I know, has done more to ruin his sister than Lovelace himself, and *this* with the approbation of you all), that I will not again enter into *your* doors or *theirs*. My servants shall have orders whither to bring what belongs to me from your house. I will see my dear Cousin Clary as soon as I can. And so God bless you all together!

I took the liberty again, but with fear and trembling, to desire leave to attend you.

There never was a creature so criminal, said your father, looking with displeasure at me, who had not some weak heads to pity and side with her.

I wept. Your mother was so good as to take me by the hand: Come, good woman, said she, come along with me.

Your mother led me to her chamber; and there we sat and wept together for several minutes without being able to speak either of us one word to the other. At last she broke silence; asking me if you were really and indeed so ill as it was said you were?

I answered in the affirmative; and would have shown her your last letter; but she declined seeing it.

I would fain have procured from her the favour of a line to you, with her blessing. I asked what was *intended* by your brother and sister? Would nothing satisfy them but your final reprobation? I insinuated how easy it would be, did not your duty and humility govern you, to make yourself independent as to circumstances; but that nothing but a blessing, a *last* blessing, was requested by you.

"Mr. Brand's account of your intimacy with the friend of the obnoxious man, your mother said, had, for the time, very unhappy effects; for before that she had gained some ground: but afterwards dared not, nor indeed had inclination, to open her lips in your behalf. Your continued intimacy with that Mr. Belford was wholly unaccountable, and as wholly inexcusable.

"What made the wished-for reconciliation, she said, more difficult was, first, that you yourself acknowledged yourself dishonoured (and it was too well known that it was your own fault that you ever were in the power of so great a profligate); of consequence, that their and your disgrace could not be greater than it was: yet that you refused to prosecute the wretch. Next, that the pardon and blessing hoped for must probably be attended with your marriage to the man they hate, and who hates them as much: very disagreeable circumstances, she said, I must allow, to found a reconciliation upon."

To my plea of your illness: "She could not but flatter herself, she answered, that it was from lowness of spirits and temporary dejection. A young creature, she said, so very considerate as you naturally were, and fallen so low, must have enough of that. Should they lose you, which God forbid! the scene would then indeed be sadly changed; for then those who now most resented would be most grieved; all your fine qualities would rise to their remembrance, and your unhappy error would be quite forgotten.

"She wished you would put yourself into your cousin's protection entirely, and have nothing more to say to Mr. Belford."

And I would recommend it to your most serious consideration, my dear Miss Clary, whether now, as your cousin is come, you should not give over all thoughts of Mr. Lovelace's intimate friend for your executor. And suppose, my dear young lady, you were to write one letter more to each of your uncles, to let them know how ill you are? and to ask their advice, and offer to be governed by it, in relation to the disposition of your estate and effects? Methinks I wish you would.

They seem to expect that you will wish to live at your grandfather's house, in a private manner, if your cousin prevail not upon you to go abroad for a year or two.

Friday Morning.

Betty was with me just now. She tells me that your Cousin Morden is so much displeased with them all that he has refused to lodge any more at your Uncle Antony's; and has even taken up with inconvenient lodgings till he is provided with others to his mind. This very much concerns them; and they repent their violent treatment of him: and the more as he is resolved, he says, to make you his sole executrix, and heir to all his fortune.

Your mother wished me not to attend you as yet, because she hopes that I may give myself that pleasure soon with everybody's good liking, and even at their desire. Your Cousin Morden's reconciliation with them, which they are very desirous of, I am ready to hope will include theirs with you.

But if that should happen which I so much dread, and I not with you, I should never forgive myself. Let me, therefore, my dearest young lady, desire you to command my attendance, if you find any danger, and if you wish me peace of mind; and no consideration shall withhold me.

I hear that Miss Howe has obtained leave from her mother to see you; and intends next week to go to town for that purpose; and (as it is believed) to buy clothes for her approaching nuptials.

For Miss Howe's sake, who, in her new engagements, will so much want you; for your Cousin Morden's sake; for your mother's sake, if I must go no farther in your family; and yet I can say, for all their sakes; and for my sake, my dearest Miss Clary; let your resumed and accustomed magnanimity bear you up. You have many things to do which I know not the person who will if you leave us.

Your
Judith Norton.

MR. BELFORD TO ROBERT LOVELACE, ESQ.

Monday, Sept. 4.

THE LADY would not read the letter she had from Mrs. Norton till she had received the Communion, for fear it should contain anything that might disturb that happy calm which she had been endeavouring to obtain for it. And when that solemn office was over, she was so composed, she said, that she thought she could receive any news, however affecting, with tranquillity.

When I was admitted to her presence, I have received, said she, a long and not very pleasing letter from my dear Mrs. Norton. It will soon be in your hands.

I would fain write an answer to it, continued she: but I have no distinct sight, Mr. Belford, no steadiness of fingers. This mistiness, however, will perhaps be gone by and by. Then turning to Mrs. Lovick: I don't think I am dying yet—not *actually* dying, Mrs. Lovick—for I have no bodily pain—no numbnesses; no signs of immediate death, I think.—And my breath, which used of late to be so short, is now tolerable, my head clear, my intellects free—I think I cannot be dying yet—I shall have agonies, I doubt—life will not give up so blessedly easy, I fear—yet how merciful is the Almighty, to give His poor creature such a sweet serenity! 'Tis what I have prayed for!

Mrs. Smith, as well as Mrs. Lovick, was with her. They were

both in tears; nor had I, any more than they, power to say a word in answer.

But, Mr. Belford, said she, assuming a still sprightlier air and accent, let me talk a little to you, while I am thus able to say what I have to say.

Mrs. Lovick, don't leave us—pray sit down; and do you, Mrs. Smith, sit down too. Dame Shelburne, take this key, and open that upper drawer.

She did, with trembling knees. Here, Mr. Belford, is my will. It is witnessed by three persons of Mr. Smith's acquaintance.

I dare to hope that my Cousin Morden will give you assistance, if you request it of him. My Cousin Morden continues his affection for me: but as I have not seen *him,* I leave all the trouble upon *you,* Mr. Belford. I will lay it by itself in this corner; putting it at the farther end of the drawer.

She then took up a parcel of letters, enclosed in one cover, sealed with three seals of black wax: This, said she, I sealed up last night. The cover, sir, will let you know what is to be done with what it encloses. This is the superscription (holding it close to her eyes, and rubbing them): *As soon as I am certainly dead, this to be broke open by Mr. Belford.* Here, sir, I put it (placing it by the will). These folded papers are letters and copies of letters, disposed according to their dates. Miss Howe will do with those as you and she shall think fit.

While we were thus solemnly engaged, a servant came with a letter from her Cousin Morden: Then, said she, he is not come *himself!*

She broke it open; but every line, she said, appeared two to her: so that, being unable to read it herself, she desired I would read it to her.

He tells her, "That the Thursday before he had procured a general meeting of her principal relations at her father's; though not without difficulty, her haughty brother opposing it, and, when met, rendering all his endeavours to reconcile them to her ineffectual.

"He tells her that he shall bring her up the accounts relating to the produce of her grandfather's estate, and adjust them with her; having actually in his hands the arrears due to her from it.

"He highly applauds the noble manner in which she resents

your usage of her. It is impossible, he owns, that you can either deserve her or to be forgiven. But as you do justice to her virtue, and offer to make her all the reparation now in your power; and as she is so very earnest with him not to resent that usage; and declares that you could not have been the author of her calamities but through a strange concurrence of unhappy causes; and as he is not at a loss to know how to place to a *proper account* that strange concurrence; he desires her not to be apprehensive of any vindictive measures from him.

"If she be so absolutely determined against marrying you, as she declares she is, he hopes, he says, to prevail upon her to take (as soon as her health will permit) a little tour abroad with him, as what will probably establish it; since travelling is certainly the best physic for all those disorders which owe their rise to grief or disappointment.

"He expresses his impatience to see her. He will set out, he says, the moment he knows the result of her family's determination; which, he doubts not, will be favourable. Nor will he wait long for that."

When I had read the letter through to the languishing lady: And so, my friends, said she, have I heard of a patient who actually died while five or six principal physicians were in a consultation, and not agreed upon what name to give to his distemper.

I asked if I should write to her cousin, as he knew not how ill she was, to hasten up.

By no means, she said; since, if he were not already set out, she was persuaded that she should be so low by the time he could receive my letter and come, that his presence would but discompose and hurry *her*, and afflict *him*.

J. Belford.

Dr. H. to James Harlowe, senior, Esq.

London, Sept. 4.

Sir,—If I may judge of the hearts of other parents by my own, I cannot doubt but you will take it well to be informed that you have yet an opportunity to save yourself and family great future regret, by dispatching hither some one of it, with your last blessing and your lady's, to the most excellent of her sex.

She knows not that I write. I must indeed acknowledge that I offered to do so some days ago, and that very pressingly: nor did she refuse me from obstinacy—but desired me to forbear for two days only, in hopes that her newly arrived cousin, who, as she heard, was soliciting for her, would be able to succeed in her favour.

But, sir, whatever you think fit to do, or permit to be done, must be speedily done; for she cannot, I verily think, live a week: and how long of that short space she may enjoy her admirable intellects to take comfort in the favours you may think proper to confer upon her, cannot be said. I am, sir,

Your most humble servant,

R. H.

MR. BELFORD TO WILLIAM MORDEN, ESQ.

London, Sept. 4.

SIR,—I understand you are employing your good offices with the parents of Miss Clarissa Harlowe, and other relations, to reconcile them to the most meritorious daughter and kinswoman that ever family had to boast of.

Generously as this is intended by you, we *here* have too much reason to think all your solicitudes on this head will be unnecessary: for it is the opinion of every one who has the honour of being admitted to her presence, that she cannot live over three days: so that if you wish to see her alive you must lose no time to come up.

She knows not that I write. I had done it sooner if I had had the least doubt that before now she would not have received from you some news of the happy effects of your kind mediation in her behalf. I am, sir,

Your most humble servant,

J. Belford.

MISS CLARISSA HARLOWE TO MRS. NORTON

MY DEAREST MRS. NORTON,—I am afraid I shall not be able to write all that is upon my mind to say to you upon the subject of your last.

As to my friends, and as to the sad breakfasting, I cannot help being afflicted for *them*. What, alas! has not my mother, in particular, suffered by my rashness! Yet to allow so much for a son!—so little for a daughter! But all now will soon be over, as to me. I hope they will bury all their resentments in my grave.

As to your advice in relation to Mr. Belford, let me only say that the unhappy reprobation I have met with, and my short time, must be my apology now. I wish I *could* have written to my mother and my uncles, as you advise. And yet favours come *so* slowly from them!

The granting of one request only now remains as a desirable one from them; which nevertheless, when granted, I shall not be sensible of. It is that they will be pleased to permit my remains to be laid with those of my ancestors—placed at the feet of my dear grandfather—as I have mentioned in my will. This, however, as they please. For, after all, this vile body ought not so much to engage my cares. It is a weakness—but let it be called a *natural* weakness, and I shall be excused; especially when a reverential gratitude shall be known to be the foundation of it.

I wish not now, at the writing of this, to see even my Cousin Morden.

Neither do I want to see even *you,* my dear Mrs. Norton. Nevertheless I must, in justice to my own gratitude, declare that there *was* a time, could you have been permitted to come, without incurring displeasure from those whose esteem it is necessary for you to cultivate and preserve, that your presence and comfortings would have been balm to my wounded mind. But were you now, even by consent, and with reconciliatory tidings, to come, it would but add to your grief; and the sight of one I so dearly love, so happily fraught with good news, might but draw me back to wishes I have had great struggles to get above.

And pray let my Miss Howe know that by the time you will receive this, and she *your* signification of the contents of it, it will, in all probability, be too late for *her* to do me the inestimable favour, as I should once have thought it, to see me.

I shall, nevertheless, love *you,* my Mamma Norton, and my Miss Howe, whose love to me *has passed the love of women,* to my latest hour! But yet, I am now above the quick sense of those pleasures which once most delighted me: and once more I say that I do not wish to see objects so dear to me which might bring me back again into sense, and rival my *supreme love*.

. . . . . .

Twice have I been forced to leave off. I *wished* that my last writing might be to you, or to Miss Howe, if it might not be to my dearest Ma——

Mamma, I would have wrote—is the word distinct? My eyes are *so* misty! If, when I apply to you, I break off in half-words, do you supply them—the kindest are *your* due.

. . . . . .

Another breaking off! But the new day seems to rise upon me with healing in its wings. I have gotten, I think, a recruit of strength: spirits, I bless God, I have not of late wanted.

Let my dearest Miss Howe purchase her wedding garments—and may all temporal blessings attend the charming preparation!

As for me, never bride was so ready as I am. My wedding garments are bought. And though not fine and gaudy to the sight, though not adorned with jewels and set off with gold and silver, yet will they be the easiest, the *happiest* suit, that ever bridal maiden wore, for they are such as carry with them a security against all those anxieties, pains, and perturbations which sometimes succeed to the most promising outsettings.

Oh, hasten, good God, if it be Thy blessed will, the happy moment that I am to be decked out in this all-quieting garb! And sustain, comfort, bless, and protect with the all-shadowing wing of Thy mercy, my dear parents, my uncles, my brother, my sister, my Cousin Morden, my ever dear and ever kind Miss Howe, my good Mrs. Norton, and every deserving person to whom *they* wish well! is the ardent prayer, first and last, of every beginning hour, as the clock tells it me (hours now are days, nay years) of

Your now not sorrowing or afflicted, but happy

Clarissa Harlowe.

MR. LOVELACE TO JOHN BELFORD, ESQ.

Wedn. Morn. Sept. 6, half an hour after Three.

I AM *not* the savage which you and my worst enemies think me. My soul is *too much* penetrated by the contents of the letter which you enclosed in your last to say one word more to it than that my heart has bled over it from every vein!

Surely it will be better when *all is over*—when I know the *worst* the Fates can do against me. Yet how shall I bear that *worst?* O Belford, Belford! write it not to me; but, if it *must* happen, get somebody else to write; for I shall curse the pen, the hand, the head, and the heart employed in communicating to me the fatal tidings. But what is this saying, when already I curse the whole world except her—myself most?

Nothing but the excruciating pangs the condemned soul feels, at its entrance into the eternity of the torments we are taught to fear, can exceed what I *now* feel, and *have* felt for almost this week past; and mayest thou have a spice of those if thou hast not a letter ready written for

Thy Lovelace.

MR. BELFORD TO ROBERT LOVELACE, ESQ.

Tuesday, Sept. 5, Six o'clock.

THE LADY remains exceedingly weak and ill. Her intellects, nevertheless, continue clear and strong, and her piety and patience are without example. Every one thinks this night will be her last. She will not, however, send away her letter to her Norton as yet. She endeavoured in vain to superscribe it: so desired me to do it. Her fingers will not hold her pen with the requisite steadiness. She has, I fear, written and read her last!

Eight o'clock.

She is somewhat better than she was. The doctor has been here, and thinks she will hold out yet a day or two. He has ordered her, as for some time past, only some little cordials to take when ready to faint. She seemed disappointed when he told her she might yet live two or three days; and said she longed for dismission! Life was not so easily extinguished, she saw, as some imagine. *Death from grief* was, she believed, *the slowest of deaths*. Her only prayer was now for submission to it: for she doubted not but by the Divine goodness she should be a happy creature as soon as she could be divested of these *rags of mortality*.

Of her own accord she mentioned you; which, till then, she had avoided to do. She asked, with great serenity, where you were?

I told her where; and read to her a few lines of yours, in which you mention your wishes to see her, your sincere affliction, and your resolution not to approach her without her consent.

I would have read more; but she said: Enough, Mr. Belford; enough! Poor man! Does his conscience begin to find him! Then need not anybody to wish him a greater punishment!

Yet let him know that I now again repeat that I forgive him. And may God Almighty, clasping her fingers and lifting up her eyes, forgive him too; and perfect his repentance, and sanctify it to him! Tell him I say so! And tell him that if I could not say so with my whole heart I should be very uneasy, and think that my hopes of mercy to myself were but weakly founded; and that I had still, in any harboured resentments, some hankerings after a life which he has been the cause of shortening.

The divine creature then turning aside her head: Poor man, said she! I once could have loved him. This is saying more than ever I could say of any other man out of my own family! Would he have permitted me to have been a humble instrument to have made him good, I think I could have made him happy! But tell him not this if he be *really* penitent—it may too much affect him!—There she paused.

But pray tell him that if I could know that my death might be a means to reclaim and save him, it would be an inexpressible satisfaction to me!

But let me not, however, be made uneasy with the apprehension of seeing him. I cannot *bear* to see him!

You see, Lovelace, that I did not forget the office of a friend, in endeavouring to prevail upon her to give you her last forgiveness personally. And I hope, as she is so near her end, you will not invade her in her last hours; since she must be extremely discomposed at such an interview; and it might make her leave the world the sooner for it.

I cannot, however, forbear to wish that the heavenly creature could have prevailed upon herself, in these her last hours, to see you; and that for *my* sake, as well as *yours:* for although I am determined never to be guilty of the crimes which till within these few past weeks have blackened my former life; and for which, at present, I most heartily hate myself; yet should I be less apprehensive of a relapse if (wrought upon by the solemnity which such an interview must have been attended with) you had become a reformed man: for no devil do I fear but one in your shape.

. . . . . .

It is now eleven o'clock at night. The lady, who retired to rest an hour ago, is, as Mrs. Lovick tells me, in a sweet slumber.

MR. LOVELACE TO JOHN BELFORD, ESQ.

Wedn. Morn., Sept. 6.

I AM OBLIGED to you for endeavouring to engage her to see me. 'Twas acting like a friend. If she *had* vouchsafed me that favour, she should have seen at her feet the most abject adorer that ever kneeled to justly offended beauty.

What she bid you, and what she *forbid* you, to tell me (the latter for *tender* considerations); that she forgives me; and that, could she have made me a *good* man, she could have made me a *happy* one! That she even *loved me!* At such a moment to own that *she once loved me!* Never *before* loved any man! That she prays for me!—O Belford, Belford! I cannot bear it!—What a dog, what a devil have I been to a goodness so superlative! Why does she not inveigh against me? Why does she not execrate me? Oh, the triumphant subduer! Ever above me! And now to leave me so infinitely below her!

Marry and repair, at any time; this, wretch that I was! was my plea to myself. To give her a lowering sensibility; to bring her down from among the stars which her beamy head was surrounded by, that my wife, so greatly above me, might not despise me; this was one of my reptile motives, owing to my *more* reptile envy, and to my consciousness of inferiority to her! Yet she, from step to step, from distress to distress, to maintain her superiority; and, like the sun, to break out upon me with the greater refulgence for the clouds that I had contrived to cast about her!—And now to escape me thus! No power left me to repair her wrongs! No alleviation to my self-reproach! No dividing of blame with her!

Tell her, oh, tell her, Belford, that her prayers and wishes, her superlatively generous prayers and wishes, shall *not* be vain: that I *can,* and *do,* repent—and *long* have repented. Tell her of my frequent deep remorses—it was impossible that such remorses should not at last produce *effectual* remorse. Yet she must not leave me—she must live, if she would wish to have my contrition perfect—for what can despair produce?

. . . . . .

But say not, Jack, that she must leave us yet. If she recover, and if I can but re-obtain her favour, then indeed will life be life to me. The world never *saw* such a husband as I will make.

MR. BELFORD TO ROBERT LOVELACE, ESQ.

Wedn. Morn. Eight o'clock (6 Sept.).

YOUR SERVANT arrived here before I was stirring. I sent him to Smith's to inquire how the lady was; and ordered him to call upon me when he came back. I was pleased to hear she had had tolerable rest. As soon as I had dispatched him with the letter I had written overnight, I went to attend her.

I found her up and dressed; in a white satin night-gown. Ever elegant; but now more so than I had seen her for a week past: her aspect serenely cheerful.

She mentioned the increased dimness of her eyes, and the tremor which had invaded her limbs. If this be dying, said she, there is nothing at all shocking in it. My body hardly sensible of pain, my mind at ease, my intellects clear and perfect as ever.

I told her it was not so serene with you.

There is not the same reason for it, replied she. 'Tis a choice comfort, Mr. Belford, at the winding-up of our short story, to be able to say I have rather *suffered* injuries *myself* than *offered* them to *others*. I bless God, though I have been unhappy, as the *world* deems it, and once I thought more so than at present I think I ought to have done; since my calamities were to work out for me my everlasting happiness; yet have I not wilfully made any one creature so. I have no reason to grieve for anything but for the sorrow I have given my friends.

But pray, Mr. Belford, remember me in the best manner to my Cousin Morden; and desire him to comfort them, and to tell them that all would have been the same had they accepted of my true penitence, as I wish and as I trust the Almighty has done.

I was called down: it was to Harry, who was just returned from Miss Howe's, to whom he carried the lady's letter. The stupid fellow, being bid to make haste with it, and return as soon as possible, stayed not till Miss Howe had it, she being at the distance of five miles, although Mrs. Howe would have had him stay, and sent a man and horse purposely with it to her daughter.

Wednesday Morning, 10 o'clock.

The poor lady is just recovered from a fainting fit, which has left her at death's door. Her late tranquillity and freedom from pain seemed but a *lightening*.

By my faith, Lovelace, I had rather part with all the friends I have in the world than with this lady. I never knew what a virtuous, a holy friendship, as I may call mine to her, was before. But to be so *new* to it, and to be obliged to forego it so soon, what an affliction! Yet, thank Heaven, I lose her not by *my own* fault!—But 'twould be barbarous not to spare thee now.

MR. LOVELACE TO JOHN BELFORD, ESQ.

Kensington, Wednesday Noon.

LIKE Æsop's traveller, thou blowest hot and cold, life and death, in the same breath, with a view, no doubt, to distract me. How familiarly dost thou use the words *dying, dimness, tremor!* Never did any mortal ring so many changes on so few bells. Thy true father, I dare swear, was a butcher or an undertaker, by the delight thou seemest to take in scenes of death and horror. Thy barbarous reflection that thou losest her not by thy own fault is never to be forgiven. Thou hast but one way to atone for the torments thou givest me, and that is by sending me word that she is better, and will recover. Whether it be true or not, let me be told so, and I will go abroad rejoicing and believing it, and my wishes and imagination shall make out all the rest.

If she live but one year, that I may acquit myself *to* myself (no matter for the world!) that her death is not owing to me, I will compound for the rest.

Will neither vows nor prayers save her? I never prayed in my life, put all the years of it together, as I have done for this fortnight past: and I have most sincerely repented of all my baseness to her—and will nothing do?

But after all, if she recover not, *this* reflection must be my comfort; and it is *truth:* that her *departure* will be owing rather to wilfulness, to downright *female* wilfulness, than to any other cause.

So this lady, as I suppose, intended only at first to vex and plague me; and, finding she could do it to purpose, her desire of revenge insensibly became stronger in her than the desire of life; and now she is willing to die, as an event which she thinks will cut my heart-strings asunder. And still the *more* to be revenged, puts on the Christian and forgives me.

But I'll have none of her forgiveness! My own heart tells me I do not deserve it; and I cannot bear it! And what is it but a mere *verbal* forgiveness, as ostentatiously as cruelly given, with a view to magnify herself and wound me deeper? A little, dear, specious—but let me stop, lest I blaspheme!

. . . . . .

Send me word by thy next, I conjure thee, in the names of all her kindred saints and angels, that she is living, and likely to live! If thou sendest ill news, thou wilt be answerable for the consequence, whether it be fatal to the messenger or to

Thy Lovelace.

Mr. Belford to Robert Lovelace, Esq.

Wednesday, 11 o'clock.

Dr. H. has just been here. He tarried with me till the minister had done praying by the lady; and then we were both admitted. Mr. Goddard, who came while the doctor and the clergyman were with her, went away with them when they went. They took a solemn and everlasting leave of her, as I have no scruple to say; blessing her, and being blessed by her; and wishing (when it came to be their lot) for an exit as happy as hers is likely to be.

She had again earnestly requested of the doctor his opinion how long it was *now* probable that she could continue: and he told her that he apprehended she would hardly see to-morrow night. She said she should number the hours with greater pleasure than ever she numbered any in her life on the most joyful occasion.

This moment a man is come from Miss Howe with a letter. Perhaps I shall be able to send you the contents.

. . . . . .

She endeavoured several times with earnestness, but in vain, to read the letter of her dear friend. The writing, she said, was too fine for her grosser sight, and the lines staggered under her eye. And, indeed, she trembled so she could not hold the paper: and at last desired Mrs. Lovick to read it to her, the messenger waiting for an answer.

Miss Howe to Miss Clarissa Harlowe

Tuesday, Sept. 5.

O my dearest Friend!—What will become of your poor Anna Howe! I see by your writing, as well as read by your own account (which, were you not very, *very* ill, you would have touched more tenderly), how it is with you! Why have I thus long delayed to attend you! Could I think that the comfortings of a faithful friend were as nothing to a gentle mind in distress, that I could be prevailed upon to forbear visiting you so much as *once* in all this time! I, as well as everybody else, to desert and abandon my dear creature to strangers! What will become of me if you be as bad as my apprehensions make you!

I will set out this moment, little as the encouragement is that you give me to do so! My mother is willing I should! Why, oh, why, was she not *before* willing!

Yet she persuades me too (lest I should be fatally affected were I to find my fears too well justified) to wait the return of this messenger, who rides our swiftest horse. God speed him with good news to me—else—but, O my dearest, dearest friend, what else? One line from your hand by him! Send me but *one* line to bid me attend you! I will set out the moment, the very moment I receive it. I am now actually ready to do so! And if you love me, as I love you, the sight of me will revive you to my hopes.

But methinks your style and sentiments are too well connected, too full of life and vigour, to give cause for so much despair as the staggering pen seems to forebode.

Your Anna Howe.

This *is* a friend, said the divine lady (taking the letter in her hand and kissing it), worth wishing to live for. O my dear Anna Howe! How uninterruptedly sweet and noble has been our friendship! But we shall one day meet (and this hope must comfort us both) never to part again! Then, divested of the shades of body, shall we be all light and all mind. Then how unalloyed, how perfect, will be our friendship! Our love then will have one and the same adorable object, and we shall enjoy it and each other to all eternity!

She said her dear friend was so earnest for a line or two that she would fain write, if she could: and she tried; but to no purpose. She could dictate, however, she believed; and desired Mrs. Lovick would take pen and paper. Which she did, and then she dictated to *her*. I would have withdrawn; but at her desire stayed.

She wandered a good deal at first.

She dictated the farewell part without hesitation; and when she came to the blessing and subscription, she took the pen,

hand, that she has from every living creature! Good God! How could your accursed friend——

And how could her cruel parents? interrupted I. We may as easily account for *him* as for *them*.

Too true! returned he, the vileness of the profligates of our sex considered, whenever they can get any of the other into their power.

I satisfied him about the care that had been taken of her; and told him of the friendly and even *paternal* attendance she had had from Dr. H. and Mr. Goddard.

He was impatient to attend her.

Mrs. Smith, at his request, stepped up, and brought us down word that Mrs. Lovick and her nurse were with her; and that she was in so sound a sleep, leaning upon the former in her elbow-chair, that she neither heard her enter the room nor go out. The colonel begged, if not improper, that he might see her, though sleeping. He said that his impatience would not let him stay till she awaked. Yet he would not have her disturbed; and should be glad to contemplate her sweet features, when she saw not him; and asked if she thought he could not go in and come out without disturbing her?

She believed he might, she answered; for her chair's back was towards the door.

He said he would take care to withdraw if she awoke, that his sudden appearance might not surprise her.

Mrs. Smith, stepping up before us, bid Mrs. Lovick and the nurse not stir when we entered: and then we went up softly together.

We beheld the lady in a charming attitude. Dressed, as I told you before, in her virgin white, she was sitting in her elbow-chair, Mrs. Lovick close by her in another chair, with her left arm round her neck, supporting it, as it were; for, it seems, the lady had bid her do so, saying she had been a mother to her, and she would delight herself in thinking she was in her mamma's arms; for she found herself drowsy; perhaps, she said, for the last time she should ever be so.

One faded cheek rested upon the good woman's bosom, the kindly warmth of which had overspread it with a faint, but charming flush; the other paler and hollow, as if already iced over by death. Her hands, white as the lily, with her meandering veins more transparently blue than ever I had seen even hers (veins so soon, alas! to be choked up by the congealment of that purple stream which already so languidly creeps rather than flows through them!); her hands hanging lifelessly, one before her, the other grasped by the right hand of the kind widow, whose tears bedewed the sweet face which her motherly bosom supported, though unfelt by the fair sleeper; and either insensibly to the good woman, or what she would not disturb her to wipe off, or to change her posture: her aspect was sweetly calm and serene; and though she started now and then, yet her sleep seemed easy; her breath indeed short and quick; but tolerably free, and not like that of a dying person.

The colonel, sighing often, gazed upon her with his arms folded, and with the most profound and affectionate attention; till at last, on her starting, and fetching her breath with greater difficulty than before, he retired to a screen that was drawn before her *house,* as she calls it. This screen was placed there at the time she found herself obliged to take to her chamber; and in the depth of our concern, and the fullness of other discourse at our first interview, I had forgotten to apprise the colonel of what he would probably see.

Retiring thither, he drew out his handkerchief, and, overwhelmed with grief, seemed unable to speak: but, on casting his eye behind the screen, he soon broke silence; for, struck with the shape of the coffin, he lifted up a purplish-coloured cloth that was spread over it, and, starting back, Good God! said he, what's here!

Mrs. Smith standing next him: Why, said he, with great emotion, is my cousin suffered to indulge her sad reflections with such an object before her?

Alas! sir, replied the good woman, who should control her? We are all strangers about her, in a manner: and yet we have expostulated with her upon this sad occasion.

I ought, said I (stepping softly up to him, the lady again falling into a doze), to have apprised you of this. I was here when it was brought in, and never was so shocked in my life. But it is not a shocking object to her, though it be to everybody else.

The lady fetched a profound sigh, and, starting, it broke off our talk; and the colonel then withdrew farther behind the screen.

Where am I? said she. How drowsy I am! How long have I dozed? Don't go, sir (for I was retiring). I am very stupid, and shall be more and more so, I suppose.

She then offered to raise herself; but, being ready to faint through weakness, was forced to sit down again, reclining her head on her chair-back; and, after a few moments: I believe now, my good friends, said she, all your kind trouble will soon be over. I have slept, but am not refreshed, and my fingers' ends seem numbed—have no feeling! (holding them up). 'Tis time to send the letter to my good Norton.

Shall I, madam, send my servant post with it?

Oh, no, sir, I thank you. It will reach the dear woman too soon (as she will think) by the post.

I told her this was not post day.

Is it Wednesday still? said she. Bless me! I know not how the time goes: but very tediously, 'tis plain. And now I think I must soon take to my bed. All will be most conveniently and with least trouble over there—will it not, Mrs. Lovick?—I think, sir, turning to me, I have left nothing to these last incapacitating hours. Nothing either to say or to do. I bless God, I have not. If I *had,* how unhappy should I be! Can you, sir, remind me of anything necessary to be done or said to make your office easy?

If, madam, your Cousin Morden should come, you would be glad to see him, I presume?

I am too weak to wish to see my cousin now. It would but discompose me, and him too. Yet, if he come while I *can* see, I *will* see him, were it but to thank him for former favours, and for his present kind intentions to me. Has anybody been here from him?

He has called, and will be here, madam, in half an hour; but he feared to surprise you.

Nothing can surprise me now, except my mamma were to favour me with her last blessing in person. That would be a welcome surprise to me, even yet. But did my cousin come purposely to town to see me?

Yes, madam. I took the liberty to let him know, by a line last Monday, how ill you were.

You are very kind, sir. I am and have been greatly obliged to you. But I think I shall be pained to see him now, because he will be concerned to see me. And yet, as I am not so ill as I shall presently be, the sooner he comes the better. But if he come, what shall I do about that screen? He will chide me, very probably; and I cannot bear chiding now. Perhaps (leaning upon Mrs. Lovick and Mrs. Smith) I can walk into the next apartment to receive him.

She motioned to rise; but was ready to faint again, and forced to sit still.

The colonel was in a perfect agitation behind the screen to hear this discourse; and twice, unseen by his cousin, was coming from it towards her; but retreated, for fear of surprising her too much.

I stepped to him and favoured his retreat; she only saying: Are you going, Mr. Belford? Are you sent for down? Is my cousin come? For she heard somebody step softly across the room, and thought it to be me; her hearing being more perfect than her sight.

I told her I believed he was; and she said: We must make the best of it. I shall otherwise most grievously shock my poor cousin: for he loved me dearly once. Pray give me a few of the doctor's last drops in water, to keep up my spirits for this one interview; and that is all, I believe, that can concern me now.

The colonel (who heard all this) sent in his name; and I, pretending to go down to him, introduced the afflicted gentleman; she having first ordered the screen to be put as close to the window as possible, that he might not see what was behind it; while he, having heard what she had said about it, was determined to take no notice of it.

He folded the angel in his arms as she sat, dropping down on one knee; for, supporting herself upon the two elbows of the chair, she attempted to rise, but could not. Excuse, my dear cousin, said she, excuse me, that I cannot stand up. I did not expect this favour now. But I am glad of this opportunity to thank you for all your generous goodness to me.

I never, my best-beloved and dearest cousin, said he (with

eyes running over), shall forgive myself that I did not attend you sooner. Little did I think you were so ill; nor do any of your friends believe it. If they did——

If they did, repeated she, interrupting him, I should have had more compassion from them. I am sure I should. But pray, sir, how did you leave them? Are *you* reconciled to them? If you are not, I beg, if you love your poor Clarissa, that you will: for every widened difference augments but my fault; since *that* is the foundation of all.

I had been expecting to hear from them in your favour, my dear cousin, said he, for some hours, when this gentleman's letter arrived, which hastened me up: but I have the account of your grandfather's estate to make up with you, and have bills and drafts upon their banker for the sums due to you; which they desire you may receive, lest you should have occasion for money. And this is such an earnest of an approaching reconciliation that I dare to answer for all the rest being according to your wishes, if——

Ah! sir, interrupted she, with frequent breaks and pauses, I wish I wish—this does not rather show that, were I to live, they would have nothing more to say to me. I never had any pride in being independent of them: all my actions, when I might have made myself *more* independent, show this—but what avail these reflections now? I only beg, sir, that you, and *this* gentleman—will adjust those matters—according to the will I have written. Mr. Belford will excuse me; but it was in truth more necessity than choice that made me think of giving him the trouble he so kindly accepts. Had I had the happiness to see you, my cousin, sooner—or to know that you still honoured me with your regard—I should not have had the assurance to ask this favour of *him.* But, though the friend of Mr. Lovelace, he is a man of honour, and he will make peace rather than break it. And, my dear cousin, let me beg of you to contribute your part to it—and remember that, while I have nearer relations than my Cousin Morden, dear as you are, and always were to me, you have no title to avenge my wrongs upon him who has been the occasion of them.

I must do Mr. Lovelace so much justice, answered he, wiping his eyes, as to witness how sincerely he repents him of his ungrateful baseness to you, and how ready he is to make you all the amends in his power. He owns *his* wickedness, and *your* merit. If he did not, I could not pass it over, though you *have* nearer relations: for, my dear cousin, did not your grandfather leave me in trust for you? And should I think myself concerned for your fortune, and not for your honour? But, since he is so desirous to do you justice, I have the less to say; and you may make yourself entirely easy on that account.

I thank you, thank you, sir, said she: all is now as I wished. But I am very faint, very weak. I am sorry I cannot hold up; that I cannot better deserve the honour of this visit: but it will not be. And saying this, she sunk down in her chair, and was silent.

Hereupon we both withdrew, leaving word that we would be at the Bedford Head, if anything extraordinary happened.

We procured Mr. Goddard (Dr. H. not being at home) once more to visit her, and to call upon us in his return. He was so good as to do so; but he tarried with her not five minutes; and told us that she was drawing on apace; that he feared she would not live till morning; and that she wished to see Colonel Morden directly.

Ten o'clock.

The colonel sent to me afterwards, to tell me that the lady having been in convulsions, he was so much disordered that he could not possibly attend me.

I have sent every half-hour to know how she does: and just now I have the pleasure to hear that her convulsions have left her; and that she is gone to rest in a much quieter way than could be expected.

Her poor cousin is very much indisposed; yet will not stir out of the house while she is in such a way; but intends to lie down on a couch, having refused any other accommodation.

MR. BELFORD. [IN CONTINUATION]

Soho, Six o'clock, Sept. 7.

THE LADY is still alive. The colonel having just sent his servant to let me know that she inquired after me about an hour ago, I am dressing to attend her. Joel begs of me to dispatch him back, though but with one line to gratify your present impatience. He expects, he says, to find you at Knightsbridge, let him make what haste he can back; and if he has not a line or two to pacify you, he is afraid you will pistol him; for he apprehends that you are hardly yourself. I therefore dispatch this; and will have another ready as soon as I can, with particulars.

Ten o'clock.

The colonel being earnest to see his cousin as soon as she awoke, we were both admitted. We observed in her, as soon as we entered, strong symptoms of her approaching dissolution.

Her breath being very short, she desired another pillow. Having two before, this made her in a manner sit up in her bed; and she spoke then with more distinctness; and, seeing us greatly concerned, forgot her own stutterings to comfort us.

I beseech ye, my good friends, proceeded she, mourn not for for one who mourns not, nor has cause to mourn, for herself. On the contrary, rejoice with me, that all my worldly troubles are so near their end. Believe me, sirs, that I would not, if I might, choose to live, although the pleasantest part of my life were to come over again: and yet *eighteen years of it,* out of *nineteen,* have been *very* pleasant. To be so much exposed to temptation, and to be so liable to fail in the trial, who would not rejoice that all her dangers are over! All I wished was pardon and blessing from my dear parents. Easy as my departure seems to promise to be, it would have been still easier had I had that pleasure. BUT GOD ALMIGHTY WOULD NOT LET ME DEPEND FOR COMFORT UPON ANY BUT HIMSELF.

She had fatigued herself so much (growing sensibly weaker) that she sunk her head upon her pillows, ready to faint; and we withdrew to the window, looking upon one another; but could not tell what to say; and yet both seemed inclinable to speak: but the motion passed over in silence.

Eleven o'clock.

MR. BELFORD. [IN CONTINUATION]

THE COLONEL tells me that he has written to Mr. Harlowe, by his servant, "That they might spare themselves the trouble of debating about a reconciliation; for that his dear cousin would probably be no more before they could resolve."

He wished he had not come to England at all, or had come sooner; and hoped I would apprise him of the whole mournful story at a proper season. He added that he had thoughts, when he came over, of fixing here for the remainder of his days: but now, as it was impossible his cousin could recover, he would go abroad again, and resettle himself at Florence or Leghorn.

. . . . . .

The lady has been giving orders, with great presence of mind, about her body; directing her nurse and the maid of the house to put her into her coffin as soon as she is cold. Mr. Belford, she said, would know the rest by her will.

. . . . . .

She has just now given from her bosom, where she always wore it, a miniature picture set in gold of Miss Howe: she gave it to Mrs. Lovick, desiring her to fold it up in white paper, and directed it, *To Charles Hickman, Esq.*, and to give it to me, when she was departed, for that gentleman.

She looked upon the picture before she gave it her. *Sweet and ever-amiable friend—companion—sister—lover!* said she—and kissed it four several times, once at each tender appellation.

. . . . . .

This event is nearly as interesting to *me* at it is to *you.* If you are more grieved than I, there can be but one reason for it; and that's at your heart! I had rather lose all the friends I have in the world (yourself in the number) than this divine lady; and shall be unhappy whenever I think of her sufferings, and of her merit; though I have nothing to reproach myself by reason of the former.

I say not this, just now, so much to reflect upon you, as to express my own grief; though your conscience, I suppose, will make you think otherwise.

Thursday Afternoon, 4 o'clock.

MR. BELFORD TO RICHARD MOWBRAY, ESQ.

Thursday Afternoon.

DEAR MOWBRAY,—I am glad to hear you are in town. Throw yourself the moment this comes to your hand (if possible with Tourville) in the way of the man who least of all men deserves the love of a worthy heart; but most that of thine and Tourville: else the news I shall most probably send him within an hour or two will make annihilation the greatest blessing he has to wish for.

You will find him between Piccadilly and Kensington, most probably on horseback, riding backwards and forwards in a crazy way; a waiter possibly, if so, watching for his servant's return to him from me.

. . . . . .

His man Will is just come to me. He will carry this to you in his way back, and be your director. Hie away in a coach or anyhow. Your being with him may save either his or a servant's life. Adieu.

J. Belford.

MR. LOVELACE TO JOHN BELFORD, ESQ.

CURSE UPON the colonel, and curse upon the writer of the last letter I received, and upon all the world! Thou to pretend to be as much interested in my Clarissa's fate as myself! 'Tis well for one of us that this was not said to me, instead of written. Living or dying, she is mine—and only mine. Have I not earned her dearly? Is not damnation likely to be the purchase to me, though a happy eternity will be hers?

An eternal separation! O God! O God! How can I bear that thought! But yet there is life! Yet, therefore, hope—enlarge my hope, and thou shalt be my good genius, and I will forgive thee everything.

For this last time—but it must not, shall not be the *last*—let me hear, the moment thou receivest this—what I *am* to be—for at present I am

The most miserable of men.

Rose, at Knightsbridge, 5 o'clock.

My fellow tells me that thou art sending Mowbray and Tourville to me. I want them not. My soul's sick of them, and of all the world; but most of myself. Yet, as they send me word they will come to me immediately, I will wait for them, and for thy next. O Belford! let it not be——But hasten it, hasten it, be it what it may!

MR. BELFORD TO ROBERT LOVELACE, ESQ.

Seven o'clock, Thursday Evening, Sept. 7.

I HAVE only to say at present: Thou wilt do well to take a tour to Paris; or wherever else thy destiny shall lead thee!!!——

John Belford.

MR. MOWBRAY TO JOHN BELFORD, ESQ.

Uxbridge, Sept. 7, between 11 and 12 at Night.

DEAR JACK,—I send, by poor Lovelace's desire, for *particulars* of the fatal breviate thou sentest him this night. He cannot bear to set pen to paper; yet wants to know every minute passage of Miss Harlowe's departure.

I wish the poor fellow had never known her.

It was well we were with him when your note came. Why, Jack, the poor fellow was quite beside himself—mad as any man ever was in Bedlam.

Will brought him the letter just after we had joined him at the Bohemia Head. He trembled like a devil at receiving it: fumbled at the seal, his fingers in a palsy; his hand shake, shake, shake, that he tore the letter in two before he could come at the contents: and, when he had read them, off went his hat to one corner of the room, his wig to the other. Damnation seize the world! and a whole volley of such-like *execratious* wishes; running up and down the room, and throwing up the sash, and pulling it down, and smiting his forehead with his double fist with such force as would have felled an ox, and stamping and tearing, that the landlord ran in, and faster ran out again.

By degrees, we brought him a little to his reason, and he promised to behave more like a man.

He won't bear the word *dead* on any account. A squeamish

puppy! How love unmans and softens! And such a *noble* fellow as this too! Rot him for an idiot and an oaf! I have no patience with the foolish *duncical* dog—upon my soul I have not!

So send the account, and let him howl over it, as I suppose he will.

I was willing to give thee some account of the hand we have had with the tearing fellow, who had certainly been a lost man, had we not been with him; or he would have killed somebody or other. I have no doubt of it. And *now* he is but very middling; sits grinning like a man in straw; curses and swears, and is confounded gloomy; and creeps into holes and corners, like an old hedgehog hunted for his grease.

And so, adieu, Jack.

R. Mowbray.

MR. BELFORD TO ROBERT LOVELACE, ESQ.

Thursday Night.

I MAY as well try to write; since, were I to go to bed, I shall not sleep. I never had such a weight of grief upon my mind in my life as upon the demise of this admirable woman; whose soul is now rejoicing in the regions of light.

You may be glad to know the particulars of her happy exit.

At four o'clock, as I mentioned in my last, I was sent for down.

The colonel was the first that took my attention, kneeling on the side of the bed, the lady's right hand in both his, which his face covered, bathing it with his tears.

On the other side of the bed sat the good widow; her face overwhelmed with tears, leaning her head against the bed's head in a most disconsolate manner; and turning her face to me, as soon as she saw me, O Mr. Belford, cried she, with folded hands—the dear lady—— A heavy sob permitted her not to say more.

Mrs. Smith, with clasped fingers and uplifted eyes, as if imploring help from the only Power which could give it, was kneeling down at the bed's feet, tears in large drops trickling down her cheeks.

Her nurse was kneeling between the widow and Mrs. Smith.

The maid of the house, with her face upon her folded arms,

as she stood leaning against the wainscot, more audibly expressed her grief than any of the others.

The lady had been silent a few minutes, and speechless, as they thought, moving her lips without uttering a word. But when Mrs. Lovick pronounced my name, O Mr. Belford, said she, with a faint inward voice, but very distinct nevertheless—Now!—Now!—I bless God for His mercies to His poor creature—all will soon be over—a few—a very few moments—will end this strife—and I shall be happy!

Comfort here, sir—turning her head to the colonel—comfort my cousin—see!—the blam—able kindness—he would not wish me to be happy—so *soon!*

Here she stopped for two or three minutes, earnestly looking upon him: then resuming: My dearest cousin, said she, be comforted—what is dying but the common lot?—The mortal frame may *seem* to labour—but that is all!—It is not so hard to die as I believed it to be!—The preparation is the difficulty—I bless God I have had time for that—the rest is worse to beholders than to me!—I am all blessed hope—hope itself.

After a short silence: Once more, my dear cousin, said she, commend me most dutifully to my father and mother—— There she stopped. And then proceeding: To my sister, to my brother, to my uncles—and tell them I bless them with my parting breath—for all their goodness to me—even for their displeasure I bless them—most happy has been to me my punishment *here!* Happy indeed!

She was silent for a few moments, lifting up her eyes, and the hand her cousin held not between his. Then: *O Death!* said she, *where is thy sting?*

Then turning towards us, who were lost in speechless sorrow: O dear, *dear* gentlemen, said she, you know not what *foretastes*—what *assurances*——And there she again stopped, and looked up, as if in a thankful rapture, sweetly smiling.

Then turning her head towards me: Do *you,* sir, tell your friend that I forgive him!—And I pray to God to forgive him! Again pausing, and lifting up her eyes, as if praying that He would: Let him know how happily I die.—And that such as my own, I wish to be his last hour.

She was again silent for a few moments: and then resuming: My sight fails me!—Your voices only—Is not this Mr. Morden's hand? pressing one of his with that he had just let go. Which is Mr. Belford's? holding out the other. I gave her mine. God Almighty bless you both, said she, and make you both—in your last hour—for you *must* come to this—happy as I am.

She paused again, her breath growing shorter; and, after a few minutes: And now, my dearest cousin, give me your hand—nearer—still nearer—drawing it towards her; and she pressed it with her dying lips—God protect you, dear, dear sir—and once more receive my best and most grateful thanks—and tell my dear Miss Howe—and vouchsafe to see and to tell my worthy Norton—she will be one day, I fear not, though now lowly in her fortunes, a saint in heaven—tell them both that I remember them with thankful blessings in my last moments!—and pray God to give them happiness *here* for many, many years, for the sake of their friends and lovers; and a heavenly crown *hereafter;* and such assurances of it as I have, through the all-satisfying merits of my blessed Redeemer.

After a short silence, in a more broken and faint accent: And you, Mr. Belford, pressing my hand, may God preserve you, and make you sensible of all your errors—you see, in me, how all ends—may *you* be——And down sunk her head upon her pillow, she fainting away, and drawing from us her hands.

We thought she was then gone; and each gave way to a violent burst of grief.

But soon showing signs of returning life, our attention was again engaged; and I besought her, when a little recovered, to complete in my favour her half-pronounced blessing. She waved her hand to us both, and bowed her head six several times, as we have since recollected, as if distinguishing every person present; not forgetting the nurse and the maid-servant; the latter having approached the bed, weeping, as if crowding in for the divine lady's last blessing; and she spoke faltering and inwardly: Bless—bless—bless—you all—and now—and now (holding up her almost lifeless hands for the last time)—come—O come—blessed Lord—JESUS!

And with these words, the last but half-pronounced, expired:

such a smile, such a charming serenity overspreading her sweet face at the instant, as seemed to manifest her eternal happiness already begun.

O Lovelace!——But I can write no more!

. . . . . .

I resume my pen to add a few lines.

The colonel sighed as if his heart would burst: at last, his face and hands uplifted, his back towards me: Good Heaven! said he to himself, support me! And is it thus, O flower of nature!—Then pausing: And must we no more—*never more!*—My blessed, blessed cousin! uttering some other words, which his sighs made inarticulate: and then, as if recollecting himself: Forgive me, sir! Excuse me, Mr. Belford! And sliding by me: Anon I hope to see you, sir. And downstairs he went, and out of the house, leaving me a statue.

She departed exactly at 40 minutes after 6 o'clock, as by her watch on the table.

And thus died Miss CLARISSA HARLOWE, in the blossom of her youth and beauty: and who, her tender years considered, has not left behind her superior in extensive knowledge and watchful prudence; nor hardly her equal for unblemished virtue, exemplary piety, sweetness of manners, discreet generosity, and true Christian charity: and these all set off by the most graceful modesty and humility; yet on all proper occasions manifesting a noble presence of mind and true magnanimity: so that she may be said to have been not only an ornament to her sex but to human nature.

One o'clock, Friday Morning.

MRS. NORTON TO MISS CLARISSA HARLOWE

Wednesday, Sept. 6.

AT LENGTH, my best-beloved Miss Clary, everything is in the wished train: for all your relations are unanimous in your favour. Even your brother and sister are with the foremost to be reconciled to you.

This happy change is owing to letters received from your physician, and from your Cousin Morden.

Colonel Morden will be with you no doubt before this can reach you, with his pocket-book filled with money-bills, that nothing may be wanting to make you easy.

And *now,* all our hopes, all our prayers are that this good news may restore you to spirits and health; and that (so long withheld) it may not come too late.

This day, being sent for by the general voice, I was received by every one with great goodness and condescension, and *entreated* to hasten up to you, and to assure you of all their affectionate regards to you: and your father bid me say all the kind things that were in my *heart* to say, in order to comfort and raise you up; and they would hold themselves bound to make them good.

Your sister will write to you, and send her letter, with this, by a particular hand.

Your uncle Harlowe will also write, and (I doubt not) in the kindest terms: for they are all extremely alarmed and troubled at the dangerous way your doctor represents you to be in; as well as delighted with the character he gives you. Would to Heaven the good gentleman had written *sooner!* And yet he writes that you know not he has *now* written. But it is all our confidence, and our consolation, that he would not have written at all had he thought it too late.

They will prescribe no conditions to you, my dear young lady; but will leave all to your own duty and discretion. Only your brother and sister declare they will never yield to call Mr. Lovelace brother: nor will your father, I believe, be easily brought to think of him for a son.

I am to bring you down with me as soon as your health and inclination will permit. You will be received with open arms. Every one longs to see you. All the servants please themselves that they shall be permitted to kiss your hands. The pert Betty's note is already changed; and she now runs over in your just praises.

Your ever affectionate and devoted

Judith Norton.

Miss Arab. Harlowe to Miss Cl. Harlowe

Wedn. Morning, Sept. 6.

Dear Sister,—We have just heard that you are exceedingly ill. We all loved you as never young creature was loved: you are sensible of that, Sister Clary. And you have been very naughty- -but we could not be angry always.

We are indeed more afflicted with the news of your being so very ill than I can express: for I see not but, after this separation (as we understand that your misfortune has been greater than your fault, and that, however unhappy, you have demeaned yourself like the good young creature you used to be), we shall love you better, if possible, than ever.

Take comfort, therefore, Sister Clary; and don't be too much cast down—whatever your mortifications may be from such noble prospects overclouded, and from the reflections you will have from *within,* on your faulty step, and from the sullying of such a charming character by it, you will receive none from *any of us*: and, as an earnest of your papa's and mamma's favour and reconciliation, they assure you by me of their blessing and hourly prayers.

If it will be any comfort to you, and my mother finds this letter is received as we expect (which we shall know by the good effect it will have upon your health), she will herself go to town to you. Meantime, the good woman you so dearly love will be hastened up to you; and she writes by this opportunity, to acquaint you of it, and of all our returning love.

I hope you'll rejoice at this good news. Pray let us hear that you do. Your next grateful letter on this occasion, especially if it gives us the pleasure of hearing you are better upon this news, will be received with the same (if not greater) delight, that we *used* to have in all your prettily penned epistles. Adieu, my dear Clary! I am

Your loving sister, and true friend,

Arabella Harlowe.

To his dear Niece Miss Clarissa Harlowe

Wedn. Sept. 6.

We were greatly grieved, my beloved Miss Clary, at your fault; but we are still more, if possible, to hear you are so very ill; and we are sorry things have been carried so far.

Forgive my part in it, my dearest Clary. I am your *second papa,* you know. And *you* used to love me.

I hope you'll soon be able to come down, and, after a while, when your indulgent parents can spare you, that you will come to me for a whole month, and rejoice my heart, as you used to do. But if, through illness, you cannot so soon come down as we wish, I will go up to you: for I long to see you. I never more longed to see you in my life; and you was always the darling of my heart, you know.

My brother Antony desires his hearty commendations to you, and joins with me in the tenderest assurance, that all shall be well, and, if possible, better than ever. Your sister and brother both talk of seeing you in town: so does my dear sister, your indulgent mother.

God restore your health, if it be His will: else I know not what will become of

Your truly loving uncle, and second papa,

John Harlowe.

Mr. Belford to Robert Lovelace, Esq.

Friday Night, Sept. 8, past Ten.

As soon as we had seen the last scene closed, we left the body to the care of the good women, who, according to the orders she had given them that very night, removed her into that last house which she had displayed so much fortitude in providing.

In the morning, between seven and eight o'clock the colonel came to me here. He was very much indisposed. We went together, accompanied by Mrs. Lovick and Mrs. Smith, into the deceased's chamber. We could not help taking a view of the lovely corpse, and admiring the charming serenity of her noble aspect.

I unlocked the drawer, in which she had deposited her papers, and found in it no less than eleven letters, each sealed with her own seal and black wax, one of which was directed to me.

I will enclose a copy of it.

To John Belford, Esq.

Sunday Evening, Sept. 3.

Sir,—I take this last and solemn occasion to repeat to you my thanks for all your kindness to me at a time when I most needed countenance and protection.

A few considerations I beg leave, as *now* at your perusal of this, from the dead, to press upon you, with all the warmth of a sincere friendship.

By the time you will see this, you will have had an instance, I humbly trust, of the comfortable importance of a pacified conscience, in the last hours of one who, *to* the last hour, will wish your eternal welfare.

In the next place, sir, let me beg of you, for *my sake,* who AM, or, as *now* you will best read it, *have been,* driven to the necessity of applying to you to be the executor of my will, that you will bear, according to that generosity which I think to be in you, with all my friends, and particularly with my brother (who is really a worthy young man, but perhaps a little too headstrong in his first resentments and conceptions of things), if anything, by reason of this trust, should fall out disagreeably; and that you will study to make peace, and to reconcile all parties; and more especially that you, who seem to have a great influence upon your *still more* headstrong friend, will interpose, if occasion be, to prevent *further* mischief—for surely, sir, that violent spirit may sit down satisfied with the evils he has already wrought; and, particularly, with the wrongs, the heinous and ignoble wrongs, he has in me done to my family, wounded in the tenderest part of its honour.

I have another request to make to you: it is only that you will be pleased, by a particular messenger, to forward the enclosed letters as directed.

Your obliged servant,
Clarissa Harlowe.

The other letters are directed to her father, to her mother, one to her two uncles, to her brother, to her sister, to her Aunt Hervey, to her Cousin Morden, to Miss Howe, to Mrs. Norton, and lastly one to you, in performance of her promise *that a letter should be sent you when she arrived at her father's house!* ——I will withhold this last till I can be assured that you will be fitter to receive it than Tourville tells me you are at present.

I gave the colonel his letter, and ordered Harry instantly to get ready to carry the others.

Meantime we opened the will, but I will avoid mentioning the particulars, as in proper time I shall send you a copy of it.

Her request to be buried with her ancestors made a letter of the following import necessary, which I prevailed upon the colonel to write; being unwilling myself (so *early* at least) to appear officious in the eye of a family which probably wishes not any communication with me.

To JAMES HARLOWE, JUN., ESQ.

SIR,—The letter which the bearer of this brings with him will, I presume, make it unnecessary to acquaint you and my cousins with the death of the most excellent of women. But I am requested by her executor, who will soon send you a copy of her last will, to acquaint her father (which I choose to do by your means) that in it she earnestly desires to be laid in the family vault, at the feet of her grandfather.

If her father will not admit of it, she has directed her body to be buried in the churchyard of the parish where she died.

I need not tell you that a speedy answer to this is necessary.

Her beatification commenced yesterday afternoon, exactly at forty minutes after six.

I can write no more, than that I am

Yours, etc.
Wm. Morden.

Friday Morn., Sept. 8.

By the time this was written, and by the colonel's leave transcribed, Harry came booted and spurred, his horse at the door; and I delivered him the letters to the family, with those to Mrs. Norton and Miss Howe (eight in all), together with the above of the colonel to Mr. James Harlowe; and gave him orders to make the utmost dispatch with them.

The colonel and I have bespoke mourning for ourselves and servants.

MR. BELFORD TO ROBERT LOVELACE, ESQ.

Sat. Ten o'clock.

POOR MRS. NORTON is come. She was set down at the door; and would have gone upstairs directly. But Mrs. Smith and Mrs. Lovick being together and in tears, and the former hinting too suddenly to the truly venerable woman the fatal news, she sunk down at her feet in fits; so that they were forced to breathe a vein to bring her to herself.

She was impatient to see the corpse. The women went up with her.

With trembling impatience she pushed aside the coffin-lid. She bathed the face with her tears, and kissed her cheeks and forehead, as if she were living. It was *she* indeed, she said! Her sweet young lady! Her very self! She admired the serenity of her aspect. She no doubt was happy, she said, as she had written to her she should be: but how many miserable creatures had she left behind her!

It was with difficulty they prevailed upon her to quit the corpse; and when they went into the next apartment, I joined them, and acquainted her with the kind legacy her beloved young lady had left her: but this rather augmented than diminished her concern. She ought, she said, to have attended her in person. What was the world to her, wringing her hands, now the child of her bosom, and of her heart, was no more?

I thought it would divert the poor gentlewoman, and not altogether unsuitably, if I were to put her upon furnishing mourning for herself; as it would rouse her, by a seasonable and necessary employment, from that dismal lethargy of grief which generally succeeds the too violent anguish with which a gentle nature is accustomed to be torn upon the first communication of the unexpected loss of a dear friend. I gave her therefore the thirty guineas bequeathed to her and to her son for mourning; the only mourning which the testatrix has mentioned: and desired her to lose no time in preparing her own, as I doubted not that she would accompany the corpse, if it were permitted to be carried down.

The colonel proposes to attend the hearse, if this kindred give him not fresh cause of displeasure; and will take with him a copy of the will. And being intent to give the family some favourable impressions of me, he desired me to permit him to take with him the copy of the posthumous letter to me: which I readily granted.

TO THE EVER-HONOURED JAS. HARLOWE, SEN., ESQ.

MOST DEAR SIR!—With exulting confidence now does your emboldened daughter come into your awful presence by these lines, who dared not but upon this occasion to look up to you with hopes of favour and forgiveness; since, when this comes to your hands, it will be out of her power ever to offend you more.

And now let me bless you, my honoured papa, and bless you, as I write, upon my knees, for all the benefits I have received from your indulgence: for your fond love to me in the days of my prattling innocence: for the virtuous education you gave me: and, for the crown of all, the happy end, which, through Divine grace, by means of that virtuous education, I hope, by the time you will receive this, I shall have made. And let me beg of you, dear venerable sir, to blot from your remembrance, if possible, the last unhappy eight months; and then I shall hope to be remembered with advantage for the pleasure you had the goodness to take in your Clarissa.

Still on her knees, let your poor penitent implore your forgiveness of all her faults and follies; more especially of that fatal error which threw her out of your protection.

When you know, sir, that I have never been faulty in my will: that ever since my calamity became irretrievable, I have been in a state of preparation: that I have the strongest assurances that the Almighty has accepted my unfeigned repentance; and that by this time you will (as I humbly presume to hope) have been the means of adding one to the number of the blessed; you will have reason for joy rather than sorrow. Since, had I escaped the snares by which I was entangled, I might have wanted those exercises which I look upon now as so many mercies dispensed to wean me betimes from a world that presented itself to me with prospects too alluring: and in that case (too easily satisfied with *worldly* felicity) I might not have attained to that blessedness in which now, on your reading of this, I humbly presume (through the Divine goodness) I am rejoicing.

That the Almighty, in His own good time, will bring you, sir, and my ever-honoured mother, after a series of earthly felicities, of which may my unhappy fault be the only interruption (and very grievous I know that must have been), to rejoice in the same blessed state, is the repeated prayer of, sir,

Your now happy daughter,

Clarissa Harlowe.

Mr. Belford gives the lady's posthumous letters to Mrs. Hervey, Miss Howe, and Mrs. Norton, at length likewise: but, although every letter varies in style as well as matter from the others; yet, as they are written on the same subject, and are pretty long, it is thought proper to omit them.

MR. BELFORD TO ROBERT LOVELACE, ESQ.

Sat. Night.

YOUR SERVANT gives me a dreadful account of your raving unmanageableness. I wonder not at it. But as nothing violent is lasting, I dare say that your habitual gaiety of heart will quickly get the better of your frenzy: and the rather do I judge so, as your fits are of the raving kind (suitable to your natural impetuosity), and not of that melancholy species which seizes slower souls.

Harry is returned from carrying the posthumous letters to the family and to Miss Howe; and that of the colonel which acquaints James Harlowe with his sister's death, and with her desire to be interred near her grandfather.

Harry was not admitted into the presence of any of the family. They were all assembled together, it seems, at Harlowe Place, on occasion of the colonel's letter which informed them of the lady's dangerous way.

Every one was in such disorder that he could get no commands, nor obtain any notice of himself. The servants seemed more inclined to execrate than welcome him. O master! O young man! cried three or four together, what dismal tidings have you brought!

He proceeded to Miss Howe's with the letter for her.

He had the precaution to desire to speak with Miss Howe's woman or maid, and communicated to her the fatal tidings, that she might break them to her young lady. The maid was herself so affected, that her old lady (who, Harry said, seemed to be *everywhere at once)* came to see what ailed her; and was herself so struck with the communication that she was forced to sit down in a chair: O the sweet creature! said she. And is it come to this! O my poor Nancy! How shall I be able to break the matter to my Nancy!

Mr. Hickman was in the house. He hastened in to comfort the old lady—but he could not restrain his own tears.

Mrs. Howe, when a little recovered, went up, in order to break the news to her daughter. She took the letter, and her salts in her hand. And they had occasion for the latter. For the housekeeper soon came hurrying down into the kitchen, her face overspread with tears. Her young mistress had fainted away, she said. Nor did she wonder at it.

I know how terribly this *great* catastrophe affects *thee.* I should have been glad to have had particulars of the distress which the first communication of it must have given to the *Harlowes.* Yet who but must pity the unhappy mother?

The answer which James Harlowe returned to Colonel Morden's letter of notification of his sister's death, and to her request as to interment, will give a faint idea of what their concern must be.

To William Morden, Esq.

Saturday, Sept. 9

Dear Cousin,—I cannot find words to express what we all suffer on the most mournful news that ever was communicated to us.

My sister Arabella was preparing to follow Mrs. Norton up; and I had resolved to escort her.

God be merciful to us all! To what purpose did the doctor write if she was so near her end?

The most admirable young creature that ever swerved! Alas! sir, I fear my mother will never get over this shock—she has been in hourly fits ever since she received the fatal news. My poor father has the gout thrown into his stomach; and Heaven knows—O cousin, O sir!—I meant nothing but the honour of the family; yet have I all the weight thrown upon me (O this cursed Lovelace! may I perish if he escape the deserved vengeance!).

We can have nothing to do with her executor—he cannot expect we will—nor, if he be a gentleman, will he think of acting. Do you, therefore, be pleased, sir, to order an undertaker to convey the body down to us.

If we know her will in relation to the funeral, it shall be punctually complied with: as shall everything in it that is fit or reasonable to be performed; and this without the intervention of strangers.

Will you not, dear sir, favour us with your presence at this melancholy time? Pray do; and pity and excuse, with the generosity which is natural to the brave and the wise, what passed at our last meeting.

Your inexpressibly afflicted cousin and servant,

Ja. Harlowe, jun.

Everything that is fit or reasonable to be performed (repeated I to the colonel, from the above letter, on his reading it to me): that is everything which she has directed, that *can* be performed. I hope, colonel, that I shall have no contention with them. I wish no more for *their* acquaintance than they do for *mine*. But you, sir, must be the mediator between them and me; for I shall insist upon a literal performance in every article.

The colonel was so kind as to declare that he would support me in my resolution.

Mr. Belford to Robert Lovelace, Esq.

Sunday Morn. 8 o'clock, Sept. 10.

I stayed at Smith's till I saw the last of all that is mortal of the divine lady.

As she has directed rings by her will to several persons, with her hair to be set in crystal, the afflicted Mrs. Norton cut off, before the coffin was closed, four charming ringlets; one of which the colonel took for a locket, which, he says, he will cause to be made, and wear next his heart in memory of his beloved cousin.

Between four and five in the morning the corpse was put into the hearse; the coffin before being filled, as intended, with flowers and aromatic herbs, and proper care taken to prevent the corpse suffering (to the eye) from the jolting of the hearse.

Poor Mrs. Norton is extremely ill. I gave particular directions to Mrs. Smith's maid (whom I have ordered to attend the good woman in a mourning chariot) to take care of her. The colonel, who rides with his servants within view of the hearse, says that he will see my orders in relation to her enforced.

When the hearse moved off, and was out of sight, I locked up the lady's chamber, into which all that had belonged to her was removed.

Mr. Mowbray to John Belford, Esq.

Uxbridge, Sunday Morn. 9 o'clock.

Dear Jack,—I send you enclosed a letter from Mr. Lovelace. You will see by it what the mad fellow had intended to do, if we had not all of us interposed. He was actually setting out with a surgeon of this place, to have the lady opened and embalmed. Rot me if it be not my full persuasion that, if he had, her heart would have been found to be either iron or marble.

We have got Lord M. to him. His lordship is also much afflicted at the lady's death. His sisters and nieces, he says, will be ready to break their hearts What a rout's here about a woman! For after all she was no more.

We have taken a pailful of black bull's blood from him; and

this has lowered him a little. But he threatens Colonel Morden, he threatens you for your cursed reflections (cursed reflections indeed, Jack!), and curses all the world and himself, still.

Last night his mourning (which is full as deep as for a wife) was brought home, and his fellows' mourning too. And though eight o'clock, he would put it on, and make them attend him in theirs.

But he has had no rest for these ten days: that's the thing! You must write to him; and prithee coax him, Jack, and send him what he writes for, and give him all his way: there will be no bearing him else. And get the lady buried as fast as you can; and don't let him know where.

MR. LOVELACE TO JOHN BELFORD, ESQ.

Uxbridge, Sat. Sept. 9.

JACK,—I think it absolutely right that my ever-dear and beloved lady should be opened and embalmed.

I will see everything done with that decorum which the case, and the sacred person of my beloved, require.

Everything that can be done to preserve the charmer from decay shall also be done. And when she *will* descend to her original dust, or cannot be kept longer, I will then have her laid in my family vault, between my own father and mother. Myself, as I am in my *soul,* so in *person,* chief mourner. But her *heart,* to which I have such unquestionable pretensions, in which once I had so large a share, and which I will prize above my own, I *will* have. I will keep it in spirits. It shall never be out of my sight. And all the charges of *sepulture* too shall be mine.

Surely nobody will dispute my right to her. Whose was she living?—Whose is she dead, but mine? Her cursed parents, whose barbarity to her, no doubt, was the *true* cause of her death, have long since renounced her. She left *them* for *me.* She chose *me* therefore: and I was her husband. What though I treated her like a villain? Do I not pay for it now? Would she not have been mine had I not? Nobody will dispute but she would. And has she not forgiven me? I am then in *statu quo prius* with her—am I not?—as if I had never offended? Whose then can she be but mine?

I will free you from your executorship and all your cares.

Her bowels, if her friends are very solicitous about them, and very humble and sorrowful (and none have they of their own), shall be sent down to them—to be laid with *her* ancestors—unless she has ordered otherwise.

I send in the meantime for a lock of her hair.

I will take her papers. And as no one can do her memory justice equal to myself, and I will not spare myself, who can better show the world what she was, and what a villain he that could use her ill? And the world shall also see what implacable and unworthy parents she had.

All shall be set forth in words at length. No mincing of the matter. Names undisguised as well as facts. For as I shall make the worst figure in it myself, and have a right to treat myself as nobody else shall, who will control me? Who dare call me to account?

Adieu, Jack! I am preparing to be with you. I charge you, as you value my life or your own, do not oppose me in anything relating to my Clarissa Lovelace.

R. Lovelace.

In a separate paper enclosed in the above

I know not what I have written. But her dear heart and a lock of her hair I will have, let who will be the gainsayers! For is she not mine? Whose else can she be? She has no father nor mother, no sister, no brother; no relations but me. And my beloved is mine; and I am hers: and that's enough—but oh!

She's out! The damp of death has quench'd her quite!
Those spicy doors, her lips, are shut, close lock'd,
Which never gale of life shall open more!

And is it so? Is it *indeed* so? Good God! Good God!—But they will not let me write on. I must go down to this officious peer—who the devil sent for him?

MR. BELFORD TO RICHARD MOWBRAY, ESQ.

Sunday, Sept. 10, 4 in the Afternoon.

I HAVE yours, with our unhappy friend's enclosed. I am glad my lord is with him. As I presume that his frenzy will be but of short continuance, I most earnestly wish that on his recovery he could be prevailed upon to go abroad. Mr. Morden, who is inconsolable, has seen by the will (as indeed he suspected before he read it) that the case is more than a common seduction; and has dropped hints already that he looks upon himself, on that account, as freed from his promises made to the dying lady, which were that he would not seek to avenge her death.

You must make the recovery of his health the motive for urging him on this head; for if you hint at his own safety, he will not stir, but rather seek the colonel.

As to the lock of hair, you may easily pacify him (as you once saw the angel) with hair near the colour, if he be intent upon it.

J. Belford.

COLONEL MORDEN TO JOHN BELFORD, ESQ.

Sunday Night, Sept. 10.

DEAR SIR,—According to my promise, I send you an account of matters here. Poor Mrs. Norton was so very ill upon the road, that, slowly as the hearse moved, and the chariot followed, I was afraid we should not have got her to St. Albans. We put up there as I had intended. I was in hopes that she would have been better for the stop: but I was forced to leave her behind me. I ordered the servant-maid you were so considerately kind as to send down with her, to be very careful of her; and left the chariot to attend her. She deserves all the regard that can be paid her; not only upon my cousin's account, but on her own—she is an excellent woman.

When we were within five miles of Harlowe Place, I put on a hand-gallop. I ordered the hearse to proceed more slowly still, the cross-road we were in being rough; and having more time before us than I wanted; for I wished not the hearse to be in till near dusk.

I got to Harlowe Place about four o'clock.

At my entrance into the court, they were all in motion. Every servant whom I saw had swelled eyes, and looked with so much concern, that at first I apprehended some new disaster had happened in the family.

Mr. John and Mr. Antony Harlowe and Mrs. Hervey were there. They all helped on one another's grief, as they had before done each other's hardness of heart.

My Cousin James met me at the entrance of the hall. His countenance expressed a fixed concern; and he desired me to excuse his behaviour the last time I was there.

My Cousin Arabella came to me full of tears and grief.

O cousin! said she, hanging upon my arm.

I myself was full of grief; and without going farther or speaking, sat down in the hall in the first chair.

The brother sat down on one hand of me, the sister on the other. Both were silent. The latter in tears.

Mr. Antony Harlowe came to me soon after. His face was overspread with all the appearance of woe. He requested me to walk into the parlour; where, as he said, were all his fellow-mourners.

I attended him in. My Cousins James and Arabella followed me.

My Cousin Harlowe, the dear creature's father, as soon as he saw me, said: O cousin, cousin, of all our family, you are the only one who have nothing to reproach yourself with!

The poor mother, bowing her head to me in speechless grief, sat with her handkerchief held to her eyes with one hand. The other hand was held by her Sister Hervey between both hers; Mrs. Hervey weeping upon it.

Near the window sat Mr. John Harlowe, his face and his body turned from the sorrowing company; his eyes red and swelled.

My Cousin Antony, at his re-entering the parlour, went towards Mrs. Harlowe: Don't—dear sister! said he. Then towards my Cousin Harlowe: Don't—dear brother! Don't thus give way. And without being able to say another word, went to a corner of the parlour, and, wanting himself the comfort he would fain have given, sunk into a chair, and audibly sobbed.

Miss Arabella followed her Uncle Antony, as he walked in before me; and seemed as if she would have spoken to the pierced mother some words of comfort.

Young Mr. Harlowe, with all his vehemence of spirit, was now subdued.

How to be pitied, how greatly to be pitied, all of them! But how much to be cursed that abhorred Lovelace, who, as it seems, by arts uncommon, and a villainy without example, has been the sole author of a woe so complicated and extensive! God judge me, as——But I stop—the man (the *man* can I say?) is your friend! He already suffers, you tell me, in his intellect. Restore him, Heaven, to that—if I find the matter come out as I *apprehend* it will—indeed her own hint of his usage of her, as in her will, is enough—nor think, my beloved cousin, thou darling of my heart! that thy gentle spirit, breathing charity and forgiveness to the vilest of men, shall avail him!

But once more I stop—forgive me, sir! Who could behold such a scene, and not be exasperated against the author of all?

As I was the only person (grieved as I was myself) from whom any of them, at that instant, could derive comfort: Let us not, said I, my dear cousin, approaching the inconsolable mother, give way to a grief which, however just, can now avail us nothing. We hurt ourselves, and cannot recall the dear creature for whom we mourn. Nor would you wish it, if you knew with what assurances of eternal happiness she left the world. She is happy, madam!

O cousin, cousin! cried the unhappy mother, withdrawing her hand from that of her Sister Hervey, and pressing mine with it, you know not what a child I have lost! Then in a lower voice, And *how* lost!—That it is that makes the loss insupportable.

They all joined in a kind of melancholy chorus, and each accused him and herself, and some of them one another. But the eyes of all, in turn, were cast upon my Cousin James as the person who had kept up the general resentment against so sweet a creature. While he was hardly able to bear his own remorse: nor Miss Harlowe hers; she breaking out into words: How tauntingly did I write to her! How barbarously did I insult her! Yet how patiently did she take it! Who would have thought that she had been so near her end! O brother, brother! but for *you!*—but for *you——!*

Double not upon me, said he, my own woes! I have every thing before me that has passed! I thought only to reclaim a dear creature that had erred! But it was the villainous Lovelace who did that—not any of us! Yet, cousin, did she not attribute all to *me?* I fear she did! I hope she, who could forgive the greatest villain on earth, I *hope* she could forgive *me.*

She died blessing you all; and justified rather than condemned your severity to her.

Would to Heaven, proceeded, exclaiming, the poor mother, I had but *once* seen her! Then turning to my Cousin James and his sister: O my son! O my Arabella! If WE were to receive as little mercy——

And there again she stopped, her tears interrupting her further speech: every one, all the time, remaining silent.

O this cursed friend of yours, Mr. Belford! This detested Lovelace! To him, to him is owing——

Pardon me, sir. I will lay down my pen till I have recovered my temper.

One in the morning.

In vain, sir, have I endeavoured to compose myself to rest.

About six o'clock the hearse came to the outward gate. The parish church is at some distance; but the wind setting fair, the afflicted family were struck, just before it came, into a fresh fit of grief, on hearing the funeral bell tolled in a very solemn manner.

A servant came in to acquaint us with what its lumbering heavy noise up the paved inner courtyard apprised us of before.

I stepped out. No one else could then stir. Her brother, however, soon followed me.

When I came to the door I beheld a sight very affecting.

The servants of the family, it seems, had told *their* friends, and those *theirs,* that though, living, their dear young lady could not be received nor looked upon, her body was permitted to be brought home. The space of time was so confined, that those who knew when she died, must easily guess *near the time* the hearse was to come, so that the hearse, and the solemn tolling of the bell, had drawn together at least fifty of the neighbouring men, women, and children, and some of good appearance.

These, when the coffin was taken out of the hearse, crowding about it, hindered, for a few moments, its being carried in; the young people struggling who should bear it; and yet with respectful *whisperings,* rather than clamorous *contention.*

At last, six maidens were permitted to carry it in by the six handles.

The corpse was thus borne, with the most solemn respect, into the hall, and placed for the present upon two stools there. The plates, and emblems, and inscription, set every one gazing upon it and admiring it. They wished to be permitted a sight of the corpse; but rather mentioned this as their *wish* than as their *hope*. When they had all satisfied their curiosity, they dispersed with blessings upon her memory, and with tears and lamentations; pronouncing her to be happy; and inferring, that were *she* not so, what would become of them?

The servants of the family then got about the coffin. They could not before: and that afforded a new scene of sorrow: but a silent one; for they spoke only by their eyes, and by sighs, looking upon the lid, and upon one another, by turns, with hands lifted up.

As for Mr. James Harlowe (who accompanied me, but withdrew when he saw the crowd), he stood looking upon the lid, when the people had left it, with a fixed attention. In a profound reverie he stood, his arms folded, his head on one side, and marks of stupefaction imprinted upon every feature.

But when the corpse was carried into the lesser parlour, adjoining to the hall, which she used to call *her* parlour, and put upon a table in the middle of the room, and the father and mother, the two uncles, her Aunt Hervey, and her sister came in, joining her brother and me, with trembling feet, and eager woe, the scene was still more affecting. Their sorrow was heightened, no doubt, by the remembrance of their unforgiving severity: and now seeing before them the receptacle that contained the glory of their family, who so lately was driven thence by their indiscreet violence; never, never more to be restored to them! no wonder that their grief was more than common grief.

They would have withheld the mother, it seems, from coming

in: but when they could not, though undetermined before, they all bore her company, led on by an impulse they could not resist. The poor lady but just cast her eye upon the coffin, and then snatched it away, retiring with passionate grief towards the window; yet addressing herself, with clasped hands, as if to her beloved daughter: O my child, my child! cried she; thou pride of my hope! Why was I not permitted to speak pardon and peace to thee!—O forgive thy cruel mother!

Her son (his heart then softened, as his eyes showed) besought her to withdraw: and her woman looking in at that moment, he called her to assist him in conducting her lady into the middle parlour: and then returning, met his father going out at the door, who also had but just cast his eye on the coffin, and yielded to my entreaties to withdraw.

His grief was too deep for utterance, till he saw his son coming in; and then, fetching a heavy groan, Never, said he, was sorrow like my sorrow! O son! son! in a reproaching accent, his face turned from him.

I attended him through the middle parlour, endeavouring to console him. His lady was there in agonies. She took his eye. He made a motion towards her: O my dear, said he—but turning short, his eyes as full as his heart, he hastened through to the great parlour: and when there he desired me to leave him to himself.

The uncles and the sister looked and turned away, looked and turned away, very often, upon the emblems, in silent sorrow.

Colonel Morden. [*In continuation*]

When the unhappy mourners were all retired, I directed the lid of the coffin to be unscrewed, and caused some fresh aromatics and flowers to be put into it.

The corpse was very little altered, notwithstanding the journey. The sweet smile remained.

When my cousins were told that the lid was unscrewed, they pressed in again, all but the mournful father and mother, as if by consent. Mrs. Hervey kissed her pale lips. Flower of the world! was all she could say; and gave place to Miss Arabella; who, kissing the forehead of *her* whom she had so cruelly treated, could only say to my Cousin James (looking upon the corpse, and upon him): O brother! While he, taking the fair lifeless hand, kissed it, and retreated with precipitation.

Her two uncles were speechless. They seemed to wait each other's example, whether to look upon the corpse or not. I ordered the lid to be replaced; and then they pressed forward, as the others again did, to take a last farewell.

And then, once more, the brother took the lifeless hand, and vowed revenge upon it, on the cursed author of all this distress.

The unhappy parents proposed to take one last view and farewell of their once darling daughter. The father was got to the parlour door, after the inconsolable mother: but neither of them were able to enter it. The mother said she must once more see the child of her heart, or she should never enjoy herself. But they both agreed to refer their melancholy curiosity till the next day; and hand in hand retired inconsolable, and speechless.

When all were withdrawn I retired, and sent for my Cousin James, and acquainted him with his sister's request in relation to the discourse to be pronounced at her interment; telling him how necessary it was that the minister, whoever he were, should have the earliest notice given him that the case would admit. He lamented the death of the Reverend Doctor Lewen, who, as he said, was a great admirer of his sister, as she was of him, and would have been the fittest of all men for that office.

Mr. Melvill, Doctor Lewen's assistant, must, he said, be the man; and he praised him for his abilities, his elocution, and unexceptionable manners; and promised to engage him early in the morning.

He called out his sister, and she was of his opinion.

They both, with no little warmth, hinted their disapprobation of you, sir, for their sister's executor, on the score of your intimate friendship with the author of her ruin.

You must not resent anything I shall communicate to you of what they say on this occasion: depending that you will not, I shall write with the greater freedom.

I told them how much my dear cousin was obliged to your friendship and humanity: the injunctions she had laid you under, and your own inclination to observe them. I said that you were a man of honour: that you were desirous of consulting me, because you would not willingly give offence to any of them.

They said there was no need of an executor out of their family; and they hoped that you would relinquish so *unnecessary* a trust, as they called it. My Cousin James declared that he would write to you as soon as the funeral was over, to desire that you would do so, upon proper assurances that all that the will prescribed should be performed.

I said you were a man of resolution: that I thought he would hardly succeed; for that you made a point of honour of it.

I then showed them their sister's posthumous letter to you; in which she confesses her obligations to you, and regard for you, and for your future welfare. You may believe, sir, they were extremely affected with the perusal of it.

They were surprised that I had given up to you the produce of her grandfather's estate since his death. I told them plainly that they must thank themselves if anything disagreeable to them occurred from their sister's device; deserted, and thrown into the hands of strangers, as she had been.

They said they would report all I had said to their father and mother; adding that, great as their trouble was, they found they had more still to come. But if Mr. Belford *were to be* the executor of her will, contrary to their hopes, they besought me to take the trouble of transacting everything with you; that a friend of the man to whom they owed all their calamity might not appear to them.

They were extremely moved at the text their sister had chosen for the subject of the funeral discourse. I had extracted from the will that article, supposing it probable that I might not so soon have an opportunity to show them the will itself, as would otherwise have been necessary on account of the interment: which cannot be delayed.

Monday Morning, between Eight and Nine.

Miss Howe is expected here by and by, to see, for the last time, her beloved friend.

Miss Howe, by her messenger, desires she may not be taken

any notice of. She shall not tarry six minutes, was the word. Her desire will be easily granted her.

Her servant, who brought the request, if it were denied, was to return and meet her; for she was ready to set out in her chariot when he got on horseback.

If he met her not with the refusal, he was to stay here till she came.

COLONEL MORDEN. [*In continuation*]

Monday Afternoon, Sept. 11.

I WAS SUMMONED to breakfast about half an hour after nine.

By the time we were well seated, the bell ringing, the outward gate opening, a chariot rattling over the pavement of the court-yard, put them into emotion.

I left them; and was just time enough to give Miss Howe my hand, as she alighted: her maid in tears remaining in the chariot.

A fixed melancholy on her whole aspect, overclouded a vivacity and fire which, nevertheless, darted now and then through the awful gloom.

Never did I think, said she, as she gave me her hand, to enter more these doors: but, living or dead, my *Clarissa* brings me after her anywhither!

She entered with me the little parlour; and seeing the coffin, withdrew her hand from mine, and with impatience pushed aside the lid. As impatiently she removed the face-cloth. In a wild air, she clasped her uplifted hands together; and now looked upon the corpse, now up to Heaven, as if appealing to that. Her bosom heaved and fluttered discernible through her handkerchief, and at last she broke silence: O sir!—see you not here!—see you not here—the glory of her sex? Thus by the most villainous of yours—*thus*—laid low!

O my blessed friend! said she—my sweet companion!—my lovely monitress!—kissing her lips at every tender appellation. And is this all!—is it all, of my CLARISSA'S story!

Then, after a short pause, and a profound sigh, she turned to me, and then to her breathless friend. But *is* she, *can* she be, really dead! O no! She only sleeps. Awake, my beloved friend! My sweet, clay-cold friend, awake! Let thy Anna Howe revive thee; by her warm breath revive thee, my dear creature! And, kissing her again, Let my warm lips animate thy cold ones!

She was silent a few moments, and then, seeming to recover herself, she turned to me: Forgive, forgive, Mr. Morden, this wild frenzy! I am not myself! I never shall be! You knew not the excellence, no, not *half* the excellence, that is thus laid low!

But why, sir, why, Mr. Morden, was she sent *hither?* Why not to *me?* She has no father, no mother, no relations; no, not *one!* They had all renounced her. I was her sympathizing friend—and had not I the best right to my dear creature's remains? O my blessed friend! Who knows, who knows, had I come in time, what my cordial comfortings might have done for thee!

But—looking round her, as if she apprehended seeing some of the family—one more kiss, my angel, my friend, my ever-to-be-regretted, lost companion! And let me fly this hated house, which I never loved but for thy sake! Adieu, then, my dearest Clarissa! *Thou* art happy, I doubt not, as thou assuredst me in thy last letter! O may we meet, and rejoice together, where no villainous *Lovelaces,* no hard-hearted *relations,* will ever shock our innocence, or ruffle our felicity!

Again she was silent, unable to go, though seeming to intend it; struggling, as it were, with her grief, and heaving with anguish. At last, happily, a flood of tears gushed from her eyes. Now!—now! said she, shall I—shall I—be easier. But for this kindly relief, my heart would have burst asunder.

But looking round her, on a servant's stepping by the door, as if again she had apprehended it was some of the family: Once more, said she, a solemn, an everlasting adieu!

Then again embracing her face with both her hands, and kissing it, and afterwards the hands of the dear deceased, she gave me her hand; and, quitting the room with precipitation, rushed into her chariot; and, when there, with profound sighs, and a fresh burst of tears, unable to speak, she bowed her head to me, and was driven away.

COLONEL MORDEN. [*In continuation*]

Thursday Night, Sept. 14.

WE ARE just returned from the solemnization of the last mournful rite. My Cousin James and his sister, Mr. and Mrs. Hervey, and *their* daughter, a young lady whose affection for my departed cousin shall ever bind me to her, my Cousins John and Antony Harlowe, myself, and some other more distant relations.

The father and mother would have joined in these last honours, had they been able: but they were both very much indisposed; and continue to be so.

The whole solemnity was performed with great decency and order. The distance from Harlowe Place to the church is about half a mile. All the way the corpse was attended by great numbers of people of all conditions.

It was nine when it entered the church; every corner of which was crowded. Such a profound, such a silent respect did I never see paid at the funeral of princes.

The eulogy pronounced by Mr. Melvill was a very pathetic one. He wiped his own eyes often, and made everybody present still oftener wipe theirs.

It is said that Mr. Solmes was in a remote part of the church, wrapped round in a horseman's coat: and that he shed tears several times. But I saw him not.

Another gentleman was there incognito, in a pew near the entrance of the vault, who had not been taken notice of, but for his great emotion when he looked over his pew at the time the coffin was carried down to its last place. This was Miss Howe's worthy Mr. Hickman.

My Cousins John and Antony, and their nephew James, chose not to descend into the vault among their departed ancestors.

Miss Harlowe was extremely affected. Her *conscience,* as well as her love, was concerned on the occasion. She would go down with the corpse of her dear, her only sister, she said: but her brother would not permit it. And her overwhelmed eye pursued the coffin till she could see no more of it: and then she threw herself on the seat, and was near fainting away.

I accompanied it down, that I might not only satisfy myself, but you, sir, her executor, that it was deposited, as she had directed, at the feet of her grandfather. I am

Sir,
Your most faithful and obedient servant,
Wm. Morden.

MR. JAMES HARLOWE TO JOHN BELFORD, ESQ.

Harlowe Place, Friday Night, Sept. 15.

SIR,—I hope from the character my worthy Cousin Morden gives you, that you will excuse the application I make to you, to oblige a whole family in an affair that much concerns their peace, and cannot equally concern anybody else. You will immediately judge, sir, that this is the executorship of which my sister has given you the trouble by her last will.

We shall all think ourselves extremely obliged to you, if you please to relinquish this trust to our own family.

We are the more concerned, sir, to wish you to decline this office, because of your short and accidental knowledge of the dear testatrix, and long and intimate acquaintance with the man to whom *she* owed her ruin, and *we* the greatest loss and disappointment that ever befell a family.

You will allow due weight, I dare say, to this plea, if you make our case your own: and so much the readier, when I assure you that your interfering in this matter so much against our inclinations (excuse, sir, my plain-dealing) will very probably occasion an opposition in some points, where otherwise there might be none.

What, therefore, I propose is, not that my father should assume this trust: he is too much afflicted to undertake it—nor yet myself—I might be thought too much concerned in interest: but that it may be allowed to devolve upon my two uncles; whose known honour, and whose affection to the dear deceased, nobody ever doubted: and they will treat with you, sir, through my Cousin Morden, as to the points they will undertake to perform.

The trouble you have already had will well entitle you to the legacy she bequeaths you, together with the reimbursement of all the charges you have been at, and allowance of the legacies you have discharged, although you should not have qualified yourself to act as an executor; as I presume you have not *yet* done; nor will *now* do.

Your compliance, sir, will oblige a family (who have already distress enough upon them) in the circumstance that occasions this application to you; and more particularly, sir,

Your most humble servant,

James Harlowe, jun.

MR. BELFORD TO JAMES HARLOWE, JUN., ESQ.

Saturday, Sept. 16.

SIR,—You will excuse my plain-dealing in turn: for I must observe that if I had *not* the just opinion I have of the sacred nature of the office I have undertaken, some passages in the letter you have favoured me with would convince me that I ought not to excuse myself from acting in it.

I need name only one of them. You are pleased to say that your uncles, if the trust be relinquished to them, will *treat with me,* through Colonel Morden, *as to the points they will undertake to perform.*

Permit me, sir, to say that it is the *duty* of an executor to see *every point* performed that *can* be performed. Nor will I leave the performance of mine to any other persons, especially where a qualifying is so directly intimated, and where all the branches of your family have shown themselves, with respect to the incomparable lady, to have but one mind.

I am sorry for the hints you give of an *opposition,* where, as you say, there might be none, if I did not interfere. I see not, sir, why your animosity against a man who cannot be defended, should be carried to such a height against one who never gave you offence: and this only because he is acquainted with that man.

As to the legacy to myself, I assure you, sir, that neither my circumstances nor my temper will put me upon being a gainer by the executorship.

Occasions of litigation or offence shall not proceed from me. You need only apply to Colonel Morden, who shall command me in everything that the will allows me to oblige your family in. I do assure you that I am as unwilling to obtrude myself upon it, as any of it can wish.

I own that I have not yet proved the will; nor shall I do it till next week at soonest, that you may have time for amicable objections, if such you think fit to make through the colonel's mediation.

Permit me to add, that when you have perused the will, and coolly considered everything, it is my hope that you will yourself be of opinion that there can be no room for dispute or opposition: and that if your family will join to expedite the execution, it will be the most natural and easy way of shutting up the whole affair, and to have done with a man so causelessly, as to his *own* particular, the object of your dislike, as is, sir,

Your very humble servant (notwithstanding),

John Belford.

THE WILL

To my Executor

I, Clarissa Harlowe, now, by strange melancholy accidents, lodging in the Parish of St. Paul, Covent Garden, being of sound and perfect mind and memory, as I hope these presents, drawn up by myself, and written with my own hand, will testify; do (this second day of September), in the year of our Lord——,[1] make and publish this my last will and testament, in manner and form following:

In the first place, I desire that my body may lie unburied three days after my decease, or till the pleasure of my father be known concerning it. But the occasion of my death not admitting of doubt, I will not, on any account, that it be opened; and it is my desire that it shall not be touched but by those of my own sex.

I have always earnestly requested that my body might be deposited in the family vault with those of my ancestors. If it might be granted, I could now wish that it might be placed at

[1] The date of the year is left blank for particular reasons.

the feet of my dear and honoured grandfather. But as I have, by one very unhappy step, been thought to disgrace my whole lineage, and therefore this last honour may be refused to my corpse; in this case, my desire is that it may be interred in the churchyard belonging to the parish in which I shall die; and that in the most private manner, between the hours of eleven and twelve at night; attended only by Mrs. Lovick, and Mr. and Mrs. Smith, and their maidservant.

And I bequeath five pounds to be given, at the discretion of the churchwardens, to twenty poor people, the Sunday after my interment; and this whether I shall be buried here or elsewhere.

I have already given verbal directions, that after I am dead, I may be put into my coffin as soon as possible: it is my desire that I may not be unnecessarily exposed to the view of anybody; except any of my relations should vouchsafe, for the last time, to look upon me.

And I could wish, if it might be avoided without making ill-will between Mr. Lovelace and my executor, that the former might not be permitted to see my corpse. But if, as he is a man very uncontrollable, and as I am nobody's, he insist upon viewing *her dead* whom he ONCE before saw in a manner dead, let his gay curiosity be gratified. Let him behold and triumph over the wretched remains of one who has been made a victim to his barbarous perfidy: but let some good person, as by my desire, give him a paper, whilst he is viewing the ghastly spectacle, containing these few words only: "Gay, cruel heart! behold here the remains of the once ruined, yet now happy, Clarissa Harlowe! See what thou thyself must quickly be;—and REPENT!"—

Yet, to show that I die in perfect charity with *all the world,* I do most sincerely forgive Mr. Lovelace the wrongs he has done me.

If my father can pardon the error of his unworthy child, so far as to suffer her corpse to be deposited at the feet of her grandfather, as above requested, I could wish (my misfortunes being so notorious) that a short discourse might be pronounced over my remains before they be interred. The subject of the discourse I shall determine before I conclude this writing.

And *now,* with regard to the worldly matters which I shall die possessed of, as well as to those which of right appertain to me, either by the will of my said grandfather, or otherwise; thus do I dispose of them.

In the first place, I give and bequeath all the real estates in or to which I have any claim or title by the said will, to my ever-honoured father, James Harlowe, Esq.; and that rather than to my brother and sister, to whom I had once thoughts of devising them, because, if they survive my father, those estates will assuredly vest in them, or one of them, by virtue of his favour and indulgence, as the circumstances of things with regard to marriage-settlements, or otherwise, may require; or as they may respectively merit by the continuance of their duty.

The house, late my grandfather's, called *The Grove,* and by him, in honour of me, and of some of my voluntary employments, *my Dairy-house,* and the furniture thereof as it now stands (the pictures and large iron chest of old plate excepted), I also bequeath to my said father; only begging it as a favour that he will be pleased to permit my dear Mrs. Norton to pass the remainder of her days in that house; and to have and enjoy the apartments in it known by the name of *The Housekeeper's Apartments,* with the furniture in them; and which (plain and neat) was bought for me by my grandfather, who delighted to call me his housekeeper; and which therefore in his lifetime I used as such: the office to go with the apartments. And I am the more earnest in this recommendation, as I had once thought to have been very happy there with the good woman; and because I think her prudent management will be as beneficial to my father as his favour can be convenient to her.

But with regard to what has accrued from that estate since my grandfather's death, and to the sum of nine hundred and seventy pounds, which proved to be the moiety of the money that my said grandfather had by him at his death, and which moiety he bequeathed to me for my sole and separate use; and which sum I gave into my father's hands, together with the management and produce of the whole estate devised to me—these sums, however considerable when put together, I hope I may be allowed to dispose of absolutely, as my love and my gratitude may warrant: and which therefore I shall dispose of in the manner hereafter mentioned.

My father, of his love and bounty, was pleased to allow me the same quarterly sums that he allowed my sister for apparel and other requisites; and (pleased with me then) used to say that those sums should not be deducted from the estate and effects bequeathed to me by my grandfather: but having *mortally* offended him (as I fear it may be said) by one unhappy step, it may be expected that he will reimburse himself those sums. It is therefore my will and direction that he shall be allowed to pay and satisfy himself for all such quarterly or other sums which he was so good as to advance me from the time of my grandfather's death; and that his account of such sums shall likewise be taken without questioning: the money, however, which I left behind me in my escritoire, being to be taken in part of those disbursements.

My grandfather, who, in his goodness and favour to me, knew no bounds, was pleased to bequeath to me all the family pictures at his late house, some of which are very masterly performances; with command that if I died unmarried, or if married and had no descendants, they should then go to that son of his (if more than one should be then living) whom I should think would set most value by them. Now, as I know that my honoured uncle, John Harlowe, Esq., was pleased to express some concern that they were not left to him, as eldest son; and as he has a gallery where they may be placed to advantage; and as I have reason to believe that he will bequeath them to my father, if he survive him; who, no doubt, will leave them to my brother; I therefore bequeath all the said family pictures to my said uncle, Joseph Harlowe. In these pictures, however, I include not one of my own, drawn when I was about fourteen years of age; which I shall hereafter in another article bequeath.

My said honoured grandfather having a great fondness for the old family plate, which he would never permit to be changed, having lived, as he used to say, to see a great deal of it come into request again in the revolution of fashions; and having left the same to me, with a command to keep it entire; and with power at my death to bequeath it to whomsoever I pleased that I thought would forward his desire; which was, as he expresses it, that it should be kept *to the end of time;* this family plate, which is deposited in a large iron chest, in the strong-room at his late dwelling-house, I bequeath entire to my honoured uncle, Antony Harlowe, Esq., with the same injunctions which were laid on me; not doubting but he will confirm and strengthen them by his own last will.

I bequeath to my ever valued friend Mrs. Judith Norton, to whose piety and care, seconding the piety and care of my ever honoured and excellent mother, I owe, morally speaking, the qualifications which, for eighteen years of my life, made me beloved and respected, the full sum of six hundred pounds, to be paid her within three months after my death.

I bequeath also to the same good woman thirty guineas, for mourning for her and for her son, my foster-brother.

To Mrs. Dorothy Hervey, the only sister of my honoured mother, I bequeath the sum of fifty guineas, for a ring; and I beg of her to accept of my thankful acknowledgments for all her goodness to me from my infancy; and particularly for her patience with me, in the several altercations that happened between my brother and sister and me, before my unhappy departure from Harlowe Place.

To my kind and much valued cousin, Miss Dolly Hervey, daughter of my Aunt Hervey, I bequeath my watch and equipage, and my best Mechlin and Brussels head-dresses and ruffles; also my gown and petticoat of flowered silver of my own work; which having been made up but a few days before I was confined to my chamber, I never wore.

To the same young lady I bequeath likewise my harpsichord, my chamber-organ, and all my music-books.

As my sister has a very pretty library; and as my beloved Miss Howe has also her late father's, as well as her own; I bequeath all my books in general, with the cases they are in, to my said cousin, Dolly Hervey. As they are not ill-chosen for a woman's library, I know that she will take the greater pleasure in them because they were mine; and because there are observations in many of them of my own writing; and some very judicious ones, written by the truly reverend Dr. Lewen.

I also bequeath to the same young lady twenty-five guineas for a ring, to be worn in remembrance of her true friend.

If I live not to see my worthy cousin, William Morden, Esq., I desire my humble and grateful thanks may be given to him for his favours and goodness to me; and particularly for his endeavours to reconcile my other friends to me at a time when I was doubtful whether he would forgive me himself. As he is in great circumstances, I will only beg of him to accept of two or three trifles, in remembrance of a kinswoman who always honoured *him* as much as he loved *her*. Particularly, of that piece of flowers which my Uncle Robert, his father, was very earnest to obtain, in order to carry it abroad with him.

I desire him likewise to accept of the little miniature picture set in gold, which his worthy father made me sit for to the famous Italian master whom he brought over with him; and which he presented to me, that I might bestow it, as he was pleased to say, upon the man whom I should be one day most inclined to favour.

To the same gentleman I also bequeath my rose-diamond ring, which was a present from his good father to me; and will be the more valuable to him on that account.

I humbly request Mrs. Annabella Howe, the mother of my dear Miss Howe, to accept of my respectful thanks for all her favours and goodness to me, when I was so frequently a visitor to her beloved daughter; and of a ring of twenty-five guineas price.

My picture at full length, which is in my late grandfather's closet (excepted in an article above from the family pictures), drawn when I was near fourteen years of age; about which time my dear Miss Howe and I began to know, to distinguish, and to love one another so dearly—I cannot express how dearly—I bequeath to that sister of my heart; of whose friendship, as well in adversity as prosperity, when I was deprived of all other comfort and comforters, I have had such instances, as that our love can only be exceeded in that state of perfection, in which I hope to rejoice with her hereafter, to all eternity.

I bequeath also to the same dear friend my best diamond ring, which, with other jewels, is in the private drawer of my escritoire: as also all my finished and framed pieces of needlework; the flower-piece excepted, which I have already bequeathed to my Cousin Morden.

These pieces have all been taken down, as I have heard; and my relations will have no heart to put them up again: but if my good mother chooses to keep back any one piece (the above capital piece, as it is called, excepted), not knowing but some time hence she may bear the sight of it; I except that also from this general bequest; and direct it to be presented to her.

My whole-length picture in the Vandyke taste, that used to hang in my own parlour, as I was permitted to call it, I bequeath to my Aunt Hervey, except my mother shall think fit to keep it herself.

I bequeath to the worthy Charles Hickman, Esq., the locket, with the miniature picture of the lady he best loves, which I have constantly worn, and shall continue to wear near my heart till the approach of my last hour. It must be the most acceptable present that can be made him, next to the *hand* of the dear original. "And, O my dear Miss Howe, let it not be long before you permit his claim to the *latter*—for indeed you know not the value of a virtuous mind in that sex; and how preferable such a mind is to one distinguished by the more dazzling flights of unruly wit; although the latter were to be joined by that specious outward appearance which too, too often attracts the hasty eye and susceptible heart."

Permit me, my dear friends, this solemn apostrophe, in this last solemn act, to a young lady so deservedly dear to me!

I make it my earnest request to my dear Miss Howe, that she will not put herself into mourning for me. But I desire her acceptance of a ring with my hair; and that Mr. Hickman will also accept of the like; each of the value of twenty-five guineas.

I bequeath to Lady Betty Lawrance, and to her sister, Lady Sarah Sadleir, and to the Right Honourable Lord M., and to their worthy nieces, Miss Charlotte and Miss Martha Montague, each an enamelled ring, with a cipher Cl. H. with my hair in crystal, and round the inside of each, the day, month, and year of my death; each ring, with brilliants, to cost twenty guineas. And this as a small token of the grateful sense I have of the honour of their good opinions and kind wishes in my favour; and of their truly noble offer to me of a very considerable annual provision, when they apprehended me to be entirely destitute of any.

To the reverend and learned Dr. Arthur Lewen, by whose instructions I have been equally delighted and benefited, I bequeath twenty guineas for a ring. If it should please God to call him to Himself before he can receive this small bequest, it is my will that his worthy daughter may have the benefit of it.

In token of the grateful sense I have of the civilities paid me by Mrs. and Miss Howe's domestics, from time to time in my visits there, I bequeath thirty guineas to be divided among them, as their dear young mistress shall think proper.

To each of my worthy companions and friends, Miss Biddy Lloyd, Miss Fanny Alston, Miss Rachel Biddulph, and Miss Cartwright Campbell, I bequeath five guineas for a ring.

To my late maidservant, Hannah Burton, an honest, faithful creature, who loved *me,* reverenced my *mother,* and respected my *sister,* and never sought to do anything unbecoming of her character, I bequeath the sum of fifty pounds, to be paid within one month after my decease, she labouring under ill-health: and if that ill-health continue, I commend her for further assistance to my good Mrs. Norton, to be put upon my poor's fund, hereafter to be mentioned.

To the coachman, groom, and two footmen, and five maids, at Harlowe Place, I bequeath ten pounds each; to the helper five pounds.

To my sister's maid, Betty Barnes, I bequeath ten pounds, to show that I resent not former disobligations; which I believe were owing more to the insolence of office, and to natural pertness, than to personal ill-will.

All my wearing apparel, of whatever sort, that I have not been obliged to part with, or which is not already bequeathed (my linen excepted), I desire Mrs. Norton will accept of.

The trunks and boxes in which my clothes are sealed up, I desire may not be opened, but in presence of Mrs. Norton (or of someone deputed by her) and of Mrs. Lovick.

To the worthy Mrs. Lovick above-mentioned, from whom I have received great civilities, and even maternal kindnesses; and to Mrs. Smith (with whom I lodge), from whom *also* I have received great kindnesses; I bequeath all my linen, and all my unsold laces; to be divided equally between them, as they shall agree; or, in case of disagreement, the same to be sold, and the money arising to be equally shared by them.

And I bequeath to the same two good women, as a further token of my thankful acknowledgments of their kind love and compassionate concern for me, the sum of twenty guineas each.

To Mr. Smith, the husband of Mrs. Smith above-named, I bequeath the sum of ten guineas, in acknowledgment of his civilities to me.

To Katherine, the honest maidservant of Mrs. Smith, to whom (having no servant of my own) I have been troublesome, I bequeath five guineas; and ten guineas more, in lieu of a suit of my wearing apparel, which once, with some linen, I thought of leaving to her. With this she may purchase what may be more suitable to her liking and degree.

To the honest and careful widow, Anne Shelburne, my nurse, over and above her wages, and the customary perquisites that may belong to her, I bequeath the sum of ten guineas. Hers is a careful and (to persons of such humanity and tenderness) a melancholy employment, attended in the latter part of life with great watching and fatigue, which is hardly ever enough considered.

In the middle drawer of my escritoire at Harlowe Place are many letters and copies of letters, put up according to their dates, which I have written or received in a course of years. As these letters exhibit a correspondence that no person of my sex need to be ashamed of, allowing for the time of life when mine were written; and as many excellent things are contained in those written to me; and as Miss Howe, to whom most of them have been communicated, wished formerly to have them, if she survived me: for these reasons, I bequeath them to my said dear friend Miss Anna Howe; and the rather, as she had for some years past a very considerable share in the correspondence.

I do hereby make, constitute, and ordain John Belford, of Edgware in the County of Middlesex, Esq., the sole executor of this my last will and testament; having previously obtained his leave so to do. I have given the reasons which induced me to ask this gentleman to take upon him this trouble to Miss Howe. I therefore refer to her on this subject.

But I do most earnestly beg of him, the said Mr. Belford, that, in the execution of this trust, he will (as he has repeatedly promised) studiously endeavour to promote peace with, and suppress resentments in, every one; so as that all further mischiefs may be prevented, as well *from* as *to* his friend. And in order to this, I beseech him to cultivate the friendship of my worthy Cousin Morden; who, as I presume to hope (when he understands it to be my dying request), will give him his advice and assistance in every article where it may be necessary; and who will perhaps be so good as to interpose with my relations, if any difficulty should arise about carrying any of the articles of this my last will into execution, and to soften them into the wished-for condescension: for it is my earnest request to Mr. Belford, that he will not seek by law, or by any sort of violence, either by word or deed, to extort the performance from *them*. If there be any articles of a merely domestic nature that my relations shall think unfit to be carried into execution; such articles I leave entirely to my said Cousin Morden and Mr. Belford to vary, or totally dispense with, as they shall agree upon the matter; or, if they two differ in opinion, they will be pleased to be determined by a third person, to be chosen by them both.

Having been pressed by Miss Howe and her mother to collect the particulars of my sad story, and given expectation that I would, in order to do my character justice with all my friends and companions: but not having time before me for the painful task, it has been a pleasure to me to find, by extracts kindly communicated to me by my said executor, that I may safely trust my fame to the justice done me by Mr. Lovelace, in his letters to him my said executor. And as Mr. Belford has engaged to contribute what is in his power towards a compilement to be made of all that relates to my story, and knows my whole mind in this respect; it is my desire that he will cause two copies to be made of this collection; one to remain with Miss Howe, the other with himself; and that he will show or lend his copy, if required, to my Aunt Hervey, for the satisfaction of any of my family; but under such restrictions as the said Mr.

Belford shall think fit to impose; that neither any other person's safety may be endangered, nor his own honour suffer, by the communication.

I bequeath to my said executor the sum of one hundred guineas, as a grateful, though insufficient acknowledgment of the trouble he will be at in the execution of the trust he has so kindly undertaken. I desire him likewise to accept of twenty guineas for a ring. And that he will reimburse himself for all the charges and expenses which he shall be at in the execution of this trust.

In the worthy Dr. H. I have found a physician, a father, and a friend. I beg of him, as a testimony of my gratitude, to accept of twenty guineas for a ring.

I have the same obligations to the kind and skilful Mr. Goddard, who attended me as my apothecary. His very moderate bill I have discharged down to yesterday. I have always thought it incumbent upon testators to shorten all they can the trouble of their executors. I know I underrate the value of Mr. Goddard's attendances, when over and above what may accrue from yesterday, to the hour that will finish all, I desire fifteen guineas for a ring may be presented to him.

To the Reverend Mr. ——, who frequently attended me, and prayed by me in my last stages, I also bequeath fifteen guineas for a ring.

There are a set of honest indigent people, whom I used to call *My Poor,* and to whom Mrs. Norton conveys relief each month (or at shorter periods), in proportion to their necessities, from a sum I deposited in her hands, and from time to time recruited, as means accrued to me; but now nearly, if not wholly expended: *now,* that my fault may be as little aggravated as possible by the sufferings of the worthy people whom Heaven gave me a heart to relieve; and as the produce of my grandfather's estate (including the moiety of the sums he had by him, and was pleased to give me, at his death, as above mentioned), together with what I shall further appropriate to the same use in the subsequent articles, will, as I hope, more than answer all my legacies and bequests; it is my will and desire that the remainder, be it little or much, shall become a fund to be appropriated, and I hereby direct that it be appropriated, to the like purposes with the sums which I put into Mrs. Norton's hands, as aforesaid—and this under the direction and management of the said Mrs. Norton, who knows my whole mind in this particular. And in case of her death, or of her desire to be acquitted of the management thereof, it is my earnest request to my dear Miss Howe, that she will take it upon herself, and at her own death, that she will transfer what shall remain undisposed of at the *time,* to such persons, and with such limitations, restrictions, and provisos as she shall think will best answer my intention. For, as to the management and distribution of all or any part of it, while in Mrs. Norton's hands, or her own, I will that it be entirely discretional, and without account, either to my executor or any other person.

It is my will and desire, that the set of jewels which was my grandmother's, and presented to me, soon after her death, by my grandfather, be valued; and the worth of them paid to my executor, if any of my family choose to have them; or otherwise, that they be sold, and go to the augmentation of my poor's fund. But if they may be deemed an equivalent for the sums my father was pleased to advance to me since the death of my grandfather, I desire that they may be given up to him.

I presume that the diamond necklace, solitaire, and buckles, which were properly my own, presented by my mother's uncle, Sir Josias Brookland, will not be purchased by any one of my family, for a too obvious reason: in this case I desire that they may be sent to my executor; and that he will dispose of them to the best advantage; and apply the money to the uses of my will.

In the beginning of this tedious writing, I referred to the latter part of it the naming of the subject of the discourse which I wished might be delivered at my funeral, if permitted to be interred with my ancestors: I think the following will be suitable to my case. I hope the alterations of the words *her* and *she,* for *him* and *he,* may be allowable.

"Let not *her* that is deceived trust in vanity; for vanity shall be *her* recompense. *She* shall be accomplished before *her* time; and *her* branch shall not be green. *She* shall shake off *her* unripe grape as the vine, and shall cast off *her* flower as the olive."

But if I am to be interred in town, let only the usual Burial Service be read over my corpse.

If my body be permitted to be carried down, I bequeath ten pounds to be given to the poor of the parish, at the discretion of the churchwardens, within a fortnight after my interment.

And now, O my blessed REDEEMER, do I, with a lively faith, humbly lay hold of Thy meritorious death and sufferings; hoping to be washed clean in Thy precious blood from all my sins: in the bare hope of the happy consequences of which, how light do those sufferings seem (grievous as they were at the time) which, I confidently trust, will be a means, by Thy grace, to work out for me a more exceeding and eternal weight of glory!

Clarissa Harlowe.

Signed, sealed, published, and declared, the day and year above written, by the said Clarissa Harlowe, as her last will and testament; contained in seven sheets of paper, all written with her own hand, and every sheet signed and sealed by herself, in the presence of us,

John Williams,
Arthur Bedall,
Elizabeth Swanton.

COLONEL MORDEN TO JOHN BELFORD, ESQ.

Sat. Sept. 16.

I HAVE BEEN employed in a most melancholy task: in reading the will of the dear deceased.

The unhappy mother and Mrs. Norton chose to be absent on the affecting occasion. But Mrs. Harlowe made it her earnest request that every article of it should be fulfilled.

The directions for her funeral, in case she were or were not permitted to be carried down; the mention of her orders having been given for the manner of her being laid out, and the presence of mind visible throughout the whole, obtained their admiration, expressed by hands and eyes lifted up, and by falling tears.

But when I came to the address to be made to the accursed man, "if he were not to be diverted from seeing *her* dead, whom

ONCE before he had seen in a manner dead"—execration, and either vows or wishes of revenge, filled every mouth.

These were still more fervently renewed when they came to hear read her forgiveness of even this man.

You remember, sir, on our first reading of the will in town, the observations I made on the foul play which it is evident the excellent creature met with from this abandoned man, and what I said upon the occasion. I am not used to repeat things of that nature.

When the article was read which bequeathed to the father the grandfather's estate, and the reason assigned for it (so generous and so dutiful), the father could sit no longer; but withdrew, wiping his eyes, and lifting up his spread hands at Mr. James Harlowe; who arose to attend him to the door, as Arabella likewise did—all he could say: O son! son!—O girl! girl! as if he reproached them for the parts they had acted, and put him upon acting.

Let tongue and eyes express what they will, Mr. Belford, the first reading of a will, where a person dies worth anything considerable, generally affords a true test of the relations' love to the deceased.

The clothes, the thirty guineas for mourning to Mrs. Norton, with the recommendation of the good woman for housekeeper at *The Grove,* were thought sufficient, had the article of £600, which was called monstrous, been omitted.

My Cousin Dolly Hervey was grudged the library. Miss Harlowe said that as she and her sister never bought the same books, she would take that to herself, and would *make it up* to her Cousin Dolly *one way or other.*

I intend, Mr. Belford, to save you the trouble of interposing —the library *shall* be my Cousin Dolly's.

The £600 bequeathed to Mrs. Norton, the library to Miss Hervey, and the remembrances to Miss Howe, were not the only articles grudged. Yet to what purpose did they regret the pecuniary bequests, when the poor's fund, and not themselves, would have had the benefit, had not those legacies been bequeathed?

But enough passed to convince me that my cousin was

absolutely right in her choice of an executor out of the family.

I will only add, that they could not bear to hear read the concluding part, so solemnly addressed to her Redeemer. They all arose from their seats, and crowded out of the apartment we were in: and then, as I afterwards found, separated, in order to seek that consolation in solitary retirement which, though they could not hope for from their own reflections, yet, at the time, they had less reason to expect in each other's company. I am,

Sir,

Your faithful and obedient servant,

Wm. Morden.

MR. BELFORD TO THE RIGHT HONOURABLE LORD M.

London, Sept. 14.

MY LORD,—I am very apprehensive that the affair between Mr. Lovelace and the late excellent Miss Clarissa Harlowe will be attended with further bad consequences, notwithstanding her dying injunctions to the contrary. I would therefore humbly propose that your lordship and his other relations will forward the purpose your kinsman lately had to go abroad; where I hope he will stay till all is blown over. But as he will not stir, if he know the true motives of your wishes, the avowed inducement, as I hinted once to Mr. Mowbray, may be such as respects his own health both of person and mind.

I am glad to hear that he is in a way of recovery: but this the rather induces me to press the matter. And I think no time should be lost.

He then transcribes the article which so gratefully mentions this nobleman, and the ladies of his family, in relation to the rings she bequeaths them, about which he desires their commands.

MISS MONTAGUE TO JOHN BELFORD, ESQ.

M. Hall, Friday, Sept. 15.

SIR,—My lord having the gout in his right hand, his lordship, and Lady Sarah, and Lady Betty, have commanded me to inform you that, before your letter came, Mr. Lovelace was preparing for a foreign tour. We shall endeavour to hasten him away on the motives you suggest.

We are all extremely affected with the dear lady's death. Lady Betty and Lady Sarah have been indisposed ever since they heard of it.

Everybody is assured that you will do all in your power to prevent *further* ill consequences from this melancholy affair. My lord desires his compliments to you. I am, sir,

Your humble servant,

Ch. Montague.

THIS collection having run into a much greater length than was wished, it is thought proper to omit several letters that passed between Colonel Morden, Miss Howe, Mr. Belford, and Mr. Hickman, in relation to the execution of the lady's will, etc.

CLARISSA'S POSTHUMOUS LETTER TO MR. LOVELACE

Thursday, Aug. 24.

I TOLD YOU, in the letter I wrote to you on *Tuesday* last, that you should have another sent you when I had got to *my father's house.*

I presume to say that I am *now,* at your receiving of this, arrived there; and I invite you to follow me, as soon as you can be *prepared* for so great a journey.

Not to allegorize further—my fate is *now,* at your perusal of this, accomplished. My doom is unalterably fixed: and I am either a miserable or a happy being to all eternity. If *happy,* I owe it solely to the Divine mercy: if *miserable,* to your undeserved cruelty.—And consider now, for your own sake, gay, cruel, fluttering, unhappy man! consider whether the barbarous and perfidious treatment I have met with from you was worthy of the hazard of your immortal soul; since your wicked views were not to be effected but by the wilful breach of the most solemn vows that ever were made by man; and those aided by a violence and baseness unworthy of a human creature.

In time then, once more, I wish you to consider your ways. Your golden dream cannot long last. Your present course can yield you pleasure no longer than you can keep off thought or reflection. A hardened insensibility is the only foundation on which your inward tranquillity is built. When once a dangerous sickness seizes you; when once effectual remorse breaks in upon you; how dreadful will be your condition! How poor a triumph will you then find it, to have been able, by a series of black perjuries, and studied baseness, under the name of gallantry or intrigue, to betray poor inexperienced young creatures, who perhaps knew nothing but their duty till they knew you!—Not one good action in the hour of languishing to recollect, not one worthy intention to revolve, it will be all reproach and horror; and you will wish to have it in your power to compound for annihilation.

Reflect, sir, that I can have no other motive, in what I write, than your good, and the safety of other innocent creatures, who may be drawn in by your wicked arts and perjuries. You have not, in my wishes for your future welfare, the wishes of a suppliant wife, endeavouring for her *own* sake, as well as for *yours,* to induce you to reform those ways. They are wholly as disinterested as undeserved. But I should mistrust my own penitence, were I capable of wishing to recompense evil for evil—if, black as your offences have been against me, I could not forgive as I wish to be forgiven.

I repeat, therefore, that I *do* forgive you. And may the Almighty forgive you too! Nor have I, at the writing of this, any other essential regrets than what are occasioned by the grief I have given to parents, who till I knew you were the most indulgent of parents; by the scandal given to the other branches of my family; by the disreputation brought upon my sex; and by the offence given to virtue in my fall.

To say I once respected you with a preference, is what I ought to blush to own, since, at the very time, I was far from thinking you even a moral man; though I little thought that you, or indeed that any man breathing, could be—what you have proved yourself to be. But indeed, sir, I have long been greatly above you: for from my heart I have despised you, and all your ways, ever since I saw what manner of man you were.

Hear me, therefore, O Lovelace! as one speaking from the dead—Lose no time. Set about your repentance instantly. Be no longer the instrument of Satan, to draw poor souls into those subtile snares, which at last shall entangle your own feet. Seek not to multiply your offences, till they become beyond the *power,* as I may say, of the Divine mercy to forgive; since *justice,* no less than *mercy,* is an attribute of the Almighty.

Whenever you shall be inclined to consult the sacred oracles, you will find doctrines and texts which a truly penitent and contrite heart may lay hold of for its consolation.

And may you be entitled to the mercies of a long-suffering and gracious God, is the sincere prayer of

Clarissa Harlowe.

MR. LOVELACE TO JOHN BELFORD, ESQ.

M. Hall, Thursday, Sept. 14.

EVER SINCE the fatal seventh of this month, I have been lost to myself, and to all the joys of life.

They tell me of an odd letter I wrote to you. I remember I did write. But very little of the contents of what I wrote do I remember.

I have been in a cursed way. Methinks something has been working strangely retributive. I never was such a fool as to disbelieve a Providence: yet am I not for resolving into judgments everything that seems to wear an avenging face. Yet if we must be punished either here or hereafter for our misdeeds, better *here,* say I, than *hereafter.* Have I not then an interest to think my punishment already not only begun, but completed; since what I have suffered, and do suffer, passes all description?

To give but one instance of the *retributive*—here I, who was the barbarous cause of the loss of senses for a week together to the most inimitable of women, have been punished with the loss of my own—preparative to—who knows what? When, Oh, when, shall I know a joyful hour?

I am kept excessively low; and excessively low I *am.* This sweet creature's posthumous letter sticks close to me. All her excellences rise up hourly to my remembrance.

Yet dare I not indulge in these melancholy reflections. I find my head strangely working again. Pen, begone!

Monday, Sept. 18.

Heavy, damnably heavy, and sick at soul, by Jupiter! I must see what change of climate will do.

You tell these fellows, and you tell me, of repenting and reforming: but I can do neither. He who *can,* must not have the *extinction* of a Clarissa Harlowe to answer for. Harlowe!—Curse upon the name!—and curse upon myself for not changing it, as I might have done! Yet have I no need of urging a curse upon myself—I have it effectually.

"To say I once respected you with a preference."—In what stiff language does maidenly modesty on these nice occasions express itself!—*To say I once loved you,* is the English; and there is truth and ease in the expression. "To say I once loved you," then let it be, "is what I ought to blush to own."

And dost thou own it, excellent creature? and dost thou then own it?—What music in these words from such an angel! What would I give that my Clarissa were in being, and *could* and *would* own that she loved me?

"But indeed, sir, I have long been greatly above you."

Long, my blessed charmer!—Long indeed, for you have been *ever* greatly above me, and above your sex, and above all the world.

"Your golden dream cannot long last."—Divine prophetess! my golden dream is *already* over. "Thought and reflection *are* no longer to be kept off."—No *longer continues* that "hardened insensibility" thou chargest upon me. "Remorse *has* broken in upon me." "Dreadful *is* my condition!" "It *is* all reproach and horror with me!"—A thousand vultures in turn are preying upon my heart!

Acquaint me with all thou knowest which I do *not* know: how her relations, her cruel relations, take it; and whether, now, the barbed dart of after-reflection sticks not in their hearts, as in mine, up to the very feathers.

. . . . . .

I will soon quit this kingdom. For now my Clarissa is no more, what is there in it (in the world indeed) worth living for? But should I not first, by some masterly mischief, avenge her and myself upon her cursed family?

They govern me as a child in strings: yet did I suffer so much in my fever, that I am willing to bear with them till I can get tolerably well.

At present I can neither eat, drink, nor sleep. Yet are my disorders nothing to what they were: for, Jack, my brain was on fire day and night: and had it not been of the *asbestos* kind, it had all been consumed.

I had no distinct ideas, but of dark and confused misery: *it was all remorse and horror* indeed! Thoughts of hanging, drowning, shooting; then rage, violence, mischief, and despair took their turns with me. My lucid intervals still worse, giving me to reflect upon what I *was* the hour before, and what I was likely to be the next, and perhaps for life—the sport of enemies! the laughter of fools! and the hanging-sleeved, go-carted property of hired slaves; who were perhaps to find their account in manacling, and (abhorred thought!) in personally abusing me by blows and stripes!

MR. LOVELACE TO JOHN BELFORD, ESQ.

Wedn. Sept. 20.

WHY, *why did my mother bring me up to bear no control?* Why was I so educated, *as that to my very tutors it was a request that I should not know what contradiction or disappointment was?* Ought she not to have known what cruelty there was in her kindness?

What a punishment, to have my first very great disappointment touch my intellect! And intellects once touched—— but that I cannot bear to think of—only thus far; the very repentance and amendment wished me so heartily by my kind and cross dear have been invalidated and postponed, who knows for how long?—the *amendment* at least:—can a madman be capable of either?

How my heart sickens at looking back upon what I was! Denied the sun, and all comfort: *all* my visitors low-born, tiptoe attendants: even those tiptoe slaves never approaching me but periodically, armed with gallipots, boluses, and cephalic draughts; delivering their orders to me in hated whispers; and answering other curtain-holding impertinents, inquiring how I was, and how I took their execrable potions, whisperingly too!

What a cursed still-life was this! Nothing active in me, or about me, but the worm that never dies.

Again I hasten from the recollection of scenes which *will,* at times, obtrude themselves upon me.

Adieu, Belford!

MR. LOVELACE TO JOHN BELFORD, ESQ.

I AM PREPARING to leave this kingdom. Mowbray and Tourville promise to give me their company in a month or two.

I'll give thee my route.

I shall first to Paris; and, for amusement and diversion's sake, try to renew some of my old friendships: thence to some of the German courts: thence, perhaps, to Vienna: thence descend through Bavaria and the Tyrol to Venice, where I shall keep the carnival: thence to Florence and Turin: thence again over Mount Cenis to France: and, when I return again to Paris, shall expect to see my friend Belford, who by that time, I doubt not, will be all crusted and bearded over with penitence, self-denial, and mortification; a very anchorite, only an itinerant one, journeying over in hope to cover a multitude of his own sins, by proselyting his old companion.

Thou hast made good resolutions. If thou keepest them not, thou wilt never be able to keep any. But, nevertheless, the devil and thy time of life are against thee: and six to one thou failest. Were it only that thou hast *resolved,* six to one thou failest. And if thou dost, thou wilt become the scoff of men, and the triumph of devils. Then how will I laugh at thee! For this warning is not from principle. Perhaps I wish it were: *but I never lied to man, and hardly ever said truth to woman.* The first is *what all free-livers cannot say:* the second, *what every one can.*

I am mad again, by Jupiter! But, thank my stars, not gloomily so! Farewell, farewell, farewell, for the third or fourth time, concludes

Thy Lovelace.

MR. BELFORD TO ROBERT LOVELACE, ESQ.

Friday, Sept. 22.

I SHOULD be glad to know when you intend to set out. I have too much concern for your welfare, not to wish you in a thinner air and more certain climate.

What have Tourville and Mowbray to do, that they cannot set out with you?

I will not, however, forswear making you a visit at Paris, at your return from Germany and Italy: but hardly with the hope of reclaiming you, if due reflection upon what I have set before you, and upon what you have written in your two last, will not by that time have done it.

I suppose I shall see you before you go. Once more, I wish you were gone. This heavy island air cannot do for you what that of the Continent will.

I do not think I ought to communicate with you, as I used to do, on this side of the Channel: let me then hear from you on the opposite shore, and you shall command the pen, as you please; and, honestly, the power, of

J. Belford.

MR. BELFORD TO COLONEL MORDEN

Thursday, Sept. 21.

GIVE ME LEAVE, dear sir, to address myself to you in a very serious and solemn manner on a subject that I must not, cannot, dispense with; as I promised the divine lady that I would do everything in my power to prevent that further mischief of which she was so very apprehensive.

I will not content myself with distant hints. It is with very great concern that I have just now heard of a declaration which you are said to have made to your relations at Harlowe Place, that you will not rest till you have avenged your cousin's wrongs upon Mr. Lovelace.

Far be it from me to offer to defend the unhappy man, or even *unduly* to extenuate his crime: but yet I must say that the family, by their persecutions of the dear lady at first, and by their implacableness afterwards, ought, *at least,* to *share* the blame with him.

When I have the pleasure of seeing you next, I will acquaint you, sir, with all the circumstances of this melancholy story; from which you will see that Mr. Lovelace was extremely ill-treated at first, by the whole family, this admirable lady excepted. This exception, I know, heightens his crime: but as his principal intention was but to try her virtue; and that he became so earnest a suppliant to her for marriage; and as he has suffered so deplorably in the loss of his reason, for not having it in his power to repair her wrongs; I presume to hope that much is to be pleaded against such a resolution as you are said to have made.

Let me *also* (though I presume to hope there is no need, when you cooly consider everything) remind you of your own promise to your departing cousin; relying upon which, her last moments were the easier.

Reflect, my dear Colonel Morden, that the highest injury was to *her:* her family all have a share in the *cause: she* forgives it: why should we not endeavour to imitate what we admire?

Excuse me, sir, for the sake of my executorial duty and promise, keeping in eye the dear lady's *personal injunctions,* as well as *written will,* enforced by *letters posthumous.* Every article of which (solicitous as we *both* are to see it truly performed) she would have dispensed with, rather than further mischief should happen on her account. I am,

Dear sir,
Your affectionate and faithful servant,
J. Belford.

The following is the posthumous letter to Colonel Morden.

SUPERSCRIBED: TO MY BELOVED COUSIN, WILLIAM MORDEN, ESQ.

MY DEAREST COUSIN,—As it is uncertain, from my present weak state, whether, if living, I may be in a condition to receive as I ought the favour you intend me of a visit, when you come to London, I take this opportunity to return you, while able, the humble acknowledgments of a grateful heart, for all your goodness to me from childhood till now: and more particularly for your present kind interposition in my favour.

God Almighty for ever bless you, dear sir, for the kindness you endeavoured to procure for me.

One principal end of my writing to you in this solemn manner, is to beg of you, which I do with the utmost earnestness, that when you come to hear the particulars of my story, you will not suffer *active* resentment to take place in your generous breast on my account.

Remember, my dear cousin, that vengeance is God's province, and He has undertaken to repay it; nor will you, I hope, invade that province:—especially as there is no necessity for you to attempt to vindicate my fame; since the offender himself (before he is called upon) has stood forth, and offered to do me all the justice that you could have extorted from him, had I lived: and when your own person may be endangered by running an *equal* risk with a *guilty man.*

Seek not then, I beseech you, sir, to aggravate my fault by a pursuit of blood, which must necessarily be deemed a consequence of that fault. Give not the unhappy man the merit (were you assuredly to be the victor) of falling by your hand. At present he is the perfidious, the ungrateful deceiver; but will not the forfeiture of his life, and the probable loss of his soul, be a dreadful expiation for having made me miserable for *a few months* only, and through that misery, by the Divine favour, happy to all eternity?

In such a case, my cousin, where shall the evil stop? And who shall avenge on you? And who on your avenger?

Let the poor man's conscience, then, dear sir, avenge me. He will one day find punishment more than enough from that. Leave him to the chance of repentance.

Be a comforter, dear sir, to my honoured parents, as you have been to me: and may we, through the Divine goodness to us both, meet in that blessed eternity, into which, as I humbly trust, I shall have entered when you read this.

So prays, and to her latest hour will pray, my dear Cousin Morden, my friend, my guardian, but *not* my avenger—(dear sir! remember that!)

Your ever affectionate and obliged

Clarissa Harlowe.

Colonel Morden to John Belford, Esq.

Sat. Sept. 23.

Dear Sir,—I am very sorry that anything you have heard I have said should give you uneasiness.

I am obliged to you for the letters you have communicated to me; and still further for your promise to favour me with others occasionally.

I leave to your own discretion, what may or may not be proper for Miss Howe to see from a pen so free as mine.

I admire her spirit. Were she a *man,* do you think, sir, *she, at this time,* would have your advice to take upon such a subject as that upon which you write?

Fear not, however, that your communications shall put me upon any measures that otherwise I should not have taken. The wickedness, sir, is of such a nature as admits not of aggravation.

I have indeed expressed myself with vehemence upon the occasion. Who could forbear to do so? But it is not my way to resolve in matters of moment, till opportunity brings the execution of my purposes within my reach. We shall see by what manner of spirit this young man will be acted, on his recovery. If he continue to brave and defy a family, which he has so irreparably injured—if——But resolutions depending upon future contingencies are best left to future determination, as I just now hinted.

Meantime, I will own that I think my cousin's arguments unanswerable. No *good* man but must be influenced by them. But, alas! sir, who *is* good?

As to your arguments; I hope you will believe me, when I assure you, as I now do, that your opinion, and your reasoning, have, and will always have, great and deserved weight with me: and that I respect you still more than I did, if possible, for your expostulations in support of my cousin's pious injunctions to me. They come from *you,* sir, with the greatest propriety, as her executor and representative; and likewise as you are a man of humanity, and a well-wisher to both parties.

I am not exempt from violent passions, sir, any more than

your friend; but then I hope they are only capable of being raised by other people's insolence, and not by my own arrogance.

That the author of this diffusive mischief perpetrated it premeditatedly, wantonly, in the gaiety of his heart. To *try* my cousin, say you, sir? To try the virtue of a Clarissa, sir! Had she then given him any cause to doubt her virtue? It could *not* be. If he avers that she did, I am indeed called upon——But I will have patience.

That he carried her, as now it appears, to a vile brothel, purposely to put her out of all human resource; himself out of the reach of all humane remorse: and that, finding her proof against all the common arts of delusion, base and unmanly arts were there used to effect his wicked purposes. *Once dead,* the injured saint, in her will, says, *he has seen her.*

That I could not know this when I saw him at M. Hall: that, the object of his attempts considered, I could not suppose there was such a monster breathing as he.

That, disgrace as he is to his name, and to the character of a gentleman, the man would not want merit who, in vindication of the *dishonoured* distinction, should expunge and blot him out of the worthy list.

That the injured family has a son who, however unworthy of such a sister, is of a temper vehement, unbridled, fierce; unequal, therefore (as he has once indeed been found), to a contention with this man: the loss of which son, by a violent death, on such an occasion, and by a hand so justly hated, would complete the misery of the whole family: and who, nevertheless, resolves to call him to account, if I do not: his very *misbehaviour* perhaps to such a sister stimulating his perverse heart to do her memory the *more signal* justice; though the attempt might be fatal to himself.

You, sir, who know more of the barbarous machinations and practices of this strange man, can help me to still more inflaming reasons, were they needed, why a man *not perfect* may stand excused to the generality of the world, if he should pursue his vengeance; and the rather, as through an absence of six years he could not till now know one half of her excellences—

till now! that we have lost, for ever lost, the admirable creature! I am, sir,

Your most faithful and obliged servant,

Wm. Morden.

Mr. Belford, in his answer to this letter, further enforces the lady's dying injunctions; and rejoices that the colonel has made no vindictive resolutions; and hopes everything from his prudence and consideration, and from his promise given to the dying lady.

He desires the colonel will give him a day's notice of his coming to town, lest otherwise he may be absent at the time.

This he does, though he tells him not the reason, with a view to prevent a meeting between him and Mr. Lovelace; who might be in town (as he apprehends) *about the same time, in his way to go abroad.*

COLONEL MORDEN TO JOHN BELFORD, ESQ.

Tuesday, Sept. 26.

DEAR SIR,—I cannot help congratulating myself, as well as you, that we have already got through with the family every article of the will, where *they* have any concern.

You left me a discretional power in many instances; and, in pursuance of it, I have had my dear cousin's personal jewels valued; and will account to you for them, at the highest price, when I come to town.

These jewels I have presented to my Cousin Dolly Hervey, in acknowledgment of her love to the dear departed. I have told Miss Howe of this; and she is as well pleased with what I have done as if she had been the purchaser of them herself.

The grandmother's jewels are also valued; and the money will be paid me for you, to be carried to the uses of the will.

Mrs. Norton is preparing, by general consent, to enter upon her office as housekeeper at *The Grove*. But it is my opinion that she will not be long on this side heaven.

Having now seen everything that relates to the will of my dear cousin brought to a desirable issue, I will set about making my own. I shall follow the dear creature's example, and give my reasons for every article, that there may be no room for after-contention.

I hope soon to pay my respects to you in town. Meantime I am, with great respect, dear sir,

Your faithful and affectionate humble servant,

Wm. Morden.

Lord M. to John Belford, Esq.

M. Hall, Friday, Sept. 29.

Dear Sir,—My kinsman Lovelace is now setting out for London; proposing to see you, and then to go to Dover, and so embark.

What I mostly write for is to wish you to keep Colonel Morden and him asunder; and so I give you notice of his going to town. I should be very loath there should be any mischief between them, as you gave me notice that the colonel threatened my nephew. But my kinsman would not bear that; so nobody let him know that he did. But I hope there is no fear: for the colonel does not, as I hear, threaten now. For his own sake I am glad of that; for there is not such a man in the world as my kinsman is said to be at all the weapons—as well he was not; he would not be so daring.

Your very humble servant,

M.

Mr. Belford to Lord M.

London, Tuesday Night, Oct. 3.

My Lord,—I obey your lordship's commands with great pleasure.

Yesterday in the afternoon Mr. Lovelace made me a visit at my lodgings. As I was in expectation of one from Colonel Morden about the same time, I thought proper to carry him to a tavern which neither of us frequented (on pretence of a half-appointment); ordering notice to be sent me thither, if the colonel came: and Mr. Lovelace sent to Mowbray, and Tourville, and Mr. Doleman of Uxbridge (who came to town to take leave of him), to let them know where to find us.

Mr. Lovelace is *too well* recovered, I was going to say. I never saw him more gay, lively, and handsome.

We parted about four; he not a little dissatisfied with me; for we had some talk about subjects which, he said, he loved not to think of; to wit, Miss Harlowe's will; my executorship; papers I had in confidence communicated to that admirable lady (with no unfriendly design, I assure your lordship); and he insisting upon, and I refusing, the return of the letters he had written to me, from the time that he had made his first addresses to her.

He would see me once again, he said; and it would be upon very ill terms if I complied not with his request. Which I bid him not expect. But, that I might not deny him everything, I told him that I would give him a copy of the will; though I was sure, I said, when he read it, he would wish he had never seen it.

I had a message from him about eleven this morning, desiring me to name a place at which to dine with him, and Mowbray, and Tourville, for the last time: and soon after, another from Colonel Morden, inviting me to pass the evening with him at the Bedford Head in Covent Garden. And, that I might keep them at distance from one another, I appointed Mr. Lovelace at the Eagle in Suffolk Street.

There I met him, and the two others. We began where we left off at our last parting; and were very high with each other. But, at last, all was made up, and he offered to forget and forgive everything, on condition that I would correspond with him while abroad, and continue the series which had been broken through by his illness; and particularly give him, as I had offered, a copy of the lady's will.

With much reluctance they let me go to my evening's appointment: they little thought with whom: for Mr. Lovelace had put it as a case of honour to all of us, whether, as he had been told that Mr. Morden and Mr. James Harlowe had thrown out menaces against him, he ought to leave the kingdom till he had thrown himself in their way.

Mowbray gave his opinion that he ought to leave it like a man of honour, as he was; and if he did not take those gentlemen to task for their opprobrious speeches, that, at least, he should be seen by them in public before he went away; else they might give themselves airs, as if he had left the kingdom in fear of them.

To this he himself so much inclined, that it was with difficulty

I persuaded him that, as they had neither of them proceeded to a *direct* and *formal challenge;* as they knew he had not made himself difficult of access; and as he had already done the family injury enough; and it was Miss Harlowe's earnest desire that he would be content with that; he had no reason, from any point of honour, to delay his journey; especially as he had so just a motive for his going as the establishment of his health; and as he might return the sooner, if he saw occasion for it.

I found the colonel in a very solemn way. We had a good deal of discourse upon the subject of certain letters which had passed between us in relation to Miss Harlowe's will, and to her family.

He has some accounts to settle with his banker; which, he says, will be adjusted to-morrow; and on Thursday he proposes to go down again, to take leave of his friends; and then intends to set out directly for Italy.

I wish Mr. Lovelace could have been prevailed upon to take any other tour than that of France and Italy. I did propose Madrid to him; but he laughed at me, and told me that the proposal was in character from a *mule;* and from one who was become as grave as a Spaniard of the *old cut,* at *ninety*.

I expressed to the colonel my apprehensions that his cousin's dying injunctions would not have the force upon him that were to be wished.

"They have *great force* upon me, Mr. Belford, said he; or *one world* would not have held Mr. Lovelace and me thus long. But my intention is to go to Florence; not to lay my bones there, as upon my cousin's death I told you I thought to do; but to settle all my affairs in those parts, and then to come over, and reside upon a little paternal estate in Kent, which is strangely gone to ruin in my absence. Indeed, were I to meet Mr. Lovelace, either here or abroad, I might not be answerable for the consequence."

He would have engaged me for to-morrow. But having promised to attend Mr. Lovelace on his journey, as I have mentioned, I said I was obliged to go out of town, and was uncertain as to the time of my return in the evening. And so I am to see him on Thursday morning at my own lodgings.

I will do myself the honour to write again to your lordship to-morrow night. Meantime, I am, my lord,

Your lordship's, etc.

MR. BELFORD TO LORD M.

Wedn. Night, Oct. 4.

MY LORD,—I am just returned from attending Mr. Lovelace as far as Gad's Hill, near Rochester. He was exceeding gay all the way. Mowbray and Tourville are gone on with him. They will see him embark, and under sail; and promise to follow him in a month or two; for they say there is no living without him, now he is once more himself.

He and I parted with great and even solemn tokens of affection; but yet not without gay intermixtures, as I will acquaint your lordship.

Taking me aside, and clasping his arms about me, "Adieu, dear Belford! said he. May you proceed in the course you have entered upon!—Whatever airs I give myself, this charming creature has fast hold of me *here* (clapping his hand upon his heart); and I must either appear what you see me, or be what I so lately was. O the divine creature!" lifting up his eyes——

"But if I live to come to England, and you remain fixed in your present way, and can give me encouragement, I hope rather to follow your *example,* than to ridicule you for it. This will (for I had given him a copy of it) I will make the companion of my solitary hours. You have told me part of its melancholy contents; and that, and her posthumous letter, shall be my study; and they will prepare me for being your disciple, if you hold on.

"*You,* Jack, may marry, continued he; and I have a wife in my eye for you. Only thou'rt such an awkward mortal" (he saw me affected, and thought to make me smile): "but we don't make ourselves, except it be worse by our dress. Thou art in mourning now, as well as I: but if ever thy ridiculous turn lead thee again to be beau-brocade, I will *bedizen* thee, as the girls say, on my return, to my own fancy, and according to thy own *natural appearance*—thou shalt doctor my soul, and I will doctor thy body: thou shalt see what a clever fellow I will make of thee.

"As for *me,* I never *will,* I never *can,* marry. That I will not take a few liberties, and that I will not try to start some of my former game, I won't promise—habits are not easily shaken off—but they shall be by way of weaning. So *return* and *reform* shall go together.

"And now, thou sorrowful monkey, what aileth thee?" (I do love him, my lord.)

"Adieu!—and once more adieu!—embracing me. And when thou thinkest thou hast made thyself an interest *out yonder* (looking up), then put in a word for thy Lovelace."

I return your lordship my humble thanks for the honour of your invitation to M. Hall. The first letter I receive from Mr. Lovelace shall give me the opportunity of embracing it. I am, my lord,

Your most faithful and obedient servant,

J. Belford.

Mr. Lovelace to John Belford, Esq.

Paris, Octob. 14.

I ought to have written to you sooner. But I loitered two days at Calais, for an answer to a letter I wrote to engage my former travelling valet, De la Tour; an ingenious, ready fellow, as you have heard me say. I *have* engaged him, and he is now with me.

I shall make no stay here; but intend for some of the Electoral Courts. That of Bavaria, I think, will engage me longest. Perhaps I may step out of my way (if I can be out of my way anywhere) to those of Dresden and Berlin: and it is not impossible that you may have one letter from me at Vienna. And then perhaps I may fall down into Italy by the Tyrol; and so, taking Turin in my way, return to Paris; where I hope to see Mowbray and Tourville: nor do I despair of you.

I have my former lodgings in the Rue St. Antoine: which I shall hold, notwithstanding my tour: so they will be ready to accommodate any two of you, if you come hither before my return: and for this I have conditioned.

Thy Lovelace.

Mr. Belford to Robert Lovelace, Esq.

London, Oct. 25.

I write to show you that I am incapable of slighting even the minutest requests of an absent and distant friend.

Yet you may believe that there cannot be any great alterations in the little time that you have been out of England, with respect to the subjects of your inquiry.

The Harlowes continue inconsolable; and I dare say will to the end of their lives.

Miss Howe is not yet married; but I have reason to think will soon. I have the honour of corresponding with her; and the more I know of her, the more I admire the nobleness of her mind.

As to Mowbray and Tourville, I suppose they'll be at Paris before you can return from Germany; for they cannot live without you: and you gave them such a specimen of your recovered volatility, in the last evening's conversation, as equally delighted *them*, and concerned *me*.

I wish, with all my heart, that thou wouldst bend thy course towards the Pyrenean. I wonder thou wilt not; since then thy subjects would be as new to thyself as to

Thy Belford.

MR. LOVELACE TO JOHN BELFORD, ESQ.

Paris, Oct. 16–27

I FOLLOW my last of the 14/25th, on occasion of a letter just now come to hand from Joseph Leman. The fellow is conscience-ridden, Jack; and tells me "that he cannot rest either day or night for the mischiefs which he fears he has been, and may still further be the means of doing." He wishes, "if it please God, and if it please *me*, that he had never seen my Honour's face."

And what is the cause of his present concern, as to his own particular? What but "the *slights* and *contempts* which he receives from every one of the Harlowes; from those particularly, he says, whom he has endeavoured to serve as faithfully as his engagements to *me* would let him serve them? And I always made him believe, he tells me (*poor weak soul as he was from his cradle!*), that serving me was serving both, *in the long run.* But this, and the death of his dear young lady, is a grief, he declares, that he shall never *claw off*, were he to live to the age of *Matthew-Salem: althoff*, and *howsomever*, he is sure that he shall not live *a month to an end;* being strangely pined, and his *stomach* nothing like what it was: and Mrs. Betty being also (now she *has got his love*) very *cross* and *slighting:* but, thank his God for punishing her! she is in a poor way *hersell.*

"But the chief occasion of troubling my Honour now, is not his own griefs only, althoff they are very great; but to prevent future mischiefs to me: for he can assure me that Colonel Morden has set out from them all, with a full resolution to *have his will of me:* and he is well assured that he said, and swore to it, as *how* he was resolved that he would either have my Honour's heart's blood, or I should have his; or *some such-like sad threatenings:* and that all the family rejoice in it, and hope I shall *come short home.*"

This is the substance of Joseph's letter; and I have one from Mowbray, which has a hint to the same effect. And I recollect now that you was very importunate with me to go to Madrid, rather than to France and Italy, the last evening we passed together.

What I desire of you is, by the first dispatch, to let me faithfully know all that you know on this head.

I can't bear to be threatened, Jack. Nor shall any man, unquestioned, give himself airs in my absence, if I know it, that shall make me look mean in anybody's eyes: that shall give my friends *pain* for me: that shall put them upon wishing me to change my intentions, or my plan, to avoid him. Upon such despicable terms as these, think you that I could bear to live?

But why, if such were his purpose, did he not let me know it before I left England? Was he unable to work himself up to a resolution till he knew me to be out of the kingdom?

As soon as I can inform myself where to direct to him, I will write to know his purpose; for I cannot bear suspense in such a case as this: that solemn act, were it even to be marriage or hanging, which must be done to-morrow, I had rather should be done to-day.

If he come to Paris, although I should be on my tour, he will very easily find out my *lodgings:* for I every day see someone or other of my countrymen, and divers of them have I entertained *here.* I go frequently to the opera and to the play, and appear at court, and at all public places. And, on my quitting this city, will leave a direction whither my letters from England, or elsewhere, shall from time to time be forwarded. Were I sure that his intention is what Joseph Leman tells me it is, I would stay here, or shorten his course to me, let him be where he would.

I cannot get off my regrets on account of this dear lady for the blood of me. If the colonel and I are to meet, as he has done me no injury, and loves the memory of his cousin, we shall engage with the same sentiments as to the object of our dispute: and that, you know, is no very common case.

In short, I am as much convinced that I have done wrong as he can be; and regret it as much. But I will not bear to be threatened by any man in the world, however conscious I may be of having deserved blame.

Adieu, Belford! be sincere with me. No palliation, as thou valuest

Thy Lovelace.

MR. BELFORD TO ROBERT LOVELACE, ESQ.

London, Oct. 26.

I CANNOT THINK, my dear Lovelace, that Colonel Morden has either threatened you in those gross terms mentioned by the vile, hypocritical, and ignorant Joseph Leman, or intends to follow you. They are the words of people of that fellow's class, and not of a gentleman: not of Colonel Morden, I am sure. You'll observe that Joseph pretends not to say that he heard him speak them.

I have been very solicitous to sound the colonel, for your sake, and for his own, and for the sake of the injunctions of the excellent lady to me, as well as to him, on that subject. He is (and you will not wonder that he should be) extremely affected; and owns that he has expressed himself in terms of resentment on the occasion. Once he said to me, that had his beloved cousin's case been that of a *common seduction,* her own credulity or weakness contributing to her fall, he could have forgiven you. But, in so many words, he assured me that he had not taken any resolutions; nor had he declared himself to the family in such a way as should bind him to resent; on the contrary, he has owned that his cousin's injunctions have hitherto had the force upon him which I could wish they should have.

He went abroad in a week after you. When he took his leave of me, he told me that his design was to go to Florence; and that he would settle his affairs there; and then return to England, and here pass the remainder of his days.

I was indeed apprehensive that if you and he were to meet, something unhappy might fall out: and as I knew that you proposed to take Italy, and very likely Florence, in your return to France, I was very solicitous to prevail upon you to take the Court of Spain into your plan. I am still so. And if you are not to be prevailed upon to do that, let me entreat you to avoid Florence or Leghorn in your return, since you have visited both heretofore. At least, let not the proposal of a meeting come from you.

It would be matter of serious reflection to me, if the *very fellow,* this *Joseph Leman,* who gave you such an opportunity to turn all the artillery of his masters against themselves, and to play them upon one another to favour your plotting purposes, should be the instrument in the devil's hand (unwittingly too) to avenge them all upon *you:* for should you even get the better of the colonel, would the mischief end there? It would but add remorse to your present remorse; since the interview *must* end in death; for he would not, I am confident, take his life at your hand. The Harlowes would, moreover, prosecute you in a legal way. You hate *them;* and *they* would be gainers by *his* death: rejoicers in *yours*—and have you not done mischief enough already?

Let *me,* therefore (and through me all your friends), have the satisfaction to hear that you are resolved to avoid this gentleman. Time will subdue all things. Nobody doubts your bravery. Nor will it be known that your plan is changed through persuasion.

Young Harlowe talks of calling you to account. This is a plain evidence that Mr. Morden has not taken the quarrel upon himself for their family.

I am in no apprehension of anybody but Colonel Morden. I know it will not be a means to prevail upon you to oblige me, if I say that I am well assured that this gentleman is a skilful swordsman; and that he is as cool and sedate as skilful. But yet I will add, that if I had a value for my life, he should be the last man, except yourself, with whom I would choose to have a contention.

I have, as you required, been very candid and sincere with you. I have not aimed at palliation. If you seek not Colonel Morden, it is my opinion he will not seek you: for he is a man of principle. But if you seek him, I believe he will not shun you.

Let me re-urge (it is the effect of my love for you!) that you know your own guilt in this affair, and should not be again an aggressor. It would be pity that so brave a man as the colonel should drop, were you and he to meet: and, on the other hand, it would be dreadful that you should be sent to your account unprepared for it, and pursuing a fresh violence.

Thy true friend,
John Belford.

MR. LOVELACE TO JOHN BELFORD, ESQ.

Munich, Nov. 11–22.

I RECEIVED yours this moment, just as I was setting out for Vienna.

As to going to Madrid, or one single step out of the way, to avoid Colonel Morden, let me perish if I do!

And so you own that he *has* threatened me; but not in gross and ungentlemanly terms, you say. But he has not done as a man of honour, if he has threatened me at all behind my back.

As to what you mention of my guilt; of a legal prosecution, if he meet his fate from my hand; of his skill, coolness, courage, and such-like poltroon stuff; what can you mean by it? Surely you cannot believe that such insinuations as those will weaken either my hands or my heart.

He had not taken any resolutions, you say, when you saw him. He *must* and *will* take resolutions, one way or other, very quickly; for I wrote to him yesterday, without waiting for this or your answer to my last. I have directed my letter to Florence. But I have couched it in such moderate terms, that he has fairly his option. He will be the challenger, if he take it in the sense in which he may so handsomely avoid taking it.

I will enclose the copy of the letter I sent him.

. . . . . .

On reperusing yours in a cooler moment, I cannot but thank you for your friendly love and good intentions. I could almost wish I had not written to Florence till I had received thy letter now before me. But it is gone. Let it go. If he wish peace, and to avoid violence, he will have a fair opportunity to embrace the one, and shun the other.

But be this as it may, you may contrive to let young Harlowe know (he is a menacer too!) that I shall be in England in March next at farthest.

This of Bavaria is a gallant and polite court. Nevertheless, being uncertain whether my letter may meet with the colonel at Florence, I shall quit it, and set out, as I intended, for Vienna; taking care to have any letter or message from him conveyed to me there: which will soon bring me back hither, or to any other place to which I shall be invited.

Lovelace.

Mr. Lovelace to William Morden, Esq.

[*Enclosed in the above*]

Munich, Nov. 10–21.

Sir,—I have heard, with a great deal of surprise, that you have thought fit to throw out some menacing expressions against me.

I should have been very glad that you had thought I had punishment enough in my own mind, for the wrongs I have done to the most excellent of women; and that it had been possible for two persons, so ardently joining in one love (especially as I was desirous, to the utmost of my power, to repair those wrongs), to have lived, if not on amicable terms, in such a way, as not to put either to the pain of hearing of threatenings thrown out in absence, which either ought to be despised for, if he had not spirit to take notice of them.

Now, sir, if what I have heard be owing only to warmth of temper, or to sudden passion, while the loss of all other losses the most deplorable to me was recent, I not only excuse but commend you for it. But if you are really *determined* to meet me on any other account (which, I own to you, is not however what I wish), it would be very blamable, and very unworthy of the character I desire to maintain, as well with you as with every other gentleman, to give you a difficulty in doing it.

Being uncertain when this letter may meet you, I shall set out to-morrow for Vienna; where any letter directed to the post-house in that city, or to Baron Windisgratz's (at the Favorita), to whom I have commendations, will come to hand.

Meantime, believing you to be a man too generous to make a wrong construction of what I am going to declare, and knowing the value which the dearest of all creatures had for you, and your relation to her, I will not scruple to assure you that the most acceptable return will be, that Colonel Morden chooses to be upon an amicable, rather than upon any other footing, with

His sincere admirer, and humble servant,

R. Lovelace.

MR. LOVELACE TO JOHN BELFORD, ESQ.

Lintz, Nov. 28. / Dec. 9.

I AM NOW on my way to Trent, in order to meet Colonel Morden, in pursuance of his answer to my letter enclosed in my last. I had been at Pressburgh, and had intended to visit some other cities of Hungary: but having obliged myself to return first to Vienna, I there met with his letter: which follows:

Munich, Nov. 21. / Dec. 2.

SIR,—Your letter was at Florence four days before I arrived there.

That I might not appear unworthy of your favour, I set out for this city the very next morning.

But being disappointed in my hope of finding you here, it becomes me to acquaint you that I have such a desire to stand well in the opinion of a man of your spirit, that I cannot hesitate a moment upon the option, which I am sure Mr. Lovelace in my situation (thus called upon) would make.

I own, sir, that I have, on all occasions, spoken of your treatment of my ever dear cousin as it deserved. And it behoves me to convince you, that no words fell from my lips, of you, merely because you were absent. I acquaint you, therefore, that I will attend your appointment; and would, were it to the farthest part of the globe.

I shall stay some days at this court; and if you please to direct for me at M. Klinefurt's in this city, whether I remain here or not, your commands will come safely and speedily to the hands of, sir,

Your most humble servant,
Wm. Morden.

So you see, Belford, that the colonel, by his ready, his even eagerly expressed acceptance of the offered interview, *was determined.* And is it not much better to bring such a point as this to an issue, than to give pain to friends for my safety, or continue in suspense myself; as I must do, if I imagined that another had aught against me?

This was my reply:

Vienna, { *Nov. 25.* / *Dec. 6.* }

SIR,—I have this moment the favour of yours. I will suspend a tour I was going to take into Hungary, and instantly set out for Munich: and, if I find you not there, will proceed to Trent. This city being on the confines of Italy, will be most convenient, as I presume, to you, in your return to Tuscany; and I shall hope to meet you in it on the $\frac{3}{14}$th of December.

I shall bring with me only a French valet and an English footman. Other particulars may be adjusted when I have the honour to see you. Till when, I am, sir,

Your most obedient servant,
R. Lovelace.

Now, Jack, I have no manner of apprehension of the event of this meeting. And I think I may say he seeks me; not I him. And so let him take the consequence.

What is infinitely nearer to my heart is my ingratitude to the most excellent of women—my *premeditated* ingratitude!

But as my loss in her departure is the greatest of any man's, and as she was nearer to me than to any other person in the world, and once she herself *wished to be so,* what an insolence in any man breathing to pretend to avenge her on *me!* Happy! happy! thrice happy! had I known how to value, as I ought to have valued, the glory of such a preference!

I will not aggravate to myself this aggravation of the colonel's pretending to call me to account for my treatment of a lady so much *my own,* lest, in the approaching interview, my heart should relent for one so nearly related to her, and who means honour and justice to her memory; and I should thereby give him advantages which otherwise he cannot have. For I know that I shall be inclined to trust to my skill, to save a man who was so much and so justly valued by her; and shall be loath to give way to my resentment, as a threatened man. And in this respect only am I sorry for his skill, and his courage, lest I should be obliged, in my own defence, to add a chalk to a score that is already too long.

. . . . . .

Indeed, indeed, Belford, I am, and shall be, to my latest hour, the most miserable of beings. Such exalted generosity!—Why didst thou put into my craving hands the copy of her will? Why sentest thou to me the posthumous letter? What though I was earnest to see the will? Thou knewest what they *both* were (*I* did not); and that it would be cruel to oblige me.

The meeting of twenty Colonel Mordens, were there twenty to meet in turn, would be nothing to me; would not give me a moment's concern, as to my own safety: but my reflections upon my vile ingratitude to so superior an excellence will ever be my curse.

Had she been a Miss Howe to me, and treated me as if I were a Hickman, I had had a call for revenge; and policy (when I had intended to be a husband) might have justified my attempts to humble her. But a *meek and gentle temper* was hers, though a *true heroine,* whenever honour or virtue called for an exertion of spirit.

Nothing but my cursed devices stood in the way of my happiness. Rememberest thou not how repeatedly, from the *first,* I poured cold water upon her rising flame, by meanly and ungratefully turning upon her the *injunctions* which *virgin delicacy,* and *filial duty,* induced her to lay me under, before I got her into my power?

Did she not tell me, and did I not *know it,* if she had *not* told me, *that she could not be guilty of affectation or tyranny to the man whom she intended to marry?* My ipecacuanha trial alone was enough to convince an infidel that she had a mind in which love and tenderness would have presided, had I permitted the charming buds to put forth and blow.

She *would have had no reserves,* as once she told me, *had I not given her cause of doubt.* And did she not own to thee, *that once she could have loved me; and, could she have made me good, would have made me happy?* O Belford! here was love; a love of the noblest kind! A love, as she hints in her posthumous letter, that extended to the soul; and which she not only avowed in her dying hours, but contrived to let me know it after death, in that letter filled with warnings and exhortations, which had for their sole end my eternal welfare!

Divine creature! Her very doubts, her reserves (so justly doubting) would have been my assurance, and my glory! And what other trial needed her virtue? What other needed a purity so angelic (blessed with such *a command of her passions in the bloom of youth*), had I not been a villain—and a wanton, a conceited, a proud fool, as well as a villain?

These reflections sharpened, rather than their edge by time abated, accompany me in whatever I do, and wherever I go; and mingle with all my diversions and amusements. And yet I go into gay and splendid company. I have made new acquaintance in the different courts I have visited. I am both esteemed and sought after by persons of rank and merit. I visit the colleges, the churches, the palaces. I frequent the theatre: am present at every public exhibition; and see all that is worth seeing, that I had not seen before, in the cabinets of the curious: am sometimes admitted to the toilette of an eminent toast, and make one with distinction at the assemblies of others—yet can think of nothing, nor of anybody, with delight, but of my CLARISSA. Nor have I seen one woman with advantage to herself, but as she resembles in stature, air, complexion, voice, or in some feature, that charmer, that *only* charmer, of my soul.

What greater punishment than to have these astonishing perfections, which she was mistress of, strike my remembrance with such force, when I have nothing left me but the remorse of having deprived myself and the world of such a blessing?

. . . . . .

If I find myself thus miserable abroad, I will soon return to England, and follow your example, I think—turn hermit, or some plaguy thing or other, and see what a constant course of penitence and mortification will do for me. There is no living at this rate—d—n me if there be!

If any mishap should befall me, you'll have the particulars of it from De la Tour. He indeed knows but little of English: but every modern tongue is yours. He is a trusty and ingenious fellow: and, if anything happen, will have some other papers, which I shall have ready sealed up, for you to transmit to Lord M. And since thou art so expert and so ready at executorships, prithee, Belford, accept of the office for me, as well as for my Clarissa—CLARISSA LOVELACE let me call her.

By all that's good, I am bewitched to her memory. Her very name, with mine joined to it, ravishes my soul, and is more delightful to me than the sweetest music.

Had I carried her (I must still recriminate) to any other place than to that accursed woman's—for the potion was her invention and mixture; and all the persisted-in violence was at her instigation, and at that of her wretched daughters.

But this looks so like the confession of a thief at the gallows, that possibly thou wilt be apt to think I am intimidated in prospect of the approaching interview. But far otherwise. On the contrary, most cheerfully do I go to meet the colonel; and I would tear my heart out of my breast with my own hands, were it capable of fear or concern on that account.

Thus much only I know, that if I should kill him (which I will not do if I can help it), I shall be far from being easy in my mind; *that* shall I never more be. But as the meeting is evidently of his own seeking, against an option fairly given to the contrary, and I cannot avoid it, I'll think of that hereafter. It is but repenting and mortifying for all at once: for I am as sure of victory as I am that I now live, let him be ever so skillful a swordsman; since, besides that I am no unfleshed novice, this is a sport that, when provoked to it, I love as well as my food. And, moreover, I shall be as *calm and undisturbed* as the bishop at his prayers: while he, as is evident by his letter, must be actuated by revenge and passion.

Doubt not, therefore, Jack, that I shall give a good account of this affair. Meantime, I remain

Yours most affectionately, etc.

Lovelace.

MR. LOVELACE TO JOHN BELFORD, ESQ.

Trent, Dec. 3–14.

TO-MORROW is to be the day that will, in all probability, send either one or two ghosts to attend the manes of my CLARISSA.

I arrived here yesterday; and inquiring for an English gentleman of the name of Morden, soon found out the colonel's lodgings. He had been in town two days; and left his name at every probable place.

He was gone to ride out; and I left *my* name, and where to be found: and in the evening he made me a visit.

He was plaguy gloomy. That was not I. But yet he told me that I had acted like a man of true spirit in my first letter; and with honour, in giving him so readily this meeting. He wished I had in other respects; and then we might have seen each other upon better terms than now we did.

I said there was no recalling what was passed; and that I wished some things had not been done, as well as he.

To recriminate now, he said, would be as exasperating as unavailable. And as I had so cheerfully given him this opportunity, words should give place to business. *Your* choice, Mr. Lovelace, of time, of place, of weapon, shall be *my* choice.

The two latter be yours, Mr. Morden. The time to-morrow, or next day, as you please.

Next day, then, Mr. Lovelace; and we'll ride out to-morrow to fix the place.

Agreed, sir.

Well, now, Mr. Lovelace, do you choose the weapon.

I said I believed we might be upon an equal foot with the

single rapier; but, if he thought otherwise, I had no objection to a pistol.

I will only say, replied he, that the chances may be more equal by the sword, because we can neither of us be to seek in that: and you would stand, says he, a worse chance, as I apprehend, with a pistol: and yet I have brought two; that you may take your choice of either: for, added he, I never missed a mark at pistol-distance, since I knew how to hold a pistol.

I told him that he spoke like himself: that I was expert enough that way, to embrace it, if he chose it; though not so sure of my mark as he pretended to be. Yet the devil's in't, colonel, if I, who have slit a bullet in two upon a knife's edge, hit not my man. So I have no objection to a pistol, if it be *your* choice. No man, I'll venture to say, has a steadier hand or eye than I have.

They may both be of use to you, sir, at the sword, as well as at the pistol: the sword, therefore, be the thing, if you please.

With all my heart.

We parted with a solemn sort of ceremonious civility: and this day I called upon him; and we rode out together to fix upon the place: and both being of one mind, and hating to put off for the morrow what could be done to-day, would have decided it then: but De la Tour, and the colonel's valet, who attended us, being unavoidably let into the secret, joined to beg we would have with us a surgeon from Brixen, whom La Tour had fallen in with there, and who had told him he was to ride next morning to bleed a person in a fever, at a lone cottage, which, by the surgeon's description, was not far from the place where we then were, if it were not that very cottage within sight of us.

They undertook so to manage it that the surgeon should know nothing of the matter till his assistance was called in. And La Tour being, as I assured the colonel, a ready contriving fellow (whom I ordered to obey him as myself, were the chance to be in *his* favour), we both agreed to defer the decision till to-morrow, and to leave the whole about the surgeon to the management of our two valets; enjoining them absolute secrecy: and so rode back again by different ways.

We fixed upon a little lone valley for the spot—ten to-morrow morning the time—and single rapier the sword. Yet I repeatedly told him that I valued myself so much upon my skill in that weapon that I would wish him to choose any other.

He said it was a gentleman's weapon; and he who understood it not, wanted a qualification that he ought to suffer for not having: but that, as to him, one weapon was as good as another throughout all the instruments of offence.

So, Jack, you see I take no advantage of him: but my devil must deceive me if he take not his life or his death at my hands before eleven to-morrow morning.

His valet and mine are to be present; but both strictly enjoined to be impartial and inactive: and, in return for my civility of the like nature, he commanded *his* to be assisting to me, if he fell.

We are to ride thither, and to dismount when at the place; and his footman and mine are to wait at an appointed distance, with a chaise to carry off to the borders of the Venetian territories the survivor, if one drop; or to assist either or both, as occasion may demand.

And thus, Belford, is the matter settled.

A shower of rain has left me nothing else to do: and therefore I write this letter; though I might as well have deferred it till to-morrow twelve o'clock, when I doubt not to be able to write again, to assure you how much I am

Yours, etc.
Lovelace.

TRANSLATION OF A LETTER FROM F. J. DE LA TOUR TO JOHN BELFORD, ESQ., NEAR SOHO SQUARE, LONDON

Trent, Dec. 18. N.S.

SIR,—I have melancholy news to inform you of, by order of the Chevalier Lovelace. He showed me his letter to you before he sealed it; signifying that he was to meet the Chevalier Morden on the 15th. Wherefore, as the occasion of the meeting is so well known to you, I shall say nothing of it here.

I had taken care to have ready, within a little distance, a surgeon and his assistant, to whom, under an oath of secrecy, I had revealed the matter (though I did not own it to the two gentlemen); so that they were prepared with bandages, and all things proper. For well was I acquainted with the bravery and skill of my chevalier; and had heard the character of the other; and knew the animosity of both. A post-chaise was ready, with each of their footmen, at a little distance.

The two chevaliers came exactly at their time: they were attended by Monsieur Margate (the colonel's gentleman) and myself. They had given orders overnight, and now repeated them in each other's presence, that we should observe a strict impartiality between them: and that, if one fell, each of us should look upon himself, as to any needful help or retreat, as the servant of the survivor, and take his commands accordingly.

After a few compliments, both the gentlemen, with the greatest presence of mind that I ever beheld in men, stripped to their shirts, and drew.

They parried with equal judgment several passes. My chevalier drew the first blood, making a desperate push, which, by a sudden turn of his antagonist, missed going clear through him, and wounded him on the fleshy part of the ribs of his right side; which part the sword tore out, being on the extremity of the body: but, before my chevalier could recover himself, the colonel, in return, pushed him into the inside of the left arm, near the shoulder: and the sword (raking his breast as it passed), being followed by a great effusion of blood, the colonel said, Sir, I believe you have enough.

My chevalier swore by G—d he was not hurt: 'twas a pin's point: and so made another pass at his antagonist; which he, with a surprising dexterity, received under his arm, and run my dear chevalier into the body; who immediately fell, saying, The luck is yours, sir—Oh, my beloved Clarissa!—Now art thou—— Inwardly he spoke three or four words more. His sword dropped from his hand. Mr. Morden threw his down, and ran to him, saying in French, Ah, monsieur, you are a dead man!—Call to God for mercy!

We gave the signal agreed upon to the footmen; and they to the surgeons; who instantly came up.

Colonel Morden, I found, was too well used to the bloody work; for he was as cool as if nothing so extraordinary had happened, assisting the surgeons, though his own wound bled much.

But my dear chevalier fainted away two or three times running, and vomited blood besides.

However, they stopped the bleeding for the present; and we helped him into the voiture; and then the colonel suffered his own wound to be dressed; and appeared concerned that my chevalier was between whiles (when he could speak and struggle) extremely outrageous. Poor gentleman! he had made quite sure of victory!

The colonel, against the surgeons' advice, would mount on horseback to pass into the Venetian territories; and generously gave me a purse of gold to pay the surgeons; desiring me to make a present to the footman; and to accept of the remainder as a mark of his satisfaction in my conduct; and in my care and tenderness of my master.

The surgeons told him that my chevalier could not live over the day.

When the colonel took leave of him, Mr. Lovelace said, You have well revenged the dear creature.

I have, sir, said Mr. Morden: and perhaps shall be sorry that you called upon me to this work, while I was balancing whether to obey or disobey the dear angel.

There is a fate in it! replied my chevalier—a cursed fate!—or this could not have been! But be ye all witnesses that I have provoked my destiny, and acknowledge that I fall by a man of honour.

Sir, said the colonel, with the piety of a confessor (wringing Mr. Lovelace's hand), snatch these few fleeting moments, and commend yourself to God.

And so he rode off.

The voiture proceeded slowly with my chevalier; yet the motion set both his wounds bleeding afresh; and it was with difficulty they again stopped the blood.

We brought him alive to the nearest cottage; and he gave orders to me to dispatch to you the packet I herewith send sealed up; and bid me write to you the particulars of this most unhappy affair: and give you thanks, in his name, for all your favours and friendship to him.

Contrary to all expectation, he lived over the night: but *suf-*

fered much, as well from his *impatience* and *disappointment* as from his *wounds;* for he seemed *very unwilling to die.*

He was delirious at times in the two last hours; and then several times cried out, as if he had seen some frightful spectre, Take her away! take her away! but named nobody. And sometimes praised some lady (that Clarissa, I suppose, whom he had invoked when he received his death's wound), calling her, Sweet Excellence! Divine Creature! Fair Sufferer! And once he said, Look down, Blessed Spirit, look down!——And there stopped; his lips, however, moving.

At nine in the morning he was seized with convulsions, and fainted away; and it was a quarter of an hour before he came out of them.

His few last words I must not omit, as they show an ultimate composure; which may adminster some consolation to his honourable friends.

Blessed—said he, addressing himself no doubt to Heaven; for his dying eyes were lifted up. A strong convulsion prevented him for a few moments saying more, but recovering, he again, with great fervour (lifting up his eyes and his spread hands), pronounced the word *blessed.* Then, in a seeming ejaculation, he spoke inwardly, so as not to be understood: at last, he distinctly pronounced these three words,

LET THIS EXPIATE!

And then, his head sinking on his pillow, he expired, at about half an hour after ten.

He little thought, poor gentleman! his end so near: so had given no direction about his body. I have caused it to be embowelled, and deposited in a vault, till I have orders from England.

This is a favour that was procured with difficulty; and would have been refused, had he not been an Englishman of rank: a nation with reason respected in every Austrian Government For he had refused ghostly attendance, and the Sacraments in the Catholic way. May his soul be happy, I pray God!

I have had some trouble also, on account of the manner of

his death, from the magistracy here: who have taken the requisite informations in the affair. And it has cost me some money. Of which, and of my dear chevalier's effects, I will give you a faithful account in my next. And so, waiting at this place your commands, I am, sir,

Your most faithful and obedient servant,

F. J. De la Tour.